D1237712

American Combat Planes

PA
64
PA
41
PA
65
PA
66

AMERICAN COMBAT PLANES

by Ray Wagner

Hanover House, Garden City, New York

1960

Library of Congress Catalog Card Number 60-14913

Printed in the United States of America

Design: Natasha Sylvester with Charles Kaplan

First Edition

Preface

PURPOSE:

Combat planes by the thousands have been built in the United States since 1917. Fighters, bombers, and attack types are the striking weapons of air power and have made world history. Yet, despite their importance, a complete and accurate history of these planes and their characteristics was not available.

The purpose of *American Combat Planes* is to offer this history, both as a reference and as an interesting story of aviation and war. All combat types built in the United States for the Air Force, Air Navy, or for foreign governments are included, together with foreign aircraft bought for American fighting outfits.

PLAN:

This book describes the planes designed to attack an enemy with guns, bombs, or rockets. It excludes the trainers, transports, and observation types which also contribute to air power, but can better be described in separate studies.

Attention is given both little-known experimentals and famous mass-production jobs with their major modifications. The description, armament, and history of each type is related to other designs, and to their intended military missions.

Photographs enable identification of each type, and are accompanied by dimensions, weights, and performances. Most of these characteristics are drawn from flight tests and specifications given in official documents once classified, but recently made available.

Part One orients readers on historical and technical factors influencing aircraft design and gives a brief summary of information needed to follow war-plane history, such as aircraft and engine designations.

The body of the work has sections on attack planes, bombers, and fighters, with parallel sections for the corresponding naval types. Planes of each class are discussed in order of their appearance. This provides a more understandable review of progress than listing them by official designation, which is often a poor guide to chronology or even design antecedents.

ACKNOWLEDGMENTS:

The origins of this material are discussed in full in the Appendix on sources. Official reports, characteristics charts, correspondence, and specifications were examined to the extent that they had been declassified and located in the National Archives, the Navy's Bureau of Aeronautics, the National Air Museum, and the Wright-Patterson Air Force Base. On current types, of course, most data is still classified; only published materials can be used. The annotated bibliography lists the books and articles used to provide background and much information not readily available in original form.

Particular acknowledgment for aid in obtaining data should be given to William Engelhardt of the WADC Design Branch; Paul Garber and Winthrop Shaw of the National Air Museum; Lee M. Pearson, Bureau of Aeronautics; Robert Houston and Marc Sloan at the Central Air Force Museum; Robert Krauskopf of the National Archives; Major Jesse D. Thompson USAF; Lewis Zarem, Public Information Branch USAF; and the helpful personnel of their several offices.

Major James F. Sunderman of the Air Force Book Program gave this project invaluable aid and encouragement. Photographs were obtained from the Air Force, Navy, and many agencies and companies mentioned in the credits, but the largest number came from Peter M. Bowers' fabulous collection, one of the largest private stocks in the country. Mr. Bowers also volunteered his unpublished study of fighter history. Other members of the American Aviation Historical

Society contributing pictures or information were William Larkins, Gerald Balzer, Harry Gann, Mauno Salo, Victor Seeley, and James J. Sloan.

Among company people who supplied photos, Convair's Betty Gosset deserves special credit for locating rare prints, along with Bell's Don N. Tranter, Boeing's Jack Fraser, Chance Vought's Arthur Schoeni, Lockheed's Eric Miller, Northrop's Charley Barr, Republic's Leon Shloss, and Frank Delear of Sikorsky.

Finally, for the trying and difficult job of typing the manuscript, very special and personal thanks to Beatrice Wagner, my wife.

Contents

List of Tables

Part 1 Introducing the Wars and the Airplanes

Chapter 1: The Role of the Combat Plane: A Historical Sketch

In the fifty-seven years since powered flight began in America, many different airplane designs have been built. From the viewpoint of their effect on world history, those intended for air combat have been the most important.

Each of these planes has its own story. The original experimental model is rolled, fresh and untried, out of the factory. Shining and new, it is the talk of the aviation world which eagerly awaits the newcomer's performance.

But on many designs, that's all you ever hear. Somewhere, something has gone wrong, and the hopeful prototype drops from sight. Sometimes a new job receives no publicity, and disappears without comment. Luckier types go into production, and then a long series of modifications fill the trade journals.

Each such design represents a response to a challenge, an invention mothered by some necessity, an actor hoping to fill a role written by forces far removed from the engineer's drawing board and often imperfectly understood by the artists of the slide rule and T square.

The value of a design depends on its mission and how well the plane fulfills it. Defective concepts of military mission have crippled as many aircraft as errors in engineering. Before describing particular types, therefore, the study begins with a short discussion of the roles that the American combat plane has had to perform.

The limited role expected of the first military plane purchased by the American, or indeed by any government, was indicated by its assignment to the Signal Corps. In December 1907, a specification was issued for a two-place aircraft with a speed of 40 mph, a range of 125 miles, "and the ability to steer in all directions without difficulty." A contract was signed on February 10, 1908, with the Wright brothers, who began testing the 25 hp aircraft that September. The first fatal airplane crash of history delayed acceptance of the aircraft until August 2, 1909.

Like all of the following 229 "flying machines" delivered to the U. S. Army prior to the April 6, 1917, declaration of war, the Wright brothers model B had no bloodthirsty intentions. Its capacity was only to train aviators for the work of communications and scouting done by its frail and kite-like successors. Nor were the aircraft purchased by the Navy any more militant.

Grimmer uses for aircraft had been anticipated, and H. G. Wells as early as 1908 had portrayed aerial attacks on New York in his novel *The War in the Air*. Weapons were experimentally fired from Army aircraft: a rifle on August 20, 1910, live bombs dropped in January 1911, and a Lewis machine gun fired on June 7, 1912.

Nevertheless, when the U.S. declared war on Germany, the Army possessed but 55 aircraft, all unarmed and primitive trainers. But if youthful American aviation had no weapons, and no deadly purposes, less than three years of warfare in Europe had already defined the basic roles of today's combat planes.

THE FIRST WAR IN THE AIR

When the war opened on July 28, 1914, Europe's airplanes were as naked of weapons as America's, but existed in much larger numbers. The initial mission of these aircraft was reconnaissance, and however violent the ground fighting, the soldiers of the skies found their flights across the lines relatively peaceful. For such purposes unarmed single-engined, two-place air craft were adequate.

But the temptation to use the advantage of flight for purposes of attack was too strong. On August 14, 1914, a pair of French biplanes dropped artillery shells on hangars at Metz, and on November 21, three British

SIGNAL CORPS

French-built fighters, like Nieuport 28, equipped U.S. fliers in 1918.

PMB

Early monoplane fighter, the metal Boeing P-26A of 1934 had open cockpit, wheel pants.

Avros bombed Zeppelin sheds. A German plane dropped the first bomb on English soil on December 19, 1914. Zeppelins began raids in January 1915, and warfare had truly entered a new dimension.

Later chapters of this book will describe how the "military aeroplane" became the combat plane by developing a series of specialties. Single-engined, two-seat observation biplanes were fitted with bomb racks under the wings and became light bombers. Smaller single-seaters with a machine gun became *avions de chasse,* or pursuit ships, for attacking enemy aircraft, while larger multiengined machines were built for long-range bombing. Naval aviation developed its own specialties; flying boats to patrol the sea and torpedo-carrying seaplanes to attack enemy shipping were joined by fighters carried by the fleet on vessels with flight decks.

The airplane as a scout had developed into the airplane as a bomber and as a destroyer of other aircraft, but this development was European, not American, and happened without any comparable activity on this side of the Atlantic.

THE A.E.F.'S AIR ARM

Although the United States had produced the world's first successful powered plane, and purchased the first military plane, it had not participated in the wartime development of the air weapon. Not even a prototype of up-to-date pattern was available when we entered the war.

In June 1917 an Aircraft Production Board was established, and the Bolling Mission sailed for Europe to gain information for an American aircraft program. Samples of several Allied warplanes were selected and shipped to the U.S. for reproduction here, while orders were placed in France and Britain for planes to be given to our airmen as they arrived.

United States production of training planes aided the dispatch of fliers to France, but of the combat types selected, only the DH-4 was produced in quantity. As the following chapters will tell, the American squadrons at the front depended principally on French equipment. The 36 squadrons at the front on November 1, 1918, included 15 with the Spad and one with the SE-5A single-seater, and 10 with the Salmson, eight with the U.S.-built DH-4, and two with the Breguet two-seaters. None had twin-engined equipment.

"During the war, the Army received a total of 16,831 planes; 6287 were delivered to the A.E.F. before the Armistice," including 2696 trainers and 3591 service types. The origin of these A.E.F. planes is shown in Table 1. On Armistice Day the A.E.F. had 740 planes at the front. Table 2 shows how this number compared with the forces of other countries.

Too late for war was American-built Thomas-Morse MB-3 biplane.

MFR

Enclosed cockpit and retractable wheels were included on 1937s Curtiss XP-37.

AMC

MFR

Prewar patterns, with more guns, are included on wartime fighters like Bell P-63A lend-leased to U.S.S.R. in 1944.

Table 1

SOURCES OF A.E.F. AIRCRAFT

From France		4791	(incl. 2186 service types)
" Britain		261	(" 189 " ")
" Italy		19	trainers
" U.S.			
	DH-4	1213	service types
	LePere	2	experimental
	DH-9	1	experimental
		6287	(incl. 3591 service types)

Table 2

COMPARISON OF AIRPLANE STRENGTHS OF ALLIED AND ENEMY AIR SERVICES, NOVEMBER 11, 1918

	Pursuit	Observation	Bombardment Day	Bombardment Night	Total Airplanes
British	759	503	306	190	1758
French	1344	1505	225	247	3321
American	330	293	117	0	740
Italian	336	360	36	80	812
Belgian	45	100	0	8	153
German	1020	1442	0	268	2730
Austrian	220	391	0	11	622
Combined Allies	2814	2761	684	525	6784
Combined Enemy	1240	1833	0	279	3352

MFR
Supersonic speeds were achieved by Lockheed XF-104 in 1954.

BEGINNINGS OF NAVY AIR

The Navy's air arm at the opening of the war included 45 training seaplanes, six flying boats, and three landplanes, none of them armed or designed for combat. Experience had been obtained in operating aircraft at sea, and Britain supplied information on her use of planes over the North Sea.

U-boats were the war's chief naval threat, so when a British flying boat sank one for the first time on May 20, 1917, the immediate role for naval aircraft was written. Orders were placed for hundreds of flying boats for shore-based antisub patrol.

Because of the difficulty encountered getting enough planes, the government built its own Naval Aircraft Factory in Philadelphia. States a Navy text:

> The Army's requirements for an enormous quantity of planes created a decided lack of interest among aircraft manufacturers in the Navy's requirements for a comparatively small quantity of machines. The Navy Department therefore concluded that it was necessary to build and put into production an aircraft factory to be owned by the Navy, in order, first, to assure a part, at least, of its aircraft supply; second, to obtain cost data for the Department's guidance in its dealings with private manufacturers; and third, to have under its own control a factory capable of producing experimental work.

While the flying boats proved of great value in spotting submarines, it was seen that a more direct attack could be made by bombing the sub bases. For this purpose, the Northern Bombing Group was organized, with DH-4, DH-9, and Caproni landplanes obtained from the Army and the Allies.

Unlike the A.E.F., the Navy obtained most of its planes at home. Only 142 of the Navy's 2705 machines were procured abroad. U.S.-built were 1444 service types, 1084 training planes, and 36 experimentals, as well as 155 DH-4s and 144 trainers transferred from the Army.

AMERICAN AIR POWER BETWEEN WARS

The Armistice left the United States with a stockpile of aircraft, some limited experience in air warfare, and the rudiments of a theory of air power.

The major item in the Army's stock of airplanes was the thousands of DH-4s designed for day bombing and observation, together with several hundred pursuits of foreign origin, and a few night bombers. Just what should be done to replace this rapidly aging armada? Viewpoints on this depended in part on viewpoints on the role of air power.

The existing organization of the Army Air Service reflected the conservative view that aviation existed

MFR

First U.S.-designed bomber was this Martin MB-1 biplane in 1918.

primarily to assist the ground army, and that bombing and pursuit aircraft in themselves were unlikely to affect the course of war. (An example of this thinking is the lengthy World War I history that mentions only scouting as a wartime aviation activity.) The view once expressed that "the duty of the aviator is to see, not to fight" seemed to be reflected in the dispersal of air force strength into observation squadrons attached to various ground units.

Subordination of the Air Service to the Army had a bad effect on both morale and equipment. Of 517 Air Service crash deaths from January 1919 to June 1925, all but 12 were in aging aircraft built before the end of the war. The lack of improved and safer replacements was criticized, and a long debate on the control of air power ensued. Since this argument centered around the use of the bomber, it is discussed in that weapon's chapters.

The organizational impasse of the period was reflected in the relatively slow technical advance. Most of the aviation headlines were made by the skill of individual aviators, rather than by a startling advance in performance. Compare the service aircraft of 1930, a dozen years after the Armistice, with those of the war period. Still we see the same open cockpit, fabric-covered biplanes dragging struts and exposed undercarriages. Advances in top speed were modest. Fighters had gone from the 135 mph of the Spad to 166 mph for the P-12B, bombers from 94 mph for the Handley-Page to 114 mph for the B-3A, two-seaters from 124 mph for the DH-4 to 139 mph for the A-3B.

Naval aviation in the 1920s made progress by beginning the organization of a carrier-based striking force. In 1918, most operational Navy service planes were shore-based flying boats, plus some Marine DH-4s. A small postwar force, including fighting, observation, and torpedo planes, was established to operate on wheels or floats from shore bases. The next step was obviously to perfect means by which these aircraft could accompany the fleet to sea, and the Bureau of Aeronautics, established in 1921, devoted itself to that problem.

Early shipboard operations were by seaplanes catapulted from battleships and cruisers, and lifted back by cranes after landing on the sea. There were disadvantages to this method: only a few seaplanes could be carried without impairing the ship's fighting ability, it was difficult to recover the launched aircraft, and most important, the seaplanes were inferior in performance to land planes.

As early as July 1917, the British Royal Navy had commissioned HMS *Furious,* which answered the problem by adding to the fleet a specialized aircraft carrier which could launch and recover landplanes from a large flight deck. In 1922, the U.S. completed the conversion of the carrier *Langley* from a collier, and on October 17, a Vought VE-7-SF made the first take-off from a Navy carrier. Conventional landplanes were thus able to begin operations with the fleet, modified by strengthened landing gear and arresting hooks.

Spurred by the sinking of battleships in the 1921–23 bombing tests, the Navy had the battlecruisers *Lexington* and *Saratoga* finished as carriers. In March 1925, the Navy called upon designers for new aircraft to fit the fine new ships, and the industry responded with the Curtiss F6C fighter, the Vought O2U scout, and the Martin T3M torpedo plane.

In 1928 the two carriers began operations, each with two squadrons of fighters, two of torpedo bombers, and one of observation planes. Their operational success soon relegated seaplanes from the status of combat planes to that of gun spotters for individual warships.

The relatively slow-paced aviation progress of the '20s contrasts sharply with the changes that took place in the air forces during the '30s. The depression knocked the bottom from the private plane market, although U.S. expenditures on military aircraft rose

Modern monoplane design is seen on 1935s Martin B-10B.

PMB

MFR

Heavy armament characterized North American B-25J and other World War II bombers.

from $25,000,000 in fiscal 1925 to $69,000,000 in fiscal 1931. This circumstance, together with Japan's invasion of Manchuria in 1931, the beginnings of German rearmament, and an administration friendlier to new ideas, gave a new impetus to the design of combat aircraft.

A complete change in the appearance of the combat plane took place in this period. Beginning in 1931 with the XA-7, XA-8, XB-7, XB-8, XB-9, and YP-24, and in 1932 with the XB-10, we see the sudden replacement of the biplane with the all-metal monoplane. Retractable landing gear, enclosed cockpits, and controllable-pitch propellers became standard on combat planes.

And in 1935, the year that Mussolini attacked Ethiopia, Hitler officially announced the formation of his air force, and Congress passed a vast legislative program of social reforms, was also a big year in combat aviation. The Baker Board (aviation had become the most investigated service) had had a majority of ground officers, but had recommended an Air Corps of 2320 planes and a General Headquarters Air Force for operations free of dependence on particular ground armies. Officially begun in March 1935, the GHQ Air Force could be concentrated for a blow in any direction.

The new air force was also presented with some brand-new planes. Their newness enhanced by the elimination of traditional blue-yellow paint for the bare metal, the prototypes of the Curtiss pursuits and the Boeing B-17 bomber were a complete departure from the traditional pattern of aircraft design. Naval aviation also began an expansion around three new carriers, and new monoplanes replaced the traditional carrier-based biplanes.

By the time the first bombs of the Second World War crashed on Spain and China, the combat plane had lost its World War One aspect. As airplanes became more numerous, they also became more elaborate and expensive, and the aircraft industry got to be really big business. When, in 1939, Orville Wright inspected the Douglas DC-4, the old man of aviation commented not on its size, or speed, but on its cost. "I can't believe that there is so much money wrapped up in a plane of this size—more than $2,000,000."

HISTORY'S LARGEST AIR FORCE

The B-17 was the most successful of all the prototypes which appeared in the '30s, and together with developments of its contemporaries, provided the basic air weapons to fight the Second World War. Both two- and four-engined bomber designs were available, and tactical support to ground forces would be offered through Attack units (later renamed Light Bombardment). Leadership in Pursuit ships (renamed now Fighters) was not as marked as in the case of the big bombers, for it took a long time for America's aeronautical engineers to catch up to the Spitfire's speed and firepower.

The Army and Navy had some 2400 and 1700 planes respectively when the 1939 expansion program proposed an Army Air Corps of 5500 planes in 24 groups, and a Naval Air Service with 3000. This expansion had hardly gotten under way when German successes in

Largest bomber built was SACs postwar B-36D, shown here with ancient Curtiss pusher.

MFR

MFR

First bomber with supersonic, 1000 mph-plus speed is the Convair B-58, carrying weapons pod.

Europe led President Roosevelt in May 1940 to call for 50,000 service planes. The figure seemed preposterous, but was authorized—13,500 for the Navy, and 36,500 for the Army in 54 groups.

In 1941, still another plan called for 84 groups by mid-1942, seemed hardly realistic in view of lend-lease commitments. Although by December 7, 1941, 70 groups had been organized in the now virtually autonomous "Army Air Forces" (the name replacing Air Corps in 1941), the 25 fighter, 14 heavy bomber, 9 medium bomber, 5 light bomber, 11 observation, and 6 transport groups had only 3305 combat planes plus 7024 other types. Navy aviation had expanded in 1941 from 2553 planes in January to 5260 in December.

Foreign countries bought U.S. combat types in large quantities even before the war began in 1939. On March 25, 1940, permission was granted for the sale of Army and Navy service types as soon as a newer type was available, while a year later lend-lease took over the cost of thousands of planes built for our Allies.

By 1945, the U.S. had the largest air force ever built in history, with 245 groups and 72,726 aircraft (41,961 combat) in the Army Air Force on January 1, and 41,180 naval aircraft (28,032 combat) on June 30. Great air armadas were assembled for the major battles of the war. For Overlord, the cross-Channel invasion of Europe, the AAF alone assembled 10,637 planes (8351 combat) in 98 groups: 40 heavy bomber, 8 medium bomber, 3 light bomber, 33 fighter, and 14 troop carrier. The Navy assaulted Okinawa with the support of 919 planes on fast carriers and 564 planes on escort carriers. Navy combat planes on hand in mid-1945 included 13,940 fighters, 5101 scout bombers, 4937 torpedo bombers, and 4054 patrol bombers, operating from 28 large carriers, 72 escort carriers, and numerous land bases. What these planes did in the war has been described in detail in official histories. Air power, both carrier and land-based, was the largest single factor in Japan's defeat. More controversial is the role of air power against Germany, although it is significant that no Allied victories were won until after Germany's early control of the air was smashed.

NAVY
Naval aviation began with shore-based, biplane flying boats. This PN-7 (1924) was first designed and built by Navy itself.

MFR

Convair Catalina was World War IIs most widely used sub-hunting patrol plane.

MFR
Antisubmarine warfare with Lockheed P2V-5s remains major Navy mission.

Folding wings allowed metal monoplanes, including Douglas TBD-1, aboard ship.

PMB

Carrier-based biplanes, like Curtiss BF2C-1, of 1935, were to control air above fleet.

NAVY

MFR
Grumman Avenger (TBF-1) helped destroy Japanese Navy.

MFR

Korean War found carriers attacking shore targets with Grumman F9F-5 jets.

NAVY

Fast-moving aircraft carriers like *Bennington* have replaced battleships, giving U.S. mobile airbases.

In any case, the role of aviation in war was vindicated beyond the boldest claims of its advocates. The Congress passed an act creating a National Military Establishment with Secretaries of Army, Navy, and Air co-equal under the Secretary of Defense. Established in September 1947, the United States Air Force has three basic combat missions: air defense, strategic air bombardment, and tactical air support for ground forces.

In the postwar international situation, Soviet-American conflicts gave the Air Force an opportunity to assert itself as the leading military element. Since the U. S. Navy was already larger than all other navies of the world put together, while Soviet ground strength could not soon be matched, national policy made strategic atomic bombing the central element and prime priority of the armed forces. To this end, the Finletter Commission had endorsed, in January 1948, an Air Force of 70 groups: 20 strategic bomber, 5 light bomber, 22 day fighter, 3 all-weather fighter, 4 tactical and 6 strategic reconnaissance, and 10 troop carrier.

Resistance arose to the program as the Navy demanded renewed recognition for carrier and antisub aviation, the Army charged neglect of tactical air, and development of Soviet atomic weapons raised concern over continental defense. Skyrocketing cost of air weapons limited procurement, and thus the Air Force on January 1, 1950, had 48 groups with some 17,000 aircraft (8000 combat), about half of which were Second World War types held in storage. Naval Air had 4900 planes attached to the fleet, plus 1900 in the Reserve and 550 in storage.

Outbreak of war in Korea led to the new rearmament program, from which by 1956 the Air Force had 134 wings with 26,000 planes, while the Navy had 12,548 planes in 17 carrier groups, three Marine air wings, and 19 shore-based antisub squadrons. Debate over the relative value of carriers and strategic bombers continued, but aircraft production reached new heights.

By this time, the role of the combat plane in American history is clear. Even if it is still questionable whether air power alone will decide a future war, a nation's position in the twentieth century will depend more on the quality of its weapons than on any other single material military factor. When history poses problems for weapons, solutions must be found from the background of existing technology. Before we begin our study of the airplanes developed to play such a part in history, we must understand the resources with which engineers might create such air weapons.

Chapter 2: Building the Warplane

THE DESIGNER'S TASK

Military leaders demand of the plane builders not only a machine to do a certain job, but a machine which can do that job better than foreign types. Since the physical laws of aerodynamics are true all over the world, and the engineering textbooks everywhere have much the same formulas, the engineer can only hope to be a little earlier than his competitors.

Essentially, the combat plane is an airborne weapons carrier whose value is its ability to get from point to point in the skies. The four physical forces which act on aircraft in flight are, on the negative side, *drag* and *gravity*, and, on the positive side, *thrust* and *lift*.

This age of streamlining has made us conscious of the problem of reducing drag, or air resistance. Counteracting drag is thrust, the energy converted into forward motion by the engine. The effect of air movement around the wings creates lift to counteract gravity. The designer's task is to manipulate these forces to produce the best possible performance.

Progress in the struggle against drag can be easily seen throughout the illustrations in this history. Landing gear development reflects, for example, the flight against drag. At first wheels hung naked below the aircraft, then they were dressed with "pants" or spats, then partial retraction (with some of the wheel left exposed in case of mechanical failure), and finally the entire undercarriage disappears within the aircraft.

Retractable landing gear, however, is heavier than the more simple fixed type, and thus a reduction of drag may also add to weight. It can easily be appreciated that the greater the weight of the aircraft the more power required for movement, and thus the weight of both the airframe and its load must be kept at a minimum.

CONVAIR

The designer's task.

ARMAMENT AND EQUIPMENT

Consider now armament, the part of the combat plane's weight that is the reason for its existence. The weapons carried must be sufficient for their task but yet not unduly hamper performance. In this respect, a lesson was taught by the first British effort to attack an enemy plane.

On August 22, 1914, a Farman pusher, with a Lewis gun attached to the bow, took off in pursuit of an Albatros patrolling at 5000 ft. altitude. The added weight of the gun had had a deplorable effect on the Farman's climb, however, and the Allied plane found itself unable to pass the 3500 ft. level, while the Albatros went home undisturbed.

Such incidents suggest why armament is always limited by the power of the aircraft. With improvements in design, the weights carried have steadily increased. The aerial bombs used most often by the Allies in the First World War were 112 lbs. each. Those of the Second World War were commonly ten times that weight while 4000- and 8000-lb. bombs were sometimes used. (A 42,000-lb. bomb was tested by the U.S. in 1947.) Throughout Part 3 the reader will watch the gradual increase of bomber loads, and will also be aware of the growing weight of *bomb-aiming* systems from the simple sights of 1917 to the elaborate radar systems of today.

Side by side with bomb development came progress in weapons to attack other aircraft. The Lewis was the first machine gun favored for aircraft work. Of light weight, it was used throughout the 1914–18 war, but its drum feeding required frequent reloading. The belt feeding of the heavier water-cooled Vickers gun was more suitable for a pilot-fired synchronized weapon. Between wars, the U.S. used the air-cooled Browning, also a belt-fed .30-caliber gun, but reliable and light. The Browning was used both as a fixed gun to replace the Vickers, and as a flexible gun to replace the Lewis.

In the '30s, with the higher speeds, larger loads, sturdier aircraft, and the growing danger of war, both the incentive and opportunity appeared to increase firepower. In single-seaters, the old two-gun standard which followed 1917 was changed to four guns for the Spanish Civil War, and in 1936 Britain adopted the eight-gun Hurricane and Spitfire. In 1940, twelve-gun fighters were introduced to the R.A.F. Most multi-gun fighters mounted their weapons in the wings where there was more room than in the nose, and where synchronization was unnecessary.

U.S. service planes were slow to follow this trend, although a six-gun XP-6H and an eight-gun XP-36E were tested. Instead, Americans had been considering a departure from the .30-caliber (7.6-mm.) gun for the heavier .50-caliber (12.7-mm.) gun. Standard armament on American fighters from 1922 to 1938 was an alternate mount of either two .30-caliber, or one .30- and one .50-caliber gun. In 1939 both guns on the P-40s ordered were of .50-caliber, while in 1941 four .50-caliber guns were fitted to the P-40D and F4F-3. Mixtures of .30-caliber and .50-caliber guns were sometimes used, but six .50-caliber guns became standard on most World War II fighters like the P-51D and the Navy's Corsairs and Hellcats. When weight had to be especially light, only four .50s were thought sufficient, while the eight .50s on the P-47 made it the hardest-hitting single-seater in action.

Larger caliber guns have a slower rate of fire, but are especially effective against bombers and ground targets. A 37 mm. aircraft gun firing explosive shells was developed by France in 1917, but its hand loading was slow and inconvenient. The Baldwin 37-mm. gun tested in the U.S. in 1919 was little better. The first

Experimental types face long performance trials before they become useful as air weapons, and not all survive. Vought's XTBU-1 was completed in December 1941, eventually produced by Convair as TBY-2, but never reached successful fleet service.

ARC

NAVY

Wheels on Curtiss XF13C-1 retracted into fuselage, but wing struts still caused drag on this 1934 fighter.

AMC

Vickers guns on Spad 13 were synchronized with propeller.

WL
Enclosed teardrop waist mount for .30-caliber gun on early B-17.

AF
Browning .30-caliber M-2 flexible gun.

really practical aircraft gun with exploding shells was the Swiss 20-mm. Oerlikon adopted by several European powers before the 1939 war. When Britain accepted it in 1940, solid ammunition was substituted.

The U.S. had planes designed for high-caliber guns before it had the guns. A 37-mm. gun built by a private firm in 1937 had too low a muzzle velocity for Army adoption, so the XFM-1 had only wooden dummies, while 23-mm. Madsens were imported from Denmark for the XP-38 and the XP-36F. By 1940 a satisfactory 37-mm. gun was available for the Airacobra and early Lightnings, while the Oerlikon was placed in mass production by 1941 for use in both aircraft and anti-aircraft work.

Flexible guns could not be as easily enlarged in caliber until a mounting could be perfected on which guns could be aimed by the gunner without interference by the slip stream. The Scarff ring was used to about 1930, when a smoother mount was devised. Two Lewis guns were carried on the ring in 1918, but a single Browning sufficed during the period between wars. Enclosed turrets appeared in 1932 on the XB-10, while .50-caliber guns in the British-invented power-operated turrets came with the new war. Remote-controlled turrets were introduced in 1942, but the most elaborate flexible armament has been the retractable, remote-controlled twin 20-mm. turrets on the B-36.

Browning .50-caliber M-2 at B-24 waist windows.
CONVAIR

Lewis guns on early Scarff ring had drum magazines.
AF

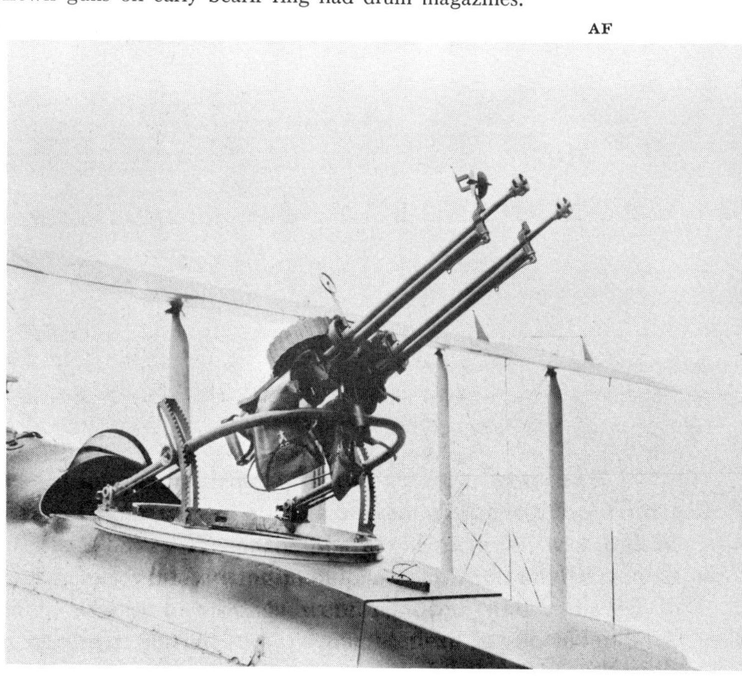

MFR

First U.S. tail turret was on Sikorsky XPBS-1. A single .50-caliber gun was hand-operated.

MFR
Power-operated tail turret on Consolidated XB-41 (B-24) had two .50-caliber guns.

A complete discussion of the guns themselves would fill a book, but the table below gives enough information for most purposes and references are given in the notes. The reader should bear in mind that the problem was not only the need to reduce weight, but the choice between the advantages of a high number of strikes-per-second from small-caliber ammunition, and the penetration and destructiveness of the larger guns.

Necessary combat equipment may also include rockets, armor, leakproof tanks, and radar. Rockets were adopted for use against ground targets by the U.S. in 1943 and are now used on interceptors for anti-bomber work. Air-to-air missiles have grown in importance in the last decade to the point where they are replacing guns as the primary fighter weapon.

Table 3

AMERICAN AIRCRAFT GUNS

Type	Length (inches)	Weight of Gun (pounds)	Weight of Bullet (ounces)	Muzzle Velocity (ft./sec.)	Rate of Fire (rds/min)	Range (yards)
.30-cal. M-2	40	21	.34	2600	1350	1,800
.50-cal. M-2	57	64	1.71	2810	800	7,200
.50-cal. M-3	—	52	1.71	2500	1100	—
20-mm. M-2	94	102	4.82	2850	650	5,500
20-mm. M-3	78	112	4.82	2750	800	—
20-mm. M-39	—	170	4.82	3400	1500	—
37-mm. M-4	89	213	21.44	2000	150	4,000
37-mm. M-9	104	365	21.44	2900	125	8,875
75-mm. M-4	141	1297	—	2090	—	12,000

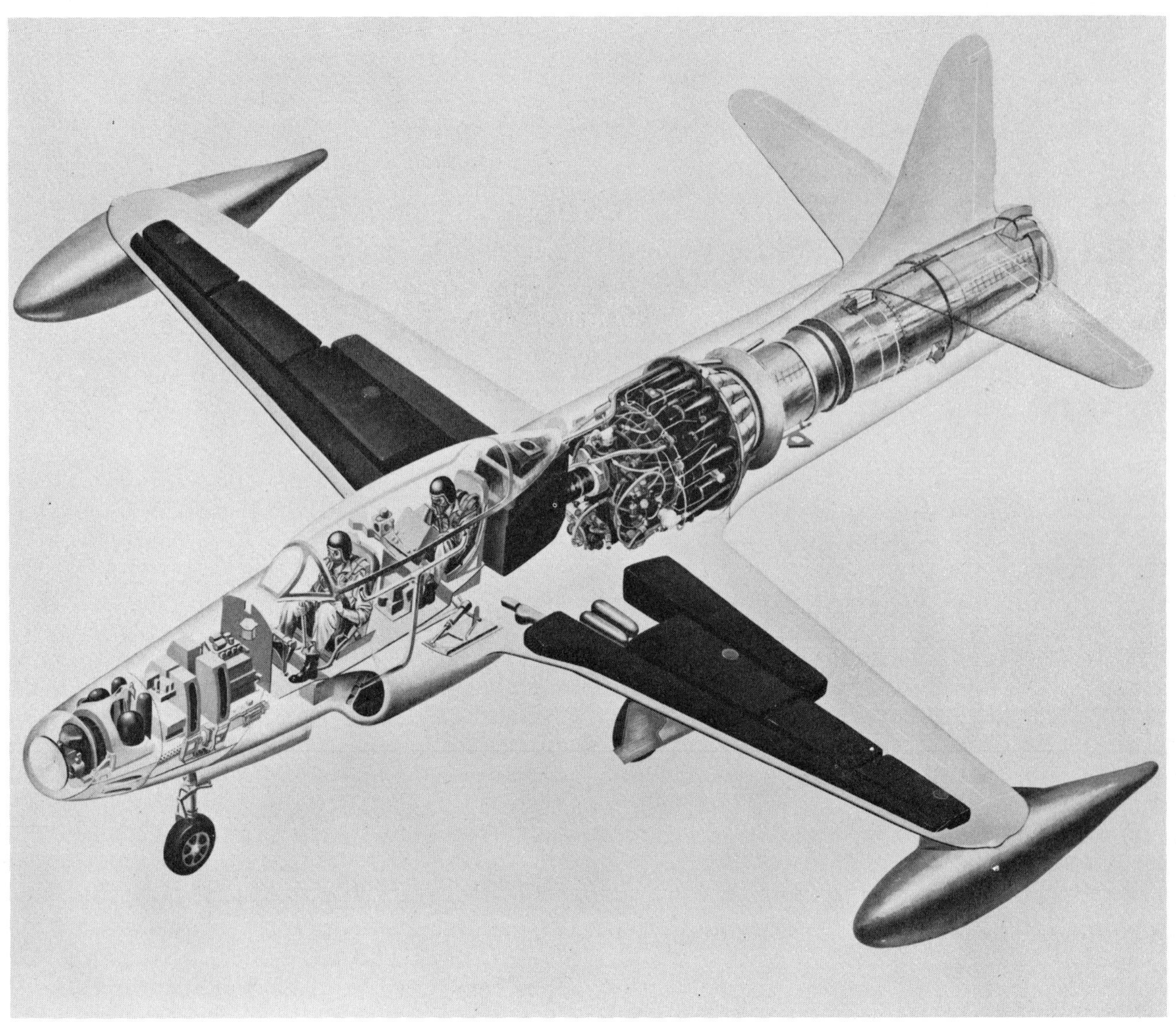

MFR
Fighter armament and equipment are seen in Lockheed F-94A cutaway.

Armor was tried out in 1918, but the weight hampered performance too much. Curtiss fighters in 1939 found it possible to have a ¼ in. plate behind the pilot without handicapping performance. European experience indicated that armor was essential and it was made standard on all American combat planes after 1940. That same year revived "self-sealing" or "leakproof" fuel tanks, originally tested in 1918 to prevent loss or ignition of fuel from bullet-punctured tanks.

The effect of this internal protection was to make many of 1941's planes slower than those of the year before, and to speed the trend toward heavier caliber armament. The weight of the P-40 fighter went up in a few months from 7215 to 8058 lbs. due to such changes, and top speed dropped from 357 to 345 mph.

Another World War II item added to the combat plane was radar, which has done much to reduce the effect of weather upon air war. Airborne radar may now weigh over 2000 lbs. and aids navigation, bomb-aiming, and the aiming of guns and rockets.

Bomber insides are shown in arrangement originally plann for Convair XB-36 prototype, with long bomb bay, retracta turrets. Production B-36s had 20-mm. guns in eight turrets.

1. PLASTIC NOSE
2. RADAR ANTENNA
3. RADAR MODULATOR
4. OXYGEN BOTTLE
5. RADAR RANGE SERVO GEAR BOX
6. AMMUNITION BOXES (4)
7. C-1 POSITION LIGHT FLASHER
8. AN/ARC-3 AND AN/ARN-6 RADIO RECEIVERS
9. GUN-SIGHT
10. PILOT'S RADAR INDICATOR
11. INSTRUMENT PANEL
12. PILOT'S SEAT
13. AN/ARN-6 RADIO COMPASS LOOP ANTENNA
14. RADAR INDICATOR POWER SUPPLY
15. RADAR MANUAL CONTROL
16. OPERATOR'S RADAR INDICATOR
17. RADAR OPERATOR'S SEAT
18. FUSELAGE FUEL TANK
19. ELEVATOR CONTROL ROD
20. J33-A-33 ENGINE
21. FUSELAGE AFT-SECTION ATTACHING POINT
22. AFTERBURNER
23. AN/ARC-3 RADIO ANTENNA
24. AFTERBURNER TRACK
25. AFTERBURNER EYELID ACTUATOR
26. ELEVATOR TAB MOTOR
27. GYROSYN COMPASS FLUX VALVE
28. AILERON BOOSTER UNIT
29. WING BEAMS
30. DIVE FLAPS
31. TURBINE AND COOLER UNIT
32. AILERON TORQUE TUBE
33. CABIN AIR MIXING VALVE
34. INTERPHONE AMPLIFIER
35. D-2 INVERTER
36. RADAR INVERTER
37. RADAR VERTICAL GYRO
38. RADAR
39. BATTERIES
40. AILERON-ELEVATOR CONTROL ASSEMBLY
41. RUDDER PEDALS
42. NOSE ALIGHTING GEAR
43. FUSELAGE NOSE-SECTION ATTACHING POINT
44. CASE EJECTION DOOR
45. MACHINE GUNS (4)
46. AIR-SPEED PITOT
47. GUN-SIGHT COMPUTER
48. GUN-SIGHT AMPLIFIER SERVO

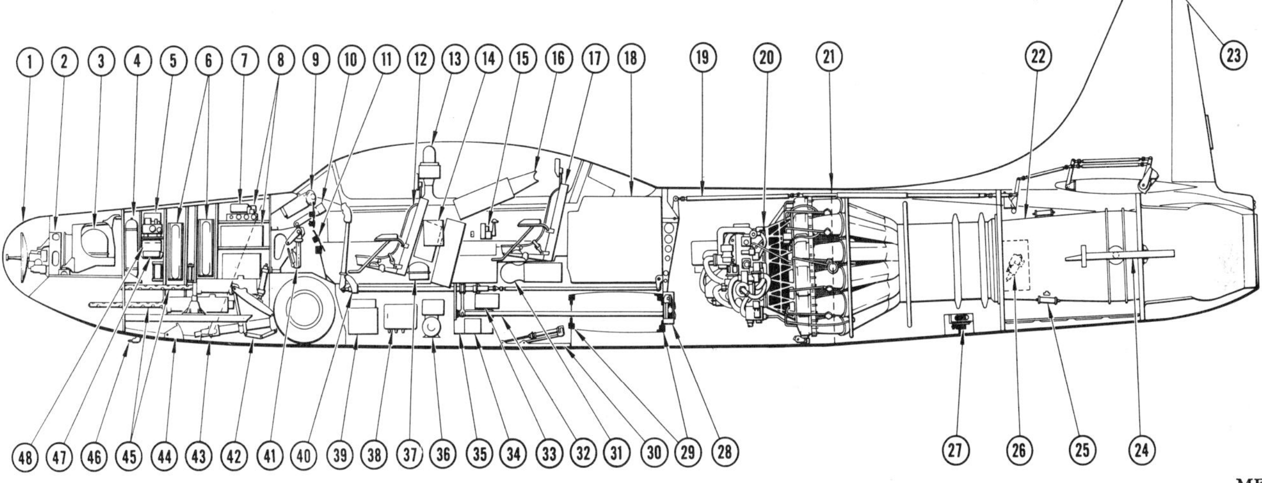

Side view below gives key to internal installations.

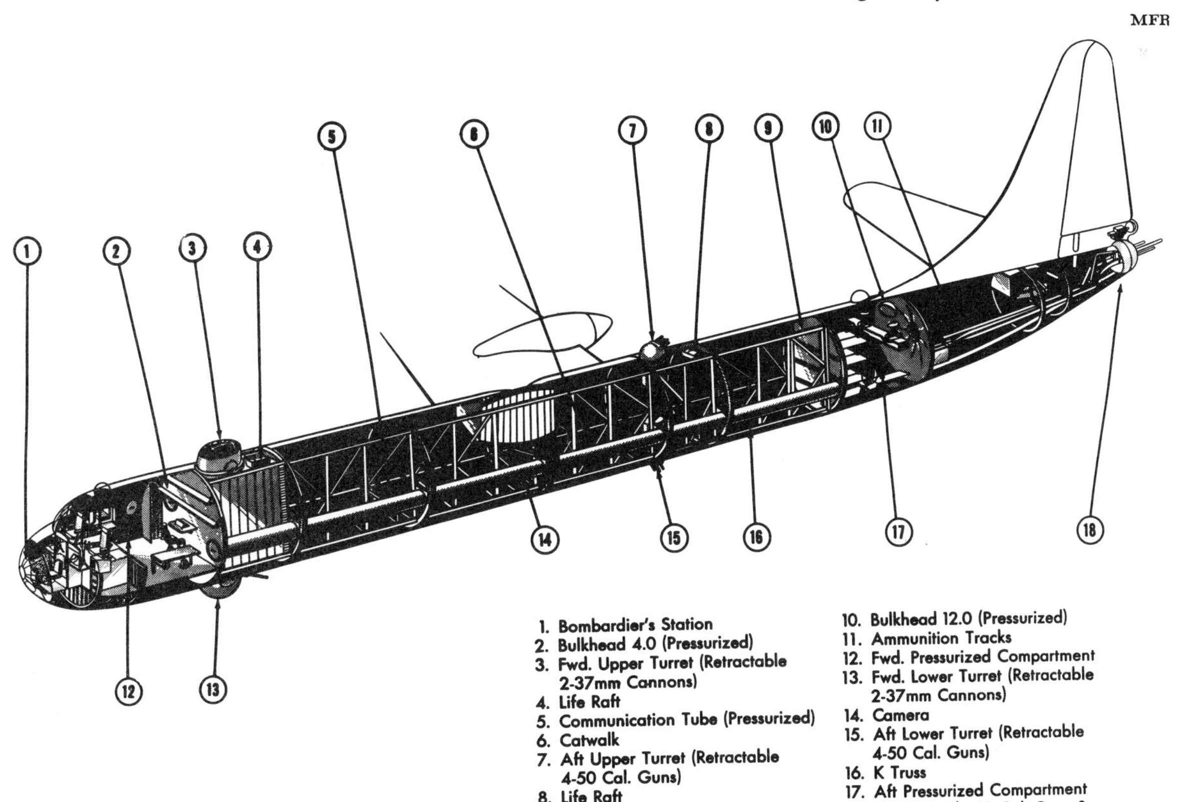

1. Bombardier's Station
2. Bulkhead 4.0 (Pressurized)
3. Fwd. Upper Turret (Retractable 2-37mm Cannons)
4. Life Raft
5. Communication Tube (Pressurized)
6. Catwalk
7. Aft Upper Turret (Retractable 4-50 Cal. Guns)
8. Life Raft
9. Bulkhead 10.0 (Pressurized)
10. Bulkhead 12.0 (Pressurized)
11. Ammunition Tracks
12. Fwd. Pressurized Compartment
13. Fwd. Lower Turret (Retractable 2-37mm Cannons)
14. Camera
15. Aft Lower Turret (Retractable 4-50 Cal. Guns)
16. K Truss
17. Aft Pressurized Compartment
18. Tail Turret (2-50 Cal. Guns & 1-37mm Cannon)

MFR

Early 5″ rockets on Lockheed P-38 were for ground attack.

PERFORMANCE GOALS

After all the paraphernalia has been provided for, the warplane's value is determined by its mobility, or performance. Speed, climb, ceiling, and range are the measurements of performance—how fast, high, and far the plane's weapons can be taken.

For years the designer has been impressed with the necessity of suppressing protruberances and gaping intakes so that drag will be reduced, and it is difficult to see how aircraft could be made much more streamlined than they are at present. Weight remains as the chief enemy of performance, against whom thrust and lift must be arrayed.

The measurement of the burden of gravity against thrust is *power loading*—the gross weight divided by the power or thrust available. The measurement of the burden upon lift is *wing loading*—the gross weight divided by the area of the wing. These expressions must be kept in mind in describing the achievement of high performance.

Falcon guided missiles with 2.75″ rockets on Northrop F-89H pod.

PMB

Sparrow air-to-air missiles on McDonnell F3H-2M.

PMB

Top speed is the measurement of the airplane's ability to catch or escape the enemy. Primarily, it is determined by an aircraft's power loading and its drag.[1] The lower the power loading the faster the aircraft, thus the lighter the weight and the greater the power, the higher the speed. The drag of any airframe is steadily reduced as the aircraft gains in altitude, due to the thinning density of the air. Therefore, the higher the altitude of a given power loading, the faster the plane. Unfortunately the thinner density of the air also means poorer engine performance, a condition which may be corrected by supercharging the engine so that sea-level pressures are maintained up to a high altitude. Without supercharging, an engine giving 1000 hp at sea level may give only 700 hp at 10,000 ft., 470 hp at 20,000 ft., and 295 hp at 30,000 ft.

An airplane makes its highest speed at the altitude at which the advantage of the lower drag is greater than the disadvantage of the loss of power due to the thinning air. This is known as the critical altitude. In unsupercharged airplanes, the critical altitude is at sea level, for the loss of power as the plane goes higher is not compensated by the reduction in drag. In the Curtiss P-6E, the last of our unsupercharged Army pursuits, top speed dropped from 198 mph at sea level to 196 at 5000 ft., 189 at 10,000 ft., and 182 at 15,000 ft. On the other hand, the Boeing 281 had a single-stage supercharger which maintained power into higher altitudes. Top speed therefore went from 215 mph at sea level to 235 at 6000 ft. (its critical altitude), and to 232 at 11,000 ft.

This effect was gained by a built-in, or integral supercharger run by the crankshaft of the engine. Later types used turbo-superchargers, run by the exhaust gases of the engine, which are heavier, and can maintain power up to 35,000 ft. The disadvantage of superchargers is their increased weight, which handicaps the supercharged aircraft's performance at sea level.

As far as fighter aircraft are concerned, rate of climb and ceiling come second only to top speed as performance criteria. *Rate of climb* is simply the time taken to reach a given altitude, or the feet gained in one minute's climb. *Service ceiling* is the altitude at which rate of climb is 100 ft. per minute, while *absolute ceiling* is the highest altitude an aircraft may achieve. Service ceiling is the criteria for tactical purposes.

The climbing ability of an aircraft is determined by both power loading and wing loading. The lower each is, the better the climb. Unfortunately a low power loading and high speed are not always compatible with a low wing loading and good climb. The larger the wing, the lower the wing loading, but the larger the wing, the more the drag. Therefore it can be seen that a fast plane with a small wing may not match in climbing ability a slower plane with a more generous wing area. An example of this was the Japanese Zero, whose low wing loading gave it a distinct advantage in climb and maneuverability over faster American types.

Maneuverability is the plane's ability to change direction. Wing loading and inertia are determining factors here. Maneuverability is adversely affected by aircraft inertia, or the natural resistance to any rotation about its center of gravity. Any heavy weights at a distance from the center of gravity will make maneuvers more difficult. The more compact and lighter the aircraft, the more maneuverable it will be, forcing designers to choose often between a fighter's ability to catch his enemy and his ability to maneuver into a good firing position. Diving speed is often useful in fighters, but today's streamlined aircraft often need brake devices to restrict diving speeds to safe limits.

Range is another vital characteristic and is determined by the number of hours an aircraft's fuel will allow it to stay in the air times the cruising speed. *Cruising speed* depends on altitude, gross weight, and power used, and thus is very variable. The range of an aircraft also has numerous possibilities depending on the amount of fuel carried. Throughout this book range is usually given at the normal cruising condition with the usual fuel load. Maximum ranges suggest the possibilities of the plane with its largest possible fuel load, and the most economical speed and altitude. *Endurance,* more easily measured in older aircraft than range, is given in hours and minutes, and is most often quoted at top speed. *Radius of action* is about 40 per cent of range.

Running engines at too high a speed may waste fuel, as in this example: With 2290 gals. of fuel and a gross weight of 55,000 lbs. the B-24D could achieve a range of about 2950 miles at a cruising speed of 200 mph at 25,000 ft. Increasing the speed to 250 mph reduces the range to 2400 miles. At an altitude of 5000 ft. however, B-24D range is only 1000 miles at 250 mph, and 2400 miles at 200 mph. The inefficiency of the supercharged engines at lower altitudes is evident. Any increase in the bomb load carried will reduce this range, while a substitution of fuel for bombs can increase the range.

Landing speed, while not tactically significant, is included in the specifications because it is a measure of relative safety, and is one of the earliest limiting points selected in the design of an aircraft. The faster the necessary landing speed, the more difficult the landing. Landing speed depends on wing loading and the lifting efficiency of the wing.

A designer begins his task with a proposed specification which gives the armament and performance required. Design procedure starts with an estimate of weight, as this is the prime limiting factor of aircraft. A list of the essential parts of the *useful load* is totaled,

[1] Propulsive efficiency is also a factor, but since propellers tended to be standardized, they are not considered in comparing aircraft designs in this book.

Salvo of 2.75″ rockets is fired from Convair F-102A in this picture sequence. Twenty-four rockets from 12 tubes in four missile bay doors are fired in less than half a second, leaving in 12 rapid pulses, two at a time.

MFR

31793

31793

CONVAIR
Inline, liquid-cooled Curtiss V-1570-59 powered Consolidated A-11, 1934 attack type.

including crew, armament, equipment, and probable fuel required. This is added to a rough estimate, from past experience, of the engine and airframe weight required to support such a load. Useful load and empty weight are added to make estimated gross weight.

An appropriate wing section and form is then selected; a hi-lift airfoil for a bomber, or a low drag airfoil for the fighter. *Aspect ratio* (the ratio of the wing span to the mean wing chord) is decided upon; a high aspect ratio for a long-range machine like the B-29, or a short, stubby wing for an interceptor.

The wing loading is then determined which would permit the desired landing speed. Dividing the gross weight by the wing loading gives the necessary *wing area.* Since 1930, lift-increasing devices such as landing flaps and wing slots have been added to reduce the wing area without raising the landing speed. The introduction of tricycle landing gear on combat planes in 1939 made feasible higher landing speeds, since the nose wheel permits more sudden stops. However wing loading should not be increased to a point detrimental to climb and maneuverability.

Once the weight has been estimated, the wing chosen, and the general layout planned, the performance of aircraft depends on its power loading. This leads us to the next problem: the selection of a power plant.

POWER PLANTS

To a designer the important features of an airplane engine are its power, weight, size, arrangement and number of cylinders, and the method of cooling. The reader should notice what the official designation tells about an engine. Allison's V-1710 has an inline *Vee* cylinder arrangement, and an approximate piston displacement of 1710 cubic inches, while Wright's R-2600 is a *radial* of some 2600 cubic inch piston displacement.

A piston engine's power is rated in horsepower available for take-off, and at a rated altitude. Jet (gas turbine) engines are rated by pounds of static thrust.

Early aircraft engines had their cylinders lined up behind one another in two rows, and were liquid cooled. (Water until the '30s; chemicals since then.) The most widely used inline engines were the Liberty 12 (V-1650) of 1918, the Curtiss D-12 (V-1150) of 1922, the Curtiss Conqueror (V-1570) of 1926, the Allison V-1710 of 1935, and the Packard Merlin (V-1650) of 1941. All had 12 cylinders. Experimental inline engines of the war period displayed other arrangements. The 12-cylinder Continental XIV-1430 was an inverted Vee type, while Allison's 24-cylinder V-3420 was two V-1710s coupled together side by side.

The radiator and cooling systems required by liquid-cooled engines added weight, drag, and maintenance problems. Air cooling offered the obvious advantage of low weight and simplified servicing, if only the engine could be kept from overheating. The rotary engines used on the World War I Nieuports, with their circle of whirling cylinders, represented an effort in this direction, but could develop only limited power.

The radial engine first used on American combat planes was the 9-cylinder Lawrence J-1 of 1922, used in the Navy's Curtiss TS fighter. Air cooling became so popular in the Navy, that after the more powerful 9-cylinder Pratt & Whitney Wasp (R-1340), Hornet (R-1690), and the early Wright Cyclone (R-1750) became available in 1927, radial engines were standard on Navy combat planes.

The National Advisory Committee for Aeronautics perfected a circular cowling which not only streamlined exposed cylinders more than early "anti-drag" rings, but improved cooling and made possible placement of a second row of cylinders behind the first. In 1934, the first 14-cylinder twin-row radials appeared as the successful Pratt & Whitney R-1830 Twin Wasp and the unlucky Wright R-1510 Twin Whirlwind. Together with the newer Wright single-row Cyclone (R-1820) this array of air-cooled power almost completely superseded, by 1938, liquid-cooled engines in both the Army and Navy.

PMB
Turbo-supercharger fitted to same basic engine and three-bladed propeller developed aircraft to P-30 high-altitude pursuit.

The inline engine, however, retained the advantage of a smaller frontal area, and permitted a streamlined nose especially helpful on fighters. The Second World War saw a revival of liquid-cooled engines which powered most fighters, although bombers and Navy

Radial, air-cooled engines like Pratt & Whitney R-2800-59 under P-47D-21s cowl, developed over 2000 hp in 1944.
AF

PMB
Wing flaps, like those extended on Lockheed Hudson V, permitted higher wing loading.

AMC
Bell XP-39 put engine behind pilot, and tricycle landing gear made high landing speeds safe.

Fighter production 1922; Boeing sold 2500 lb., wood-and-fabric MB-3As for $7240 each.

MFR

planes utilized the power offered by the 18-cylinder R-2800 Wasp and the R-3350 Cyclone. At the end of the war, the big 28-cylinder Wasp Major (R-4360) was available.

Wartime research indicated that propeller-driven aircraft could not be expected to achieve speeds much beyond 500 mph. When information was received in 1941 on the British Whittle jet engine, General Electric began developing this centrifugal-flow gas turbine into the J-31 and J-33 units. Meanwhile, Westinghouse in 1943 developed an axial-flow turbine, the J-34.

Axial-flow units are smaller in diameter, but longer than the centrifugal-flow types. Although the Pratt & Whitney J-48 is of the latter type, the Allison J-35, General Electric J-47 and J-73, Pratt & Whitney J-57, and Westinghouse J-40, are axial-flow units. Another type of gas turbine, the propeller-turbine, or turboprop, has been developed in the hope that it will provide some of the speed of the jet without sacrificing cruising range.

The chief disadvantage of the jet engine has been its thirsty consumption of fuel, which delayed its acceptance as a bomber power plant long after it had become standard for new fighters. Use of the afterburner, which doubles the already high fuel consumption, is limited to interceptors, which turn on the "A.B." for only a few minutes of emergency power.

In spite of the fuel problem, the gas turbine has replaced the piston engine as the power plant of nearly all combat planes now in production.

Fighter production 1958; increased complexity has raised cost of 30,000-lb. Convair F-106A past $1,500,000 mark.

MFR

Before leaving the subject of engines, the reader should note that modifications in basic types are indicated by dash numbers after the main designations. Odd dash numbers, as R-3350-23 and J-33-A-31, indicate Army and Air Force models, while even dash numbers are Navy models, as the A-3350-24 and J-34-WE-22.

PRODUCTION COSTS IN TIME AND MONEY

With the power plant chosen, preliminary estimates rechecked, and the plans of their project ready, the engineers have what is now called a "design study." The project is sent to the government, which after comparing it with competing designs, orders construction of a prototype. If field tests of additional examples seem desirable, the "X" models may be joined by "Y" or service test models. Then, a production order may be placed.

The cost of designing and engineering a prototype has gone up tremendously. The three XPW-9 fighters of 1923 cost $40,734, but the single XP-38 of 1938 cost $763,000. In 1949, it cost $5,091,000 to get the XF-90 into the air. In 1940 the P-51 took 97 engineers and 1100 drawings before it was flown, but ten years later, the F-86D required 600 engineers and 6572 drawings. Yet the costs of fighters are small beside those of bombers. The Boeing XB-17 of 1935 took 138,000 engineering hours and $500,000 to build. The XB-47 of 1947 required 3,464,000 engineering hours and nearly $12,000,000.

Mass production copies cost less than experimental planes, yet the P-51 airframes cost, "less general, administrative, and profit," $26,741 each, compared to $121,132 for the F-86. Today's supersonic fighters cost over $1,000,000 each. The cost of the B-36 hit $3,500,000 each, when all equipment was included.

No doubt about it, the air weapon, once hailed as a cheap substitute for the battleship, has become the most expensive element of the military establishment. The growing use of the huge hydraulic presses in production, and complicated electronics systems in the finished aircraft, has made military aircraft building possible only for the most advanced industrial combinations. When one remembers the Wright brothers' bicycle shop in Dayton, one wonders whether any fifty years of history have ever seen such an example of the impact of a scientific development upon society.

Chapter 3: A Guide to Designations

All Air Force combat types since June 11, 1948, have had but two designations: "F" for fighter, and "B" for bomber, as in the F-86 and B-50. Reconnaissance versions are prefixed by "R" as the RF-80 and RB-45C. Previous to that, a variety of letters are seen, beginning with the random names and designations made by individual firms up to 1919. Most companies continue their own numbering series, but from 1919 to 1924 the Air Service used an adaption of the French system. A more simplified classification was then used until 1948, with many modifications. Table 4 lists older designations used by Army combat planes, with the dates in use.

We might mention the block designations used on World War II Army planes to denote minor modifications and factory of origin. Thus, the Douglas A-24A-DE was built at the El Segundo, California, plant; the A-20B-DL at the Long Beach, California, facility; the A-20C-DO at the main Santa Monica, California, shop, and the A-24-DT at the firm's Tulsa, Oklahoma, shop. The Boeing-designed B-17G-VE was built by Lockheed's subsidiary, Vega. Since there are only a few cases in which the block designation was important, they are not often used in this work.

Navy combat aircraft today are known as "F" for fighter, "A" for attack, and "P" for patrol. These designations were simplified in March 1946 from the older system which included combinations of "TB" (torpedo bomber) and "PB" (patrol bomber). Naval aircraft are listed by a manufacturer's letter, with modification letters following. Thus, the P5M-2 is the fifth patrol design by Martin, second model, and the F6C-1 the sixth fighter by Curtiss, first model. Designations previous to about 1925 are an anarchy of privately placed labels. Like the Army, the Navy uses X as a prefix for experimental, as the XF12C-1.

Table 4

ARMY COMBAT TYPE DESIGNATIONS

A—Attack and light bombardment, 1926–48
B—Bombardment, 1926 to present
DB—Day bombardment, 1920–23
F—(Photographic reconnaissance, 1938–46)
Fighter, 1948 to present
FM—Fighter-multiplace, 1937–40
GA—Ground attack, 1920–22
HB—Heavy bombardment, 1926–27
LB—Light bombardment, 1925–30
NBL—Night bombardment—long distance, 1923
NBS—Night bombardment—short distance, 1921–24
P—Pursuit, 1925–48
PA—Pursuit—air cooled, 1922
PB—Pursuit—biplace, 1935
PG—Pursuit—ground attack, 1922
PN—Pursuit—night, 1921
PW—Pursuit—water cooled, 1921–28

Table 5

LETTERS ASSIGNED TO MANUFACTURERS OF NAVY COMBAT TYPES
(Dates indicate last deliveries of now defunct firms)

A	Brewster (1944)	Long Island City, New York
A	Atlantic-Fokker (1930)	
B	Boeing	Seattle, Washington
C	Curtiss (1947)	Buffalo, New York
D	Douglas	Santa Monica, California
E	Bellanca	New Castle, Delaware
F	Grumman	Bethpage, L. I., New York
G	Goodyear	Akron, Ohio
G	Great Lakes (1935)	Cleveland, Ohio
H	McDonnell	St. Louis, Missouri
H	Hall (1940)	Bristol, Pennsylvania
J	North American	Inglewood, California
J	Berliner-Joyce (1934)	Dundalk, Maryland
K	Kaiser	Bristol, Pennsylvania
K	Keystone (1930)	Bristol, Pennsylvania
L	Bell	Buffalo, New York
M	Martin	Baltimore, Maryland
M	Eastern (Div. of General Motors)	Trenton, New Jersey
N	Naval Aircraft Factory	Philadelphia, Pennsylvania
O	Lockheed (Plant One)	Burbank, California
R	Ryan	San Diego, California
S	Sikorsky	Stratford, Connecticut
T	Northrop	Hawthorne, California
U	Chance-Vought	Fort Worth, Texas
V	Lockheed (Vega plant)	Burbank, California
W	Canadian Car & Foundry (1945)	Fort William, Ontario, Canada
Y	Consolidated	San Diego, California

To the above list should be added suffixes sometimes added since World War II to denote special modifications, such as the F4U-5N. On combat types they include:

A—Amphibious version
B—Special Armament version
C—Carrier version
D—Special Drop Tank version
E—Special Electronic Gear version
G—Search-Rescue version
K—Target Drone version
L—Searchlight version
M—Missile launcher
N—Night version
P—Photographic version
Q—Radar Countermeasure version
S—Antisubmarine version
W—Early Warning version

Part 2 Army Attack and Light Bombers

Chapter 4: Airplanes against Infantry 1917-23

SHADOW OVER THE TRENCHES

When World War I airmen began using their planes to bomb enemy soldiers and civilians, aircraft specifically designed for this purpose soon appeared. Some were developments of the older single-engined, two-seat scouts, and could be used both for light bombing and reconnaissance. Larger and slower machines with bigger crews and two or more engines were ancestors of the medium and heavy bombers to be discussed later.

Here our concern is with the two-seaters carrying comparatively small bomb loads for short distances. By 1917, they were known as "day" or light bombers. This work required a plane larger than a fighter, smaller than a night bomber, and with the best speed possible from the burdened single engine. A pilot chauffeured the aircraft to the target, while the observer released bombs and hoped to discourage enemy fighters with his flexible guns.

While these light bombers shuttled back and forth across the lines, a more daring tactic of machine-gunning enemy trenches was developed by fighter pilots diverted from their more usual tasks. Low-flying planes buzzing hostile infantry lowered enemy morale and inflicted casualties. The Germans were so impressed by these tactics that two-seat fighters originally detailed to protect artillery spotting planes were given trench-strafing duty during the Battle of Arras in April 1917. Later these units were redesignated "battle flights" and used entirely for low-flying attack work. By 1918, they had specially designed Junkers and A.E.G. two-seaters with armor and belly guns.

The British also went in for ground-strafing, although they were more likely to use single-seat fighters. The standard types generally used would have been joined by Sopwith Salamanders designed as armored attack planes, had the war lasted longer.

By the end of the war, two tendencies in the tactics and design of close-support planes were evident. Although the more spectacular ground-strafers made a sharp impression, the conventional light bombers remained more widely used, eschewing the dangerous fire of enemy infantry for flight at safer heights and to more respectable distances with a bomb load more important than armor or extra guns. But the issue was unsettled, and we will see how planes for U. S. Army "attack" squadrons vacillated between the two tendencies.

If the "day bomber" squadrons of the A.E.F. followed the more common European mode, then the early '20s found the Army testing the German armored idea. During most of the period between the wars, a more conservative two-seater specialized for ground-strafing became the American substitute for Europe's "day" or light bomber.

FIRST SERVICE TYPES

Having no combat planes at all when it entered the First World War, the U.S. turned to French-built Breguet 14s and British-designed de Havilland 4s for its first light-bomber squadrons. Typical of the period, both were biplanes with two open cockpits, noses squared by big flat radiators for the water-cooled engines, wooden frame construction and fabric-covered wings held together with four pairs of struts and numerous wires.

The Breguet usually had a 300 hp Renault engine, and carried a single Vickers gun over it, firing through the propeller. The observer handled two Lewis guns on a Scarff ring, and 520 lbs. of bombs could be fitted on wing racks. After July 1918, self-sealing fuel tanks were installed. The 376 Breguets given us by France were used for training and observation work more often than for bombing, with but two squadrons of

AF

DE HAVILLAND DH-4
Liberty 12, 400 hp
DIMENSIONS: Span 42′ 5½″, Lg. 29′ 11″, Ht. 9′ 8″, Wing Area 440 sq. ft.
WEIGHT: Empty 2391 lb., Gross 3582 lb. Fuel 66 gal.
PERFORMANCE: Speed—Top 124 mph at s. l., 120 mph at 6500′. Service Ceiling 19,600′, Climb 10,000′/14 min. Range 270 miles.

Breguets at the front in November 1918. Table 6 gives data for the bomber version, 47 of which were received from March 1918 onward.

In August 1917 a British DH-4 arrived in the United States minus its engine. This sample model was fitted with the hastily designed 400 hp Liberty engine and flown on October 29, 1917. The mating of British plane and American engine was successful, and the design became the first combat plane to go into production in the United States.

The first American DH-4 was completed in February 1918, and by October production was greater than 1000 a month. Three firms participated in the program, producing 3431 before the end of the war, and 4846 before work stopped in 1919. On August 2, 1918, the DH-4 became the *first and only* American-built plane to fly over enemy territory in the First World War, and Armistice Day found the type equipping five bombing and seven observation squadrons of the A.E.F.

Table 6

PRODUCTION OF DE HAVILLAND-4 IN UNITED STATES

Company	No. Built	Canceled after Armistice
Dayton-Wright	3106	1900
Fisher Body	1600	2400
Standard	140	860

Armed with two Vickers or Marlin guns on the cowl, two Lewis guns at the rear pit, and 220 lbs. of bombs in wing racks, the DH-4s least popular feature was

AMC

BREGUET 14B.2
Renault 12-F, 300 hp
DIMENSIONS: Span 47′ 3″, Lg. 29′ 7″, Ht. 10′ 9″, Wing Area 560 sq. ft.
WEIGHT: Empty 2730 lb., Gross 3868 lb., Max. 4300 lb. Fuel 82 gal.
PERFORMANCE: Speed—Top 115 mph at s. l., Landing 55 mph. Service Ceiling 18,900′, Climb 16,400′/47 min. Range 280 miles.

AMC

ENGINEERING DIV. USD-9A
Liberty 12, 400 hp
DIMENSIONS: Span 45′ 11″, Lg. 30′ 3″, Ht. 10′ 6″, Wing Area 490 sq. ft.
WEIGHT: Empty 2815 lb., Gross 4521 lb., Max. 4987 lb. Fuel 142 gal.
PERFORMANCE: Speed—Top 121 mph at s. l. as bomber, 124 mph as reconnaissance, Landing 64 mph. Service Ceiling 13,500′, Absolute Ceiling 15,000′, Climb 6500′/13 min. Range 400 miles.

JAMES MORROW

DE HAVILLAND DH-4B
Liberty 12A, 416 hp
DIMENSIONS: Span 42′ 5″, Lg. 29′ 11″, Ht. 9′ 8″, Wing Area 439 sq. ft.
WEIGHT: Empty 2939 lb., Gross 4595 lb. Fuel 88 gal.
PERFORMANCE: Speed—Top 118 mph at s. l., Cruising 94 mph, Landing 64 mph. Service Ceiling 12,800′, Absolute Ceiling 14,700′, Climb 5000′/8.2 min.

the placement of the gas tank between the pilot and observer. Suspicious fliers dubbed the DH-4 the Flaming Coffin, but wartime statistics show a loss rate no higher than that shown by other two-seaters.

In October 1918, a standard DH-4 was converted to a DH-4B which used the 416 hp Liberty 12A. The gas tank on this model was larger, leakproof, and placed in front of the pilot, who was moved back. There were 1538 wartime DH-4s so rebuilt by 1923, when production was resumed on the modernized DH-4M, with 135 built by Atlantic, and 150 by Boeing. There were numerous variations, but these were intended for observation work or for commercial jobs, rather than combat.

Over 1000 of these two-seaters were still in Army hands in 1925, and their replacement in 1928 by the A-3 ended a varied postwar career in attack and observation squadrons, as well as on pioneer airmail routes and miscellaneous activities. The last was not scrapped until 1932. The DH-4 also remained standard Marine Corps equipment for many years.

AMERICAN-BUILT LIGHT BOMBERS

Meanwhile, designers in the United States hastened to provide native versions of foreign designs, all following the standard European pattern of two-seat, biplane light bombers. Two sample de Havilland 9s arrived from Britain in July 1918, were fitted with Liberty engines, and labeled USD-9. An improved, larger DH-4 with gas tank moved to a less dubious spot, the design was promptly copied as the Army's Engineering Division USD-9A, and 14,000 were ordered.

Flight tests began on September 24, 1918. Dayton-Wright finished four, and the Engineering Division eight, before the war ended. Armament included a .30-caliber Browning gun under the right-hand side of the cowl with 750 rounds and two Lewis guns with 970 rounds in the rear cockpit. Usual bomb load was 520 lbs. carried in racks below the wings and fuselage, while wireless and camera equipment could be fitted to the reconnaissance version.

The next light bomber to appear, the Packard LUSAGH-11 powered by a 408 hp Liberty engine, was tested in August 1918. Designed with the assistance of the French engineer, LePere, it was a double-bay biplane undistinguished in appearance and performance, armed with two Lewis guns and 450 lbs. of bombs. A second prototype, the LUSAGH-21

ENGINEERING DIV. LUSAGH-11 AF
Liberty 12, 408 hp
DIMENSIONS: Span 47′ 1″, Lg. 24′ 4″, Wing Area 601 sq. ft.
WEIGHT: Empty 3913 lb., Gross 5109 lb., Max. 5600 lb. Fuel 67 gal.
PERFORMANCE: Speed—Top 114 mph at s. l., 107 mph at 10,000′, Cruising 95 mph, Landing 61 mph. Service Ceiling 15,300′, Absolute Ceiling 17,000′, Climb 6500′/9.4 min., 875′/1 min. Range 275 miles at 107 mph.

AMC

POMILIO BVL-12
Liberty 12, 400 hp
DIMENSIONS: Span 48′ 3″, Lg. 31′ 7″, Ht. 9′ 9″, Wing Area 578 sq. ft.
WEIGHT: Empty 2824 lb., Gross 4552 lb. Fuel 115 gal.
PERFORMANCE: Speed—Top 111 mph at s. l., 106.5 mph at 6500′, Cruising 94 mph, Landing 61.5 mph. Service Ceiling 13,700′, Absolute Ceiling 15,900′, Climb 6500′/11.8 min., 710′/1 min. Range 485 miles/350 lbs. bombs.

appeared in January 1919, with a 420 hp Bugatti engine.

Also in this month appeared the first of six Pomilio BVL-12s with the Liberty engine. Based on an Italian design with three pairs of struts, the fuselage was suspended between the wings, and three .30-caliber guns and 350 lbs. of bombs were carried.

The LWF-G was flown in January 1918, but crashed on its first flight. It was rebuilt as the G-2 the following summer. Using the 435 hp Liberty, the G-2 was well equipped for warfare, with 66 pounds of cockpit armor, 592 lbs. of bombs, four fixed nose guns, two Lewis guns on the rear gunner's mount, and another Lewis gun firing through an opening in the belly. It was an interesting design, but none went into service.

PMB

L.W.F. G (Similar to G-2)

FLYING ARSENALS

Shortly after the war, the Army began experiments with armored aircraft designed to attack ground troops with gunfire. The first was the GAX (Ground Attack Experimental) built by the Engineering Division in May 1920. A contract for twenty more, designated GA-1, was given to Boeing on June 7, 1920, but the quantity was reduced to ten before the first example was delivered in May 1921.

Powered by Liberty engines driving four-bladed pusher propellers, these planes are the only twin-engined triplanes in Air Force history. A ton of ¼″ armor was installed to protect the engines and crew of three. Slow and awkward, the Boeing had a 37-mm. Baldwin cannon for the front gunner, and eight .30-caliber Lewis guns. Four of these pointed front and downward, another one faced aft over the wings, and all were fired by the busy front gunner. The rear gunner handled two belly guns and one upper gun. Some

PMB

L.W.F. G-2
Liberty 12, 435 hp
DIMENSIONS: Span 41′ 7″, Lg. 29′ 1″, Ht. 9′ 4″, Wing Area 516 sq. ft.
WEIGHT: Empty 2675 lb., Gross 4023 lb., Max. 4880 lb. Fuel 120 gal.
PERFORMANCE: Speed—Top 138 mph at s. l., 130 mph at 10,000′, Landing 50 mph. Absolute Ceiling 21,000′, Climb 10,000′/9.3 min. Range 550 miles at 130 mph.

of these guns had to be removed to permit carrying ten small fragmentation bombs. Service tests in Texas proved these planes to be unmaneuverable and gen-

AMC

ENGINEERING DIV. GAX
Liberty 12, 400 hp
DIMENSIONS: Span 65′ 6″, Lg. 33′ 7″, Ht. 14′ 3″, Wing Area 1016 sq. ft.
WEIGHT: Empty 7532 lb., Gross 9740 lb. Fuel 103 gal.
PERFORMANCE: Speed—Top 105 mph at s. l., 102 mph at 4000′, Cruising 89 mph, Landing 64 mph. Service Ceiling 11,500′, Climb 600′/1 min., 2000′/3.7 min. Range 160 miles.

erally unsatisfactory. Pilots complained of the long take-off run, poor visibility, and especially of vibration and noise from the armored sides.

A smaller single-engined attack biplane designed around an experimental 700 hp Engineering Division W-1A-18 engine was planned by Army Engineers. Two of these three-place GA-2s were built by Boeing in 1922. Behind the engine, at the leading edge of the lower wing, was mounted a 37-mm. cannon and two .50-caliber guns movable 60° in the vertical plane (downward and forward) and 15° in the horizontal. Another .50-caliber gun fired back and down through a tunnel, while two Lewis guns guarded the upper hemisphere. Protection was furnished by 1600 lbs. of ¼″ armor and the duplication of all struts, bracing and control wires, and spars. The GA-2 is the sole example of this weighty and expensive safety device. Like the GA-1, this Boeing sacrificed performance for ferocity.

The American sales representative of a famous German firm offered the Army in December 1921 an attack monoplane with remarkable armament. Based on a wartime design, the Junkers-Larsen JL-12 had what was then the unusual low-wing arrangement and corrugated metal fuselage characterizing Junkers planes, and used a 420 hp Liberty engine. Its biggest threat was twenty-eight Thompson .45-caliber submachine guns fixed to fire downward. Another pair was mounted in the crew's enclosed cabin, one firing through a window on each side. Some protection was offered by 400 lbs. of ⅛″ armor plate.

The 28 belly guns were mounted in the floor; twelve pointed slightly forward, six directly down, and ten inclined to the rear. Half the guns could be fired at once, or a single trigger could set off all 28, delivering a fire volume for once justifying the old cliché about a rain of bullets. The test pilot opposed purchase of the plane, however, as a bad flier, expensive, and with an armament array of doubtful efficiency.

In 1923, three examples of a different design appeared. The Aeromarine PG-1 (pursuit, ground) was a small single-seater biplane designed for strafing and for destroying armored attack planes of the GA-1 type. The latter function proved unnecessary, for foreign nations, perhaps appalled by the designs inspired here, did not then adopt ground-strafers!

Completed by Boeing, the PG-1 used a 330 hp Wright K2 engine with a 37-mm. cannon mounted in the crankshaft, and a .50-caliber cowl gun. (One was tested with a Packard 1237.) Vee struts connected the wings and ¼″ armor plate guarded the cockpit. However, placing the radiator above the engine and in front of the pilot, and lowering the upper wing so that his head poked through the center section, had a distressing effect on the pilot's visibility. Pilots welcomed the type's abandonment.

The general failure of these armored ground-strafers was due to inadequacies of the time's engineering: not enough strength and power, and too much weight and drag. All through the decade following the war, therefore, attack-squadron equipment, like that of the observation outfits, had to be drawn from the wartime stock of DH-4s.

One effort was made to develop a light bomber of really advanced layout. Stimulated by the success of the metal low-wing, internally braced monoplanes built by Junkers and Dornier, the Army ordered the

AMC

BOEING GA-2
Engineering Div. W-1A-18, 700 hp
DIMENSIONS: Span 54′, Lg. 37′, Ht. 12′, Wing Area 851 sq. ft.
WEIGHT: Empty 6784 lb., Gross 9085 lb., Max. 9150 lb.
PERFORMANCE: Speed—Top 110 mph, Cruising 100 mph. Service Ceiling 11,100′, Absolute Ceiling 13,000′, Climb 6500′/16.5 min. Range 165 miles.

JUNKERS JL-12 [*Photo unavailable*]
Liberty 12, 420 hp
DIMENSIONS: Span 49′, Lg. 33′, Ht. 10′ 4″, Wing Area 417 sq. ft.
WEIGHT: Empty 2900 lb., Gross 5000 lb. Fuel 140 gal.
PERFORMANCE: Speed—Top 125 mph at s. l., Landing 60 mph. Climb 10,000′/18 min. Range 400 miles.

Gallaudet DB-1 on December 24, 1920. A low-wing two-seater minus outside wing bracing, it had a 700 hp Engineering Division W-1A water-cooled engine. Between the pilot and gunner's cockpit was a bay for 600 lbs. of bombs and fuel to last, they hoped, for eight hours. Top speed was expected to be 141 mph.

But when the DB-1 (Day Bomber One) was delivered in December 1921, it proved to be overweight; 9207 lbs. instead of the 7050 lbs. estimated. When the control system tended to buckle the duralumin skin, it was decided not to fly the ship, but use it for static tests only. A lighter second machine with a new wing was ordered in February 1922 as the DB-1B.

The DB-1B made the first of its few flights on August 1, 1923, showing eccentricities that discouraged many further tests. It was armed with 600 lbs. of bombs and about 1400 rounds for four guns; one in the nose, two Lewis in the rear cockpit, and the last a belly gun. Unlike other postwar attack planes, it was intended for daylight bombing raids instead of ground strafing, but the design was too advanced for the day's structural knowledge.

AMC

AEROMARINE PG-1
Wright K-2, 330 hp
DIMENSIONS: Span 40′, Lg. 24′ 6″, Ht. 8′, Wing Area 389 sq. ft.
WEIGHT: Empty 3030 lb., Gross 3918 lb. Fuel 45 gal.
PERFORMANCE: Speed—Top 130 mph, Landing 58 mph. Service Ceiling 17,000′, Absolute Ceiling 19,000′, Climb 6500′/9.5 min. Range 195 miles at top speed.

AMC

GALLAUDET DB-1
Engineering Div. W-1A-18, 700 hp
DIMENSIONS: Span 67′, Lg. 44′, Ht. 10′ 2″, Wing Area 663 sq. ft.
WEIGHT: Empty 9207 lb., Gross 11,160 lb. Fuel 248 gal.
PERFORMANCE: (Estimated) Speed—Top 144 mph at s. l., 140 mph at 10,000′, Cruising 128 mph. Service Ceiling 17,150′, Absolute Ceiling 18,850′, Climb 10,000′/12.4 min. Endurance 8 hrs.

GALLAUDET DB-1B [*Photo unavailable*]
Engineering Div. W-1A-18, 700 hp
DIMENSIONS: Span 66′ 7″, Lg. 42′ 6″, Ht. 12′ 7″, Wing Area 684 sq. ft.
WEIGHT: Empty 5060 lb., Gross 8600 lb. Fuel 250 gal.
PERFORMANCE: Speed—Top 127 mph at s. l. Service Ceiling 13,400′, Absolute Ceiling 15,500′, Climb 706′/1 min.

Chapter 5: The Single-Engined Attack Plane 1925–40

CURTISS FALCONS

All the foregoing experiments had convinced the Army that armor and cannons were not worth their cost in flying performance. After a four-year breathing space, it was decided to try again with designs less bloodthirsty and original but thoroughly proven in service. Such types were found in the two-place biplanes then used by observation squadrons.

First of the new pattern was the Douglas XA-2,[1] whose conversion from a single O-2 observation plane was approved in March 1926. An orthodox two-place biplane, the XA-2 utilized an inverted 433 hp Liberty V-1410 engine altered for air-cooling, presumably to dispense with the vulnerable radiator. Armament included six .30-caliber Brownings firing forward, and two flexible Lewis guns for the gunner. Two of the fixed guns were in the nose, two were in the upper wing, two were in the lower wing, and bombs were in internal racks.

The first attack design actually approved for large-scale use was the Curtiss Falcon, already in service as the O-1. In July 1926, the Falcon was recommended "as a substitute until a more satisfactory type can be developed." The first contract placed on February 28, 1927, was increased in June and August, and deliveries began in October 1927 on the seventy-six A-3s that became the first production attack types to replace the DH-4s in service. Five with minor modifications were redesignated A-3A. They were followed by orders in June 1929 and March 1930 for seventy-eight A-3B models. Tested in April 1930, the A-3B had new ailerons and a tail wheel, and cost $11,215 per plane.

The A-3 had typical Curtiss lines. A 435 hp Curtiss D-12D engine was under the smooth cowling, the radiator was underneath and a neat prop spinner gave the nose the characteristic "Eversharp pencil" appearance. The lower wing was straight, while the upper wing was swept back from a straight center section. There were two nose guns and two wing guns firing forward, and two flexible Lewis rear guns. All were .30-caliber, with 400 rounds provided for the wing guns and 600 rounds for the others. Wing racks for 200 lbs. of bombs were attached, in the belief that a supplementary bomb load was more useful than a surplus of automatic weapons.

While the A-3 was successful enough to remain in service several years, Curtiss used one in May 1928 for an experimental air-cooled engine installation. When fitted with a 410 hp Pratt & Whitney R-1340-1 Wasp, the Falcon was known as the XA-4.

The same machine with a Curtiss V-1570 Conqueror of 600 hp was to be known as the XA-5, while the XA-6 was planned to test the odd Curtiss H-1640 hexagonal 600 hp unit. Both of these projects were canceled before completion as attack planes, but the XO-16 and the XO-18 were similar.

THE MONOPLANES

The demand for faster speeds brought the monoplane into the attack classification. First were the Fokker XA-7 and the Curtiss XA-8, two-place low-wing monoplanes powered with the 600 hp Curtiss Conqueror, an inline liquid-cooled engine. Each was armed with four .30-caliber guns firing forward outside of the propeller arc, a fifth Browning for the rear gunner, and could carry 488 lbs. of bombs for a two-hour flight.

The former model, built by the Atlantic-Fokker Company, had been ordered in December 1929, and was tested in January 1931 with a thick wing minus external bracing, the radiator beneath the engine,

[1] A new series had begun under the simplified designation system of 1924, but XA-1 had already been used for an ambulance plane.

AMC

DOUGLAS XA-2
Liberty V-1410, 433 hp
DIMENSIONS: Span 39′ 8″, Lg. 29′ 7″, Ht. 11′, Wing Area 414 sq. ft.
WEIGHT: Empty 3179 lb., Gross 4985 lb. Fuel 65 gal.
PERFORMANCE: Speed—Top 130 mph. Climb 800′/1 min.

wheel pants, and open cockpits close together. Later, the prototype re-emerged from the shops with changes in the nose and wheel fairings.

Its competitor, the Curtiss XA-8 Shrike, had thin wings externally braced by wires, and landing gear entirely enclosed in spats. Construction was all-metal, the structure used in all attack- or light-bomber aircraft following this machine. Cooling was accomplished by a radiator below and behind the engine, which was neatly streamlined behind the prop spinner. Modern features of the XA-8 were its wing slots and

PMB

CURTISS A-3B
Curtiss V-1150-5, 435 hp
DIMENSIONS: Span 38′, Lg. 27′ 2″, Ht. 10′ 6″, Wing Area 353 sq. ft.
WEIGHT: Empty 2875 lb., Gross 4458 lb., Max. 4476 lb. Fuel 113–149 gal.
PERFORMANCE: Speed—Top 139 mph at s. l., 136 mph at 5000′, Cruising 110 mph, Landing 60 mph. Service Ceiling 14,100′, Absolute Ceiling 16,100′, Climb 948′/1 min., 5000′/6.25 min. Range 628 miles.

flaps to minimize landing speed, the first to appear on a U.S. combat plane. It also had the first enclosed cockpits, several feet apart, for both crewmen. The prototype was ordered in May 1930 and flown the following year.

The Curtiss design was judged the better of the pair, and was awarded a contract on September 29, 1931, for 13 service test examples. These went into

AF

CURTISS A-3
Curtiss V-1150-3, 435 hp
DIMENSIONS: Span 38′, Lg. 28′ 4″, Ht. 10′ 1″, Wing Area 353 sq. ft.
WEIGHT: Empty 2612 lb., Gross 4378 lb. Fuel 113–169 gal.
PERFORMANCE: Speed—Top 141 mph, Cruising 116 mph, Landing 61 mph. Service Ceiling 15,600′, Absolute Ceiling 17,300′, Climb 1046′/1 min., 5000′/5.8 min. Range 630 miles at top speed.

MFR

CURTISS XA-4
Pratt & Whitney R-1340-1, 410 hp (421 hp actual)
DIMENSIONS: Span 38′, Lg. 28′ 4″, Ht. 10′ 1″, Wing Area 353 sq. ft.
WEIGHT: Empty 2348 lb., Gross 4114 lb. Fuel 114 gal.
PERFORMANCE: Speed—Top 139 mph at s. l., 136 mph at 5000′, Cruising 112 mph, Landing 58 mph. Service Ceiling 15,975′, Absolute Ceiling 17,700′, Climb 1040′/1 min.

MFR

FOKKER XA-7
Curtiss V-1570-27, 600 hp
DIMENSIONS: Span 46′ 9″, Lg. 31′, Ht. 9′ 5″, Wing Area 333 sq. ft.
WEIGHT: Empty 3866 lb., Gross 5650 lb.
PERFORMANCE: Speed—Top 184 mph, Landing 61 mph.

AF

CURTISS XA-8

MFR

CURTISS XA-8
Curtiss V-1570-23, 600 hp
DIMENSIONS: Span 44′, Lg. 32′ 6″, Ht. 9′, Wing Area 285 sq. ft.
WEIGHT: Empty 3673 lb., Gross 5413 lb. Fuel 96–123 gal.
PERFORMANCE: Speed—Top 197 mph at s. l., 191 mph at 5000′, Cruising 162.5 mph, Landing 75 mph (65 mph/flaps). Service Ceiling 19,800′, Absolute Ceiling 21,450′, Climb 1265′/1 min. Range 682 miles.

service in June 1932 as the YA-8 (later A-8). Heavier than the original, they also had a pair of forward guns in each wheel spat, with 600 rounds for each of these, and the rear gun. The last of these ships, the Y1A-8A,

PMB

CURTISS YA-8
Curtiss V-1570-31, 600 hp
DIMENSIONS: Span 44′ 3″, Lg. 32′ 10″, Ht. 9′, Wing Area 285 sq. ft.
WEIGHT: Empty 3938 lb., Gross 5706 lb. Fuel 101–153 gal.
PERFORMANCE: Speed—Top 183 mph at s. l., 179.5 mph at 5000′, Cruising 157.5 mph, Landing 69 mph. Service Ceiling 18,100′, Absolute Ceiling 19,700′, Climb 1325′/1 min., 5000′/4.4 min. Range 425 miles/464 lbs. bombs, 734 miles max.

was tested in February 1933 with a geared Conqueror "F" engine; less noisy, but heavier than the standard model. The field trials of the Shrike were successful enough to merit a 46 plane production order on February 27, 1933.

However, by 1933 the Army was reviewing the aircraft power-plant situation to determine future policy. The air-cooled radial engine had proven to be less expensive to operate than the liquid-cooled inline type. Another advantage, especially telling in the attack classification, was that the radial was free of the radiator area the inline engine exposed to the retaliatory fire of ground forces. The Army's policy was then set as favoring air-cooled engines on all attack planes, even though this caused a loss in top speed, as a comparison of the A-12 and A-17 with the A-8 and A-11 will show.

First product of this policy was the YA-10 of 1933, a regular YA-8 rebuilt to use the Pratt & Whitney Hornet of 625 hp. The cowling and mount of this air-cooled radial was poorly streamlined. Another version of this ship was offered to the Navy with a Wright engine as the XS2C-1 for scouting work.

When the 46 production Shrikes began tests in March 1934, they were of the A-12 type instead of the A-8B as originally planned. An air-cooled radial, the 690 hp Wright Cyclone, was the power plant, and the two cockpits were close together, with the pilot's cockpit open, and the gunner's semienclosed. In other respects, the design was similar to the previous models, with the usual five guns and 488 lbs. of bombs. An external 52 gallon drop tank could replace the latter. The forward guns in the wheel pants could be adjusted 2° down, and 1° up, and 1° to either side.

While attack squadrons were receiving the Curtiss

PMB

CURTISS Y1A-8A (A-8A)
Curtiss V-1570-57, 675 hp
DIMENSIONS: Span 44′ 3″, Lg. 33′ 7″, Ht. 9′ 2″, Wing Area 285 sq. ft.
WEIGHT: Empty 4330 lb., Gross 6287 lb. Fuel 105–157 gal.
PERFORMANCE: Speed—Top 181 mph at s. l., 176 mph at 5000′, Cruising 156 mph, Landing 75.5 mph. Service Ceiling 17,000′, Absolute Ceiling 18,600′, Climb 1225′/1 min. Range 624 miles.

PMB

CURTISS YA-10
Pratt & Whitney R-1690-9, 625 hp at s. l.
DIMENSIONS: Span 44′ 3″, Lg. 32′ 6″, Ht. 9′, Wing Area 285 sq. ft.
WEIGHT: Gross 6135 lb. Fuel 101–153 gal.
PERFORMANCE: Speed—Top 175 mph at s. l.

products, testing also proceeded on some more advanced projects. The first of these was the Lockheed YA-9, projected in 1931 from the YP-24 experimental. This design incorporated the most modern features then available, including fully retractable landing gear, flaps, and enclosed cockpits. Top speed was 214 mph with a 600 hp Conqueror engine. This design and its misfortune is described more fully in the chapter on fighters.

When Lockheed proved unable to fulfill the five plane service test order placed in September 1931,

CURTISS A-12
Wright R-1820-21, 670 hp at s. l.
DIMENSIONS: Span 44′, Lg. 32′ 3″, Ht. 9′ 4″, Wing Area 285 sq. ft.
WEIGHT: Empty 3898 lb., Gross 5756 lb., Max. 5900 lb. Fuel 114–166 gal.
PERFORMANCE: Speed—Top 177 mph at s. l., 173.5 mph at 5000′, Cruising 150.5 mph, Landing 69.5 mph. Service Ceiling 15,150′, Absolute Ceiling 16,600′, Climb 5000′/5.1 min. Range 510 miles/464 lbs. bombs.

AF

CONSOLIDATED A-11
Curtiss V-1570-59, 675 hp PMB
DIMENSIONS: Span 43′ 11″, Lg. 29′ 3″, Ht. 9′ 10″, Wing Area 297 sq. ft.
WEIGHT: Empty 3805 lb., Gross 5490 lb. Fuel 90–180 gal.
PERFORMANCE: Speed—Top 227.5 mph at s. l., Cruising 193 mph, Landing 84 mph. Service Ceiling 23,300′, Absolute Ceiling 24,900′, Climb 5000′/3.4 min. Range 470 miles/327 lbs. bombs, 950 miles max.

Consolidated produced a development of the basic design in January 1933, called the YA-11, and won the defaulted contract. With increased power and improved nose, the YA-11 was similar to the YP-25 but minus the turbo-supercharger. Tests of the four A-11s purchased began in January 1935. Using the 675 hp V-1710-59 Curtiss Conqueror engine, and armed with 300 lbs. of bombs, two cowl and two wing fixed guns and one flexible gun, the A-11 had a performance far advanced over its contemporaries. Apparently the Army's policy opposing liquid-cooled engines in attack ships blocked its wider acceptance. However, the pursuit versions of the ship (P-30 and PB-2A) won larger orders. A modified XA-11A engine test ship became the first plane to take the Allison 1000 hp V-1710 into the air.

In February 1933, Vought tried to reintroduce the biplane into the attack picture with the V-70A proposal; a five-gun version of the O3U with wheel pants and cowl for the Pratt & Whitney R-1690C Hornet. Designed to weigh 5300 lbs. and do 193 mph top, it did not pass the drawing-board stage.

NORTHROP ATTACK PLANES

In August 1933, Northrop completed a military development of the popular commercial Gamma and Delta models. An all-metal, low-wing monoplane with pleasing lines, the Model 2-C, or XA-13, had enclosed cockpits and the wheel pants that were a Northrop

NORTHROP XA-13
Wright R-1820-37, 712 hp at 3300′
DIMENSIONS: Span 48′, Lg. 29′ 2″, Ht. 9′ 2″, Wing Area 362 sq. ft.
WEIGHT: Empty 3600 lb., Gross 6463 lb., Max. 6575 lb. Fuel 245–262 gal.
PERFORMANCE: Speed—Top 207 mph at 3300′, 198 mph at s. l., Cruising 172 mph, Landing 70 mph. Service Ceiling 21,750′, Absolute Ceiling 23,600′, Climb 1300′/ min., 5000′/4.3 min. Range 1100 miles.
AF

trademark in that period. Armament was the standard four fixed guns tucked into the wing, plus the flexible gunner's Browning and 600 lbs. of bombs. A Wright R-1820-37 turned the two-bladed propeller.

An improved light-bomber version was the Northrop 2E, which carried three machine guns and 1100 lbs. of bombs, and had a semiretractable bombardier's window beneath the rear cockpit. A single 2E was sold in 1934 to the R.A.F., and some 150 were built for China in 1935. Powered by a supercharged R-1820, it achieved 210 mph with bomb load and 228 mph without bombs.

The XA-13 itself was purchased in June 1934 by the Army, which on December 19 gave Northrop this period's largest attack-plane order—110 planes at a cost of $2,047,774. Since these planes were to use Pratt & Whitney R-1830 Wasps, one was installed on the prototype for testing.

However, when in March 1935, Northrop flew the rebuilt prototype as the Model 2F with Pratt & Whitney R-1830-7 engine, troubles began. Designated XA-16 by the Army, this model had 800 hp, a three-bladed propeller, and changes about the tail surfaces and cockpit enclosures. Yet on April 25, 1935, the company notified the Army that either a larger tail or a smaller engine would be necessary. To prevent disruption of production, the Army chose a smaller engine, and received its first A-17 in August 1935.

Delivered through 1936, the production models were heavier machines using the smaller R-1535-11 Wasp, Jr., new open-sided wheel fairings, perforated flaps, and further changes about the tail. The armament was five .30-caliber guns and twenty 30-lb. fragmentation bombs carried in chutes inside the fuselage. Larger bombs might be carried externally, maximum bomb load being 654 lbs.

In December 1935 the Army ordered the Northrop A-17A, which was identical except for its retractable wheels, an 825 hp Wasp, Jr., and paintless Alclad finish. (An order of March 15, 1935, eliminated most paint on Army planes until wartime camouflage.) Between August 1936 and September 1938, 129 were completed, together with two special 600 hp R-1340-45 powered three-place Command "taxis" known as the A-17AS. Ninety-three of these A-17As were transferred back to Douglas on June 20, 1940, to be resold to Britain and France for training and emergency use. In exchange, Douglas added twenty planes to the current A-20A order. Of the 93 A-17As, 32 were detained at the French colony of Martinique, and the remainder, after a stay in England, went to South Africa.

MFR

NORTHROP 2E
Wright R-1820-F53, 750 hp at 11,000′
DIMENSIONS: Span 48′, Lg. 28′ 10″, Ht. 9′ 1″, Wing Area 363 sq. ft.
WEIGHT: Empty 3850 lb., Gross 6400 lb., Max. 7600 lb. Fuel 362 max.
PERFORMANCE: Speed—Top 210 mph at 11,500′ (7600 lb.), 228 mph (6400 lb.). Service Ceiling 23,600′, Absolute Ceiling 30,700′, Climb 5000′/5 min.

PMB

NORTHROP XA-16
Pratt & Whitney R-1830-9, 950 hp take-off, 850 hp at 8000′
DIMENSIONS: Span 48′, Lg. 29′ 8″, Wing Area 362 sq. ft.
WEIGHT: Gross 6750 lb.
PERFORMANCE: Speed—Top 212 mph.

ATTACK BOMBERS FOR EXPORT

The Northrop design enjoyed many foreign sales. Sweden purchased two model 8A-1s as well as a license to build the design in Sweden as the B-5. Like thirty 8A-2s built in 1938 for Argentina, the 8A-1 had the A-17s fixed landing gear, but was powered with a British engine, the Bristol Hercules. The Argentine 8A-2 used a Wright Cyclone.

After the Northrop factory and designs were sold to Douglas, production continued on more powerful export versions of the A-17A with retractable wheels. In 1939, ten single-row Cyclone-powered 8A-3Ps for Peru were followed by twenty twin-row Wasp-powered 8A-3Ns for the Netherlands, delivered in time to meet the German invasion of 1940. From April to June 1940, fifteen 8A-4s went to Iraq, followed, from October on, by 36 8A-5s for Norwegian forces in Canada.

In 1942, thirty-one were requisitioned by the U. S. Army for defense needs and designated the Douglas A-33. This model was similar to the A-17A in appearance and size, but had a Wright R-1820-87 Cyclone

MFR

NORTHROP A-17

Pratt & Whitney R-1535-11, 750 hp

DIMENSIONS: Span 47′ 9″, Lg. 32′, Ht. 12′, Wing Area 362 sq. ft.

WEIGHT: Empty 4913 lb., Gross 7337 lb. Fuel 150–287 gal.

PERFORMANCE: Speed—Top 206 mph at s. l., Cruising 170 mph, Landing 67.5 mph. Service Ceiling 20,700′, Absolute Ceiling 22,150′, Climb 5000′/3.8 min. Range 650 miles/654 lbs. bombs, 1242 miles max.

AF

PMB

developing 1200 hp for take-off and 860 hp at 11,000 ft. The export model had an armament of two .50-caliber and two .30-caliber wing guns, a .30-caliber upper gun, and had a semiretractable enclosure under the fuselage for the bombardier. Up to 1800 lbs. of bombs might be carried.

The Vultee V-11 was a development of that firm's 1934 V-1A transport. The transport had lost its commercial market with the banning of single-engined planes from commercial airlines, and so Vultee turned to the military market for new sales. As a three-place, low-wing monoplane with retractable wheels and a long cockpit enclosure, the V-11 met with immediate success, in spite of the destruction of the prototype in a fatal crash in September 1935.

The first order was received in 1935 from China for thirty planes, and was followed by an order from the U.S.S.R. By November 1938, forty more V-11s had been delivered to Turkey, and work was started on a 26-plane Brazilian contract. Some of the latter's planes were twin float torpedo-carrying seaplanes with modified tails. The Soviets even built some themselves under license. Armament of the V-11 included four .30-caliber guns in the wings, and two flexible .30s for the rear gunner. One of these was the usual type of upper gun, while the other was a retractable belly gun. All guns had 600 rounds of ammunition each.

The V-11 could be operated as an attack plane with 600 lbs. of bombs in internal racks and a 1125 mile range. Alternatively, it was a bomber carrying 1100 lbs. with a 2380 mile range, or 3000 lbs. for 640 miles. Various Wright Cyclone single-row engines were utilized, but the one most frequently used was the 850 hp (at 5000 ft.) R-1820-G2.

Not until after the V-11 became popular abroad was it tested by the U. S. Army. Seven service test exam-

NORTHROP A-17A

Pratt & Whitney R-1535-13, 825 hp at 2500′

DIMENSIONS: Span 47′ 9″, Lg. 31′ 8″, Ht. 12′, Wing Area 362 sq. ft.

WEIGHT: Empty 5106 lb., Gross 7550 lb. Fuel 151–247 gal.

PERFORMANCE: Speed—Top 220 mph at 2500′, Cruising 170 mph, Landing 64 mph. Service Ceiling 19,400′, Absolute Ceiling 20,800′, Climb 1350′/1 min., 5000′/3.9 min. Range 732 miles/654 lbs. bombs, 1195 miles max.

MFR

NORTHROP 8A-1
Bristol Hercules, 875 hp
DIMENSIONS: Span 47′ 9″, Lg. 31′ 9″, Ht. 12′ 11″, Wing Area 363 sq. ft.
WEIGHT: Empty 4680 lb., Gross 7500 lb. Fuel 290 gal.
PERFORMANCE: Speed—Top 219 mph at 6250′, Cruising 190 mph, Landing 66 mph. Service Ceiling 22,500′, Climb 1430′/1 min. Range 1380 miles max.

MFR

NORTHROP 8A-2
Wright R-1820G-3, 840 hp
DIMENSIONS: Span 47′ 9″, Lg. 31′ 6″, Ht. 12′ 4″, Wing Area 363 sq. ft.
WEIGHT: Empty 4899 lb., Gross 7500 lb. Fuel 225 gal.
PERFORMANCE: Speed—Top 223 mph at 8700′, Cruising 200 mph, Landing 65 mph. Service Ceiling 25,400′, Climb 1300′/1 min. Range 1190 miles max.

MFR

DOUGLAS 8A-3N
Pratt & Whitney R-1830-SC3G, 1050 hp take-off, 900 hp at 12,000′
DIMENSIONS: Span 47′ 9″, Lg. 32′ 5″, Ht. 9′ 9″, Wing Area 363 sq. ft.
WEIGHT: Empty 5508 lb., Gross 7848 lb., Max. 8948 lb. Fuel 250 gal.
PERFORMANCE: Speed—Top 260 mph, Cruising 205 mph, Landing 66 mph. Service Ceiling 29,600′, Climb 1430′/1 min. Range 910 miles.

PMB

DOUGLAS 8A-5 (A-33)
Wright R-1820-87, 1200 hp take-off, 1000 hp at 6900′
DIMENSIONS: Span 47′ 9″, Lg. 32′ 6″, Ht. 9′ 4″, Wing Area 363 sq. ft.
WEIGHT: Empty 5510 lb., Gross 8600 lb., Max. 9200 lb. Fuel 173–252 gal.
PERFORMANCE: Speed—Top 248 mph at 15,700′, Landing 67 mph. Service Ceiling 29,000′.

MFR

VULTEE V-11
Wright R-1820-G2, 850 hp at 5800′
DIMENSIONS: Span 50′, Lg. 37′ 6″, Ht. 10′, Wing Area 384 sq. ft.
WEIGHT: Empty 6176 lb., Gross 9441 lb., Max. 11,437 lb. Fuel 250–504 gal.
PERFORMANCE: Speed—Top 229 mph at 5800′, 214 mph at s. l., Cruising 207 mph, Landing 68 mph. Service Ceiling 23,000′, Climb 1285′/1 min. Range 1225 miles/600 lbs. bombs, 2380 miles max.

PMB

VULTEE YA-19
Pratt & Whitney R-1830-17, 1200 hp take-off, 1050 hp at 6500′
DIMENSIONS: Span 50′, Lg. 37′ 10″, Ht. 10′, Wing Area 384 sq. ft.
WEIGHT: Empty 6452 lb., Gross 10,421 lb. Fuel 311–330 gal.
PERFORMANCE: Speed—Top 230 mph at 6500′, Cruising 207 mph, Landing 80 mph. Service Ceiling 20,400′, Absolute Ceiling 22,000′, Climb 1320′/1 min. Range 1110 miles/1080 lbs. bombs, 1385 miles max.

JACK CANARY

VULTEE XA-19A
Lycoming 0-1230-1, 1275 hp
DIMENSIONS: Span 50′, Lg. 38′ 3″, Wing Area 384 sq. ft.
WEIGHT: Empty 6605 lb., Gross 10,285 lb.
PERFORMANCE: Speed—Top 232 mph.

ples for comparison with twin-engined types were ordered in June 1938, and delivered the following year as the YA-19. Unlike the export versions, they were powered by Pratt & Whitney Wasps, the R-1830-17 giving 1200 hp for take-off. Six .30-caliber guns, and 1080 lbs. of bombs were the armament. Two ships were completed as engine test beds, the most unique being the XA-19A with the 1200 hp Lycoming O-1230-1 inline engine and lengthened tail.

In 1939, Vultee tried again with the V-12 which had improved streamlining and the Wright R-1820-G105A of 900 hp at 6500 ft. Armament was similar to that on the V-11 except for the substitution of .50-caliber guns for two of the wing guns. China ordered twenty-six V-12Cs (R-1820-105B) and fifty-two V-12Ds (R-2600-A5B). One of each was completed by Vultee in 1940, but the rest were shipped in parts for assembly in Asia.

A curious episode in American warplane history brought another firm into the light-bomber picture. This was the conversion of a small five-place cabin job for personal use to a two-seat warplane used in the China war in 1938. Powered with a 400 hp Pratt & Whitney Wasp, the Spartan "Executive" was a clean-looking low-wing monoplane with retractable wheels. Cabin furnishings were removed, and replaced by two .30-caliber nose guns, a flexible gun mounted at a hatch, and an outside rack for 300 lbs. of bombs.

A few months later, the Spartan firm offered an avowed military design in the form of the "Zeus," several of which went to Mexico. Based on the Executive, it had a 500 hp Wasp, and its two crew members under a conventional canopy, with two machine guns and 250 lbs. of bombs.

Another two-seat monoplane appearing in 1938 was the North American NA-44 light bomber, also intended for the economy-minded air force. A souped-up version of that firm's famous AT-6 trainer, the demonstration model was shown to South American purchasers. Delivery began in July 1940, on 31 machines built for Brazil. Ten more ordered on November 29, 1939, by Siam were shipped abroad, but were intercepted by the Army in the Philippines, in October 1941, for fear they might reach Japanese hands. As the A-27, these NA-69s were with General MacArthur's forces when the war began.

Powered by the Wright R-1820-75 giving 745 hp at 9600 ft., the A-27 carried 400 lbs. of bombs and five .30-caliber guns; two in the nose, two in the wings, and the flexible rear gun.

SWISHER-PMB

VULTEE V-12C
Wright GR-1820-105B, 1050 hp take-off
DIMENSIONS: Span 50′, Lg. 38′ 2″, Ht. 12′ 11″, Wing Area 384 sq. ft.
WEIGHT: Empty 6641 lb., Gross 10,111 lb., Max. 12,078 lb. Fuel 494 gal.
PERFORMANCE: Speed—Top 254 mph at 18,000′ as attack (231 mph as bomber), Cruising 226 mph (194 mph), Landing 70 mph. Service Ceiling 25,200′ (20,200′), Climb 6560′/5.8 min.

VULTEE V-12D
Wright GR-2600-A5B, 1600 hp take-off, 1275 hp at 11,500′
DIMENSIONS: As V-12C
WEIGHT: Empty 7416 lbs., Gross 10,886 lbs., Max. 12,853 lbs. Fuel 350 gal.
PERFORMANCE: Speed—Top 281 mph at 11,000′ as attack (270 mph as bomber), Cruising 248 mph (230 mph). Service Ceiling 28,000′ (25,400′), Climb 2000′/1 min.

MFR

WILLIAMS

SPARTAN ZEUS
Pratt & Whitney R-1340-S3H-1, 550 hp
DIMENSIONS: Span 39′, Lg. 27′ 3″, Ht. 8′ 6″, Wing Area 256 sq. ft.
WEIGHT: Empty 3440 lb., Gross 4953 lb. Fuel 112 gal.
PERFORMANCE: Speed—Top 234 mph at 5000′, Cruising 218 mph, Landing 65 mph. Service Ceiling 29,400′, Climb 2100′/1 min. Range 760 miles.

NORTH AMERICAN A-27 (NA-69)
Wright R-1820-75, 785 hp take-off, 745 hp at 9600′
DIMENSIONS: Span 42′, Lg. 29′, Ht. 12′ 2″, Wing Area 258 sq. ft.
WEIGHT: Empty 4520 lb., Gross 6006 lb., Max. 6700 lb. Fuel 120–170 gal.
PERFORMANCE: Speed—Top 250 mph at 11,500′, Cruising 220 mph, Landing 70 mph. Service Ceiling 28,000′. Range 575 miles/400 lbs. bombs, 800 miles max.

MFR

Chapter 6: Attack Bombers with Two Engines 1935–44

DEVELOPMENTS OF 1935–39

Although the use of two engines would improve performance and safety, the Army was cautious about adding to the cost and complexity of its attack planes, and it took a decade before twin-engined types replaced the smaller ships used through the 1930s.

In May 1934, an attack version of the Martin YB-10 bomber was projected. Designated XA-15, it was to have two Wright R-1820-25s, weigh 12,356 lbs. gross, and do 214 mph at 4500 ft. This design was dropped in the paper stage in favor of the faster Curtiss XA-14.

Completed in September 1935, the XA-14 was a carefully streamlined all-metal monoplane with retractable wheels, pencil-pointed nose, and crew of two under a long enclosure. Two Wright twin-row R-1670-5 Whirlwinds of 775 hp turned two-bladed propellers. Although top speed was much higher than other attack or bomber types, the Army hesitated at large-scale production. Curtiss wanted to try to break some records with the prototype, but it was used instead for 37-mm. gun tests.

Thirteen examples were ordered on July 23, 1936, at $82,497 each for service tests. Powered by single-row R-1820-47 Cyclones with 850 hp and three-bladed propellers, these ships were designated YA-18, and began tests in December 1937. Standard armament of the XA-14 and YA-18 included four .30-caliber nose guns and another for the rear gunner, and a 654-lb.

CURTISS XA-14
Wright R-1670-5, 775 hp at 10,000′
DIMENSIONS: Span 59′ 5″, Lg. 40′ 3″, Ht. 10′ 9″, Wing Area 526 sq. ft.
WEIGHT: Empty 8456 lb., Gross 11,738 lb. Fuel 287–617 gal.
PERFORMANCE: Speed—Top 254 mph at 9750′, Cruising 211 mph, Landing 75 mph. Service Ceiling 27,125′, Absolute Ceiling 28,500′, Climb 1685′/1 min. Range 816 miles/600 lbs. bombs.

AF

AF

CURTISS XA-14

PMB

CURTISS A-18
Wright R-1820-47, 930 hp take-off, 850 hp at 2000′
DIMENSIONS: Span 59′ 6″, Lg. 42′ 4″, Ht. 15′, Wing Area 526 sq. ft.
WEIGHT: Empty 9410 lb., Gross 12,679 lb., Max. 13,170 lb. Fuel 287–630 gal.
PERFORMANCE: Speed—Top 238.5 mph at 3500′, Cruising 211 mph, Landing 73 mph. Service Ceiling 28,650′, Absolute Ceiling 30,000′, Climb 5000′/2.2 min. Range 1443 miles/654 lbs. bombs, 1700 miles max.

internal bomb load. An export version, the Curtiss 76-D with the Cyclone G-3 of 840 hp at 10,200 ft. was offered, but found no buyers.

Twin-engined attack types meant more than improved performance and safety. Additional power also allowed larger bomb loads, so that American attack planes could match the capabilities of the swift twin-engined light bombers then being acquired by European powers. Prodded by the threatening war, the Army announced a design competition for "attack bombers," a new specification foreshadowed by the A-18s two engines and the A-19s larger bomb load. The minimum requirements included a 1200-lb. bomb load to be carried 1200 miles at an operating speed of at least 200 mph.

The preliminary designs submitted in July 1938 included one with inline engines, Bell's Model 9. Two Allison V-1710s were expected to yield a top speed of 255 mph at 3000 ft. with a 19,500-lb. gross weight, including two 37-mm. guns. Faster speeds, however, were promised by the radial-engined proposals including the 17,470-lb. Stearman X-100 at 269 mph, the 15,800-lb. Martin 167F at 275 mph, and the 14,700-lb. Douglas Model 7 offering 280 mph. Encouraged by results, the Army invited the companies to build sample planes and submit bids to be opened March 17, 1939. Bell dropped out, but the other three firms, plus North American did build prototypes for the competition that determined the World War II attack-bomber pattern.

All four prototypes were three-place all-metal monoplanes with two radial engines, three-bladed propellers, and retractable wheels, reflecting European light bombers like the Bristol Blenheim and Dornier DO-17. All had four .30-caliber fixed guns for ground attack and an internal bay for the bomb load.

Two Pratt & Whitney R-2180-7 Twin Hornets powered the Stearman X-100, which had its wing mounted high on a squared-off fuselage. Appearing first with its bombardier and pilot under an unbroken Plexiglas nose, it was later reworked to have a separate pilot's windshield, the broken nose sacrificing streamlining for drag. This caused the top speed to drop below early estimates, but the Army bought the prototype as the XA-21. A socket in the nose allowed a flexible front gun, while the rear gunner had a .30-caliber gun in a turret behind the wing, and another in a belly fixture. Four wing guns and up to 2700 lbs. of bombs could be used against ground targets.

STEARMAN XA-21 (Photo shows original nose)
Pratt & Whitney R-2180-7, 1400 hp take-off, 1150 hp at 7000′
DIMENSIONS: Span 65′, Lg. 53′ 1″, Ht. 14′ 2″, Wing Area 607 sq. ft.
WEIGHT: Empty 12,760 lb., Gross 18,230 lb. Fuel 450–520 gal.
PERFORMANCE: Speed—Top 257 mph at 5000′, Cruising 232 mph, Landing 72 mph. Service Ceiling 20,000′. Range 720 miles/1200 lbs. bombs, 1500 miles max.

MFR

STEARMAN XA-21

AMC

AF

NORTH AMERICAN NA-40B
Wright R-2600-A71, 1500 hp take-off, 1275 hp at 12,000′
DIMENSIONS: Span 66′, Lg. 48′ 3″, Ht. 23′, Wing Area 598.5 sq. ft.
WEIGHT: Empty 13,961 lb., Gross 19,741 lb. Fuel 476 gal.
PERFORMANCE: Speed—Top 309 mph at 14,000′, Cruising 282 mph. Service Ceiling 25,000′. Range 1200 miles/1200 lbs. bombs.

Another high-wing design was offered in the North American NA-40, which had two Wright R-2600-A2 Cyclones, twin rudders, and featured tricycle landing gear. Armament included seven .30-caliber guns; four in the wings, one in the nose ball and socket turret, and the rear gunner's upper and lower flexible guns. The layout was a forerunner of the B-25 bomber.

During its tests at Wright Field, the NA-40 crashed, eliminating it from the competition. The Douglas 7B prototype had met the same fate while still in the builder's hands, leaving the Stearman ship and Martin's 167 the only survivors. To these firms' disappointment, no contract was awarded; the Army instead calling for new bids in April for design proposals without prototypes. The same firms submitted new bids, in addition to Vincent Burnelli, who offered an Allison-powered job with a radical airfoil fuselage and twin tail booms.

Douglas offered a new version of their plane, with Wright R-2600 engines instead of the R-1830 Wasps used on the 7B prototype. This won an order for 186 attack bombers, while only the prototypes of Stearman and Martin were purchased. Glenn L. Martin protested the decision in a letter to Secretary of War Harry H. Woodring, but to no avail.

FROM BALTIMORE, MARYLAND

Although the Martin 167 won no Army contract, there was no need for the Baltimore builder to be disappointed, for France had ordered 115 on January 26, 1939.

The XA-22 prototype flown to Wright Field on March 14, 1939, was like the low-wing, tail-down 167s bought by France, but had R-1830-37 Wasps giving 1100 hp at 5000 ft. and a hatch sliding forward over the rear retractable gun turret. Armament included four .30-caliber wing guns, one in the turret, another in a deeply cut lower position, and up to 1800 lbs. of bombs dropped by the bombardier in the transparent nose.

By August 1939, the first French 167 flew, but deliveries could not begin until the arms embargo was repealed in October, when an additional order was

MARTIN XA-22
Pratt & Whitney R-1830-37, 1200 hp take-off, 1100 hp at 5000′
DIMENSIONS: Span 61′ 4″, Lg. 46′ 8″, Ht. 10′, Wing Area 538.5 sq. ft.
WEIGHT: Empty 11,170 lb., Gross 16,000 lb., Max. 17,000 lb. Fuel 390–530 gal.
PERFORMANCE: Speed—Top 280 mph at 5000′, Cruising 260 mph. Service Ceiling 20,000′. Range 750 miles/1800 lbs. bombs, 1200 miles/1200 lbs. bombs, 1900 miles max.

MFR

placed. The first contract was completed in November, but before completion of the second in July 1940, France was defeated, and the last 75 ships went to Britain. Known there as the Maryland I, they were powered by R-1830-SC3G Wasps of 900 hp at 12,000 ft. Between December 1940 and April 1941, 150 Maryland IIs were delivered to the R.A.F. with R-1830-S3C4-G Wasps of 1000 hp at 12,500 ft.

French 167s had gone into action against the Nazis on May 22, 1940, and were used by Vichy supporters against Britain in September, while the R.A.F. ships were used in North Africa.

Meanwhile an improved version, the XA-23, was planned with Wright R-3350-11 engines. This project was dropped, but in May 1940 an order had been placed for 400 Martin 187s, designed to meet British requirements for increased power and armament. The Lend-Lease Act made available more funds to the British, and 575 more were ordered in June 1941, plus 600 in July 1942.

First flown June 14, 1941, the Martin 187B was dubbed the "Baltimore," and differed from the Maryland by having Wright 1600 hp R-2600-A5B engines, self-sealing fuel tanks, 211 lbs. of armor, and a deeper fuselage for a four-man crew and a ton of bombs. Fifty Baltimore I and one hundred Baltimore II types had eleven .30-caliber guns; four fixed in the wings, two flexible guns for the upper rear cockpit, another for the ventral spot, and an unusual mounting of four belly guns pointing aft and fixed at an angle 9° down and 1½° out. Hand-held upper guns were replaced on the 250 Baltimore IIIs by a Boulton Paul power turret with four .30-caliber guns. Known as the A-30 on U.S. records, 281 Baltimore IV lend-lease ships substituted a Martin power turret with two .50-caliber guns.

Wright R-2600-29 Cyclones of 1700 hp powered the Baltimore V, or A-30A, which appeared in December 1942. When Baltimore production ended in May 1944, 894 Vs had been built. Both the 1575 Baltimores and the R.A.F.'s Maryland served entirely in the Mediterranean theatre.

MFR

MARTIN 167 (MARYLAND I)
Pratt & Whitney R-1830-SC3G, 1050 hp take-off, 900 hp at 12,000′
DIMENSIONS: As XA-22
WEIGHT: Empty 10,586 lb., Gross 15,297 lb., Max. 16,571 lb. Fuel 255–510 gal.
PERFORMANCE: Speed—Top 304 mph at 13,000′, 275 mph at s. l., Cruising 248 mph, Landing 71 mph. Service Ceiling 29,500′, Climb 2000′/1 min. Range 1300 miles.

MARTIN BALTIMORE I (187B)
Wright R-2600-19 (A5B), 1600 hp take-off, 1400 hp at 10,000′
DIMENSIONS: Span 61′ 4″, Lg. 48′ 6″, Ht. 11′ 3″, Wing Area 538.5 sq. ft.
WEIGHT: Empty 15,149 lb., Gross 21,750 lb., Max. 22,958 lb. Fuel 490–980 gal.
PERFORMANCE: Speed—Top 308 mph at 13,000′, 284 mph at s. l., Cruising 230 mph. Service Ceiling 22,300′, Climb 13,130′/7.9 min. Range 1082 miles/1000 lbs. bombs, 2800 miles max.

MFR

HAVOC FROM DOUGLAS

One attack bomber from the competition remains for discussion—the design originally by Jack Northrop

MARTIN BALTIMORE II (As BALTIMORE I)

SI

AMC

MARTIN A-30 (BALTIMORE IV)
Wright R-2600-19, 1600 hp take-off, 1275 hp at 11,500′
DIMENSIONS: Span 61′ 4″, Lg. 48′ 6″, Ht. 14′ 2″, Wing Area 538.5 sq. ft.
WEIGHT: Empty 15,460 lb., Gross 22,600 lb., Max. 27,100 lb. Fuel 490–1440 gal.
PERFORMANCE: Speed—Top 305 mph at 11,500′, Cruising 225 mph, Landing 87 mph. Service Ceiling 23,300′, Climb 10,000′/7 min. Range 800 miles/2000 lbs. bombs, 1100 miles/1000 lbs. bombs, 2800 miles ferry.

that came out as the Douglas 7B in December 1938. This ship made headlines when it crashed the following month with a French official aboard. Discovery by the press of a Frenchman on a secret ship was the first tip-off that the U.S. had reversed its usual policy and was allowing France to inspect and buy our latest designs.

A high-wing monoplane with two 900 hp Pratt & Whitney Wasps and the first tricycle landing gear on an American warplane, the 7B had four .30-caliber guns in the metal nose, one in a rotating rear turret, and another in the belly.

France ordered 105 in February 1939, and the first flew August 17, 1939, with R-1830-SC3G Wasps like those on the Maryland I. The French DB-7 could be distinguished from the prototype by a transparent bombardier's nose, engine nacelles below the wings, intakes on the cowl top instead of the leading edge, and a ring mount instead of the turret. Another order placed in October was completed in 1940 with R-1830-S3C-4G Wasps giving 1200 hp for take-off and 1000 hp at 12,500 ft. Armament of the 100 SC3-G and 170 S3C-4G DB-7s included 2080 lbs. of bombs, four 7.5-mm. fixed guns, a 7.5-mm. flexible upper rear gun, and one aimed through a ventral aperture. Fighting began for the DB-7 on May 31, 1940, with attacks on invading German columns.

Of 270 Wasp-powered DB-7s built on French contracts, 15 with the SC3-G and 147 with the S3C4-G were transferred to Britain after France's surrender in June 1940. Named Boston I, the former became trainers introducing tricycle landing gear to R.A.F. pilots. The 147 Boston IIs went to Fighter Command for night work. Painted black and fitted with flame-dampening exhaust, they were renamed Havoc I. Some were used for intruder attacks on enemy bases, others had AI (Aircraft Intercept) radar and a solid nose with eight .30-caliber fixed guns to hit enemy bombers.

Britain also inherited contracts for 100 ships with Wright R-2600-A5B Cyclones of 1600 hp for take-off, longer nacelles, and broader vertical tail. Designated DB-7A, and first accepted in November 1940, they had noses and guns like the DB-7, plus armor, and one was tested with twin tails. Except for one that crashed before delivery, the DB-7As were converted in England to Havoc II night fighters with radar and twelve .30-caliber nose guns.

The 123 A-20As the Army had ordered on May 20, 1939, began appearing in December 1940, followed by twenty more added to the contract in exchange for the A-17s resold to the Allies. (See p. 61.) Powered by Wright R-2600-3 Cyclones, the A-20A had a larger nose enclosure, more fuel or up to 2600 lbs. of bombs, and seven .30-caliber guns: four set low in the nose, two in the rear cockpit, and one in the belly. Another A-20A and eight A-20Bs were purchased by the Navy in October 1940 and became the BD-1 and BD-2s.

Sixty-three A-20 light bombers ordered the same day were to get R-2600-7 Cyclones turbo-supercharged to give 1500 hp at 20,000 ft. Delivery was delayed by the engines, however, and it was realized that high altitude performance (395 mph at 20,000 ft. was anticipated) was of little value when small bomb loads required accurate, low-level bombing. Flight tests on the first A-20 in 1941 showed the turbo-supercharged engines almost impossible to cool, and the supercharging was deleted from further aircraft, while the lone A-20 became the XP-70 night fighter. In March 1940, conversion of three of the A-20s into F-3 photo-reconnaissance ships was ordered, and another order on October 15, 1941, authorized conversion of the remainder to P-70 night fighters with AI-4 radar. These versions are discussed further in Chapter 17.

Britain's version of the A-20A were 541 DB-7Bs delivered in 1941, which had seven .303-caliber guns, self-sealing tanks and armor. The Royal Air Force name was Boston III, and 240 additional DB-7Bs were built by Boeing between August 1941 and January 1942. First tested in February 1941, the R.A.F. Bostons became famous for their raids against German-held territory from France to Libya. Bomber Command's first Boston III sortie was made in February 1942, against Occupied France. Two Boston III squadrons had four 20-mm. guns under the fuselage for intruder sorties. Some DB-7Bs were passed on to Russia, and 213 were transferred to Army Air Force units after Pearl Harbor.

On October 11, 1940, the AAF ordered 999 A-20Bs and 775 O-53 reconnaissance versions. The O-53s were

MFR

MARTIN A-30A (BALTIMORE V)
Wright R-2600-29, 1700 hp take-off, 1450 hp at 12,000′
DIMENSIONS: As A-30
WEIGHT: Empty 15,875 lb., Gross 22,622 lb., Max. 27,850 lb. Fuel 490–1440 gal.
PERFORMANCE: Speed—Top 320 mph at 15,000′, Cruising 224 mph, Landing 87 mph. Service Ceiling 25,000′, Climb 10,000′/4.8 min. Range 920 miles/2000 lbs. bombs, 980 miles/1000 lbs. bombs 2600 miles ferry.

DOUGLAS 7B (Prototype A-20)
Pratt & Whitney R-1830-S6C3-6, 1100 hp at 5000′
DIMENSIONS: Span 61′, Lg. 45′ 5″, Wing Area 464 sq. ft.
WEIGHT: Gross 15,000 lb.
PERFORMANCE: Speed—Top 304 mph at 5000′. Service Ceiling 27,600′

MFR

DOUGLAS DB-7 (BOSTON I)
Pratt & Whitney R-1830-SC3G, 1050 hp take-off, 900 hp at 12,000′

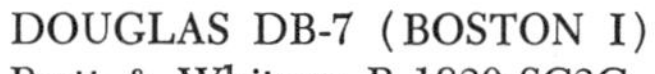

DIMENSIONS: Span 61′ 4″, Lg. 46′ 11″, Ht. 15′ 10″, Wing Area 464 sq. ft.
WEIGHT: Empty 11,400 lb., Design Gross 16,000 lb., Max. 17,031 lb. Fuel 325 gal.
PERFORMANCE: Speed—Top 314 mph at 15,000′, Cruising 270 mph, Landing 81 mph. Service Ceiling 28,570′, Climb 2440′/1 min. Range 630 miles.

MFR

IWM

DOUGLAS HAVOC I
Pratt & Whitney Wasp SC4-G, 1100 hp at 6200′; 1000 hp at 12,500′
DIMENSIONS: As DB-7
WEIGHT: Empty 11,520 lb., Max. 17,151 lb. Fuel 325 gal.
PERFORMANCE: Speed—Top 320 mph at 15,000′. Service Ceiling 32,300′.

H. LEVY

DOUGLAS DB-7A (Twin-tailed modification)

MFR

DOUGLAS DB-7A
Wright R-2600-A5B, 1500 hp take-off, 1275 hp at 11,500′
DIMENSIONS: Span 61′4″, Lg. 48′, Ht. 15′10″, Wing Area 464 sq. ft.
WEIGHT: Empty 13,584 lb., Design Gross 16,700 lb., Max. 19,322 lb. Fuel 325 gal.
PERFORMANCE: Speed—Top 323 mph at 12,800′, Cruising 275 mph, Landing 89 mph. Service Ceiling 27,680′, Climb 2420′/1 min. Range 490 miles.

MFR

DOUGLAS DB-7B (BOSTON III)
Wright R-2600-A5BO, 1500 hp take-off, 1275 hp at 11,500′
DIMENSIONS: Span 61′ 4″, Lg. 47′ 3″, Ht. 18′ 1″, Wing Area 464 sq. ft.
WEIGHT: Empty 15,051 lb., Design Gross 19,750 lb., Max. 21,580 lb. Fuel 390 gal.
PERFORMANCE: Speed—Top 321 mph at 12,800′, Cruising 273 mph, Landing 96 mph. Service Ceiling 25,170′, Climb 2000′/1 min. Range 525 miles.

PMB

DOUGLAS DB-7B (BOSTON III)

DOUGLAS A-20
Wright R-2600-7, 1700 hp at 20,000′ (turbosuperchargers)
DIMENSIONS: As A-20A
WEIGHT: Gross 20,329 lb. Fuel 414 gal.
PERFORMANCE: (Estimated) Speed—Top 388 mph at 20,000′, Cruising 218 mph, Landing 93 mph. Service Ceiling 31,500′, Climb 10,000′/5 min. Range 767 miles/1200 lbs. bombs, 1100 miles max.

MFR

AF

canceled in June 1942, but the A-20Bs were delivered at the new Douglas Long Beach plant between December 1941 and January 1943. Eight went to the U. S. Navy as the BD-2 in May 1942, while Russia got 665 on lend-lease. The A-20B had R-2600-11 engines, armor, leakproof tanks, two .50-caliber fixed nose guns, one .50-caliber flexible upper gun, and a pair of .30-caliber guns in the engine nacelles firing rearward by remote control. Provision was made for auxiliary tanks to increase fuel capacity from a normal 394 gallons to 1094 internal overload, or as much as 1479 gallons with a belly tank.

Concurrently, production continued at the main Douglas plant at Santa Monica on 808 A-20Cs for lend-lease. Like 140 more built early in 1942 by Boeing under license, they had R-2600-23 Cyclones, seven .30-caliber guns, 415 lbs. of armor, and carried 2076 lbs. of bombs. British name for the A-20C was Boston IIIA, for it was like the DB-7B but for exhaust stacks. Forty-eight similar DB-7Cs purchased for the Dutch were lend-leased to Russia.

There was no A-20D model built, but the A-20Es were 17 A-20As fitted with R-2600-11 engines like the B. The XA-20F was an A-20A with a 37-mm. fixed nose gun and two General Electric remote-control turrets installed to test and develop a gunnery system for the projected A-26.

DOUGLAS A-20A
Wright R-2600-3, 1600 hp take-off, 1275 hp at 12,000′
DIMENSIONS: Span 61′ 4″, Lg. 47′ 7″, Ht. 17′ 7″, Wing Area 464 sq. ft.
WEIGHT: Empty 15,165 lb., Design Gross 19,750 lb., Max. 20,711 lb. Fuel 390 gal.
PERFORMANCE: Speed—Top 347 mph at 12,400′, Cruising 295 mph, Landing 85 mph. Service Ceiling 28,175′, Climb 10,000′/5.1 min. Range 525 miles/2400 lbs. bombs, 675 miles/1200 lbs. bombs, 1000 miles max.

After America came into the war, the A-20 found itself in action all over the world. The name "Havoc" was given to all models, the British dropping "Boston" for conformity. A squadron of A-20As was a victim of the Pearl Harbor attack. Havocs reached New Guinea in April 1942, but did not go into action until August. By 1944, there were three Havoc groups in the Southwest Pacific. On the Fourth of July 1942, American pilots made their first attack from England on German airfields with DB-7B Havocs, and an A-20B group appeared later in North Africa. Three more Havoc groups supported the invasion of Europe in June 1944. In March 1942 deliveries began to the Soviet Union, a trickle at first, and then more and more, until 3125 had been sent, 2900 actually arriving.

In February 1943 the A-20G appeared with more firepower, armor, and fuel. Powered by the R-2600-23,

DOUGLAS A-20B
Wright R-2600-11, 1600 hp take-off, 1275 hp at 11,500′
DIMENSIONS: Span 61′ 4″, Lg. 48′, Ht. 18′ 1″, Wing Area 464 sq. ft.
WEIGHT: Empty 14,830 lb., Gross 21,000 lb., Max. 23,800 lb. Fuel 394–490 gal.
PERFORMANCE: Speed—Top 350 mph at 12,000′, Cruising 278 mph, Landing 95 mph. Service Ceiling 28,600′, Climb 10,000′/5 min. Range 825 miles/1000 lbs. bombs, 2300 miles ferry.

H. LEVY

MFR

DOUGLAS A-20C (Photo shows Boeing-built A-20C-BO, data for A-20C-DO)
Wright R-2600-23, 1600 hp take-off, 1275 hp at 11,500′
DIMENSIONS: Span 61′ 4″, Lg. 47′ 3″, Ht. 17′ 7″, Wing Area 464 sq. ft.
WEIGHT: Empty 15,625 lb., Gross 21,000 lb., Max. 24,500 lb. Fuel 400–540 gal.
PERFORMANCE: Speed—Top 342 mph at 13,000′, 314 mph at s. l., Cruising 280 mph, Landing 100 mph. Service Ceiling 25,320′, Climb 10,000′/6.3 min. Range 745 miles/1000 lbs. bombs, 1400 miles max.

PMB

DOUGLAS A-20G-5
Wright R-2600-23, 1600 hp take-off, 1275 hp at 11,500′
DIMENSIONS: Span 61′ 4″, Lg. 48′, Ht. 17′ 7″, Wing Area 464 sq. ft.
WEIGHT: Empty 15,984 lb., Gross 21,971 lb., Max. 27,200 lb. Fuel 540–916 gal.
PERFORMANCE: Speed—Top 339 mph at 12,400′, Cruising 272 mph, Landing 95 mph. Service Ceiling 25,800′, Climb 10,000′/7.1 min. Range 1090 miles.

AF

DOUGLAS A-20G-20
Wright R-2600-23, 1600 hp
DIMENSIONS: As A-20G-5
WEIGHT: Empty 16,993 lb., Gross 24,127 lb., Max. 27,000 lb. Fuel 725–1105 gal.
PERFORMANCE: Speed—Top 333 mph at 12,300′, Cruising 272 mph, Landing 95 mph. Service Ceiling 23,700′, Climb 10,000′/8.8 min. Range 1000 miles normal, 2100 miles ferry.

MFR

DOUGLAS A-20H-1 (BOSTON V)
Wright R-2600-29, 1700 hp take-off
DIMENSIONS: As A-20G-5
WEIGHT: Empty 16,842 lb., Gross 23,987 lb., Max. 27,000 lb. Fuel 725–1105 gal.
PERFORMANCE: Speed—Top 333 mph at 15,600′, Cruising 269 mph, Landing 100 mph. Service Ceiling 25,300′, Climb 10,000′/6.6 min. Range 880 miles normal, 2200 miles ferry.

WILLIAMS

DOUGLAS A-20J
Wright R-2600-23, 1600 hp take-off
DIMENSIONS: Span 61′ 4″, Lg. 48′ 4″, Ht. 17′ 7″, Wing Area 464 sq. ft.
WEIGHT: Empty 17,117 lb., Gross 23,748 lb., Max. 27,000 lb. Fuel 725–1105 gal.
PERFORMANCE: Speed—Top 317 mph at 10,700′, Cruising 257 mph, Landing 95 mph. Service Ceiling 23,100′, Climb 10,000′/8.8 min. Range 1000 miles/2000 lbs. bombs, 2100 miles max.

it introduced a solid "gun nose" instead of the former bombardier's enclosure. The first 250 (A-20G-1 for Russia) had four 20-mm. and two .50-caliber nose guns, while the remaining 2600 Gs used six .50-caliber bow guns, with 350 rounds per gun. A hand-operated .50-caliber gun in the rear seat of the first 750 (to A-20G-15) was replaced in the rest by two .50s in a power-operated Martin turret. The .30-caliber belly gun was also replaced by a .50-caliber gun in the A-20G-20 and all further models.

The 451 A-20Js built after October 1943 were identical to later Gs but had a revised bombardier's transparent nose with two .50-caliber guns. Britain received 169 and named them Boston IV. Wright R-2600-29 Cyclones of 1700 hp were fitted to the A-20H and A-20K. Solid noses with six .50-caliber guns distinguished 412 Hs from the 413 Ks with the bombardier nose. Ninety of the latter became the R.A.F.'s Boston V.

When Havoc production ended in September 1944, 7098 had been built by Douglas, and 380 under license

WL

DOUGLAS A-20K
Wright R-2600-29, 1700 hp take-off
DIMENSIONS: As A-20J
WEIGHT: Empty 17,266 lb., Gross 23,953 lb., Max. 27,000 lb. Fuel 725–1105 gal.
PERFORMANCE: Speed—Top 333 mph at 15,600′, Cruising 269 mph, Landing 100 mph. Service Ceiling 25,100′, Climb 10,000′/6.6 min. Range 830 miles normal, 2200 miles ferry.

SWISHER

LOCKHEED HUDSON I
Wright R-1820-G102A, 1100 hp take-off, 900 hp at 6700′
DIMENSIONS: Span 65′ 6″, Lg. 44′ 4″, Ht. 11′ 10″, Wing Area 551 sq. ft.
WEIGHT: Empty 11,630 lb., Gross 17,500 lb.
PERFORMANCE: Speed—Top 246 mph, Cruising 220 mph, Landing 70 mph. Service Ceiling 25,000′, Absolute Ceiling 26,000′, Climb 2180′/1 min. Range 1960 miles.

LOCKHEED HUDSON III
Wright R-1820-G205A, 1200 hp take-off, 900 hp at 15,200′
DIMENSIONS: As Hudson I
WEIGHT: Empty 12,536 lb., Gross 18,500 lb., Max. 20,000 lb.
PERFORMANCE: Speed—Top 255 mph, Cruising 223 mph. Service Ceiling 24,500′. Range 2160 miles max.

PMB

PMB

by Boeing, while AAF inventories were at a peak of over 1700 A-20s.

LOCKHEED A-28
Pratt & Whitney R-1830-45, 1050 hp take-off, 1000 hp at 11,500′
DIMENSIONS: As Hudson I
WEIGHT: Empty 12,810 lb., Gross 18,500 lb., Max. 20,500 lb. Fuel 644 gal.
PERFORMANCE: Speed—Top 260 mph at 12,500′, Cruising 206 mph, Landing 68 mph. Service Ceiling 26,000′, Climb 10,000′/7.8 min. Range 1500 miles/1400 lbs. bombs, 1800 miles max.

THE HUDSONS

Another twin-engined light bomber built at the same time as the Havoc and Maryland actually originated as the Lockheed 14 transport. Before the war, when a British Purchasing Commission came looking for good warplane buys, Lockheed hastily put together a mockup of a fuselage equipped for coastal reconnaissance work.

Impressed, the British ordered 250 on June 23, 1938, and the first Hudson I flew on December 10, 1938. Outbreak of war brought more orders and 351 Hudson Is were built, followed by 20 Hudson IIs, alike but for propellers. The Hudson I had 1000 hp Wright R-1820-G102A Cyclones and had the tapered wings, twin rudders, and tail-down landing gear of previous Lockheed transports. Five .30-caliber guns were carried: two fixed in the nose above the bombardier's windows, two in a British-built power turret, and the belly gun. In January 1940, some Hudsons received ASV radar for searching the sea's surface.

More powerful Wright G-205A Cyclones giving 1200 hp at take-off powered the 410 Hudson IIIs which began to appear in August 1940. One hundred Hudson IVs for Australia and 30 for the R.A.F. had Pratt & Whitney SC3G Wasps of 1050 hp at take-off, while 309 Hudson Vs had 1200 hp S3C4-G Wasps.

Additional Hudsons were ordered under the Lend-Lease Act in April 1941 and later received Army designations. Fifty-two A-28s (Hudson IVA) of 1941 had 1050 hp R-1830-45 Wasps, and 450 A-28A (Hudson VI) of 1942 had the 1200 hp R-1830-67. Wright R-1820-87 Cyclones powered 417 A-29 and 383 A-29A (382 became the R.A.F. Hudson IIIA). The A-28A and A-29A could be fitted with troop benches and used as transports. During 1941 and 1942 both the Army and Navy took over some Hudsons for antisubmarine patrol.

Army Hudsons carried 1600 lbs. of bombs, and usually replaced the British power turret, unnecessary for antisubmarine work, with a hand-operated .50-caliber gun on an open mount. Twenty Hudsons were oper-

MFR

LOCKHEED A-28A (HUDSON VI)
Pratt & Whitney R-1830-67, 1200 hp
DIMENSIONS: Span 65′ 6″, Lg. 44′ 4″, Ht. 11′ 10″, Wing Area 551 sq. ft.
WEIGHT: Empty 13,195 lb., Gross 18,500 lb., Max. 22,360 lb. Fuel 644–1028 gal.
PERFORMANCE: Speed—Top 261 mph, Cruising 224 mph, Landing 72 mph. Service Ceiling 27,000′, Climb 2160′/1 min. Range 2160 miles max.

MFR

LOCKHEED A-29 (HUDSON IIIA)
Wright R-1820-87, 1200 hp take-off, 1000 hp at 14,200′
DIMENSIONS: Span 65′ 6″, Lg. 44′ 4″, Ht. 11′ 11″, Wing Area 551 sq. ft.
WEIGHT: Empty 12,825 lb., Gross 20,500 lb., Max. 21,000 lb. Fuel 644–1028 gal.
PERFORMANCE: Speed—Top 253 mph at 15,000′, Cruising 205 mph, Landing 68 mph. Service Ceiling 26,500′, Climb 10,000′/6.3 min. Range 1550 miles/1400 lbs. bombs, 2800 miles max.

ated by the Navy as the PBO-1. It was the Navy Hudsons that got the first two U-boats sunk by U.S. forces, and an Army Hudson hit the first U-boat destroyed by the Army Air Forces. Hudsons fought over many points in the Atlantic, Pacific, and Indian oceans, and thirty-three A-29s even went to China. Some 2522 Hudsons had been delivered when production was completed in May 1943, in addition to 300 AT-18 Cyclone-powered training and target-towing models.

MFR

Chapter 7: Close Support for the Front 1941–45

THE ARMY'S DIVE BOMBERS

Reports of how French defense points were smashed by Junkers dive bombers supporting Nazi tanks startled American authorities into the realization that conventional bombing technique was inefficient against small or moving targets. "Can the A-20 bomb from a dive?" asked an official on the first of June 1940. No, not from angles over 30°, but the Army might get some dive bombers like the Navy's Douglas SBD. Get them, said General Henry H. Arnold, and, in July 1940, 78 were ordered under designation A-24 (Navy SBD-3A).

Delivery began in June 1941 and was completed in October. Similar to Navy models but for a different tail wheel and no carrier gear, the A-24 had a Wright R-1820-52 giving 1000 hp at take-off. Armament included 1200 lbs. of bombs, two .50-caliber nose guns, and two .30-caliber flexible rear guns.

They were followed in 1942 by 170 similar A-24As (SBD-4), also built at the Douglas El Segundo plant. A Wright R-1820-60 of 1200 hp for take-off powered the A-24B (SBD-5), 615 of which were delivered between March and November 1943 from the Douglas factory at Tulsa.

Not many of the Army's A-24s were used in action. Some were sent to Java in 1942, and made a few sorties from there and from Port Moresby. In July 1942, they were withdrawn from action as too slow, short-ranged, and ill-armed. This same type, of course, did excellent Navy work, but the Air Force was comparing it to land-based twin-engined types. The only combat appearance of the A-24B model was in December 1943, in the Gilbert Islands. Some of these ships were also given to Mexico.

The next Navy dive bomber ordered by the Air Force was the Curtiss SB2C-1, designated A-25. The original A-25 specification of April 1941 called for a weight of 7868 lbs. empty, 10,982 lbs. gross, and 12,175 lbs. maximum. By the time the first production model A-25A was accepted in December 1943, so many changes had been made that the weight had increased to 10,290 lbs. empty, and 16,000 lbs. gross. Expected performance indicated a top speed of 313 mph and a service ceiling of 29,000 ft.; the A-25A actually had a top speed of 275 mph and a 26,800 ft. service ceiling. These figures are presented as an example of what wartime increases in armament, armor, and fuel often cost in performance.

The A-25A lacked the folding wings and arresting gear of its carrier twin, and was armed with four .50-caliber wing guns, a single .50-caliber flexible rear gun, and up to 2000 lbs. of bombs. Nine hundred were built at St. Louis by March 1945, but none was used in action by the Air Force. Most went to the Marines and to the New Zealand Air Force.

Another dive bomber for the Air Force had originated as a land-based two-seater, the Vultee V-72 ordered for the Royal Air Force in 1940. Contracts were placed for 500 from Vultee and 200 to be built under license by the reorganized Northrop corporation. Lend-lease contracts in June 1941 added 400 Vultees and 200 more Northrops to these orders, and gave the V-72 the Army designation A-31. Two preproduction prototypes were built at Downey, California, and were christened Vengeance in July 1941.

The Vengeance used the Wright R-2600-19 of 1600 hp at take-off, and had odd wings, dive brakes, armor, and leakproof tanks. Armament included six .30-caliber guns and 1000 lbs. of bombs in an internal bay. The four wing guns had 750 rounds each, while 500 rounds were provided each of the two flexible guns.

Northrop delivered 400 Vengeance I and IAs between January 1942 and April 1943 to the R.A.F. Vultee began quantity deliveries from a Nashville, Tennessee, plant in March 1942, and 500 Vengeance

PMB

DOUGLAS A-24
Wright R-1820-52, 1000 hp take-off, 800 hp at 16,000′
DIMENSIONS: Span 41′ 6″, Lg. 32′ 8″, Ht. 12′ 11″, Wing Area 325 sq. ft.
WEIGHT: Empty 6265 lb., Gross 9200 lb., Max. 10,200 lb. Fuel 260 gal.
PERFORMANCE: Speed—Top 250 mph at 17,200′, Cruising 173 mph, Landing 75 mph. Service Ceiling 26,000′, Climb 10,000′/7 min. Range 950 miles/1000 lb. bomb, 1300 miles max.

AF

DOUGLAS A-24B
Wright R-1820-60, 1200 hp take-off, 900 hp at 14,000′
DIMENSIONS: Span 41′ 6″, Lg. 33′, Ht. 12′ 11″, Wing Area 325 sq. ft.
WEIGHT: Empty 6330 lb., Gross 9250 lb., Max. 10,250 (with 1000 lb. bomb). Fuel 260 gal.
PERFORMANCE: Speed—Top 254 mph at 15,000′, Cruising 180 mph, Landing 75 mph. Service Ceiling 27,000′, Climb 10,000′/6.1 min. Range 950 miles/1000 lb. bomb, 1250 miles as scout.

IIs were followed by 100 Vengeance IIIs (A-31). One XA-31A was built in June 1942 at Downey without engine or armament to be used as an engine test ship for the Pratt & Whitney XR-4360-1 and was known as the XA-31B. Five A-31s modified to test Wright R-3350s for the B-29 program were known as YA-31s.

In July 1942, Army pilots recommended that the Vengeance be equipped according to AAF armament standards and given an increased angle of wing incidence. These changes were incorporated in the next 99 ships on the 1941 order, which were designated A-35A, and had five .50-caliber guns. The four fixed wing guns had 425 rounds each, and the flexible gun had 400 rounds. Tests on the first A-35 in September 1942 showed satisfactory flying traits, and more Vengeances were purchased.

Last model to appear was the A-35B of 1943, which had a 1700 hp R-2600-13, six .50-caliber wing guns, and up to 2000 lbs. of bombs. When A-35B production ended in May 1944, 831 had been built, 562 going to Australia and Britain as Vengeance IV, and 29 to Brazil.

The Army also considered buying Brewster's SB2A-1 dive bomber, and allotted it the designation A-34, but none was procured. It's just as well, for little combat use was made of over 1900 Vengeances built. Army ships were used for training only, while 1205 sent to the R.A.F. were used for bombing in Burma, but saw no action in the European Theater.

The disappearance of two-seat dive bombers from AAF combat groups can be attributed to the greater success of single-seat fighter bombers in the same mission. Bombed-up fighters like the A-36 and P-47 had much better performance, proved excellent for close support, and could take care of their own defense after their bombs were gone. Officials in the U.S. did not anticipate the lack of demand for the Vengeance planes, and their continued production was criticized as a "shining example of the waste caused by pressure for sheer numbers of planes not actually needed at the front."

THE DOUGLAS INVADER

As thousands of Havocs rolled out of the plant, Douglas began in January 1941 designing a better and larger light bomber. The prototype XA-26 ordered on June 2, 1941, and first flown on July 10, 1942, was a three-place, high-wing monoplane with tricycle gear powered by 2000 hp R-2800-27 Wasps.

There were three prototypes, distinguished from production models by prop spinners and camouflage. The first XA-26 had a transparent bombardier's nose, 3000 lbs. of bombs, and six .50-caliber guns (two were fixed in the nose, two in a top turret, and two in a lower rear turret). The turret guns were aimed through periscope sights and remote controls in the rear cockpit.

Night fighter equipment was installed on the second prototype, the XA-26A with radar nose, four 20-mm. fixed guns in a belly tray, and a top turret with four

PMB

CURTISS A-25A
Wright R-2600-8, 1700 hp take-off, 1450 hp at 15,000′
DIMENSIONS: Span 49′ 9″, Lg. 36′ 8″, Ht. 14′ 6″, Wing Area 422 sq. ft.
WEIGHT: Empty 10,290 lb., Gross 16,000 lb. Fuel 320–450 gal.
PERFORMANCE: Speed—Top 275 mph at 15,000′, Cruising 240 mph, Landing 80 mph. Service Ceiling 26,800′, Climb 10,000′/6.5 min. Range 700 miles/2000 lbs. bombs, 1350 miles max.

MFR

VULTEE A-31 (VENGEANCE I in photo)
Wright R-2600-19, 1600 hp take-off, 1250 hp at 11,500′
DIMENSIONS: Span 48′, Lg. 39′ 9″, Ht. 15′ 4″, Wing Area 332 sq. ft.
WEIGHT: Empty 9725 lb., Gross 12,940 lb., Max. 14,300 lb. Fuel 320 gal.
PERFORMANCE: Speed—Top 275 mph at 11,000′, Cruising 235 mph, Landing 80 mph. Service Ceiling 22,500′, Climb 19,700′/20.4 min. Range 700 miles/1500 lbs. bombs, 1400 miles ferry.

.50-caliber guns. Third prototype was the XA-26B, which had a 75-mm. gun on the right side of a short solid nose.

Delivery on the production A-26B began in August 1943, and 615 built at Long Beach (A-26B-1 to -45 DL) and 205 at Tulsa (A-26B-5 to -25 DT) had six .50-caliber guns in a short solid nose, each with 400 rounds. The upper turret, which could be cocked forward, had 500 rounds for each of its two guns. Like the lower turret's pair, they were fired normally by the rear gunner. With capacity for 4000 lbs. of bombs, these ships were powered by R-2800-27 or R-2800-71 engines.

New R-2800-79 engines with water injection were installed on the next 535 A-26Bs (A-26B-50 to -65 DL), and the added power boosted top speed from 355 to 373 mph at 10,000 ft. Increased firepower included eight .50-caliber nose guns, and provision under the wings for six more or up to fourteen 5 in. rockets. Some had their lower turret removed to allow another 125 gallons of fuel.

Five A-26C-DL and 1086 A-26C-DTs built con-

VULTEE A-35 (A-35A-1)
Wright R-2600-19, 1600 hp take-off, 1275 hp at 11,500′
DIMENSIONS: As A-31
WEIGHT: Empty 10,060 lb., Gross 13,500 lb., Max. 15,600 lb. Fuel 300 gal.
PERFORMANCE: Speed—Top 273 mph at 11,000′, Cruising 235 mph, Landing 83 mph. Service Ceiling 21,500′, Climb 15,000′/12.8 min. Range 600 miles/2000 lbs. bombs, 1250 miles ferry.

MFR

VULTEE A-35B
Wright R-2600-13, 1700 hp take-off, 1350 hp at 13,000′
DIMENSIONS: As A-31
WEIGHT: Empty 10,300 lb., Gross 16,400 lb., Max. 17,100 lb. Fuel 300–625 gal.
PERFORMANCE: Speed—Top 279 mph at 13,500′, Cruising 230 mph, Landing 84 mph. Service Ceiling 22,300′, Climb 15,000′/11.3 min. Range 550 miles/1000 lbs. bombs, 2300 miles max.

AF

DOUGLAS XA-26

Pratt & Whitney R-2800-27, 2000 hp take-off, 1600 hp at 13,500′

DIMENSIONS: Span 70′, Lg. 51′ 2″, Ht. 18′ 6″, Wing Area 540 sq. ft.

WEIGHT: Empty 21,150 lb., Gross 31,000 lb. Fuel 830–1050 gal.

PERFORMANCE: Speed—Top 370 mph at 17,000′, Cruising 212 mph, Landing 100 mph. Service Ceiling 31,300′, Climb 20,000′/10.2 min. Range 1800 miles/3000 lbs. bombs, 2500 miles ferry.

AF

currently with the Bs differed in having transparent bombardier's nose and two fixed .50-caliber nose guns. Otherwise, the A-26C used the same engines as the B, and had the same performance. Radar was fitted to some ships painted black for night bombing. V-J Day brought the end of "Invader" production, and cancellation of 445 Bs, 2809 Cs, 750 improved A-26Ds and 1250 Es.

Going into action over Europe in September 1944, the Invaders proved superior to other twin-engined bombers in service. (See p. 133 for comparative data on ETO light bombing.) It was the standard light bomber of the postwar air force and was redesignated B-26 in 1948 with the abolition of Attack planes as a

DOUGLAS A-26B-1

Pratt & Whitney R-2800-27 or -71, 2000 hp take-off, 1600 hp/13,500′

DIMENSIONS: Span 70′, Lg. 50′, Ht. 18′ 6″, Wing Area 540 sq. ft.

WEIGHT: Empty 22,370 lb., Gross 35,000 lb. Fuel 925–1600 gal.

PERFORMANCE: Speed—Top 355 mph at 15,000′, Cruising 284 mph, Landing 100 mph. Service Ceiling 22,100′, Climb 10,000′/8.1 min. Range 1400 miles/4000 lbs. bombs, 3200 miles ferry.

MFR

separate category. Enough B-26s were on hand or in storage to last through the entire Korean war.

Final ship of the series was the XA-26F of 1946, in which the rear gunner's compartment and turrets were replaced by an I-16 jet engine and 125 gallons of jet fuel. The jet intake was atop the fuselage and the exhaust was in the tail. Two 2100 hp Wasp R-2800-83 engines turned four-bladed props and large spinners. No rear guns were carried, but eight .50-caliber guns were in the nose, and six in the wing. In June 1946, the XA-26F averaged 413 mph over a 621-mile course.

The Invader remained standard equipment so long that we might forget two 1942 designs of the same class. The first was the Hughes XA-37, with two R-2800-49s and Duramold construction, which never passed drawing-board form. More progress was made by the Beech 28 Destroyer, or XA-38. Design began August 1942, and two prototypes were ordered September 23, 1942.

Flown May 7, 1944, the XA-38 was a two-place low-wing monoplane with two Wright R-3350-43 Cyclones, twin rudders, tail-down landing gear, and external studs for 2000 lbs. of bombs. Rear gun arrangement was like the A-26s: two pairs of .50-caliber guns in upper and lower remote-control turrets. The nose, however, was as individual as a swordfish's; the long barrel of a 75-mm. cannon protruded far beyond the pair of .50s in the bow. Twenty rounds of ammunition were fed to the big gun by automatic loading, and 3000 rounds were carried for the machine guns.

Delayed by the lack of availability of engines, also needed for the B-29 program, the A-38 never reached production, although it had good flying qualities.

PMB

DOUGLAS A-26C-50 (B-26C)
Pratt & Whitney R-2800-79, 2000 hp take-off, 2360 hp WE
DIMENSIONS: Span 70′, Lg. 51′ 3″, Ht. 18′ 3″, Wing Area 540 sq. ft.
WEIGHT: Empty 22,850 lb., Gross 29,700 lb., Max. 35,000 lb.
PERFORMANCE: As A-26B-50

PMB

DOUGLAS XA-26F

AF

DOUGLAS A-26B-1

SOMMERICH

DOUGLAS A-26B-50
Pratt & Whitney R-2800-79, 2000 hp take-off, 2360 hp WE
DIMENSIONS: As A-26B-1
WEIGHT: Empty 22,370 lb., Gross 35,000 lb., Max. 37,000 lb. Fuel 925–1910 gal.
PERFORMANCE: Speed—Top 373 mph at 10,000′, Cruising 284 mph. Service Ceiling 22,100′, Climb 10,000′/8 min. Range 1400 miles/4000 lbs. bombs, 3400 miles ferry.

ONE-MAN ARSENALS

Successful with twin-engined types, but disappointed with the performance of the converted Navy single-engined two-seaters, the Army looked for a small single-engined plane for dive bombing and strafing. If two-seaters were too slow, perhaps a single-seater would offer the speed and maneuverability needed for close-in support.

First modern single-seat attack design was the Brewster XA-32 begun in May 1941 and ordered on October 30, 1941. After the mockup was inspected in May 1942, and advance estimates gave top speed

MFR

BEECH XA-38

Wright R-3350-43, 2300 hp take-off, 2440 hp WE

DIMENSIONS: Span 67′ 4″, Lg. 51′ 9″, Ht. 15′ 6″, Wing Area 626 sq. ft.

WEIGHT: Empty 22,480 lb., Design Gross 29,900 lb., Max. 35,265 lb. Fuel 820–1425 gal.

PERFORMANCE: Speed—Top 376 mph at 3,100′ Cruising 167 mph, Landing 103 mph. Service Ceiling 27,800′, Climb 20,000′/11.5 min. Range 1420 miles/2000 lbs. bombs, 2700 miles ferry.

BREWSTER XA-32

Pratt & Whitney R-2800-37, 2100 hp take-off, 1600 hp at 13,500′

DIMENSIONS: Span 45′ 1″, Lg. 40′ 7″, Ht. 12′ 8″, Wing Area 425 sq. ft.

WEIGHT: Empty 11,820 lb., Gross 15,512 lb., Max. 19,960 lb. Fuel 200–530 gal.

PERFORMANCE: Speed—Top 311 mph at 13,200′, Cruising 196 mph, Landing 75 mph. Service Ceiling 26,000′, Climb 10,000′/5.7 min. Range 500 miles/3000 lbs. bombs, 1600 miles max.

AMC

as 331 mph, the XA-32 was viewed the "most desirable" dive bomber in sight. Since Brewster was tied up by Navy contracts and management troubles, A-32 production would require another facility, possibly that used by the A-25A.

The two prototypes were delayed, however, and didn't appear until April 22, 1943, with an R-2800-37, four-bladed propeller and spinner, and an internal bomb bay for 3000 lbs. of bombs. Four 37-mm. were to be mounted in the wings, but were replaced on the prototypes by six .50-caliber or four 20-mm. guns.

Unable to wait for A-32s, the Army in August 1942 ordered that North American P-51s then building be completed as fighter bombers designated A-36A. Five hundred were accepted between September 1942 and March 1943, with a 1325 hp Allison V-1710-87, six

BREWSTER XA-32

AMC

PMB

NORTH AMERICAN A-36A
Allison V-1710-87, 1325 hp at 3000′
DIMENSIONS: Span 37′, Lg. 32′ 3″, Ht. 12′ 2″, Wing Area 233 sq. ft.
WEIGHT: Empty 6610 lb., Gross 8370 lb., Max. 10,000 lb. Fuel 105–180 gal.
PERFORMANCE: Speed—Top 310 mph at 5000′/two 500 lb. bombs, 356 mph clean, Cruising 250 mph, Landing 85 mph. Service Ceiling 25,100′ (bombs), 27,000′. Range 550 miles/ two 500 lb. bombs, 2300 miles ferry.

.50-caliber guns, and wing racks for two 500-lb. bombs. Dive brakes were installed under the wings, but these were wired shut at the front and not used.

Two A-36A groups dive-bombed in Italy, and one was used by the R.A.F. Its success demonstrated the value of single-seat fighter bombers, and led to widespread use of later P-51 and P-47 models on close-support missions.

Meanwhile, development proceeded on a trio of heavily armed single-seat, single-engined monoplanes, with large internal bomb bays. They were halfway between the single-seat fighter and the two-seat dive bomber, and were close to the bomber-torpedo single-seaters developed for the Navy.

First were the Kaiser-Fleetwings XA-39 and Curtiss XA-40, neither of which got past the mockup stage. The former was to have used a 2000 hp R-2800-27, and had two 37-mm. and four .50-caliber wing guns. A 2300 hp R-3350-8 was planned for the XA-40, which

FLEETWINGS XA-39 (Aircraft not completed)
Pratt & Whitney R-2800-27, 2000 hp take-off, 1600 hp at 13,500′
DIMENSIONS: Span 55′ 9″, Lg. 43′ 9″, Ht. 17′ 6″, Wing Area 626 sq. ft.
WEIGHT: Empty 10,845 lb., Gross 16,160 lb., Max. 20,300 lb. Fuel 350–750 gal.
PERFORMANCE: Speed—Top 357 mph at 16,600′, Cruising 275 mph, Landing 74 mph. Service Ceiling 27,000′, Climb 2600′/1 min. Range 800 miles/3000 lbs. bombs, 1400 miles/ 500 lbs. bombs, 3440 miles max.

was a torpedo dive bomber similar to the Navy XSB3C-1.

More progress was made on the XA-41, which was begun in September 1942 as the Vultee 90, ordered April 30, 1943, and first flown on February 11, 1944. Powered by a 3000 hp XR-4360-9, the Convair XA-41 had four 37-mm. and four .50-caliber guns in the wings. The internal bomb bay normally carried 7000 lbs., but was large enough to accommodate a torpedo, four 1600-lb. bombs, or extra fuel tanks. Its wing shape was like the Vengeance two-seater, but main wheels for the tail-down gear folded inward.

This fat single-seater did not go into production, and, with the XA-38, were the last types completed with Attack designation. Although four other designs were allotted attack designations during the war, none were completed in that class. The twin-engined Douglas XA-42 was redesignated XB-42, while the Curtiss jet-propelled XA-43 developed into the XP-87. Convair's strange canard jet XA-44 became the XB-53, while Martin's XA-45 jet was completed as the XB-51.

CONSOLIDATED-VULTEE XA-41
Pratt & Whitney XR-4360-9, 3000 hp take-off, 2400 hp at 13,500′
DIMENSIONS: Span 54′, Lg. 48′ 8″, Ht. 14′ 6″, Wing Area 540 sq. ft.
WEIGHT: Empty 13,400 lb., Gross 18,800 lb., Max. 23,260 lb. Fuel 350–445 gal. (1140 gal. ferry).
PERFORMANCE: Speed—Top 353 mph at 15,500′, Cruising 270 mph, Landing 74 mph. Service Ceiling 27,000′, Climb 10,000′/4.3 min. Range 950 miles/3000 lbs. bombs. MFR

Chapter 8: Summary

THE QUESTION OF CLOSE SUPPORT

Between the end of World War I and the outbreak of World War II, the light bomber developed from the 400 hp DH-4 to the 4000 hp A-26. Armament had increased from four .30-caliber guns and 220 lbs. of bombs to eight .50-caliber guns and 4000 lbs. of bombs, top speed from 124 to 373 mph, and range from 270 to 1400 miles.

The A-26s which remained as the standard postwar light bomber was a twin-engined 17½ ton ship, larger than the single-engined types usually prevailing through Attack plane history. Single-engined Attack specialists were superseded during the war by standard fighter types loaded with bombs. Divergent trends in attack-bomber design, small single-engined types, and larger twin-engined ships grew so far apart that the Attack category vanished into the fighter and bomber classes.

In June 1948, the "Attack" designation was eliminated, nine months after the Air Force cast off from the Army and became an independent branch of the Defense establishment. All Douglas A-26s on hand were redesignated B-26 (the older Martin B-26 had been scrapped), and advocates of specialized close support felt alarm that concentration on strategic bombing would neglect tactical short-range types.

This fear had some justification, for although a Tactical Air Command was formed, no new types specially designed for close support were in production when the Korean war began. Army men felt that insufficient attention was given to their desire for a "tank-destroyer" type for front-line work. However, the Air Force can point to successes of its jet fighter bombers in Korea as the answer to Army needs, and to the fast B-57 and B-66 types now in service.

In the section on Air Force bombers, we will see what designs are now available for short-range work. Perhaps the difference between short-range B-57 types and the B-52 may again separate bombers into light and heavy groups clearly defined by designation.

Part 3 Bombers for the Air Force

Chapter 9: Biplanes versus Battleships 1917–30

THE FIRST BOMBERS

When land warfare settled down to a long deadlock in World War I, the airplane's appeal as an offensive weapon grew. Attacks against people on the ground became more serious, and aircraft specialized for bomb-carrying over long distances were demanded by the warring powers.

Respectable bomb loads, increased fuel supply, and a crew sufficient to operate the airplane and its armament, required much larger machines than the frail scouting types then available. Builders began bomber designs by adding a second or more engines to their aircraft for the additional power needed.

Only Russia had such a plane at the war's beginning: Igor Sikorsky's Ilya Mourometz, a February 1914 improvement on the giant Sikorsky Grand of 1913, first multiengined aircraft in the world. Powered by four 100 hp engines out on the lower wings, Ilya had an open balcony in front of an enclosed cabin. Crewmen dropped primitive bombs through a hole cut into the cabin floor. On February 15, 1915, the Ilya Mourometz V carried 600 pounds of bombs over the German lines on its first combat mission.

Seventy-three were built before the 1917 Russian Revolution halted production. When enemy fighters became dangerous, a cockpit was built in the tail for a machine gunner who had an unobstructed fire zone. This arrangement worked so well that the designer claims that only once, when a gunner left his post, was one of these bombers lost to a fighter. Yet the logic of the tail gunner's post escaped U.S. acceptance for two decades.

MFR

SIKORSKY MOUROMETZ

The general arrangement which became the classic pattern for the next dozen years of bombers was established by the first British Handley-Page bomber flown on December 18, 1915. The upper wing spanned 100 feet, overhanging a smaller lower wing; between them was suspended two 250 hp Rolls-Royce engines. A squarish fuselage began with a gunner's cockpit in the bow, followed by side-by-side seats for the pilot and co-pilot. A rear gunner sitting behind the wings had his rearward view limited by a boxlike tail of two horizontal and two vertical surfaces. A pair of .30-caliber Lewis guns were mounted at the front and rear cockpits, and a fifth gun aimed downward through a trap door. Eight 250-lb. bombs could be carried on eight-hour missions.

By the time the Handley-Page went into action in 1917, other belligerents had designed counterparts, such as Germany's Gotha and the Italian Caproni. Over a score of large bomber designs appeared during the war, including a four-engined Handley-Page of May 1918, and a German Siemens-Schuckert R-VIII whose six 300 hp engines were buried within the fuselage and turned propellers between the wings by a gear system.

Although none of these planes made any real difference as far as the strategy or outcome of the war was concerned, they brought the war to civilians behind the lines who, in past history, had not feared for their lives. The most severe of these raids was on

PMB

STANDARD HANDLEY-PAGE
Liberty 12-N, 350 hp
DIMENSIONS: Span 100′, Lg. 62′ 11″, Ht. 22′, Wing Area 1655 sq. ft.
WEIGHT: Empty 8721 lb., Gross 14,425 lb. Fuel 390 gal.
PERFORMANCE: Speed—Top 94 mph at s. l., 82 mph at 6500′, Cruising 84 mph. Service Ceiling 7400′, Absolute Ceiling 9600′, Climb 400′/1 min., 6500′/27 min. Range 550 miles/ 2000 lbs. bombs.

June 13, 1917, when twenty Gothas attacking London killed 162 and injured 432 persons. A modest piece of homicide, considering World War II, but it was the best the earlier war could offer, and caused many to feel then that the likelihood of such horrors would cause nations to abstain from any more war.

EARLY AMERICANS

After the United States entered the war, the Bolling Mission was sent to Europe to recommend types for an American aircraft program. Production of bombers here, however, was delayed by the inability to decide how many should be made, and of what type.

The former decision should have been determined by current doctrines of airpower employment, but as no such doctrines had yet been formulated, the number of bombers programed was based on an inaccurate guess of production capacity. After much wavering, the program of July 1918 finally projected a ratio of 3 : 5 : 2 for pursuit, observation, and bombardment plane production. Although the Bolling Mission had recommended Caproni bombers in July 1917, consideration of the Handley-Page caused a rivalry which, with fluctuating production targets, delayed the placing of contracts. Finally both were ordered, to be powered with U.S.-designed Liberty engines.

A pair of sample Capronis arrived from Italy in September 1917, followed in January by a technical

AF

STANDARD CAPRONI
Liberty 12-N, 350 hp
DIMENSIONS: Span 76′ 10″, Lg. 41′ 2″, Ht. 12′ 1″, Wing Area 1420 sq. ft.
WEIGHT: Empty 7700 lb., Gross 12,350 lb., Max. 12,900 lb. Fuel 400 gal.
PERFORMANCE: Speed—Top 103 mph at s. l., Landing 61.5 mph. Service Ceiling 11,500′, Absolute Ceiling 13,500′, Climb 670′/1 min., 6500′/14 min. Range 762 miles/1330 lbs. bombs.

mission whose head ordered that American-built Capronis were to have "no modification whatsoever, even in the slightest detail without formal permission from the engineer d'Annunzio."

Fifty Capronis were ordered from Standard Aircraft in February 1918, and in July contracts were signed with the Curtiss and Fisher Body Corporations for 500 Capronis each. The Standard firm also was to build 500 Handley-Pages, most to be shipped across the ocean for assembly in Britain, and the metal fittings for 1000 sets of wooden Handley-Page parts to be built by a Grand Rapids airplane company.

Standard flew its first Handley-Page on July 1, 1918, and its first Caproni on July 4. When Armistice Day halted U.S. bomber production, deliveries amounted to two Standard and three Fisher Capronis, seven Handley-Pages assembled here, and 100 other shipped in pieces to England.

Each bomber had Liberty engines and a crew of four. The Handley-Page, described earlier, carried five Lewis guns and up to 2000 lbs. of bombs, while the smaller Caproni had 1330 lbs. of bombs, and four .30-caliber Lewis guns. Three Liberty engines powered the latter ship; one at the rear of a center nacelle, and the others at the nose of twin booms leading back from between the wings to a stabilizer and three rudders. Lewis guns guarded the nose, and another pair were operated by a gunner standing on a platform over the rear engine.

Concentrating on foreign-designed planes, the government was reluctant to purchase untried native designs, but on January 17, 1918, Glenn L. Martin received a contract for a twin-engined four-place "*corps-de-Armée*" reconnaissance plane, the GMB (MB-1) which was first flown on August 15, 1918, and could also be used for bombing. That the first American bomber was ordered as a scout for land armies is symbolic of the outlook that was to limit Army bomber development through so much of its history.

The Martin GMB (MB-1) was of similar layout to the Handley-Page, but smaller. Two 400 hp Liberties were suspended between the wings, four wheels were aligned on a single axle, and the tail assembly of two rudders obstructed the rear gunner's view less than the older type's *empennage*. Five .30-caliber guns and 1040 lbs. of bombs comprised the armament. Nine were built by Armistice Day, and a tenth was completed in 1919 as a twelve-place transport.

No bombers were built in the U.S. during 1919, but in June 1920 the Army ordered twenty Martin MB-2s. An MB-1 development with wings enlarged and strengthened to lift more fuel and bombs, the MB-2 had its Liberty engines lowered to the bottom wing and two landing wheels fitted with mudguards, but crew arrangement and five-gun armament remained the same. First tested on September 3, 1920, these planes were redesignated NBS-1 (night bomber, short distance), could carry up to 2000 lbs. for a range

MARTIN GMB
Liberty 12A, 400 hp
DIMENSIONS: Span 71′ 5″, Lg. 44′ 10″, Ht. 14′ 7″, Wing Area 1070 sq. ft.
WEIGHT: Empty 6702 lb., Gross 10,225 lb. Fuel 214 gal.
PERFORMANCE: Speed—Top 105 mph at s. l., 100 mph at 6500′, Cruising 92 mph, Landing 67.5 mph. Service Ceiling 10,300′, Absolute Ceiling 12,250′, Climb 630′/1 min., 6500′/14.6 min. Range 390 miles/1040 lbs. bombs.

MFR

MARTIN MB-2
Liberty 12A, 410 hp (Photo shows supercharged version)
DIMENSIONS: Span 74′ 2″, Lg. 42′ 8″, Ht. 14′ 8″, Wing Area 1121 sq. ft.
WEIGHT: Empty 7069 lb., Gross 12,027 lb. Fuel 300 gal.
PERFORMANCE: Speed—Top 98 mph at s. l., Cruising 91 mph, Landing 59 mph. Service Ceiling 7700′, Absolute Ceiling 9900′, Climb 445′/1 min., 6500′/23.8 min. Range 400 miles/2000 lbs. bombs.

AMC

AF

MARTIN-CURTISS NBS-1
Liberty 12A, 420 hp
DIMENSIONS: Span 74′ 2″, Lg. 42′ 8″, Ht. 14′ 8″, Wing Area 1121 sq. ft.
WEIGHT: Empty 7269 lb., Gross 12,064 lb., Max. 12,119 lb. Fuel 300 gal.
PERFORMANCE: Speed—Top 98.7 mph at s. l., 91 mph at 6500′, Cruising 91 mph, Landing 62 mph. Service Ceiling 8500′, Absolute Ceiling 10,000′, Climb 391′/1 min., 6500′/22.5 min. Range 429 miles/1797 lbs. bombs, 558 miles/1262 lbs. bombs.

of 400 miles, and had a top speed of 98 mph. One MB-2 was fitted with superchargers which enabled it on December 8, 1921, to climb past its normal 9900 ft. ceiling to 25,600 ft. Superchargers wouldn't be ready for service use, however, until the B-17.

Those twenty Martins and a few survivors of 1918 made a modest force indeed, even for 1921, but with them the airmen challenged the traditional champions of American national defense.

ONE THOUSAND BOMBERS FOR ONE BATTLESHIP

After the war, a return to "normalcy" was expected, and the nation turned to the day's internal problems. Any return to conservative military habits of the past was resisted, however, by those who saw in new weapons a need for a complete re-organization of America's defense establishment.

Foremost in the campaign for greater emphasis on aviation was Brigadier General William Mitchell, Assistant Chief of Air Service, and wartime commander of the A.E.F.'s combat planes. General Mitchell's life and arguments are studied in detail elsewhere, but bomber history requires here a summary of his position.

Mitchell said that air bombardment would become the most important instrument of warfare. Instead of a tedious wearing down of hostile land forces, bombers would strike immediately at enemy industrial centers, destroying his ability and will to make war before his armies need be defeated. For a nation surrounded by the sea, bombers would replace battleships, and with the aid of submarines, cause surface fleets to "disappear" as a major military force.

If air power was to play this role, it must be freed from the dominance of ground commanders, and have its own leadership, doctrine, and equipment. The organization most suitable for this purpose was a unified department of defense, with a department of air co-equal with the Army and Navy.

Greatest resistance to these views came from those who held Mahan's theory of sea power as the basis of national strength, and so Mitchell aimed his attack at sixteen expensive 16 in. gun capital ships then being built in a naval race with Britain and Japan. His bombers could sink any battleship afloat, he insisted, and offered to prove it by actual test. Then he struck a low blow at the big ships, "1000 bombardment airplanes can be built and operated for the price of one battleship." Irritated by Mitchell's appeal to the economy-minded public, Secretary of the Navy Josephus Daniels offered to stand bareheaded on a battleship deck while bombers tried to hit it. This offer was not accepted, but target ships were provided.

The tests were carried out in July 1921, on captured German ships. Attacking with Martins from Langley Field, Virginia, the airmen first sank a destroyer with 300-lb. bombs, then a cruiser with 600-lb. bombs, and finally climaxed the demonstration by sinking a battleship with six new 2000-lb. bombs, then the largest available.

There was no agreement on the experiment's significance; a joint Army and Navy board report signed by General Pershing concluded that the "battleship was still the backbone of the fleet and the bulwark of the nation's sea defense," while Mitchell's own report flatly contradicted the other, asserting that bombers alone could accomplish the defense of our coasts. In Congress, Senator William E. Borah questioned the necessity of the expensive battleship building program, while a bill was introduced providing for conversion of two forthcoming battlecruisers into aircraft carriers.

In the midst of this debate, the Washington Conference on the Limitation of Armaments was held. At the suggestion of the United States, an agreement was made to limit battleship construction; many ships on hand or on order were to be scrapped and the size of future ships limited. As a result the United States halted work on eleven capital ships, converted two others to aircraft carriers, and scrapped some prewar battleships, including three sunk in more bombing tests in 1923.

But those who thought the end of the battleship race would result in more funds for bombers were disappointed. With Europe and Asia apparently pacified by diplomacy, there was little interest in armaments—not even in substituting economy-sized wood frame airplanes for costly steel dreadnoughts. Air Service appropriations dropped from 35.1 million in fiscal 1921 to 12.6 million in fiscal 1924.

In order to spread limited funds farthest, the Army purchased its aircraft by inviting competitive bids from prospective contractors. Proprietary rights to military designs were then held by the government, which could assign production to the company offering the lowest bid.

In February 1922, when Glenn L. Martin offered to build more NBS-1s for $23,925 each, he discovered that he had been underbid by his competitors. Instead, Curtiss received a contract for 50 NBS-1s at a price of $17,490 each, 35 were ordered from the LWF Engineering Company, and 25 more from Aeromarine. Tests on the first Curtiss ship began in September 1922 and showed characteristics like those of its predecessors. A loss of $300,000 on the NBS-1 contract was admitted, however, by Curtiss officials. Liberty engines from the wartime stockpile were used on these planes, as well as on the next four bomber projects of the Air Service.

The first of these new projects was the three-engined LWF Owl which had been built earlier as a mailplane, but was tested as a bomber at Mitchell Field in September 1922. A Caproni-like layout included a center plywood nacelle for a crew of three and the center Liberty, with booms running back from outboard engines to triple rudders. The same firm designed a smaller, metal-structured bomber with two Libertys, called the XNBS-2, but this project was canceled.

AMC

L.W.F. OWL
Liberty 12, 400 hp
DIMENSIONS: Span 106′ 8″, Lg. 53′ 9″, Ht. 17′ 6″, Wing Area 2216 sq. ft.
WEIGHT: Empty 12,600 lb., Gross 20,200 lb., Max. 21,186 lb.
PERFORMANCE: Speed—Top 110 mph, Landing 56 mph. Service Ceiling 17,500′, Climb 6000′/9 min. Range 1100 miles/2000 lbs. bombs.

AF

BARLING XNBL-1
Liberty 12A, 420 hp
DIMENSIONS: Span 120′, Lg. 65′, Ht. 27′, Wing Area 4200 sq. ft.
WEIGHT: Empty 27,703 lb., Gross 32,203 lb., Max. 42,569 lb. Fuel 2088 gal.
PERFORMANCE: Speed—Top 96 mph at s. l., 93 mph at 5000′, Cruising 61 mph, Landing 55 mph. Service Ceiling 7725′, Absolute Ceiling 10,200′, Climb 352′/1 min., 5000′/19.7 min. Range 170 miles/5000 lbs. bombs, 335 miles max.

The largest bomber of this period was designed in 1920 by Walter Barling, and built in sections by Witteman-Lewis in New Jersey. Designated XNBL-1 (night bombardment-long distance), the Barling was first flown on August 22, 1923. Three wings, four rudders, six engines, and ten landing wheels gave this behemoth a configuration more likely to antagonize the air than to pass through it. Four 420 hp Liberty 12A engines were arranged as tractors, two as pushers. Seven .30-caliber guns guarded a crew of six. Up to 2000 gallons of gasoline made a six-ton load, for two-thirds of which bombs might be substituted.

Although Mitchell said the Barling "was entirely successful from an experimental standpoint," it was elsewhere described as "Mitchell's Folly," and an Air Force history admits it had "disappointing speed, load, and endurance," with a range of 170 miles with load divided between fuel and bombs, and 335 miles with fuel only. Considering the $350,000 cost, it was hardly a great achievement. Mitchell wanted to go ahead with the Martin XNBL-2, an advanced four-place monoplane with two 700 hp, 18 cylinder, W-2779 Engineering Division engines in the 98 ft. wing's leading edge, but the order for two prototypes was canceled. The Barling triplane itself was abandoned in 1925, and nothing like its size was to be seen in U.S. bombers for a dozen years.

Traditional bomber patterns reappeared in the Elias XNBS-3 and Curtiss XNBS-4, four-place biplanes with two Libertys, boxlike biplane tails, and five .30-caliber guns in the usual nose, rear, and tunnel positions. The XNBS-3 was tested in August 1924, and did 101 mph with a 1692-lb. bomb load. The Curtiss XNBS-4 carried 1907 lbs. in the November 1924 tests of the first of two examples.

Neither of these ships was ordered, for they incorporated no real advance over service types. With little performance progress made since the war, Air Service bomber squadrons hardly seemed likely to replace the battleship as the first line of defense. In July 1925, the bomber force was limited to 90 NBS-1s, the same type used five years earlier.

AMC

ELIAS XNBS-3
Liberty 12A, 425 hp
DIMENSIONS: Span 77′ 6″, Lg. 48′ 5″, Ht. 16′ 10″, Wing Area 1542 sq. ft.
WEIGHT: Empty 8809 lb., Gross 14,343 lb. Fuel 340–356 gal.
PERFORMANCE: Speed—Top 101 mph at s. l., 96 mph at 6500′, Landing 65 mph. Service Ceiling 8680′, Absolute Ceiling 11,500′, Climb 405′/1 min., 5000′/16 min. Range 465 miles/1692 lbs. bombs.

AMC

CURTISS XNBS-4
Liberty 12A, 436 hp
DIMENSIONS: Span 90′ 2″, Lg. 46′ 5″, Ht. 15′ 9″, Wing Area 1524 sq. ft.
WEIGHT: Empty 7864 lb., Gross 13,795 lb. Fuel 334 gal.
PERFORMANCE: Speed—Top 100 mph at s. l., 95 mph at 5000′, Landing 53 mph. Service Ceiling 10,750′, Absolute Ceiling 13,000′, Climb 529′/1 min., 5000′/11.5 min. Range 620 miles/2000 lbs. bombs.

A THEORY OF WAR UNSOUND AND RUTHLESS?

Despite the modest size of his striking force Mitchell continued attacking "battleship admirals" and ground generals and predicted enormous capabilities for future aircraft. President Calvin Coolidge demoted him to the rank of colonel, and he was sent to "exile" in Texas, but the disaster of the dirigible *Shenandoah* in September 1925 gave Mitchell an excuse to issue his most violent denunciation of "incompetency, criminal negligence, and almost treasonable administration."

This statement resulted in Mitchell's famous court-martial in the fall of 1925, and the accompanying publicity led to Presidential appointment that same year of a board to investigate aviation, under chairmanship of banker-diplomat Dwight W. Morrow. Scores of witnesses presented data and opinions on air power to the board, most of them hostile to Mitchell.

It was against the limited range of the existing bombers that witnesses before the Morrow Board directed their main fire. The conservative position was put very strongly by the assistant director of the Navy's War Plans Division, Captain Claude S. Pye. In the first place, argued the Navy spokesman, since bombers were then very limited in striking radius, to abandon battleships for bombers would be to assume an "essentially defensive" military posture. "Without a fleet, our world trade would soon become a sacrifice to the air fetish." Do we wish to adopt a policy "like that of China and build a wall of air defense along our shores, outside of which the nations of the world can rob us of our commerce on which our national prosperity . . . depends?"

Even if one were to suppose, Captain Pye continued, that offensive operations by aircraft alone were possible, could Americans use such weapons? No, he said, quoting liberally from Mitchell's *Winged Defense* to show that air bombardment meant "ruthlessly" bombing "civil population and economic resources." But, under existing international law "the destruction of private property as an independent . . . means of coercing an enemy people is banned." But the Navy "does not subscribe to the theory of ruthlessness and believes that any organization based on . . . war according to such theory is unsound. The Navy further believes that if the people of the United States will seriously consider this subject they will reject this theory of ruthlessness and with such rejection the principal excuse for an independent air service will disappear."

Thus testified a representative of the Navy on October 14, 1925. Not all Navy men deprecated bomber striking power, and later chapters in this book detail progress made in carrier aviation. Yet aviation was seen by the majority as an arm of surface elements, whether fighting ships or infantry divisions. An independent air force built around bombers would

AMC

HUFF-DALAND XLB-1
Packard 2A-2540, rated 800 hp, actual 750 hp
DIMENSIONS: Span 66′ 6″, Lg. 46′ 2″, Ht. 14′ 11″, Wing Area 1137 sq. ft.
WEIGHT: Empty 5740 lb., Gross 10,346 lb. Fuel 290 gal.
PERFORMANCE: Speed—Top 121 mph at s. l., 117 mph at 6500′, Cruising 114 mph, Landing 55 mph. Service Ceiling 14,425′, Absolute Ceiling 17,300′, Climb 176′/1 min., 6500′/23.5 min. Range 940 miles.

MFR

HUFF-DALAND LB-1
Packard 2A-2540, 787 hp
DIMENSIONS: Span 66′ 6″, Lg. 46′ 2″, Ht. 14′ 11″, Wing Area 1137 sq. ft.
WEIGHT: Empty 6237 lb., Gross 12,415 lb. Fuel 295–350 gal.
PERFORMANCE: Speed—Top 120 mph at s. l., 114 mph at 5000′, Cruising 105 mph, Landing 61 mph. Service Ceiling 11,150′, Absolute Ceiling 13,700′, Climb 530′/1 min., 6500′/14 min. Range 430 miles/2750 lbs. bombs.

be unsound because it could not protect our overseas commerce, and because it would commit the U.S. to a theory of ruthlessness. The Morrow Board must have been impressed, for the final report firmly rejected Mitchell's theories, and two weeks later he was found "guilty as charged" of insubordination, and resigned from the Army effective February 1, 1926.

BOMBERS UNDER THE GENERAL STAFF

Aside from changing the Air Service name to Air Corps, and promising enough funds to build a modern force of 1800 planes, the Air Corps Act of 1926 embodied Morrow Board ideas and left the airmen still under the thumb of a General Staff of ground officers. Appropriations steadily increased from 13.5 million dollars in 1925 to 38.9 million in fiscal 1931, but much was siphoned off for observation planes. On June 30, 1925, the Army had 90 bombers compared with 249 observation planes and 28 fighters; on December 31, 1928, there were only 60 bombers to 506 observation planes, 190 fighters, and 69 attack planes.

HUFF-DALAND XHB-1
Packard 2A-2540, 787 hp
DIMENSIONS: Span 84′ 7″, Lg. 59′ 7″, Ht. 17′ 2″, Wing Area 1648.5 sq. ft.
WEIGHT: Empty 8070 lb., Gross 16,838 lb. Fuel 412 gal.
PERFORMANCE: Speed—Top 109 mph.

MFR

Bomber strength was declining, and a replacement for the NBS-1 was required. More range was needed if bombers were to grow in importance, and this aim seemed advanced by the Huff-Daland XLB-1 (light bomber), which appeared in October 1925. Substituting a single 750 hp Packard 1A-2540 for the usual two Libertys, the XLB-1 was of fabric-covered steel-tube construction with two men side by side behind the engine, and a gunner near the single tail. Two Lewis guns were mounted at the gunner's pit, a third on the floor, and two .30-caliber Brownings were fixed on the lower wings' leading edge. About 1500 lbs. of bombs could be carried $8\frac{1}{4}$ hours over a range of 940 miles, the best yet for an American bomber.

Ten LB-1s, called Pegasus by the company, were ordered in November 1925 for service trials. In July 1927, tests began on the LB-1, which had provision for a fourth crewman and larger useful loads than the prototype.

An enlarged heavy bomber version of the LB-1 appeared in August 1926 as the Huff-Daland XHB-1. Since the 1200 hp engine expected had failed to materialize, the same 787 hp Packard 2A-2540 had to be used. Christened Cyclops by the company, the only Army plane bearing "HB" letters carried four men; two in an open cockpit ahead of the wing, one near the tail with twin Lewis guns, and the other with a

HUFF-DALAND XHB-1

MFR

AMC

HUFF-DALAND XLB-5
Liberty V-1650-3, 400 hp
DIMENSIONS: Span 66′ 6″, Lg. 45′, Ht. 16′ 10″, Wing Area 1137 sq. ft.
WEIGHT: Empty 6848 lb., Gross 11,992 lb. Fuel 200–340 gal.
PERFORMANCE: Speed—Top 108 mph, Cruising 87 mph, Landing 60 mph. Service Ceiling 7875′, Absolute Ceiling 10,300′, Climb 420′/1 min.

"retractable gun platform" which could be lowered below the fuselage. Two fixed Browning wing guns and over 4000 lbs. of bombs were also carried.

The Cyclops was the Army's last single-engined bomber, for as early as April 1926 an Army board declared single-engined aircraft unsatisfactory for bombardment missions. A twin-engined layout was safer, and allowed a nose cockpit for gunnery and bomb-aiming.

The NBS-1s were aging on the flying fields, and the Army began shopping for better twin-engined replacements. Huff-Daland, which in 1927 became the

AMC

KEYSTONE LB-5A (As LB-5 with twin rudders)

Keystone Aircraft Corporation, offered the XLB-5 for tests in February 1927. This ship, called the Pirate by the company, had war-surplus Libertys, gunners in the bow and rear, and the LB-1s tapered wing and single rudder.

Ten LB-5 and 25 LB-5As were ordered at a cost of $28,000 each, and when delivered were similar to the prototype except for triple rudders on the former, and twin rudders on the LB-5A. Armament included five .30-caliber Lewis guns and 2121 lbs. of bombs.

KEYSTONE LB-5
Liberty V-1650-3, 420 hp
DIMENSIONS: Span 67′, Lg. 44′ 8″, Ht. 16′ 10″, Wing Area 1138.7 sq. ft.
WEIGHT: Empty 7024 lb., Gross 12,155 lb. Fuel 200 gal.
PERFORMANCE: Speed—Top 107 mph. Service Ceiling 8000′, Absolute Ceiling 8800′, Climb 5000′/20 min. Range 435 miles/2312 lbs. bombs.

AF

AMC

KEYSTONE XLB-3
As LB-5 inverted, air-cooled Liberty V-1410-1.

AMC

KEYSTONE XLB-3A
Pratt & Whitney R-1340-1, 410 hp
DIMENSIONS: Span 67′, Lg. 45′, Ht. 16′ 10″, Wing Area 1138.7 sq. ft.
WEIGHT: Empty 6065 lb., Gross 11,682 lb. Fuel 245–350 gal.
PERFORMANCE: Speed—Top 116 mph at s. l., 113 mph at 5000′, Cruising 93 mph, Landing 59 mph. Service Ceiling 11,210′, Absolute Ceiling 13,700′, Climb 550′/1 min., 5000′/11.3 min. Range 544 miles at top speed.

MFR

KEYSTONE XB-1B (Original version shown)
Curtiss V-1570-5, 600 hp
DIMENSIONS: Span 85′, Lg. 62′, Ht. 19′ 3″, Wing Area 1604 sq. ft.
WEIGHT: Empty 9462 lb., Gross 16,500 lb., Max. 17,039 lb. Fuel 444 gal.
PERFORMANCE: Speed—Top 117 mph at s. l., Landing 56 mph. Service Ceiling 15,000′. Range 700 miles/2508 lbs. bombs.

MFR

CURTISS XB-2
Curtiss GV-1570, 600 hp
DIMENSIONS: Span 90′, Lg. 47′ 6″, Ht. 16′ 3″, Wing Area 1499 sq. ft.
WEIGHT: Empty 8732 lb., Gross 16,344 lb. Fuel 444 gal.
PERFORMANCE: Speed—Top 130 mph at s. l., Cruising 104 mph, Landing 53 mph. Service Ceiling 16,140′, Absolute Ceiling 18,435′.

An air-cooled version of the Pirate was planned in the XLB-3 which was to be a twin to the XLB-5, using air-cooled Libertys. When this engine didn't work out, the project was replaced by the XLB-3A, which had a pair of 410 hp R-1340-1 radials. The aircraft was not completed until 1928, when it appeared with a triple rudder.

Keystone also built a heavy bomber, the XB-1, which was a twin-engined development of the XHB-1. Originally, 510 hp Packard 2A-1530s were to be used, but since this engine proved unsatisfactory during LB-1 service trials, the new 600 hp Curtiss V-1570-5 Conquerors were installed on the completed aircraft, which was labeled XB-1B.

But competition was offered by the Curtiss XB-2 Condor, which was also a large five-place biplane with twin rudders, and Curtiss Conquerors. Both the XB-1B and the XB-2 shared the first improvement in defensive armament since the war; instead of a single rear gunner with view blocked by the tail assembly, there were two gunners, one seated in each engine nacelle with a clear fire to the rear. Two Lewis guns were provided for each, with a third pair in the nose. Bomb load, normally 2508 lbs., could be increased to 4000 on short flights. First tested in September 1927, the Curtiss Condor showed the best performance of any bomber of that decade.

Other designs continued to appear, however. Igor Sikorsky, now transplanted to America, offered a descendant of the Ilya Mourometz: the Sikorsky S-37B Guardian. Powered by two air-cooled Pratt & Whitney 525 hp Hornets, the S-37B had a 100 ft. span upper wing overhanging a 58 ft. lower wing. Five men were arranged in the traditional manner in the fuselage; twin rudders made up the tail. Armed with five .30-caliber guns and 1952 lbs. of bombs, the Guardian did not attract even an official Army designation.

AF

CURTISS B-2

Curtiss V-1570-7, 633 hp

DIMENSIONS: Span 90′, Lg. 47′ 6″, Ht. 16′ 3″, Wing Area 1499 sq. ft.

WEIGHT: Empty 9039 lb., Gross 16,516 lb. Fuel 444 gal.

PERFORMANCE: Speed—Top 132 mph at s. l., 128 mph at 5000′, Cruising 114 mph, Landing 53 mph. Service Ceiling 17,100′, Absolute Ceiling 19,400′, Climb 850′/1 min., 5000′/6.8 min. Range 780 miles/2508 lbs. bombs.

SIKORSKY S-37B

Pratt & Whitney R-1690, 525 hp

DIMENSIONS: Span 100′, Lg. 45′, Ht. 16′ 2″, Wing Area 1074 sq. ft.

WEIGHT: Empty 8794 lb., Gross 15,109 lb. Fuel 350 gal.

PERFORMANCE: Speed—Top 108 mph, Landing 57 mph. Service Ceiling 12,800′, Climb 546′/1 min. Range 575 miles/1952 lbs. bombs.

MFR

MFR

ATLANTIC-FOKKER XLB-2
Pratt & Whitney R-1340, 410 hp (R-1690-1, 525 hp)
DIMENSIONS: Span 72′ 10″, Lg. 51′ 5″, Ht. 13′ 3″, Wing Area 748 sq. ft.
WEIGHT: Empty 5916 lb. (6236 lb.), Gross 12,039 lb. (12,655 lb.). Fuel 295 gal. (340 gal.).
PERFORMANCE: Speed—Top 116 mph (123 mph) at s. l., 112 mph at 5000′, Cruising 93 mph, Landing 67 mph. Service Ceiling 10,925′ (13,700′), Absolute Ceiling 13,400′, Climb 540′/1 min. (762′/1 min.), 5000′/11.5 min. Range 540 miles (650 miles)/2052 lbs. bombs.

MFR

KEYSTONE XLB-6
Wright R-1750, 525 hp
DIMENSIONS: Span 74′ 9″, Lg. 43′ 6″, Ht. 18′ 1″, Wing Area 1148 sq. ft.
WEIGHT: Empty 6605 lb., Gross 13,018 lb. Fuel 350 gal.
PERFORMANCE: Speed—Top 116 mph at s. l., 114 mph at 5000′, Cruising 93 mph, Landing 58 mph. Service Ceiling 14,770′, Absolute Ceiling 17,050′, Climb 746′/1 min., 5000′/7.9 min. Range 440 miles/2000 lbs. bombs.

The first twin-engined Air Corps bomber built as a monoplane was the Atlantic-Fokker XLB-2. Developed from the Fokker transport, the XLB-2 had 410 hp Pratt & Whitney R-1340 Wasps suspended below the high cantilever wing. Top speed with these engines was 116 mph, but speed was later increased to 123 mph by using the 525 hp R-1690-1. The crew of five was armed with five .30-caliber guns and 2052 lbs. of bombs.

This firm had planned in 1926 a larger monoplane; the XHB-2 with two Packard 2A-2540s, 108 ft.-4 in. span and 24,478 lbs. gross. It was never built, for, as in the case of Martin's XNBL-2 and a projected Huff-Daland XHB-3, authorities were unready to trust a big monoplane. Reticence about all-metal aircraft also dropped the XLB-4 project, a biplane with R-1690 Hornets proposed by Martin.

Keystone introduced another bomber type in December 1927, the XLB-6. This was actually the last LB-5 modified with a larger wing and two R-1750-1 Wrights.

When an Army board of seven officers met in February 1928 to choose a bomber type for production, it dismissed the XB-1B, XLB-2, and S-37, but disagreed on the merits of the Curtiss XB-2 and Keystone XLB-6. Although the former had by far the best performance, critics complained that it cost too much and was "too big for existing hangars." A four-to-three decision put the Keystone ship into production, but Curtiss did get in June 1928 a $1,050,473 contract for twelve B-2s, and began delivery in May 1929.

Although the Keystone bombers were conservative in design and performance, they were favored because of their low cost, economical operation and stable flying qualities. Between 1927 and 1932, 210 Keystones were delivered to the Air Corps, representing nineteen different models. All were twin-engined, five-place biplanes constructed of steel tubing covered by fabric. Below the bow gunner were windows for the bombardier, and behind and above him sat the pilots. The rear gunner behind the wings had, like the front gunner, two Lewis guns on a ring (a single Browning on later models), and another gun firing downward through the floor opening.

With their open cockpits, struts, wires, and exposed wheels they looked and performed little differently from the NBS-1s they replaced, certainly not enough to make national policymakers feel they had advanced far beyond the planes that sank the old target ships.

The first production series was the LB-5 Pirates mentioned earlier; they could be recognized by their water-cooled Libertys, triple rudders, and 67 ft. tapered wing. The last became the XLB-6 with air-cooled Cyclones and a 75 ft. wing. In May 1928, a new batch was ordered for delivery beginning the following November at a cost of $24,750 each. Labeled Panther by the company, they had a longer fuselage, 75 ft. wings and twin rudders. Seventeen were LB-6s with Wright R-1750-1 Cyclones; 18 were LB-7s with Pratt & Whitney R-1690-3 Hornets and one LB-12 had a 575 hp R-1860-1. Armament included five Lewis guns and a ton of bombs in internal racks.

Geared engine installations were tested in 1929 by converting the last four ships on that contract to the LB-8 (R-1860-3), LB-9, single-ruddered LB-10, and LB-11, which had modifications of R-1750 Cyclones. These tests resulted in the largest bomber order since 1922, for 73 ships originally labeled L-10A, LB-13, and LB-14. But by the time they were delivered, the Army had dropped the LB designation and was listing all bombers in the B series beginning with the XB-1B

MFR

KEYSTONE LB-6
Wright R-1750-1, rated 525 hp at s. l., actual 536 hp
DIMENSIONS: Span 75′, Lg. 43′ 5″, Ht. 18′ 1″, Wing Area 1148 sq. ft.
WEIGHT: Empty 6836 lb., Gross 13,440 lb. Fuel 352 gal.
PERFORMANCE: Speed—Top 114 mph at s. l., 106 mph at 5000′, Cruising 95 mph, Landing 58 mph. Service Ceiling 11,650′, Absolute Ceiling 14,000′, Climb 600′/1 min., 5000′/10.3 min. Range 632 miles/2003 lbs. bombs.

KEYSTONE LB-7
Pratt & Whitney R-1690-3, 525 hp at s. l.
DIMENSIONS: As LB-6
WEIGHT: Empty 6556 lb., Gross 12,903 lb. Fuel 350 gal.
PERFORMANCE: Speed—Top 114 mph at s. l., 110 mph at 5000′, Cruising 95 mph, Landing 55 mph. Service Ceiling 13,325′, Absolute Ceiling 15,700′, Climb 660′/1 min., 5000′/9.1 min. Range 432 miles/2000 lbs. bombs.

AMC

MFR

KEYSTONE LB-8
Pratt & Whitney GR-1860-3, 550 hp
DIMENSIONS: Span 75′, Lg. 42′ 6″, Ht. 18′ 1″, Wing Area 1148 sq. ft.
WEIGHT: Empty 7357 lb., Gross 13,745 lb. Fuel 363 gal.
PERFORMANCE: Speed—Top 126 mph at s. l., 121 mph at 5000′, Cruising 100 mph, Landing 59 mph. Service Ceiling 16,800′, Absolute Ceiling 18,700′, Climb 977′/1 min., 5000′/14.5 min.

KEYSTONE LB-10
Wright R-1750-1, 525 hp
DIMENSIONS: Span 75′, Lg. 49′ 3″, Ht. 15′ 6″, Wing Area 1148 sq. ft.
WEIGHT: Empty 6993 lb., Gross 13,285 lb. Fuel 340 gal.
PERFORMANCE: Speed—Top 116 mph at s. l., 113 mph at 5000′, Cruising 93 mph, Landing 58 mph. Service Ceiling 13,440′, Absolute Ceiling 15,800′, Climb 660′/1 min., 5000′/9 min. Range 352 miles/2587 lbs. bombs.

MFR

KEYSTONE B-4A
Pratt & Whitney R-1860-7, 575 hp at s. l.
DIMENSIONS: As B-3A
WEIGHT: Empty 7951 lb., Gross 13,209 lb. Fuel 235–535 gal.
PERFORMANCE: Speed—Top 121 mph at s. l., Cruising 103 mph, Landing 57 mph. Service Ceiling 14,000′. Range 855 miles.

AF

KEYSTONE B-6A
Wright R-1820-1, 575 hp
DIMENSIONS: Span 74′ 9″, Lg. 48′ 10″, Ht. 17′ 2″, Wing Area 1137 sq. ft.
WEIGHT: Empty 8037 lb., Gross 13,374 lb. Fuel 235–535 gal.
PERFORMANCE: Speed—Top 121 mph at s. l., 116 mph at 5000′, Cruising 103 mph, Landing 57 mph. Service Ceiling 14,100′, Absolute Ceiling 16,500′, Climb 690′/1 min. Range 363 miles/2500 lbs. bombs, 825 miles maximum.

MFR

KEYSTONE B-5A
Wright R-1750-3, 525 hp at s. l.
DIMENSIONS: As B-3A
WEIGHT: Empty 7705 lb., Gross 12,952 lb. Fuel 235-535 gal.
PERFORMANCE: Speed—Top 111 mph at s. l., 106 mph at 5000′, Cruising 98 mph, Landing 57 mph. Service Ceiling 10,600′, Absolute Ceiling 13,000′, Climb 540′/1 min., 5000′/11.7 min. Range 815 miles.

and B-2 and continuing to this day. All ships in this Keystone series had a 74 ft. 9 in. span and were distinguished from their predecessors by a single balanced rudder. Three Browning flexible guns with 500 rpg and up to 2500 lbs. of bombs were the armament. First was the B-3A, tested in December 1930 with 525 hp R-1690-3 Hornets. Thirty-six B-3A were followed by five Y1B-4 (575 hp R-1860-7), three Y1B-5 and 27 B-5A (525 hp R-1750-3), and five Y1B-6 (575 hp R-1820-1), three of the latter being reworked B-3A ships.

September 1931 saw the appearance of the final Keystone series; similar to the previous types, they were 25 B-4As with Pratt & Whitney R-1860-7s and 39 B-6As with Wright R-1820-1 Cyclones.

KEYSTONE B-3A
Pratt & Whitney R-1690-3, 525 hp at s. l.
DIMENSIONS: Span 74′ 8″, Lg. 48′ 10″, Ht. 15′ 9″, Wing Area 1145 sq. ft.
WEIGHT: Empty 7705 lb., Gross 12,952 lb. Fuel 235–535 gal.
PERFORMANCE: Speed—Top 114 mph at s. l., 109.5 mph at 5000′, Cruising 98 mph, Landing 56 mph. Service Ceiling 12,700′, Absolute Ceiling 15,000′, Climb 650′/1 min., 5000′/9.4 min. Range 860 miles.

AF

A TECHNICAL REVOLUTION BEGINS

Keystone biplanes formed almost the entire U.S. bombardment strength during the international social crisis of the late twenties and early thirties which finally led to the Second World War. If their striking power, range, and ability to defend themselves were no greater than that of their predecessors, if their top speed reflected only that improvement endowed by more horsepower, then airmen might explain the limited technical advance by asking, "What would have happened to the automobile, if the railroads had controlled its development?" A better excuse was that fabric-covered biplanes could go so fast and so far, but no farther.

But in spite of General Staff control of air power, a technical revolution in aircraft design was under way. It had appeared on drawing boards in the twenties, and unencouraged by the military, had begun flying as commercial aircraft built by Boeing, Consolidated, and Northrop, while Army squadrons still operated their old biplanes. The technical revolution had two elements: the use of new discoveries in metallurgy for lightweight all-metal structures of new strength and reliability; and the shaping of these structures into streamlined forms in which dragging struts, undercarriages, and open cockpits were submerged into cantilever wings, retractable landing gear, and Plexiglas enclosures. The availability of monoplanes, due to "increased knowledge of internally braced metal wing construction and of the cause and cure of wing flutter and other aberrations," was about to make a radical improvement in the appearance and performance of the bomber.

The revolution crept into the bomber field through the back way. In 1928, the War Department was developing a fast twin-engined monoplane designed for observation missions, and for economy's sake it appeared advantageous to utilize the same type for bombing. Two prototypes were planned of each of two designs; the Fokker XO-27 and Douglas XO-35, and in February 1929, it was decided to complete the second prototype of each as a day bomber.

When completed in 1930, they appeared as the XB-7 and XB-8, four-place high-wing monoplanes, whose landing wheels retracted back into the engine nacelles behind 600 hp Curtiss Conqueror engines. The Douglas XB-7s wing was gulled into the fuselage and braced by struts from the V-1570-25 engines, while the Fokker XB-8 had a straight, cantilever (internally braced) wing.

A dozen of the Fokker ships were ordered, but all were delivered as observation types. Douglas received a service test contract for seven YB-7s at $510,212, plus five YO-35 observation versions. These bombers achieved a speed of 182 mph with their 675 hp V-1570-27 engines, and were armed with 1200 lbs. of bombs,

MFR

DOUGLAS XB-7
Curtiss V-1570-25, 600 hp
DIMENSIONS: Span 65′, Lg. 45′ 6″, Ht. 11′ 7″, Wing Area 621 sq. ft.
WEIGHT: Empty 6865 lb., Gross 10,537 lb., Max. 11,287 lb. Fuel 200–300 gal.
PERFORMANCE: Speed—Top 169 mph at s. l., 165.5 mph at 5000′, Cruising 147 mph, Landing 66 mph. Service Ceiling 18,950′, Absolute Ceiling 20,600′, Climb 1220′/1 min., 5000′/4.7 min.

MFR

FOKKER XB-8
Curtiss V-1570-23, 600 hp
DIMENSIONS: Span 64′, Lg. 47′, Ht. 11′ 6″, Wing Area 619 sq. ft.
WEIGHT: Empty 6861 lb., Gross 10,545 lb. Fuel 209.5 gal.
PERFORMANCE: Speed—Top 160 mph.

DOUGLAS YB-7
Curtiss V-1570-27, 675 hp at s. l.
DIMENSIONS: Span 65′ 3″, Lg. 46′ 7″, Ht. 12′ 1″, Wing Area 621 sq. ft.
WEIGHT: Empty 7519 lb., Gross 9953 lb., Max. 11,177 lb. Fuel 200–300 gal.
PERFORMANCE: Speed—Top 182 mph at s. l., 177 mph at 5000′, Cruising 158 mph, Landing 78 mph. Service Ceiling 20,400′, Absolute Ceiling 21,800′, Climb 5000′/3.7 min. Range 411 miles/1200 lbs. bombs, 632 miles max.

AF

a .30-caliber Browning for the bow gunner, and another for his companion in the rear. Even for a lightweight, this performance in 1931 made the Keystone seem indeed slow.

Monoplanes built entirely of metal, including the skin, were operating successfully on airlines, and suggested themselves as bombers. A bomber version of Ford's famous tri-motor was tested by the Army in June 1931. A high-wing monoplane with anti-drag rings on three 500 hp R-1340-E radials, the Ford XB-906 was like the "Tin Goose" transport, but for bombardier's windows behind the front engine, a bay for 2000 lbs. of bombs, a front gun ring above and behind the pilot, and top and tunnel rear guns. Wheel pants did not compensate enough for the landing gear's drag, and performance was far below that of new types with retractable gear. An Army board inspecting the XB-906 reported that the front gun could not be handled in the propeller slip stream and coverage of the rear guns was inadequate.

Even less progress was made by the Keystone XB-908, designed as an all-metal low-wing monoplane with retractable wheels and two Curtiss V-1570 Conquerors. A mockup was inspected in April 1931, but neither the Army nor the company chose to finance the project further. When production of older Keystone biplanes ended in 1932, the Bristol, Pennsylvania, factory closed, and unemployment hurt the Bucks County community. A senator was asked to intercede for Army contracts, but new Boeing and Martin designs eclipsed competition, and the company suffered the penalty of inadequate technical advance.

AF

FORD XB-906
Pratt & Whitney R-1340E, 500 hp at 7000′
DIMENSIONS: Span 77′ 11″, Lg. 51′ 6″, Ht. 12′ 11″, Wing Area 835 sq. ft.
WEIGHT: Empty 8345 lb., Gross 14,137 lb. Fuel 325 gal.
PERFORMANCE: Speed—Top 145 mph at s. l., 142 mph at 5000′, Cruising 135 mph, Landing 66 mph. Service Ceiling 18,400′, Absolute Ceiling 20,000′, Climb 775′/1 min., 7000′/11.9 min.

BOEING XB-901 (YB-9)
Pratt & Whitney R-1830-13, 575 hp at s. l. (R-1830-11, 600 hp at 6000′)
DIMENSIONS: Span 76′ 9″, Lg. 51′ 6″, Ht. 12′ 8″, Wing Area 954 sq. ft.
WEIGHT: Empty 7650 lb. (8362 lb.), Gross 12,663 lb. (13,351 lb.). Fuel 250–308 gal.
PERFORMANCE: Speed—Top 163 mph at s. l., 158 mph at 5000′, (188 mph at 6000′), Cruising 137 mph (165 mph), Landing 62 mph (63 mph). Service Ceiling 19,400′ (22,600′), Absolute Ceiling 21,700′ (24,400′), Climb 950′/1 min. (1060′/1 min.), 5000′/6 min. Range (495 miles/1997 lbs. bombs).

MFR

AMC

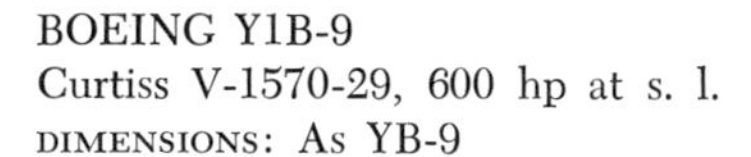

BOEING Y1B-9
Curtiss V-1570-29, 600 hp at s. l.
DIMENSIONS: As YB-9
WEIGHT: Empty 8618 lb., Gross 13,591 lb. Fuel 263–308 gal.
PERFORMANCE: Speed—Top 173 mph at s. l., 171.5 mph at 5000′, Cruising 151 mph, Landing 62 mph. Service Ceiling 19,200′, Absolute Ceiling 21,000′, Climb 1160′/1 min.

Boeing's aggressive design staff had developed in 1930 an all-metal low-wing transport with retractable wheels called the Monomail. The same principles were applied next to a twin-engined bomber built as a private venture and labeled XB-901. First flown on April 29, 1931, the XB-901 had 575 hp Pratt & Whitney commercial engines and a top speed of 163 mph at sea level. The crew of four sat in separate open cockpits along the narrow fuselage.

A contract for the prototype and six service test models was made in August 1931 for $730,730. Re-engined with Hornets supercharged to yield 600 hp at 6000 ft., the prototype was designated YB-9 and did 188 mph at that altitude during January 1932 tests. Armament included a ton of bombs and a .30-caliber gun in the front and rear cockpits.

Second example delivered was the Y1B-9, which had Curtiss V-1570-29 Conquerors, the last inline engines to be used on an Army bomber for over ten years.

AF

BOEING Y1B-9

February 1932 trials demonstrated a 173 mph speed. The remaining five ships, designated Y1B-9A and completed with R-1860-11 Hornets, did 188 mph clean, and 186 mph with external bomb load.

The Boeing bomber was a tremendous achievement, offering speeds more than 50 per cent higher than that of the Keystones built at the same time. With bomber speed now comparable to that of pursuit ships, defense problems became much greater than in biplane days. Boeing's metal monoplane became the parent of the bombers that fought the next war. But the B-9 itself was not built in quantity, for a new machine even more advanced in scope eclipsed it and became the first American-built bomber to take part in actual warfare.

BOEING Y1B-9A (Y1P-26 in background)
Pratt & Whitney R-1860-11, 600 hp at 6000′
DIMENSIONS: Span 76′ 10″, Lg. 52′, Ht. 12′, Wing Area 954 sq. ft.
WEIGHT: Empty 8941 lb., Gross 13,932 lb., Max. 14,320 lb. Fuel 263–504 gal.
PERFORMANCE: Speed—Top 188 mph at 6000′, Cruising 165 mph, Landing 67 mph. Service Ceiling 20,750′, Absolute Ceiling 22,500′, Climb 900′/1 min., 5000′/7.1 min. Range 540 miles/2260 lbs. bombs, 990 miles max.

MFR

Chapter 10: New Monoplanes for a New War 1931-37

BOMBERS IN DEMAND

Even as bombers shed their World War I configuration for a deadlier form, a new redivision of world power began. Japan occupied Manchuria, and non-recognition was the strongest objection made by the United States. A World Disarmament Conference began at Geneva in 1932, and abolition of the bombing plane was proposed by the U.S. and supported by a majority of the nations present.

Hitler came to power in January 1933 and Germany withdrew from Geneva, ending hopes for disarmament. Preparations were made in Germany, Italy, and Japan to build or strengthen bomber fleets for aggressive purposes. The ideas of Giulio Douhet, an Italian strategist, about the primacy of bombardment, awakened interest in bombers in many minds, and more attention and money was given to offensive aviation.

The Roosevelt administration was friendly to new ideas, and since William Mitchell had headed the Virginia delegation to the Democratic Convention in Chicago in 1932 that elected Roosevelt the party standard-bearer, it is not surprising that the Air Corps expenditures rose from 17.4 million dollars in 1934 to 50.9 million in 1938, and bombardment began serious preparation for a place in national strategy.

The bomber's role in America had been written by the MacArthur-Pratt agreement in January 1931, in which Army bombers assumed responsibility for coast defense, freeing the Navy for overseas offense. In July 1934, the Baker Board rejected an independent air force, but projected an increase to 2320 planes by 1940, and concentration of combat planes into a General Headquarters Air Force under central command that could strike a blow in any direction. Said the Board, "The development of aviation has increased the power of the offense where the countries at war . . . are close to each other, and has increased the power of the defense where the contestants are widely separated." Thus, the oceans around us made the bomber an asset to a policy of defense. Future technical developments would make a different evaluation necessary.

MARTIN'S TROPHY WINNER

The deep-bellied mid-wing monoplane that next equipped bomber squadrons first appeared at Wright Field in July 1932, as the Martin XB-907. It had retractable wheels, two 600 hp Wright SR-1820-E Cyclones in anti-drag rings, three open cockpits and a

MARTIN XB-10 (XB-907A)
Wright R-1820-19, 675 hp at 6000′
DIMENSIONS: Span 70′ 7″, Lg. 45′, Ht. 10′ 4″, Wing Area 640 sq. ft.
WEIGHT: Empty 7294 lb., Gross 12,230 lb., Max. 12,560 lb. Fuel 250 gal.
PERFORMANCE: Speed—Top 207 mph at 6000′, 196 mph at s. l., Cruising 169.5 mph, Landing 71 mph. Service Ceiling 21,000′, Absolute Ceiling 22,750′, Climb 1380′/1 min. Range 600 miles/2260 lbs. bombs.
AF

AF

MARTIN XB-907
Wright SR-1820E, 600 hp at 6000′
DIMENSIONS: Span 62′ 2″, Lg. 46′ 2″, Ht. 12′ 8″, Wing Area 551 sq. ft.
WEIGHT: Empty 6978 lb., Gross 10,580 lb. Fuel 200–300 gal.
PERFORMANCE: Speed—Top 197 mph at 6000′, 190 mph at s. l., Cruising 171 mph, Landing 91.5 mph. Service Ceiling 20,000′, Absolute Ceiling 21,600′, Climb 1600′/1 min. Range 650 miles, 980 miles max.

fourth crew member within the fuselage, and a top speed of 197 mph. After initial tests, it returned to the factory for rebuilding, and the new version came back to Wright in October 1932 as the XB-10. In this form, the Martin had larger wings, R-1820-F Cyclones of 675 hp in neat full cowlings, and the first rotating transparent nose turret on a U.S. bomber. It was necessary to protect the front gunner from the slip stream, for the XB-10 had an astonishing top speed of 207 mph.

Not only were the Keystones now totally obsolete, but the Martin was faster than any pursuit plane then in Army service. The technical revolution accomplished in bomber design by all-metal monoplanes would now be forced on fighter design. Little wonder that the Collier Trophy was awarded in 1932 to Glenn L. Martin for this ship.

On January 17, 1933, 48 Martins were ordered at a unit cost of $50,840 apiece. (Costs had more than doubled in the decade since Martin's last bomber, the NBS-1.) These ships differed from the prototype in having a canopy over the pilot and another for the radioman and the rear gunner. Load included a .30-caliber Browning in the nose turret, another in the rear cockpit, a third in the floor, 2260 lbs. of bombs and a fuel capacity of 226 gallons normal and 452 gallons overload.

Tests on the first of these began in June 1934, and different engines were used: 675 hp R-1820-25 Cy-

AF

MARTIN YB-10
Wright R-1820-17, 675 hp at 4500′
DIMENSIONS: Span 70′ 6″, Lg. 45′ 3″, Ht. 11′, Wing Area 678 sq. ft.
WEIGHT: Empty 7688 lb., Gross 12,829 lb., Max. 14,192 lb. Fuel 226–452 gal.
PERFORMANCE: Speed—Top 207 mph at 4500′, 196.5 mph at s. l., Cruising 178.5 mph, Landing 80 mph. Service Ceiling 21,800′, Absolute Ceiling 23,600′, Climb 1075′/1 min., 10,000′/10.2 min. Range 523 miles/2260 lbs. bombs, 1360 miles max.

clones on fourteen YB-10s and 775 hp R-1690-11 Hornets on seven YB-12 and 25 B-12A, the latter with provisions for an extra 365 gallon bomb-bay tank for long-range flights. A dozen planned R-1860-17 powered YB-13s were canceled, but one XB-14 tested in May 1935 had 950 hp R-1830-9 Twin Wasps. Last and fastest of the lot was the YB-10A, which had experimental turbo-supercharged R-1820-31 Cyclones. Several Martins temporarily fitted with floats for coast defense trials were designated B-10M and B-12AM.

Most widely used version was the B-10B, 103 being delivered in 1935 and 1936 with 775 hp R-1820-33 Cyclones and a range, with 2260 lbs. of bombs, of 590 miles on 226 gallons, 1240 miles on 452 gallons, and 1830 miles without bombs. This performance attracted attention from foreign powers waiting impatiently for the design to be released for export.

Meanwhile Bellanca and Curtiss developed for export bomber versions of transports. Bellanca's 77-140 for Colombia in 1935 was a bulky high-wing monoplane with R-1820F-3 Cyclones, externally braced, squared-off wings, and fixed landing gear. Armament included 2200 lbs. of bombs and five .30-caliber guns, located in the nose pit, and at top, bottom, and side openings in the cabin. Top speed was 190 mph as a landplane, and 165 mph when fitted with twin floats.

Chiang Kai-shek in 1934 received the Curtiss BT-32, a Condor transport armed with five .30-caliber guns and up to 3968 lbs. of bombs. Last large biplane built in the U.S., the BT-32 had two R-1820F-2 Cyclones, fabric covering, retractable wheels, pilots in the nose, top gunner before and after wings and guns in side and bottom openings. Further sales possibilities for Bellanca and Curtiss were ended by release in July 1936 of the more advanced Martin bombers for export.

The Dutch East Indies became the largest foreign purchaser of Martin bombers, buying 120 to protect their rich oil fields. The bombers delivered to the Dutch in 1937 and 1938 were Martin 139W models using the 850 hp G Cyclone, instead of the F series

MARTIN YB-12
Pratt & Whitney R-1690-11, 700 hp at 6500′
DIMENSIONS: As YB-10
WEIGHT: Empty 7728 lb., Gross 12,824 lb. Fuel 226–456 gal.
PERFORMANCE: Speed—Top 212 mph at 6500′, 190 mph at s. l., Cruising 170 mph, Landing 71 mph. Service Ceiling 24,600′, Absolute Ceiling 26,600′, Climb 1740′/1 min., 10,000′/10.1 min. Range 524 miles normal, 1360 miles max.

AF

WILLIAMS

MARTIN B-12A

MARTIN YB-10A
Wright R-1820-31, 675 hp take-off
DIMENSIONS: As YB-10
WEIGHT: Empty 8139 lb., Gross 13,212 lb. Fuel 230–456 gal.
PERFORMANCE: Speed—Top 236 mph at 25,000′. Climb 10,000′/7.1 min.

WL

PMB

MARTIN XB-14
Pratt & Whitney YR-1830-3, 950 hp take-off, 850 hp at 8000′, 800 hp at 10,000′
DIMENSIONS: As YB-10
WEIGHT: Empty 8467 lb., Gross 13,560 lb. Fuel 226–456 gal.
PERFORMANCE: Speed—Top 222.5 mph at 7900′, 190 mph at s. l., Cruising 191.5 mph. Climb 1640′/1 min. Range 600 miles/2260 lbs. bombs, 1210 miles/456 gal.

on Army ships. Bombers delivered in late 1938 and 1939 were the 166 model, which had 900 hp Cyclones and a long transparent enclosure running down the fuselage top. By the time the Japanese attacked in 1942, however, these planes were aging, and were of little effect.

Thirty-five more 139s were ordered by Argentina, while twenty were built for Turkey in 1937, and one was sold to Amtorg, the Soviet trading agency. The

MFR

MARTIN 166
Wright R-1820G-102, 900 hp at 6700′
DIMENSIONS: Span 70′ 10″, Lg. 44′ 2″, Ht. 11′ 7″, Wing Area 682 sq. ft.
WEIGHT: Empty 10,322 lb., Gross 15,624 lb. Fuel 762 gal. max.
PERFORMANCE: Speed—Top 260 mph, Cruising 205 mph, Landing 68 mph. Service Ceiling 25,200′, Climb 1680′/1 min. Range 2080 miles max.

MARTIN B-10B
Wright R-1820-33, 775 hp take-off, 750 hp at 5400′
DIMENSIONS: Span 70′ 6″, Lg. 44′ 9″, Ht. 15′ 5″, Wing Area 678 sq. ft.
WEIGHT: Empty 9681 lb., Gross 14,600 lb., Max. 16,400 lb. Fuel 226–452 gal. (702 gal. ferry).
PERFORMANCE: Speed—Top 213 mph at 10,000′, 196 mph at s. l., Cruising 193 mph, Landing 65 mph. Service Ceiling 24,200′, Climb 5000′/3.4 min. Range 590 miles normal, 1240 miles (overload)/2260 lbs. bombs, 1830 miles ferry.

AF

SI

BELLANCA 77-140
Wright R-1820F-3, 710 hp at 7000′
DIMENSIONS: Span 76′, Lg. 40′, Ht. 14′, Wing Area 770 sq. ft.
WEIGHT: Empty 8215 lb., Gross 14,136 lb., Max. 16,333 lb. Fuel 300–635 gal.
PERFORMANCE: Speed—Top 190 mph at 7000′, Cruising 172 mph, Landing 58 mph. Service Ceiling 23,500′, Absolute Ceiling 25,000′, Climb 1200′/1 min. Range 710 miles normal, 1500 miles max.

State Department refused to allow sales of American planes to combatants in the Spanish Civil War, although German and Italian bombers were used in large quantity by the Rebels. Nevertheless, at least one Martin bomber did appear in Spain, perhaps resold to the Spanish Republicans by its original purchaser.

China purchased nine 139s and Siam six. The effectiveness of Chinese planes used against the Japanese was limited by inadequate training of the Chinese crews. In February 1938, a pair of Chinese Martins flew over the Japanese mainland, but the fuel load necessary precluded dropping anything heavier than propaganda leaflets. Most Chinese bombers were soon destroyed in accidents, or while on the ground, by Japanese raids.

CURTISS-WRIGHT BT-32 CONDOR
Wright R-1820F-2, 716 hp (R-1820F-3, 750 hp for take-off)
DIMENSIONS: Span 82′, Lg. 49′ 6″, Ht. 16′ 4″, Wing Area 1276 sq. ft.
WEIGHT: Empty 11,233 lb., Gross 17,500 lb. Fuel 447–750 gal.
PERFORMANCE: Speed—Top 176 mph at 4100′ (180 mph at 7000′), Cruising 161 mph, Landing 58 mph. Service Ceiling 22,000′ (23,500′), Absolute Ceiling 24,200′ (25,300′), Climb 1290′/1 min. (1020′/1 min.). Range 840 miles/2260 lbs. bombs, 1400 miles max.

SI

FOUR ENGINES AND GREATER RANGE

That first "raid" by American planes over Japan illustrated the limited strategic value of the small aircraft that made up bomber production in this period. However useful for support of land armies they might be, it was evident that air power would require larger weapons to develop real strategic force, and the Air Corps wasn't slow to explore the new capabilities offered by all-metal monoplanes.

As early as July 1933, Wright Field had studied the problem of maximum range with a one-ton bomb load. When a 5000-mile range seemed possible, the Air Corps submitted "Project A," a proposal to build such a plane. Approval was given, and in May 1934, the Chief of Staff authorized negotiations with Boeing and Martin for preliminary designs.

The designs prepared by these firms were heroic in size compared with the existing bombers, but development abroad of such huge planes as the 157 ft. Span Dornier DO-X and the 210 ft. span Soviet Maxim Gorky had already demonstrated the practicality of large-size metal aircraft. The Boeing XB-15 was to be a 149 ft. span, four-engined, 35-ton monoplane, while the Martin XB-16 was projected as a 173 ft. span monoplane of 52 tons. Six 1000 hp Allison V-1710-3 engines were utilized: four as tractor, two as pusher. On June 28, 1934, a contract was given to Boeing for design data, wind tunnel tests, and mockup. Actual construction of the XB-15 was ordered a year later.

Meanwhile, preparations were made to select another bomber to replace the Martin B-10. A specification was issued early in 1934 for a "multiengine" bomber with approximately twice the older type's bomb load and range. Other companies based their proposals on the traditional twin engines, but Boeing remembered how, two years before, their own design had been bested by Martin, and boldly used four engines to maximize performance. When the Army announced in August 1934 a prototype competition for the following year, Boeing ventured construction of a prototype known as the Boeing 299.

First flown on July 28, 1935, four months after Hitler renounced the Versailles Pact and officially announced rearmament, the Boeing 299 had four 750 hp Pratt & Whitney R-1690-E Hornets on its low wing and could carry 2573 lbs. of bombs over 2000 miles at 204 mph. Immediately recognized as the most

AF

MARTIN 146
Wright R-1820G-5, 800 hp at 10,000′
DIMENSIONS: Span 75′, Lg. 50′, Wing Area 729 sq. ft.
WEIGHT: Empty 10,943 lb., Gross 16,000 lb., Max. 17,100 lb. Fuel 404 gal.
PERFORMANCE: Speed—Top 234 mph at 13,500′, 204 mph at s. l., Cruising 170 mph. Service Ceiling 28,500′. Range 1237 miles normal, 1589 miles max.

advanced bomber yet built, the 299 had five enclosed positions for .30-caliber guns. A nose turret could cover the whole forward hemisphere, while teardrop blisters studded the top, bottom, and sides of the rear fuselage.

Martin and Douglas also sent prototypes to Wright Field for the opening of bids and trials in August 1935. The Martin 146 was an enlarged B-10, with a wider fuselage to accommodate a larger bomb load and crew compartment, Fowler flaps on the wing, and two Wright R-1820-G5 Cyclones.

The Douglas DB-1 bore a family resemblance to that firm's transports, even to a cabin with bunks on which the six-man crew might rest. Two Wright R-1820-45 Cyclones powered this mid-wing monoplane, which was armed with three .30-caliber guns. One of these was in the nose turret, a second fired through a trap door in the floor at the rear, while the third was in a retractable, fully rotating turret just ahead of the tail. A 2260-lb. bomb load could be carried over 1000 miles at 170 mph cruising.

QUANTITY OR QUALITY?

In spite of the prototype's destruction on October 30, 1935, in a crash due to pilot error, the Air Corps recommended adoption of the Boeing 299, now officially labeled XB-17. Although airmen enthusiastically greeted the advanced performance, the General Staff was concerned with economy. Prices quoted per ship (exclusive of engines), in lots of 25 and in lots of 220, were as follows: Martin, $85,910 and $48,880; Douglas $99,150 and $58,500; and Boeing $196,730 and $99,620. Operating under budgetary limitations, the Air Corps recommended purchase of 65 B-17s instead of 185 other aircraft authorized. However, the General Staff preferred quantity to quality, and when production contracts were signed in January 1936, 13 four-engined Boeing YB-17s and 133 twin-engined Douglas B-18s were ordered.

The Air Corps received the YB-17s[1] between January and August 1937. Powered by Wright R-1820-39 Cyclones, the YB-17 had less framework on turrets and landing gear than the prototype and could be distinguished from later B-17 models by the carburetor intake on top of the engine nacelles. Top speed was 256 mph, and the range was then 2260 miles with a normal load of 2511 lbs. of bombs and 850 gallons of fuel. Range in overload condition (4000 lbs. of bombs

[1] Designated YB-17 on the 17 January 1936 contract, they became the Y1B-17 in November, and just plain B-17 in 1939.

PMB

DOUGLAS DB-1 (B-18 prototype)
Wright R-1820-45, 930 hp take-off, 810 hp at 10,200′
DIMENSIONS: Span 89′ 7″, Lg. 57′ 3″, Ht. 15′ 4″, Wing Area 959 sq. ft.
WEIGHT: Empty 14,806 lb., Gross 20,159 lb. Fuel 204–802 gal.
PERFORMANCE: Speed—Top 220 mph at 10,000′, Cruising 173 mph, Landing 62 mph. Service Ceiling 25,000′, Climb 10,000′/8.8 min. Range 1030 miles/2532 lbs. bombs.

BOEING XB-17
Pratt & Whitney R-1690E, 750 hp
DIMENSIONS: Span 103′ 9″, Lg. 68′ 9″, Ht. 15′, Wing Area 1420 sq. ft.
WEIGHT: Empty 22,125 lb., Gross 32,432 lb., Max. 43,000 lb. Fuel 1700 gal.
PERFORMANCE: Speed—Top 236 mph at 10,000′, Cruising 204 mph. Service Ceiling 24,620′. Range 2040 miles/2573 lbs. bombs, 3010 miles max.

MFR

BOEING YB-17
Wright R-1820-39, 930 hp take-off, 820 hp at 14,000′
DIMENSIONS: Span 103′ 9″, Lg. 68′ 4″, Ht. 18′ 4″, Wing Area 1420 sq. ft.
WEIGHT: Empty 24,458 lb., Gross 34,873 lb., Max. 42,600 lb. Fuel 1700–2492 gal.
PERFORMANCE: Speed—Top 256 mph at 14,000′, Cruising 217 mph, Landing 70 mph. Service Ceiling 30,600′, Climb 10,000′/6.5 min. Range 2260 miles/850 gal. with 2511 lbs. bombs, 1377 miles/10,496 lbs. bombs, 3320 miles max.

MFR

AF

DOUGLAS B-18
Wright R-1820-45, 930 hp take-off, 810 hp at 10,200′
DIMENSIONS: Span 89′ 6″, Lg. 56′ 8″, Ht. 15′ 2″, Wing Area 959 sq. ft.
WEIGHT: Empty 15,719 lb., Gross 21,130 lb., Max. 27,087 lb. Fuel 802–1170 gal.
PERFORMANCE: Speed—Top 217 mph at 10,000′, Cruising 167 mph, Landing 64 mph. Service Ceiling 24,200′, Absolute Ceiling 25,850′, Climb 1355′/1 min., 10,000′/9.1 min. Range 1082 miles/412 gal. with 2200 lbs. bombs, 1200 miles/4000 lbs. (Max. load), 2225 miles ferry.

DOUGLAS B-18A
Wright R-1820-53, 1000 hp take-off, 850 hp at 9600′
DIMENSIONS: Span 89′ 6″, Lg. 57′ 10″, Ht. 15′ 2″, Wing Area 965 sq. ft.
WEIGHT: Empty 16,321 lb., Gross 22,123 lb., Max. 27,673 lb. Fuel 802–1170 gal.
PERFORMANCE: Speed—Top 215.5 mph at 10,000′, Cruising 167 mph, Landing 69 mph. Service Ceiling 23,900′, Absolute Ceiling 25,600′, Climb 1030′/1 min., 10,000′/9.9 min.

AF

DOUGLAS DB-2 (Last B18, with powerturret)

and 1700 gallons of fuel) was 2400 miles. Without bombs and with 2492 gallons of fuel the range expanded to 3320 miles. A maximum bomb load of 10,496 lbs. might be carried 1377 miles, according to the Service Test Manual.

The first Douglas B-18 accepted was actually the DB-1 prototype. However, minor changes were made on the production models, and the last of these appeared with a power-operated nose turret in October 1937 with the company designation DB-2. The standard B-18 did 217 mph top, and had a range of 690 miles with maximum bomb load of 6502 lbs., 1082 miles with 2200 lb. normal bomb load, and 2225 miles without bombs.

Although flight tests confirmed the superiority of the four-engined types, the War Department preferred to use its limited budget on quantity rather than quality. No B-17s were ordered in the fiscal year of 1936, but Douglas received on June 10, 1937, an order for 177 B-18As at a cost of over $65,800 each.

PMB

PMB

DOUGLAS B-18B

The next fiscal year ended on June 30, 1938, with orders for 78 additional Douglas bombers (completed as 40 B-18A and 38 B-23) and 39 Boeing B-17Bs.

Changes in the neat Douglas nose had been ordered on October 11, 1937, to give more visibility and comfort to the bombardier. This resulted in the B-18As unusual nasal arrangement in which the bombardier sat above and ahead of the bow gunner. Appearing

PMB

BOEING XB-15

BOEING XB-15

Pratt & Whitney R-1830-11, 1000 hp take-off, 850 hp at 6000′

DIMENSIONS: Span 149′, Lg. 87′ 7″, Ht. 19′ 5″, Wing Area 2780 sq. ft.

WEIGHT: Empty 37,709 lb., Gross 65,068 lb., Max. 70,700 lb. Fuel 4190 gal.

PERFORMANCE: Speed—Top 197 mph at 6000′, Cruising 171 mph, Landing 70 mph. Service Ceiling 18,850′, Absolute Ceiling 20,900′, Climb 5000′/7.1 min., 10,000′/14.9 min. Range 3400 miles/2,511 lbs. bombs.

MFR

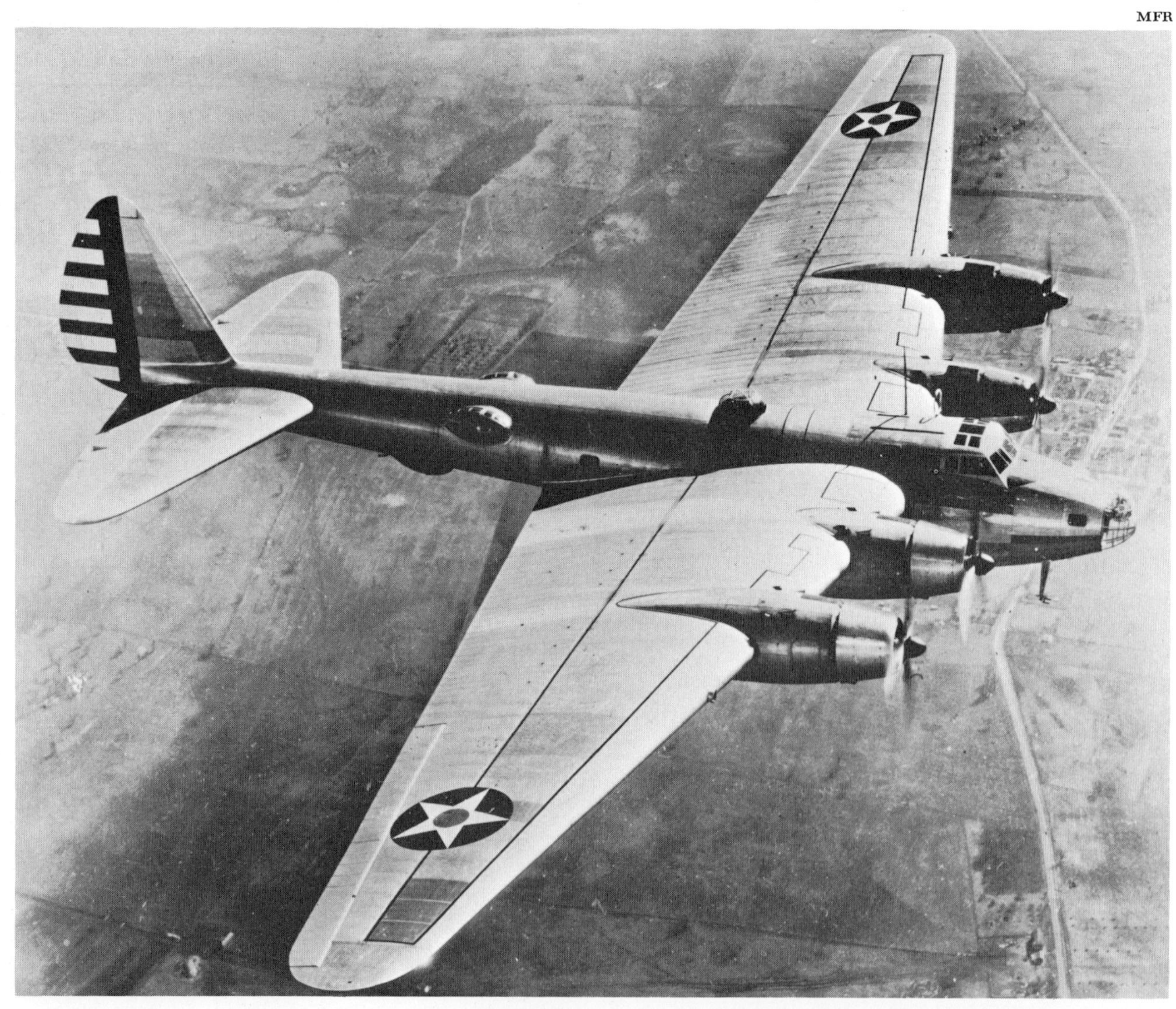

in April 1938, 217 B-18As had R-1820-53 Cyclones and a dome top on the power-operated rear turret.

Twenty B-18As for Canada were built in the opening weeks of 1940. When Axis submarines threatened in 1942, 122 aging B-18s were fitted with MAD gear (Magnetic Airborne Detector), redesignated B-18B, and used in the Caribbean.

During this period, work proceeded on long-range "Project A," including construction of the huge Boeing ordered in June of 1935 and planning of an even larger plane by Douglas. For a time these ships were designated XBLR-1 and XBLR-2 (experimental bomber long-range), but completed as the Boeing XB-15 and Douglas XB-19. On October 15, 1937, the XB-15 was flown for the first time.

The largest aircraft then built in America, the XB-15 had in the wing leading edge passageways to four 1000 hp Pratt & Whitney R-1830-11 Wasps. Double wheels and two ailerons on each wing testified to the 70,700 lbs. bulk. The crew of ten had "soundproofed, heated, and ventilated" quarters with rest bunks, kitchen and lavatory, and for the first time in an airplane, small auxiliary engines operated a 110-volt electrical system.

Armament was the heaviest then found on a bomber, three .30-caliber and three heavy .50-caliber guns. A nose turret like the XB-17s, a forward facing belly turret below the pilot's cabin, a top turret whose .50-caliber gun could rotate 360 degrees, two waist blisters behind the wings, and a rearward-facing belly turret, covered every approach to the ship except directly behind the huge tail—a weakness common to all U.S. bombers of the decade.

Strategically, the most important facts about the XB-15 were its 12,000 lb. maximum bomb capacity, and its 3400 mile range with 2511 lbs., not only much greater than any other bomber, but enough to fly from Guam to Japan and back, dropping something heavier and noisier than the leaflets sprinkled by Chiang's Martins. Eight years of flying, most of it as a converted cargo plane (XC-105), demonstrated this behemoth to be a practical aircraft. There was a weakness in that the ship was underpowered, so its 197 mph speed was the lowest of the modern bombers; but this was to be corrected in the Boeing YB-20, two of which were projected as improved B-15s with 1400 hp Pratt & Whitney R-2180-5s.

In March 1938 the Boeing Model 316 and Douglas DB-4 were offered as four-engined long-range bomber projects with tricycle landing gear. The Douglas ship, based on the DC-4 transport, was to weigh 71,000 gross, have a crew of nine, and six .50-caliber guns in four power turrets and two waist portals. Estimated performance included 260 mph at 15,000 ft. and 4000 mile range with 4500 lbs. of bombs, and 1000 miles with 20,000 lbs. of bombs. Boeing's project was offered in several forms, and the 80,000 lb. gross, 10 place, 152 ft. span 316-D version was designated YB-20 in June 1938. Prototypes of these designs were considered too expensive to warrant construction.

Abroad, war focussed public attention on bombing planes. Bombers contributed to the success of Mussolini's invasion of Ethiopia in October 1935, and the Spanish Civil War revealed the force of German and Italian raids on Republican cities. Japanese aviators began their massacre of the Chinese, and on December 12, 1937 sank the U.S. gunboat *Panay*, although a quick apology followed. Establishment of the Rome-Berlin-Tokyo Axis linked the aggressive and expanding air fleets of the fascist powers. In this situation, Air Corps leaders urged new emphasis on their favorite weapons. From the formation of the GHQ Air Force in 1935 to the end of fiscal 1937, they had persuaded the General Staff to buy 388 twin-engined and 55 four-engined bombers, compared to only 316 fighters, 147 attack planes, and 239 observation planes—quite a shift from the reconnaissance-minded force of 1928. Now the problem was to win even more funds for the expensive four-engined ships.

Enthusiastic over the performance of their one squadron of B-17s and single XB-15, airmen pressed for a larger role in the military scheme. During the May 1938 maneuvers, three B-17s flew 725 miles to sea to intercept the Italian liner *Rex*. They could have been carrying the six one-ton bombs that were used to sink the battleship in the 1921 test, so the flight demonstrated Boeing's value in coast defense. The speed and firepower of the bombers, thought their advocates, were now such that "No known agency can frustrate their mission."

In June 1937, Major General Frank M. Andrews argued that in the future only four-engined bombers should be purchased, and that they were "the basic element of air power." But the airmen were again discouraged by the General Staff, which persisted in buying additional twin-engined bombers at the expense of four-engined ships, and in June 1938, an Army and Navy Joint Board deemed it improbable that bombers of greater range and capacity than the B-17 would be needed. This policy killed Boeing's YB-20 project, and would have prevented the development of the B-29, if continued.

North American's NA-21 was offered in March 1937 as an attempt to get better performance from two engines. Powered by two 1200 hp Pratt & Whitney R-2180-1 Twin Hornets, this six-place mid-wing monoplane had five .30-caliber guns mounted in power turrets in the nose and on the top, and at transparent panels in waist and ventral orifices. A 2200-lb. bomb load on 1900-mile hauls could be increased to 10,000 lbs. for a shortened 660 mile range. Without bombs, and with a fuel overload, the range was 3100 miles. The prototype was eventually accepted by the Air Corps as the XB-21, although a plan to build five more for service tests was dropped. Once again price was a factor, for North American had bid $122,600 each in quantities of 50, while cost savings due to previous production enabled Douglas to cut B-18A unit bids to $63,977, and Douglas won the contract.

Douglas had plans to improve their twin-engined design—at first as the B-22, a B-18A with new R-2600-1 Cyclone engines. This project was superseded in November 1938 by the B-23, which had 1600 hp Wright R-2600-3 Cyclones and a new streamlined fuselage incorporating the latest ideas in armament. It was thought that the 282 mph top speed reduced the threat of frontal attacks, so the bow turret of earlier years was replaced by a simple plastic nose with a flat bomb-aimer's panel, and a ball-and-socket mount for a .30-caliber gun. Two other .30s were placed in top and belly positions, while a .50-caliber gun armed the first Air Corps tail gunner. The idea of a gun position behind the tail, of course, dated back to the Ilya Mourometz of 1914. It had also been used on British bombers, and was seen on Navy patrol bombers in 1937. The first B-23 flew on July 27, 1939, and 37 others followed between February and September 1940.

PMB

NORTH AMERICAN XB-21

Pratt & Whitney R-2180-1, 1200 hp take-off

DIMENSIONS: Span 95′, Lg. 61′ 9″, Ht. 14′ 9″, Wing Area 1120 sq. ft.

WEIGHT: Empty 19,082 lb., Gross 27,253 lb., Max. 40,000 lb. Fuel 600–2400 gal.

PERFORMANCE: Speed—Top 220 mph at 10,000′, Cruising 190 mph. Service Ceiling 25,000′, Climb 10,000′/10 min. Range 1960 miles/2200 lbs. bombs, 660 miles/10,000 lbs. bombs, 3100 miles max.

PMB

DOUGLAS B-23

Wright R-2600-3, 1600 hp take-off, 1275 hp at 12,000′

DIMENSIONS: Span 92′, Lg. 58′ 4″, Ht. 18′ 6″, Wing Area 993 sq. ft.

WEIGHT: Empty 19,059 lb., Gross 26,500 lb., Max. 30,477 lb. Fuel 870–1290 gal.

PERFORMANCE: Speed—Top 282 mph at 12,000′, Cruising 210 mph, Landing 80 mph. Service Ceiling 31,600′, Climb 10,000′/6.7 min. Range 1455 miles/4000 lbs. bombs.

Chapter 11: The Great Air Offensive 1938–44

TURNING POINT AFTER MUNICH

Twenty years after World War I, Army bombers had capabilities limited to much the same kind of raids as those made in 1918. Most squadrons used Douglas B-18s, but a single squadron had YB-17s, an early model of World War II's popular Boeing. The main Air Corps mission was still support of surface forces, rather than independent strategic bombing.

The European crisis in September 1938 led to the Munich agreement and dramatized the importance of bombers in power politics, alerting Americans to the need for air power. Some advocates of appeasement had been motivated by Hitler's professed intention to expand only eastward, but much acceptance of Czech dismemberment was due to fear of Germany's well-advertised bombers. Wrote General Henry H. Arnold, who had just been appointed Chief of the Air Corps: "the nation with the greatest navy in the world in . . . alliance with the nation having the most powerful army in the world [France was meant] capitulated without a struggle to Germany's newly created air power."

At a White House meeting on September 28, 1938, President Roosevelt emphasized air power, and rejected a War Department request for "new barracks" in Wyoming because that would not impress Hitler. The President proposed a tremendous effort to enlarge the air force, and General Arnold left the meeting feeling that his Air Corps had finally "achieved its Magna Carta," including a go ahead on long-range bombers. After Arnold had prepared expansion plans, appropriations were requested in the Presidential message to Congress in January 1939.

By April, the Air Corps was authorized to expand from 2300 planes to 5500 in 24 groups by June 1941. Bombers, in five heavy, six medium, and two attack (light) bombardment groups, were the big stick of the new force. In the words of its chief, "The No. 1 job of an air force is bombardment. We must have the long-range bombers which can hit the enemy before he hits us; . . . the best defense is attack." No longer was the bomber merely a long-range coast-defense gun.

On August 10, 1939, the Army ordered 461 new bombers of four different models. One contract was for improved Boeing B-17Cs, but others were for B-24, B-25, and B-26 types not even flown yet in prototype form.

When war was declared in Europe in September 1939, Roosevelt appealed to every belligerent government that "under no circumstances" there be any bombing of civilians in unfortified cities, upon the understanding that the same rules be observed by all belligerents. Except for the quick conquest of Poland, the "phony war" phase gave some hopes that the air weapon would remain sheathed; no one then realized that the United States itself would demonstrate bombing of cities in its most violent form.

German invasion of Western Europe in May 1940 was accompanied by unrestrained air attacks on civilians, and Britain began her struggle for survival. President Roosevelt called for expansion of Army aviation to 36,500 planes in 54 groups. Basic equipment of the bomber component was to be a pair each of four-engined and twin-engined types; the B-17 and B-24, and the B-25 and B-26. That quartet was also the bomber force for the 84 group program projected in 1941.

READYING THE BOMBER FOR WAR—1938–41

Technical progress during this expansion consisted of adopting the turbo-supercharger for heavy bombers, developing the B-24 as a B-17 counterpart, developing the B-25 and B-26 medium bombers, fitting all types with increased protection, and initiating design of new Very Long-Range bombers.

PMB

BOEING YB-17A
Wright R-1820-51, 1000 hp take-off, 800 hp at 25,000′
DIMENSIONS: Span 103′ 9″, Lg. 68′ 4″, Ht. 18′ 4″, Wing Area 1420 sq. ft.
WEIGHT: Empty 26,520 lb., Gross 37,000 lb., Max. 45,650 lb. Fuel 1700–2492 gal.
PERFORMANCE: Speed—Top 295 mph at 25,000′, Cruising 230 mph, Landing 78 mph. Service Ceiling 38,000′, Climb 10,000′/7.8 min. Range 2400 miles/4000 lbs. bombs, 3600 miles max.

The first turbo-supercharged heavy bomber was the lone Y1B-17A. Begun as a static test YB-17, it was completed in April 1938 with Wright R-1830-51 supercharged by turbos on top of the engines to yield 1000 hp at 25,000 ft. By November 1938, the turbos had been moved beneath the nacelles. Greatly improving speed and ceiling, these engines were also used on the

PMB

BOEING B-17B
Wright R-1820-51, 1000 hp take-off, 800 hp at 25,000′
DIMENSIONS: Span 103′ 9″, Lg. 67′ 11″, Ht. 15′ 5″, Wing Area 1420 sq. ft.
WEIGHT: Empty 27,650 lb., Gross 37,810 lb., Max. 46,650 lb. Fuel 850–1700 gal. (2492 gal. max.).
PERFORMANCE: Speed—Top 291.5 mph at 25,000′, Cruising 231 mph, Landing 80 mph. Service Ceiling 36,000′, Climb 1430′/1 min., 10,000′/7.1 min. Range 2400 miles/4000 lbs. bombs, 3600 miles ferry.

BOEING B-17C
Wright R-1820-65, 1200 hp at 25,000′
DIMENSIONS: As B-17B
WEIGHT: Empty 30,600 lb., Gross 39,320 lb., Max 49,650 lb. Fuel 1700 gal.
PERFORMANCE: Speed—Top 323 mph at 25,000′, Cruising 250 mph, Landing 84 mph. Service Ceiling 37,000′, Climb 10,000′/7.5 min. Range 2000 miles/4000 lbs. bombs, 3400 miles max.

MFR

B-17B, which eliminated the nose turret for a cleaner bow with a gun on a ball and socket joint. Ordered November 1937, the B-17B was first flown on June 27, 1939, and 39 more were completed by March 1940.

Thirty-eight B-17Cs, ordered on August 10, 1939 for $8,090,000, were delivered between July and November 1940. This model had 1200 hp R-1820-65 Cyclones and new flush gun panels, with a "bathtub" belly gun emplacement. Armor was added, and armament now included six .50-caliber and one .30-caliber gun. The latter was in the nose, with two .50s for the top opening, two for the bottom, and one each for the waist gunners.

Twenty B-17Cs went to Britain under the name Fortress I, and 42 B-17Ds were purchased on an option on the B-17C contract. Built between February and April 1941, the B-17D was like the B-17C, but had leakproof tanks. They reflected the March 1940 agreement under which the Allies were permitted to purchase current service types providing they supplied information on improvements developed at the front,

PMB

BOEING B-17D

CONSOLIDATED XB-24

Pratt & Whitney R-1830-33, 1200 hp take-off, 1000 hp at 14,500′

DIMENSIONS: Span 110′, Lg. 63′ 9″, Ht. 18′ 8″, Wing Area 1048 sq. ft.

WEIGHT: Empty 27,500 lb., Gross 38,360 lb., Max. 46,400 lb. Fuel 2400–3000 gal.

PERFORMANCE: Speed—Top 273 mph at 15,000′, Cruising 186 mph, Landing 90 mph. Service Ceiling 31,500′, Climb 10,000′/6 min. Range 3000 miles/2500 lbs. bombs, 4700 miles max.

MFR

AF

CONSOLIDATED B-24A
Pratt & Whitney R-1830-33, 1200 hp take-off, 1000 hp at 14,500′
DIMENSIONS: As XB-24
WEIGHT: Empty 30,000 lb., Gross 39,350 lb., Max. 53,600 lb. Fuel 2150–3100 gal.
PERFORMANCE: Speed—Top 292.5 mph at 15,000′, Cruising 228 mph, Landing 92 mph. Service Ceiling 30,500′, Absolute Ceiling 32,000′, Climb 1780′/1 min., 10,000′/5.6 min. Range 2200 miles /4000 lbs. bombs, 4000 miles max. at 190 mph.

hence the addition of self-sealing tanks. Earlier Boeings already on hand were converted to D standards.

Thirty-five B17Ds were flown to the Philippines, and those that survived the first Japanese attack were the entire U. S. Far East bombing strength in the war's first three months. The remaining Flying Fortresses were grouped in Hawaii, Panama, and Newfoundland at the end of 1941.

A companion four-engined type developed in the meantime was the Consolidated 32, a high-wing monoplane design begun September 1938. A prototype ordered March 30, 1939, was designated XB-24, and additional orders were placed before it flew; seven YB-24s were ordered on April 27, and 38 B-24As on August 10.

First flown on December 29, 1939, the seven-place XB-24 had the first tricycle landing gear on a large bomber. The nose wheel permitted faster landings and take-offs, and thus allowed a heavier wing-loading on the low-drag Clark airfoil. A bombardier's enclosure began the nose of the deep fuselage, which terminated behind twin rudders with a tail gunner's position. Armament included a .50-caliber hand-operated gun in the tail. Two more .50-caliber and four .30-caliber guns fired through panels in the fuselage sides, top and bottom, and nose sockets, while 8800 lbs. of bombs could be accommodated. Power plants were Pratt & Whitney R-1830-33 Wasps of 1000 hp at 14,500 ft.

When the prototype's speed was measured at 273 mph instead of the 311 mph estimated by the specification, the builders tried the ship with R-1830-41 Wasps turbo-supercharged to yield 1200 hp at 25,000 ft., deleted wingtip slots, and installed self-sealing fuel tanks. In this form, the prototype became the XB-24B and speed was 310 mph. In August 1940 the XB-24B was accepted and its innovations specified for 56 B-24Ds added to the 1939 contract through exercise of an option. More B-24Ds were ordered in September, but meanwhile, work continued on the earlier orders and on an LB-30 version originally ordered May 4, 1940, by France and transferred to Britain.

Averting possible bottlenecks, the Air Corps on November 9, 1940, deferred delivery on the B-24As ordered in 1939, so that the first twenty-six could go to Britain, and so that most Army B-24s could incorporate the turbo-superchargers and power turrets expected a year later. First ships off the production line in December 1940 were the seven YB-24s, identical to the original unsupercharged XB-24 but for the deletion of wingtip slots and the addition of de-icers. The next ship, flown January 17, 1941, and 25 following went to Britain as the Liberator I, or LB-30A. Six were used as unarmed transatlantic ferry transports, but the others began Coastal Command antisubmarine missions in June 1941 armed with four 20-mm. fixed guns in a trough under the fuselage, single .30-caliber guns at waist and belly apertures, and two .30-caliber tail guns. A ton of bombs could be carried on 16-hour patrols.

These ships used Pratt & Whitney R-1830-33 (S3C4-G) Wasps, like nine similar B-24As the Army got in

CONSOLIDATED LIBERATOR I (B-24A)

MFR

June 1941. Armed originally with six .50-caliber and two .30-caliber hand-held guns, they went to the newly organized Ferry Command.

Also similar were 139 Liberator IIs built on the LB-30 contract beginning in August 1941, but the nose section was lengthened, and Boulton & Paul power turrets were installed on top and in the tail by the British. Including four in each turret, eleven .303-caliber guns were installed. Fifteen LB-30s were requisitioned by the AAF in December 1941 for emergency use in the Pacific.

First production ships with turbo superchargers and American power turrets were nine B-24Cs accepted in December 1941 with 1200 hp R-1830-41 Wasps. Seven .50-caliber guns and 2900 rounds of ammunition were carried: One gun in the nose, two in a top power turret, one at each waist panel, and a pair in a tail power turret. These ships were on the deferred 1939 contract, like the first twenty of the B-24D mass-production version delivered in 1942.

Before discussing the expansion of Air Force four-engined strength after Pearl Harbor, a pair of twin-engined bombers developed in 1939–41 claim attention. With about half the bomb and fuel capacity of the larger types, medium bombers were to perform at lower altitudes the direct support missions traditionally the role of Army aircraft.

AF

CONSOLIDATED B-24C
Pratt & Whitney R-1830-41, 1200 hp at 25,000′
DIMENSIONS: Span 110′, Lg. 66′ 4″, Ht. 18′, Wing Area 1048 sq. ft.
WEIGHT: Empty 32,330 lb., Design Gross 41,000 lb., Max. 53,700 lb. Fuel 2364–3164 gal.
PERFORMANCE: Speed—Top 313 mph at 25,000′, Cruising 233 mph, Landing 93 mph. Service Ceiling 34,000′, Climb 10,000′/6.1 min. Range 2100 miles/5000 lbs. bombs, 3600 miles max.

CONSOLIDATED LIBERATOR II (LB-30)
Pratt & Whitney R-1830-S3C-4, 1000 hp at 12,500′
DIMENSIONS: Span 110′, Lg. 66′ 4″, Ht. 18′, Wing Area 1048 sq. ft.
WEIGHT: Gross 46,250 lb.
PERFORMANCE: Speed—Top 263 mph (with turrets). Service Ceiling 24,000′.

MFR

On January 25, 1939, a competition was announced for medium bomber designs to be submitted by July 5. Without the usual wait for prototypes, production contracts were awarded on August 10. North American got $11,771,000 for 184 copies of its NA-62, which became the B-25, and 201 Martin Model 179s (B-26) were bought for $15,815,000. Both were five-place high-wing monoplanes with tricycle landing gear.

North American delivered a bare airframe for static tests in July 1940, and flew its first B-25 on August 19, while the world watched the Battle of Britain test German bombers against a superb fighter defense. A prone tail gunner between the twin rudders had a .50-caliber gun. The bombardier had sockets in the nose enclosure for a .30-caliber gun, while two others fired from openings in the sides and top of the fuselage behind the bay for 3000 lbs. of bombs. Wright R-2600-9 Cyclones of 1350 hp enabled the B-25 to reach 322 mph, a speed never equalled by later models.

The first ship resembled the NA-40 attack and had natural metal finish and unbroken dihedral, but olive drab paint was added to later ships, while beginning with the tenth example the outer wing panels were made horizontal.

In September 1940, the Army ordered more protection to be added after 24 B-25s had been accepted; deliveries began in May 1941 on 40 B-25As with armor and self-sealing tanks with reduced fuel capacity. August 1941 saw the B-25B, 119 of which were delivered with Bendix power-operated turrets. Since the awkward prone tail position was eliminated, the rear was covered by two .50-caliber guns in the upper turret and two in a retractable belly turret sighted through a periscope by a kneeling gunner. The .30-caliber hand-operated gun was retained in the nose.

The B-25s squared-off lines made production easier and contrasted sharply with the perfect streamlining, round fuselage, and small wing of Martin's B-26, ordered the same day as the B-25. Although none of the 201 B-26s were completed yet, the Air Corps ordered 139 B-26As on September 16, 1940, and 791 B-26Bs on September 28.

Powered by Pratt & Whitney R-2800-5 Wasps of 1500 hp at 14,000 ft., the B-26 could also be distinguished from the B-25 by its single rudder. The original specification called for a weight of 19,250 lbs. empty and 26,625 lbs. gross, and at these weights guaranteed top speed was 323 mph, service ceiling 26,440 ft., and range 1800 miles with 2500 lbs. of bombs. On September 30, 1940, however, it was decided that the self-sealing tanks and 555 lbs. of armor specified for the B-26A should also be included on all B-26s under construction. This added nearly 2000 lbs. to B-26 weight, and, with additional loads specified for the B-26B, affected flying traits to an extent not appreciated fully until the Martin entered service.

First flown on November 25, 1940, and accepted the following February, the B-26 was armed with two .50-caliber guns in the first power-operated dorsal turret on an American bomber, and a hand-operated .50-caliber gun in the tail. A .30-caliber gun was socket-mounted in the bombardier's transparent nose cone, and another was placed at a floor aperture behind the double bay for up to 4800 lbs. of bombs. Normal bomb load was 3000 lbs. carried 1000 miles, and top speed was 315 mph. The B-26A delivered in October 1941 was similar but for lengthened fuselage and provision for additional fuel on ferry flights. Of 139 built, 52 went to British Middle East units as the Marauder I.

MFR

NORTH AMERICAN B-25A
Wright R-2600-9, 1700 hp take-off, 1350 hp at 13,000′
DIMENSIONS: Span 67′ 7″, Lg. 54′ 1″, Ht. 15′ 9″, Wing Area 610 sq. ft.
WEIGHT: Empty 17,870 lb., Gross 25,322 lb., Max. 27,100 lb. Fuel 434–670 gal. (1090 gal. max.).
PERFORMANCE: Speed—Top 315 mph at 15,000′, Cruising 262 mph, Landing 90 mph. Service Ceiling 27,000′, Climb 15,000′/8.4 min. Range 1350 miles/3000 lbs. bombs.

AF

NORTH AMERICAN B-25B
Wright R-2600-9, 1700 hp take-off, 1350 hp at 13,000′
DIMENSIONS: Span 67′ 7″, Lg. 52′ 11″, Ht. 15′ 9″, Wing Area 610 sq. ft.
WEIGHT: Empty 20,000 lb., Gross 26,208 lb., Max. 28,460 lb. Fuel 670–1090 gal.
PERFORMANCE: Speed—Top 300 mph at 15,000′, Cruising 262 mph, Landing 93 mph. Service Ceiling 23,500′, Climb 15,000′/8.8 min. Range 1300 miles/3000 lbs. bombs, 2900 miles ferry.

PMB

NORTH AMERICAN B-25
Wright R-2600-9, 1700 hp take-off, 1350 hp at 13,000′
DIMENSIONS: Span 67′ 6″, Lg. 54′ 1″, Ht. 14′ 10″, Wing Area 610 sq. ft.
WEIGHT: Empty 16,767 lb., Gross 23,714 lb., Max. 27,310 lb. Fuel 434–916 gal. (1336 gal. max.).
PERFORMANCE: Speed—Top 322 mph at 15,000′, Landing 90 mph. Service Ceiling 30,000′, Absolute Ceiling 31,200′, Climb 2090′/1 min. Range 2000 miles/916 gal. with 3000 lbs. bombs.

The weight added to the Martin design since its inception had results more serious than reduction of performance. Accidents due to landing-gear failure became frequent, and wheel struts were strengthened, but stalling speed was being lifted to dangerous heights by heavy loadings on the small wing. In July 1941, Martin proposed larger wings for B-26B and B-26Cs on order, but until these planes would be available a year later, the B-26 remained a doubtful issue.

PLANNING VERY LONG RANGE BOMBERS—1940–41

As Air Corps squadrons began to receive the bombers ordered in 1939, plans were made for larger machines of longer range, which, if England fell, could strike across oceans at the Axis. On November 10, 1939, General Arnold asked War Department permission to initiate development of a four-engine bomber of 2000 mile radius "superior in all respects to the B-17B and the B-24." Permission was granted, and on January 29, 1940, Request for Data R-40B was issued to leading aircraft builders.

When R-40B, which called for a range of 5333 miles with a ton of bombs, reached Boeing, the Seattle engineers completed a design already under way as Model 341. Sent to Wright Field by March 5, 1940, the 341 had a design gross weight of 76,000 lbs., span of 124 ft. 7 in., speed of 405 mph, capacity of 4120 gallons of fuel or five tons of bombs, and six hand-operated .50-caliber guns. A few weeks later, Wright Field requested the design be revised to incorporate leakproof tanks and heavier armament. Boeing replied on May 11, 1940, with Model 345, with a design gross of 97,700 lbs., span of 141 ft. 2 in., speed of 382 mph, capacity of 5440 gallons of fuel or eight tons of bombs, and ten .50-caliber and one 20-mm. gun in remote-controlled turrets.

AF

MARTIN B-26A
Pratt & Whitney R-2800-5, 1850 hp take-off, 1500 hp at 14,000′
DIMENSIONS: Span 65′, Lg. 58′ 3″, Ht. 19′ 10″, Wing Area 602 sq. ft.
WEIGHT: Empty 21,741 lb., Gross 28,367 lb., Max. 33,022 lb. Fuel 465–962 gal. (1462 gal. max.).
PERFORMANCE: Speed—Top 313 mph, Cruising 243 mph. Service Ceiling 23,500′. Range 1000 miles/3000 lbs. bombs, 2600 miles max.

MARTIN B-26
Pratt & Whitney R-2800-5, 1850 hp take-off, 1500 hp at 14,000′
DIMENSIONS: Span 65′, Lg. 56′, Ht. 19′ 10″, Wing Area 602 sq. ft.
WEIGHT: Empty 21,375 lb., Gross 27,200 lb., Max. 32,000 lb. Fuel 465–962 gal.
PERFORMANCE: Speed—Top 315 mph at 15,000′, Cruising 265 mph, Landing 102 mph. Service Ceiling 25,000′, Climb 15,000′/12.5 min. Range 1000 miles/3000 lbs. bombs, 2200 miles max.

AF

Other entries in the design competition also used the new 2200 hp Wright R-3350-13. "An evaluation board appraised the designs and rated the competitors in this order of preference: Boeing, Lockheed, Douglas, Consolidated. Contracts for preliminary engineering data were issued to the firms on June 27 and their planes were designated, respectively, the XB-29, XB-30, XB-31, XB-32."

On the strength of the engineering data then offered, Boeing won a $3,615,095 contract for two XB-29 prototypes on September 6, 1940. A similar contract went to the XB-32 at the same time, while a third prototype machine was added to each in November. The Douglas and Lockheed designs were withdrawn, although the latter finally appeared in transport form as the Constellation. Martin's XB-33 project, begun in October 1940 with two R-3350s, was ordered with four R-2600 Wrights, but both prototypes were later cancelled.

On July 9, 1935, Wright Field had issued the designation XBLR-2 to a Douglas project far larger than

AF

DOUGLAS XB-19A
Allison V-3420-11, 2600 hp at 25,000′
DIMENSIONS: As XB-19
WEIGHT: Empty 92,400 lb., Gross 140,230 lb. Fuel 6400 gal.
PERFORMANCE: Speed—Top 265 mph at 20,000′, Cruising 185 mph. Service Ceiling 39,000′. Range 4200 miles/2500 lbs. bombs.

the XBLR-1 (XB-15) then under way at Boeing. Engineering data was ordered from Douglas on October 31, 1935, and after inspection of a mockup in March 1936, a prototype was ordered September 29, 1936. A Sikorsky project, the XBLR-3, was dropped to limit costs. In March 1938 the Douglas project was redesignated XB-19, but on August 30 the company suggested dropping it because of the expense and the probability that the huge ship would be obsolete before completion.

The Matériel Division insisted on its completion, however, for only flight tests could provide the information needed for future giant projects, and on June 27, 1941, the XB-19 finally took to the air for the first

DOUGLAS XB-19
Wright R-3350-5, 2000 hp take-off, 1500 hp at 15,700′
DIMENSIONS: Span 212′, Lg. 132′ 2″, Ht. 42′ 9″, Wing Area 4285 sq. ft.
WEIGHT: Empty 84,431 lb., Gross 140,000 lb., Max. 162,000 lb. Fuel 10,350–11,174 gal.
PERFORMANCE: Speed—Top 224 mph at 15,700′, Cruising 135 mph, Landing 73 mph. Service Ceiling 23,000′, Absolute Ceiling 24,500′, Climb 545′/1 min. Range 7300 miles/6000 lbs. bombs, 7900 miles max.

MFR

time. This low-wing monoplane with tricycle gear was the first to use the 2000 hp Wright R-3350-5, four of these replacing six smaller power plants expected originally. Construction of the 70 to 81 ton plane had required 500 men, 9000 drawings, two million man-hours, $1,400,000 of Air Corps funds, and an estimated $4,000,000 of company money.

A 37-mm. gun was mounted in the power-operated nose turret and another in the front dorsal power turret. The rear dorsal power turret had a .50-caliber gun, as did hand-operated mounts in the belly, the waists, and tail. Single .30-caliber guns were mounted atop each 37-mm. gun, on each side of the bombardiers' windows, and on each side of the rear fuselage.

Wing fuel tanks had a 10,350 gallon capacity, and the bomb bay had room for 18,700 lbs. of bombs or 824 extra gallons of fuel. A total of 37,100 lbs. of bombs might be carried if external wing bomb racks and reduced fuel loads were carried. From 11 to 18 men were in the crew, depending on the mission.

Less of a weapon than a flying laboratory to test technical problems and the feasibility of very large aircraft, the XB-19 encouraged work on even larger long-range bombers. As a result of an April 11, 1941, design competition, Consolidated Aircraft on November 15 received a contract for two six-engined XB-36 prototypes. Northrop's giant XB-35 flying wing was ordered a week later.

Data for these designs was prepared with the aid of XB-19 experience. In 1943, 2600 hp Allison V-3420-11 inline engines were installed to improve performance. When tests were completed, the XB-19A operated as a cargo plane until it was scrapped in June 1949.

From the preceding pages we can see that all the bombers which played such a prominent part in the history of the next decade were already in production or on order before the Pearl Harbor attack. These weapons presented the United States with an opportunity to build military policy around a new spearhead of power.

RAINBOW FIVE

Since autumn of 1939, the Army had been preparing basic war plans against the potential enemies; Rainbow No. 5, code name for the plan finally adopted, contemplated an offensive in Europe while maintaining a strategic defense against Japan. After talks with British officials in February 1941, this strategy was approved on May 14, 1941, by the Joint Board of the Army and Navy.

At the President's request, the now virtually autonomous Army Air Forces prepared by August 12, 1941, AWPD/1 (Air War Plans Division), which defined the Air Force plan to fulfill Rainbow Five. AWPD/1 was approved and included in the joint Army-Navy report to Roosevelt on September 11, 1941. This remarkably precise program projected German defeat by the destruction of 154 selected targets in the electric power, petroleum, aluminum, magnesium, aircraft, and transportation industries. Required for this bombardment were 6834 bombers in 98 groups: 20 heavy (B-17 and 24), 24 very heavy (B-29 and 32), and 10 medium groups (B-25 and 26), the latter "included because of availability only." Larger planes would be "far more economical" and it was hoped that by 1944, 44 groups of bombers of 4000-mile radius would be available. Sixteen pursuit groups were to protect the bombers' bases.

Now that a war plan and the bomber designs to meet its requirements had been prepared, the problem remaining was one of improving the weapons to meet battle conditions and building them in numbers sufficient to execute the plan, and still have enough to allot some to allies.

FORTRESSES AND LIBERATORS AGAINST FORTRESS EUROPE

Rainbow Five required, according to AWPD/1, six times more bombers in three years than had been built in the U.S. during the previous twenty-three years. Furthermore, these bombers had to be well enough protected to penetrate to their targets, an ability not yet demonstrated by U.S. planes.

In this respect, the results of the Fortress (B-17C) operations begun by the British on July 8, 1941, had been disappointing. The first 39 sorties resulted in only two bomb hits certain for a combat and operational loss of eight Boeings. Americans blamed the record on excessively high attack altitudes, and on not flying in formation to promote defensive firepower and a good bombing pattern; but it was evident that something had to be done to counter the speed and firepower gained by fighter planes since the original B-17 had been designed.

On September 5, 1941, the B-17E was flown, armed with twelve .50- and one .30-caliber guns, and protected by the armor and leakproof tanks then provided on all U.S. bombers. The .50-caliber gun at each squared waist opening was hand-operated, but the rest were paired in turrets: a power-operated dome behind the pilots, a cramped ball turret[1] in the belly and a tail emplacement. The light gun was fired from sockets in the nose enclosure. Since engines were the same as on the previous models, the increased weight and drag of protruding turrets made the Fortress slower, although its ability to defend itself was greatly improved. Distinguishing feature of this and succeeding Fortresses was the large dorsal fin.

[1] On the first 112 B-17Es, the belly turret was remote-controlled from a periscopic sight, but this proved less feasible than the Sperry ball turret with the gunner curled up inside.

WILLIAMS

BOEING B-17F
Wright R-1820-97, 1200 hp at 25,000′
DIMENSIONS: Span 103′ 9″, Lg. 74′ 9″, Ht. 19′ 1″, Wing Area 1420 sq. ft.
WEIGHT: Empty 34,000 lb., Gross 55,000 lb., Max. 56,500 lb. Fuel 1730–2550 gal.
PERFORMANCE: Speed—Top 299 mph at 25,000′, Cruising 200 mph, Landing 90 mph. Service Ceiling 37,500′, Climb 20,000′/25.7 min. Range 1300 miles/6000 lbs. bombs, 2880 miles max.

MFR

BOEING XB-38
Allison V-1710-89, 1425 hp at 25,000′
DIMENSIONS: Span 103′ 9″, Lg. 74′, Ht. 19′ 2″, Wing Area 1420 sq. ft.
WEIGHT: Empty 34,748 lb., Gross 56,000 lb., Max. 64,000 lb. Fuel 1730–2520 gal.
PERFORMANCE: Speed—Top 327 mph at 25,000′, Cruising 226 mph. Service Ceiling 29,700′. Range 2400 miles/3000 lbs. bombs, 1900 miles/6000 lbs. bombs, 3600 miles max.

BOEING B-17E
Wright R-1820-65, 1200 hp at 25,000′
DIMENSIONS: Span 103′ 9″, Lg. 73′ 10″, Ht. 19′ 2″, Wing Area 1420 sq. ft.
WEIGHT: Empty 32,250 lb., Gross 40,260 lb., Max. 53,000 lb. Fuel 1730–2520 gal.
PERFORMANCE: Speed—Top 317 mph at 25,000′, Cruising 195–223 mph, Landing 80 mph. Service Ceiling 36,600′, Climb 1430′/1 min., 5000′/7 min. Range 2000 miles/4000 lbs. bombs, 3300 miles max.

MFR

AMC

BOEING XB-40 (YB-40 in photo)
Wright R-1820-97, 1200 hp at 25,000′
DIMENSIONS: As B-17F
WEIGHT: Empty 36,898 lb., Gross 58,000 lb., Max. 63,295 lb. Fuel 1730–2520 gal.
PERFORMANCE: Speed—Top 292 mph at 25,000′, 248 mph at s. l., Cruising 196 mph, Landing 94 mph. Service Ceiling 29,200′, Climb 780′/1 min., 10,000′/13.3 min. Range 2260 miles, 2460 miles max.

MFR

BOEING B-17G
Wright R-1820-97, 1200 hp at 25,000′
DIMENSIONS: Span 103′ 9″, Lg. 74′ 4″, Ht. 19′ 1″, Wing Area 1420 sq. ft.
WEIGHT: Empty 36,135 lb., Gross 55,000 lb., Max. 65,500 lb. Fuel 2810–3630 gal.
PERFORMANCE: Speed—Top 287 mph at 25,000′, Cruising 182 mph, Landing 90 mph. Service Ceiling 35,600′, Climb 20,000′/37 min. Range 2000 miles/6000 lbs. bombs, 3400 miles max.

A total of 512 B-17Es was built by May 1942, when the slightly improved B-17F began to appear. Working together in a production pool established a year before, Boeing, Douglas, and Vega together produced 3400 B-17Fs (600 by Douglas, 500 by Vega, and the rest by Boeing). This model introduced the 1200 hp R-1820-97, added additional guns and armor, and could be recognized by a new plastic nose. In the nose, two or three .50-caliber hand-operated guns had mountings that varied with the unit using the plane, while another .50 was added at the radio operator's top hatch in the rear. External racks could be added to increase the bomb load.

Capable of carrying a two-ton bomb load for 2000 miles, the B-17E arrived in Java in February 1942 and did most of the bombing in the Pacific that year, replacing older Ds originally in the Far East. On August 17 the B-17E began raids against the Nazis, while 45 sent to Britain with 19 B-17Fs served as the Fortress GR.II on antisubmarine patrols. The British fitted one with a 40-mm. gun in a Bristol nose turret for attacking ships and submarines. By 1943, the B-17F was in operation over Europe, but Boeings were withdrawn from the Pacific in favor of the longer-ranged Consolidated Liberator. (In January 1942 the Army officially adopted the British naming system for publicity reasons.)

One B-17E was fitted with 1425 hp Allison V-1710-89 inline engines and called XB-38. The first liquid-cooled bomber design in a decade was begun in March 1942, ordered the following July 10, and flown on May 19, 1943.

The disaster at Pearl Harbor did not divert the Air Force from the main ideas of the Rainbow Five plan. Bombers dispatched to the Pacific were limited to coastal defense, the role touted for them since Billy Mitchell's day. They had no significant success, for official tabulations of Japanese warships sunk in the war's first year credit none to Army bombers. Smaller ships were hit, including a halted destroyer which had neglected to start its engines when attacked. Observed the surprised captain, "Even the B-17s hit sometimes." Yet early attacks on large motionless European targets were also disappointing.

In Europe, after several experimental raids in 1942 by B-17E and B-24Ds against German-occupied countries, the Allies launched in 1943 Operation Pointblank, the Combined Bomber Offensive against Germany. "Precision" bombing in daylight was more effective than the night "area" bombing practiced by the R.A.F., and it was supposed that bomber firepower in mass formation would frustrate fighter defense. But resistance by German fighters grew more bitter and effective as bomb tonnage delivered mounted, and raids like those on Ploesti and Schweinfurt in August and September 1943 cost such losses that ability of the bombers to execute their part of the war plan was in doubt.

In August 1942, an Air Force board had suggested that bombers be accompanied by "destroyer escort" planes. Existing fighters being too short-ranged to protect the bombers, the logical proposal was a specially armed B-17. One XB-40 and thirteen YB-40 escort planes were converted from B-17Fs by replacing the bombs with more armor, 11,200 rounds of ammunition, and fourteen .50-caliber guns which were placed in pairs in a new chin turret, in a power-operated mount amidships, and in each side window, as well as the usual top, belly, and tail positions.

First used in action in May 1943, the YB-40 proved disappointing. "Being heavily armored and loaded, they could not climb or keep speed with the standard B-17, a fact which . . . resulted in the disorganization of the formation they were supposed to protect."

These four-engined fighters had to be re-equipped as bombers, but fortunately drop tanks were beginning to stretch the range of single-seat fighters. The chin turret developed for the B-40 was useful in discouraging frontal attacks and was adopted in the last Fortress production model, the B-17G (British Fortress III) which appeared in September 1943.

Armament of the B-17G included thirteen .50-caliber guns, 6380 rounds, and from 6000 to 10,800 lbs. of bombs. Two guns were placed in the chin turret below the nose; above them a pair of hand-operated "cheek" guns. The other gun locations were the same as on the B-17F, although the installations had been improved.

Of 8680 Gs built, 2395 were by Douglas, 2250 by Vega, and the rest by Boeing, who completed Fortress production in April 1945. With Germany defeated, production closed at the other plants in July. Some of those on hand were modified into radio-controlled BQ-7 missiles tested against German targets in August 1944, and the B-17H rescue model carrying radar and a lifeboat. Peak AAF inventory for B-17s was 4574 in August 1944, in 33 combat groups. Eighty-five went to Britain, and 40 became Navy PB-1W radar warning planes.

Parallel to B-17 development, the Consolidated B-24 Liberators increased in firepower and numbers. Before Pearl Harbor, Liberators were delivered without power

CONSOLIDATED B-24D

Pratt & Whitney R-1830-43, 1200 hp at 23,400′

DIMENSIONS: Span 110′, Lg. 66′ 4″, Ht. 17′ 11″, Wing Area 1048 sq. ft.

WEIGHT: Empty 32,605 lb., Gross 55,000 lb., Max. 60,000 lb. Fuel 2364–3664 gal.

PERFORMANCE: Speed—Top 303 mph at 25,000′, Cruising 200 mph, Landing 95 mph. Service Ceiling 32,000′, Climb 20,000′/22 min. Range 2850 miles/5000 lbs. bombs, 4600 miles max.

MFR

MFR

CONSOLIDATED XB-41
Pratt & Whitney R-1830-43, 1200 hp at 25,000′
DIMENSIONS: As B-24D
WEIGHT: Empty 37,050 lb., Gross 61,500 lb., Max. 63,000 lb. Fuel 2814 gal.
PERFORMANCE: Speed—Top 289 mph at 25,000′, Cruising 200 mph. Service Ceiling 28,500′, Climb 1050′/1 min. Range 3100 miles.

MFR

CONSOLIDATED XB-41

turrets or turbo-superchargers, but these features were incorporated on wartime versions. The first mass-production Liberator was the B-24D, first delivered from the company's San Diego plant in January 1942.

The first ships were built on the original B-24A contract as modified in August 1940, but most were from orders given the production pool established in February 1941 that eventually included five factories. The 18,181 Liberators produced by this pool are probably the largest number of one bomber type ever built.

Ford's Willow Run plant flew the first B-24E on September 30, 1942, and the first B-24G was delivered from North American's Dallas facility in February 1943. Only internal changes to expedite production differentiated these types from B-24Ds produced at San Diego, at the Douglas-operated Tulsa plant after February 1943, and at Convair's new Fort Worth branch after March 1943.

Powered by Pratt & Whitney R-1830-43 Wasps offering 1200 hp up to 23,400 ft., the B-24D had a top Martin power turret behind the pilots and a Consolidated power turret in the tail, each with two .50-caliber guns. Hand-held single guns were mounted at each waist window, and the nose enclosure, originally provided with one, eventually had three hand-operated .50s at the sides and bottom. Belly protection was first provided by a Bendix power turret, but this was removed and a single manual tunnel gun installed. Armor plate ⅜ in. thick protected gun stations and pilot seats.

With a crew of eight to ten men, the B-24D grossed from 55,000 to 60,000 lbs. depending on the load. The normal fuel capacity of 2364 gallons might be increased to an overload of 3664 gallons, providing a maximum ferry range of 4600 miles, without bombs. Bomb load varied from 2000 to 8800 lbs. internal, and

MFR

CONSOLIDATED B-24H
Pratt & Whitney R-1830-65, 1200 hp at 25,000′
DIMENSIONS: Span 110′, Lg. 67′ 2″, Ht. 18′, Wing Area 1048 sq. ft.
WEIGHT: Empty 36,500 lb., Gross 56,000 lb., Max. 65,000 lb. Fuel 2814–3614 gal.
PERFORMANCE: Speed—Top 290 mph at 25,000′, Cruising 215 mph, Landing 95 mph. Service Ceiling 28,000′, Climb 20,000′/25 min. Range 2100 miles/5000 lbs. bombs, 3700 miles max.

12,800 lbs. using external racks. Range varied with altitude, cruising speed, bomb load and gross weight, but at 55,000 gross, 5000 lbs. of bombs, and 2290 gallons of fuel, a cruising speed of 220 mph at 20,000 ft. yielded a range of 2850 miles.

The first B-24Ds to go abroad were those of the Halvorsen detachment originally organized to bomb Japan from China, but rerouted to Egypt. From there they struck at Ploesti in June 1942. Britain-based B-24Ds began operations in October, while the first B-24Ds went in November 1942, to the Southwest Pacific, where, because of superior range, they eventually replaced all B-17s. The following year, the quantity of Liberators was enough to supply the entire Pacific war, to provide the Navy with some for antisubmarine patrol, and to support the offensive against Germany.

Of 2738 B-24Ds accepted, 260 went to the British as the Liberator III, while 122 with radar for the

MFR

CONSOLIDATED B-24J
(Data as B-24H)

MFR

CONSOLIDATED B-24M
Pratt & Whitney R-1830-65, 1200 hp at 25,000′
DIMENSIONS: As B-24H
WEIGHT: Empty 36,000 lb., Gross 56,000 lb., Max. 64,500 lb. Fuel 2814–3614 gal.
PERFORMANCE: Speed—Top 300 mph at 30,000′, Cruising 215 mph, Landing 95 mph. Service Ceiling 28,000′, Climb 20,000′/25 min. Range 2100 miles/5000 lbs. bombs, 3700 miles max.

Coastal Command became the Liberator G.R.V. Liberator IV was to be the B-24E, but all of these were limited to domestic use only, and none of 791 Es built seem to have left the U.S.

Like the Boeing, the Liberator also suffered from enemy fighters and in August 1942 a convoy fighter counterpart to the B-40 was approved. Converted from a B-24D, the Consolidated XB-41 had fourteen .50-caliber guns paired in a "chin" turret, two top turrets, tail turret, ball turret, and each waist opening. One appeared in December 1942, but was not reproduced.

An Emerson nose turret and a retractable Sperry ball belly turret were introduced in June 1943 on the B-24H. Ten .50-caliber guns with 4700 rounds of ammunition were carried, paired in the nose, top, belly, and tail turrets, and at hand-operated waist panels. While 738 B-24H-CFs from Fort Worth used the Emerson nose turret, Consolidated turrets were used on 1780 Ford B-24H-FO and 582 Douglas B-24H-DT. Nose turrets were also fitted on all but the first 25 of 430 B-24Gs built at Dallas, and on 6728 B-24J, which appeared in August 1943 with a Motor Products nose and a Briggs ball turret. Both the B-24H and B-24J used the R-1830-65 Wasp.

Lend-lease to Britain included 772 B-24Js from San Diego and 506 from Willow Run, which were known there as the Liberator VI or VIII, depending on minor changes. Those used by Coastal Command replaced the belly turret by a radome.

Hand-held tail guns distinguished 1667 B-24L of July 1944, while 2593 B-24M of October 1944 had a lightweight tail turret and was the last production model. Experimental conversions from Ds were the XB-24F with hot air de-icers and the XB-24K with 1350 hp Wasps and a high single tail. The single tail was approved in April 1944 for all future Liberators, but of 5176 single-tailed B-24Ns ordered from Ford, only November 1944's XB-24N and seven YB-24s of May–June 1945 were completed. These ships had R-1830-75 Wasps and new nose and tail turrets.

CONSOLIDATED XB-24N
Pratt & Whitney R-1830-75, 1350 hp at 30,000′
DIMENSIONS: Span 110′, Lg. 67′ 2″, Ht. 26′ 9″, Wing Area 1048 sq. ft.
WEIGHT: Empty 38,300 lb., Gross 56,000 lb., Max. 65,000 lb. Fuel 2814–3614 gal.
PERFORMANCE: Speed—Top 294 mph at 30,000′, Cruising 213 mph, Landing 95 mph. Service Ceiling 28,000′, Climb 20,000′/29 min. Range 2000 miles/5000 lbs. bombs, 3500 miles max.

MFR

A transport version of the Liberator was known as the C-87 (R.A.F. Liberator C.VII) and 282 were delivered in 1942–43. Peak AAF B-24 inventory was in September 1944, when 45½ overseas combat groups and many home stations had 6043 Liberators. (The story of the Navy's Liberators is in Part 5 of this book.) During 1944 Liberator factories began shifting to other types until the last one was delivered by Ford in June 1945.

TWIN-ENGINED BOMBERS IN WARTIME, 1942–45

While the four-engined bombers hammered at Germany's economic strength, twin-engined types flew less spectacular missions supporting ground armies and striking at Japanese shipping in the Pacific. North American Mitchells were the most widely used ships of this class, and production totaled 9815.

The first mass-production Mitchell was the B-25C-NA, ordered September 28, 1940, and delivered from Inglewood, California, beginning in January 1942. A new plant in Kansas City began in February 1942 to deliver 2290 B-25D-NCs which were similar to 1619 B-25Cs but for modified exhaust outlets. Like the B-25B in appearance, they had R-2600-13 Cyclones, more fuel and heavier equipment. Six .50-caliber guns, 2100 rounds of ammunition, and 3000 lbs. of bombs were carried. Two guns were in each power turret, one was fixed in the nose, and there was a hand-operated gun for the bombardier.

By April 1942, Mitchells began to see action in the Southwest Pacific, although early models had hunted submarines off the East and West coasts. Mitchells also served in the Aleutians, China, India, and four groups were in the Mediterranean Theater. On April 18, 1942, sixteen B-25Bs loaded with 2000 lbs. of bombs and 1141 gallons of fuel took off from the aircraft carrier *Hornet* for the first attack on Tokyo. The only twin-engined bombers ever to fly a combat mission from an aircraft carrier's deck, they had dummy tail guns to distract the enemy; the belly turret had been removed to save weight.

In March 1942, the Mitchell became the first U.S. bomber lend-leased to Russia. Although only 102 were delivered in 1942, eventually 870 were dispatched. Britain received 23 B-25Bs (Mitchell I), 167 B-25C and 371 B-25D (Mitchell II), while 249 Mitchells went to the Netherlands, 131 to China, and 29 to Brazil.

Demands for more firepower for ground strafing arose in Southwest Pacific units, which in the year following December 1942, converted 175 Mitchells to a version with ten .50-caliber guns and a three-man

NORTH AMERICAN B-25C
Wright R-2600-13, 1700 hp take-off, 1450 hp at 12,000′
DIMENSIONS: Span 67′ 7″, Lg. 52′ 11″, Ht. 15′ 10″, Wing Area 610 sq. ft.
WEIGHT: Empty 20,300 lb., Gross 33,500 lb., Max. 34,000 lb. Fuel 974–1559 gal.
PERFORMANCE: Speed—Top 284 mph at 15,000′, Cruising 233 mph, Landing 105 mph. Service Ceiling 21,200′, Climb 15,000′/16.5 min. Range 1500 miles/3000 lbs. bombs, 2750 miles max.

MFR

NORTH AMERICAN B-25G
Wright R-2600-13, 1700 hp take-off, 1450 hp at 12,000′
DIMENSIONS: Span 67′ 7″, Lg. 51′, Ht. 15′ 9″, Wing Area 610 sq. ft.
WEIGHT: Empty 19,975 lb., Gross 33,500 lb., Max. 35,000 lb. Fuel 974–1649 gal.
PERFORMANCE: Speed—Top 281 mph at 15,000′, Cruising 248 mph, Landing 105 mph. Service Ceiling 24,300′, Climb 15,000′/15.5 min. Range 1560 miles/3000 lbs. bombs, 2450 miles max.

MFR

MFR

NORTH AMERICAN B-25H
Wright R-2600-13, 1700 hp
DIMENSIONS: As B-25G
WEIGHT: Empty 19,975 lb., Gross 33,500 lb., Max. 36,047 lb. Fuel 434–974 gal. (1624 gal. ferry).
PERFORMANCE: Speed—Top 275 mph at 13,000′, Cruising 230 mph. Service Ceiling 23,800′, Climb 15,000′/19 min. Range 1350 miles/974 gal. with 3000 lbs. bombs, 2700 miles ferry.

MFR

NORTH AMERICAN B-25J
Wright R-2600-29, 1700 hp
DIMENSIONS: Span 67′ 7″, Lg. 52′ 11″, Ht. 16′ 4″, Wing Area 610 sq. ft.
WEIGHT: Empty 19,480 lb., Gross 33,500 lb., Max. 35,000 lb. Fuel 974 gal.
PERFORMANCE: Speed—Top 272 mph at 13,000′, Cruising 230 mph, Landing 97 mph. Service Ceiling 24,200′. Range 1350 miles/3000 lbs. bombs.

crew. Four guns fired from a solid nose, and four from bulges about the nose, with two in the top turret. Other conversions were made on B-25Cs, including an XB-25E and XB-25F with experimental de-icers and an XB-25G in January 1943 with a 75-mm. cannon in the nose. This was the largest gun ever used on an American plane, and had been developed from an experimental mounting on a B-18 in 1939. A pair of .50-caliber guns was also fixed in the nose, and other pairs were in the upper and lower turrets. Twenty-one rounds of ammunition, hand-loaded by a gunner, for the big gun, 2300 rounds for the machine guns, and 3000 lbs. of bombs were carried. A total of 405 B-25G-NAs were built at Inglewood. Low-level, skip-bombing attacks by Mitchells were far more effective against ships than conventional horizontal bombing.

One thousand B-25H-NAs followed after August 1943 carrying a crew of five, a 75-mm. gun, and fourteen .50-caliber guns. Four fifties and the cannon in the nose, four guns in side packages facing forward, two in a top turret behind the pilots, a single waist gun on each side, and two guns in a new tail emplacement, eight 5 in. rockets under the wings, and 3000 lbs. of bombs made the B-25H a very dangerous weapon.

In December 1943 six-place B-25J-NCs replaced B-25Ds at the Kansas City facility, with R-2600-29s and the conventional bombardier's bow with one flexible and one fixed nose gun. Four more fixed and six flexible guns and bomb load were arranged like those of the B-25H. Eight hundred of 4318 B-25Js were modified by solid noses with eight guns, for a total of

MARTIN B-26B-2
Pratt & Whitney R-2800-41, 2000 hp take-off, 1600 hp at 13,500′
DIMENSIONS: As B-26A
WEIGHT: Empty 22,380 lb., Design Gross 27,200 lb., Max. 34,000 lb. Fuel 962–1462 gal.
PERFORMANCE: Speed—Top 317 mph at 14,500′, Cruising 260 mph, Landing 103 mph. Service Ceiling 23,500′, Climb 15,000′/12 min. Range 1150 miles/3000 lbs. bombs, 2800 miles max.

AF

AF

MARTIN B-26C-5
Pratt & Whitney R-2800-43, 2000 hp take-off, 1600 hp at 13,500′
DIMENSIONS: Span 71′, Lg. 58′ 3″, Ht. 21′ 6″, Wing Area 658 sq. ft.
WEIGHT: Empty 24,000 lb., Gross 37,000 lb., Max. 38,200 lb. Fuel 962–1462 gal.
PERFORMANCE: Speed—Top 282 mph at 15,000′, Cruising 214 mph, Landing 135 mph. Service Ceiling 21,700′, Climb 15,000′/24.5 min. Range 1150 miles/3000 lbs. bombs, 2850 miles max.

MARTIN B-26B-40

AF

AF

MARTIN B-26F
Pratt & Whitney R-2800-43, 2000 hp
DIMENSIONS: Span 71', Lg. 56' 1", Ht. 20' 4", Wing Area 658 sq. ft.
WEIGHT: Empty 23,700 lb., Gross 37,000 lb., Max. 38,000 lb. Fuel 465–1502 gal.
PERFORMANCE: Speed—Top 277 mph at 10,000', Cruising 225 mph, Landing 122 mph. Service Ceiling 20,000', Climb 15,000'/24.5 min. Range 1300 miles/3000 lbs. bombs.

PMB

MARTIN B-26G
Pratt & Whitney R-2800-43, 2000 hp take-off
DIMENSIONS: As B-26F
WEIGHT: Empty 23,800 lb., Gross 37,000 lb., Max. 38,200 lb. Fuel 465–1502 gal.
PERFORMANCE: Speed—Top 283 mph at 5000', 274 mph at 15,000', Cruising 216 mph, Landing 120 mph. Service Ceiling 19,800', Climb 5000'/8 min. Range 1100 miles/4000 lbs. bombs.

18 guns in all. Production of B-25H Mitchells stopped at Inglewood in July 1944, but the B-25J continued from Kansas City until the end of the war with Japan. Britain got 314 B-25Js, which became Mitchell IIIs.

Peak AAF inventory for the B-25 was 2656 in July 1944, compared to 1931 for the B-26 peak that March, although "B-25 and B-26 groups within the AAF were approximately equal in number." On January 14, 1943, the Navy ordered Mitchells for use by Marine Corps pilots who got 248 B-25H and 458 B-25Js. They were designated PBJ-1H and PBJ-1J, and operated in the Pacific Theater.

The Martin Marauder was not built in as large numbers as the Mitchell, because it proved more expensive to produce and maintain, and had a higher accident rate. A group began operations from New Guinea in April 1942, but in 1943 longer-ranged Mitchells replaced the B-26 in Pacific areas. In Europe the Marauder was more successful, despite a disastrous loss of the entire formation on the second mission in May 1943. Three groups operated in the Mediterranean, and eight groups aided the cross-Channel invasion. Other B-26s operated with French and British units.

The first mass production Marauder was the B-26B, ordered on September 28, 1940, and first accepted in April 1942 with two .50-caliber hand-operated tail guns distinguishing it from previous models. Originally the B-26B specification called for an airplane similar to the B-26A, with R-2800-5 engines, empty weight of 22,014 lbs. and a top speed of 311 mph. Numerous changes were made until the B-26B had R-2800-41 or R-2800-43 engines with 2000 hp for take-off, and an empty weight of 22,380 lbs. Armament included four .50-caliber guns paired in the dorsal and tail turrets, a .30-caliber nose gun, another in the belly, 3000 lbs. of bombs, and an outside attachment for a torpedo. In June 1942, B-26Bs attacked Japanese ships near Midway and the Aleutians with torpedoes; the only time Army planes used this weapon in combat.

The first 307 B-26Bs of the 791 plane 1940 contract had 65 ft. wings, six guns, and the 1850 hp R-2800-5, but 95 ships of block B-26B-2 had 2000 hp R-2800-41s, while the similar R-2800-43 of all future Marauders was first used on 28 B-26B-3s, with enlarged air intakes atop the cowl. Two .50-caliber beam guns, firing down and rearward through flank hatches, replaced the .30-caliber ventral gun in the last 141 of 211 B-26B-4s, which also had other equipment changes.

Accidents plagued the training program as added weight, including bomb loads of up to 5200 lbs., made the ship harder to handle. The wider, 71 ft. wing and a larger tail to improve handling qualities was first seen on the B-26C-5-MO ordered on June 28, 1941, and first delivered in August 1942 from the new Martin Omaha plant. The new wing and tail were also used on the last 150 ships (B-26B-10-MA) of the 1940 Baltimore contract.

Forward armament in these wide-wing ships was increased to six .50-caliber guns, including a flexible nose gun, a fixed gun in the right-hand nose, and two guns in blisters on each side of the fuselage. Armament now included 12 guns altogether, with 4250 rounds of .50-caliber ammunition.

Twin tail guns were hand-held on the first 741 Bs (to B-25B-15-MA) and 170 B-25C-5-MA, but the B-25B-20 and B-26C-10 introduced in 1943 a power-operated Martin-Bell two-gun tail turret. Seven men operated the Marauder, whose increased size and weight had reduced performance, but improved its serviceability.

Omaha continued production for a total of 1235 bombers (to B-26C-45) plus 350 AT-23B unarmed trainer and target tugs. Two hundred more went to the Navy in October 1943 as JM-1 target tugs without turret or guns. One hundred B-26C-30 became the Marauder II.

Meanwhile Baltimore continued deliveries on contracts that brought B-26B totals to 1883 ships with the B-26B-55. Baltimore-built target-towing conversions

MFR

LOCKHEED-VEGA VENTURA I

Pratt & Whitney R-2800-S1A4-G, 1850 hp take-off

DIMENSIONS: Span 65′ 6″, Lg. 51′ 5″, Ht. 11′ 11″, Wing Area 551 sq. ft.

WEIGHT: Empty 17,233 lb., Gross 22,500 lb., Max. 26,000 lb. Fuel 565 gal.

PERFORMANCE: Speed—Top 312 mph. Cruising 272 mph, Landing 80 mph. Service Ceiling 25,200′, Climb 2035′/1 min. Range 1000 miles/2500 lbs. bombs.

included 208 AT-23As (from B-26Bs) and 57 JM-2s from later B-26Gs.

The Omaha plant shifted from Marauders to Superfortresses, but Baltimore continued Marauder deliveries with 300 B-26Fs of February 1944. A 3.5° increase in the angle of incidence, an improved tail turret, eleven .50-caliber guns and 4400 rounds of ammunition, and more fuel were added to this model. The nose fixed gun was omitted, but the tail gunner had better protection and more bullets. The R.A.F. got 200 B-26Fs and 150 similar B-26Gs as the Marauder III.

Last Marauder model was the B-25G, which can be distinguished from its predecessor only by serial numbers indicating they were built to fiscal 1943 and 1944 contracts. Of 950 built, 57 were completed as TB-26G trainers. When production was completed in March 1945, 5157 Marauders had been built. Although never as popular as the Mitchell, the Martin Marauder made most of the Army's short-range bomber sorties against Germany.

Lighter than AAF twin-engined types, the Lockheed Vega Ventura was a mid-wing medium bomber with twin rudders and tail-down landing gear that had been designed in May 1940. Developed from the Hudson light bomber, 675 Venturas were ordered by the R.A.F. in 1940 and were designated B-34 when a lend-lease contract added 200 in 1941.

The Ventura I was first flown on July 31, 1941, with Pratt & Whitney R-2800-51A4-C Wasps of 1850 hp and

LOCKHEED-VEGA B-37 (VENTURA III)

Wright R-2600-13, 1700 hp take-off, 1450 hp at 12,000′

DIMENSIONS: As B-34A

WEIGHT: Empty 18,160 lb., Gross 27,000 lb., Max. 29,500 lb. Fuel 565–1300 gal.

PERFORMANCE: (26,500 lb.) Speed—Top 298 mph at 13,500′, Cruising 198 mph, Landing 77 mph. Service Ceiling 22,400′, Climb 10,000′/5.5 min. Range 1300 miles/2000 lbs. bombs, 2700 miles max.

MFR

PMB

LOCKHEED-VEGA B-34A (VENTURA IIA)

Pratt & Whitney R-2800-31, 2000 hp take-off, 1600 hp at 13,500′

DIMENSIONS: Span 65′ 6″, Lg. 51′ 5″, Ht. 11′ 11″, Wing Area 551 sq. ft.

WEIGHT: Empty 17,275 lb., Gross 25,600 lb., Max. 27,750 lb. Fuel 565–1345 gal.

PERFORMANCE: Speed—Top 315 mph at 15,500′, Cruising 230 mph, Landing 80 mph. Service Ceiling 24,000′, Climb 15,000′/8.2 min. Range 950 miles/3000 lbs. bombs, 2600 miles max.

a crew of four. Armament included 2500 lbs. of bombs, two fixed .50-caliber and two flexible .30-caliber guns in the nose, a pair of .30-caliber guns in a power-operated British top turret, and another pair at a ventral opening.

Eighty-eight Ventura Is were followed by the Ventura II, which had 2000 hp R-2800-31 engines, 3000 lbs. of bombs, a pair of .50-caliber fixed nose guns, another pair in a Martin dorsal turret, and provision for six .30-caliber flexible guns. The Ventura III, or B-37 (formerly O-56) used 1700 hp Wright R-2600-31 Cyclones, but only 18 of 550 ordered were actually delivered in 1943. The R.A.F.'s Bomber Command began Ventura sorties on November 3, 1942, but in 1943 the type was transferred to Coastal Command, for whom it was originally intended. As the B-34A, Venturas did patrol and training flying for the Army Air Forces until Ventura production was assigned entirely to the U. S. Navy. (See PV-1 in Part 5.) Before that, 875 Venturas had been built, of which 394 went to the R.A.F.

The next twin-engined bomber to appear had been designed originally in August 1939 to a specification for high altitude versions of the B-25 and B-26. Both the Martin XB-27 (Model 182) and North American XB-28 (NA-63) were to have turbo-supercharged

NORTH AMERICAN XB-28

Pratt & Whitney R-2800-11, 2000 hp take-off, 1840 hp at 25,000′

DIMENSIONS: Span 72′ 7″, Lg. 56′ 5″, Ht. 14′, Wing Area 676 sq. ft.

WEIGHT: Empty 25,575 lb., Gross 35,740 lb., Max. 37,200 lb. Fuel 1170–1508 gal.

PERFORMANCE: Speed—Top 372 mph at 25,000′, Cruising 255 mph, Landing 86 mph. Service Ceiling 34,600′, Climb 10,000′/9 min. Range 2040 miles/600 lbs. bombs.

AMC

AMC

DOUGLAS XB-42
Allison V-1710-125, 1800 hp WE
DIMENSIONS: Span 70′ 6″, Lg. 53′ 7″, Ht. 20′ 9″, Wing Area 555 sq. ft.
WEIGHT: Empty 20,888 lb., Gross 33,208 lb., Max. 35,702 lb. Fuel 650–1750 gal.
PERFORMANCE: Speed—Top 410 mph at 23,440′, 344 mph at s. l. Service Ceiling 29,400′. Range 1840 miles normal, 5400 miles max.

MFR

DOUGLAS XB-42A
Allison V-1710-133, 1325 hp take-off, 1800 hp WE at s. l., and Westinghouse 19B-2, 1600 lbs.
DIMENSIONS: Span 70′ 7″, Lg. 53′ 10″, Ht. 18′ 10″, Wing Area 555 sq. ft.
WEIGHT: Empty 24,775 lb., Gross 39,000 lb., Max. 44,900 lb. Fuel 650–2402 gal. (2570 gal. max.).
PERFORMANCE: Speed—Top 488 mph at 14,000′, Cruising 251 mph. Range 4750 miles max.

Pratt & Whitney Wasps and pressurized cabins, but the Martin project was dropped. Two XB-28s, however, were ordered on February 13, 1940, and the first was flown in April 1942. Powered by the R-2800-11, the XB-28 had tricycle landing gear, single rudder, five men in a pressure cabin, and carried 4000 lbs. of bombs, six .50-caliber and three .30-caliber guns. The heavier guns were paired in the tail and in upper and lower turrets remote-controlled from periscopic stations behind the pilots' seats. The second prototype was completed as the XB-28A photo version with R-2800-27s.

Although the high-altitude performance of the XB-28 far exceeded that of service types, wartime medium bombing was done at relatively low altitudes and authorities were unwilling to interrupt Mitchell production for an untried type.

A fitting end to the story of twin-propellered bomber design was the Douglas ship begun in May 1943 and proposed on June 15, 1943. The original design was designated XA-42 and had two Allison V-1710-93 liquid-cooled engines in the fuselage. When the experimental contract was awarded in August, however, it was seen as a way of "increasing the heavy long-range bombing attack with minimum industrial effort." Redesignated XB-42, it became a high-speed bomber which could match the B-29s striking range at much less cost in economic strain, fuel, and crew requirements. First flown on May 6, 1944, the XB-42 minimized drag by burying both inline engines in the fuselage behind the pilots and extending drive shafts (each of five P-39 shafts) to co-axial pusher propellers behind the tail. Radiators in the wings cooled 1800 hp Allison V-1710-125s.

The usual bombardier sat in the transparent nose, with the pilot and co-pilot seated under individual canopies, the latter facing backward when operating the remote-controlled guns. Two .50-caliber guns in the trailing edge of each wing had a limited azimuth, but were thought enough to meet attacks which, because of the bomber's speed, could come only from the rear. Two fixed forward guns were located in the nose, and a total of 2400 rounds were provided for all six guns. An alternate attack solid nose with eight guns was anticipated. A range of over 5000 miles with a one-ton bomb load was expected, but the bomb bay had an 8000-lb. capacity, and normal range was 1800 miles. Both XB-42 prototypes were finally destroyed in crashes, but one of the Mixmasters flew a 2295 mile transcontinental flight averaging 433 mph (with the help of 60 mph winds). The other became the XB-42A when a Westinghouse 19B auxiliary jet of 1600-lb. thrust was placed under each wing. All guns were removed, but more fuel was provided.

Although none of the experimental medium bombers designed after 1939 went into production, more than enough of earlier models to win the war were available. The table below summarizes the work of AAF bombers in the air offensive against Germany and her European Allies.

Table 7

AAF BOMBERS IN THE EUROPEAN WAR, 1942–45

	Number of Sorties	Bomb Tonnage	U. S. Aircraft Lost in Combat	Enemy Aircraft Claimed Destroyed in Air
B-17	291,508	640,036	4688	6659
B-24	226,775	452,508	3626	2617
B-26	129,943	169,382	911	402
B-25	63,177	84,980	380	193
A-20	39,492	31,856	265	11
A-26	11,567	18,054	67	7
Total	762,462	1,396,816	9937	9889

Chapter 12: The Magic Weapon 1945–59

MFR

BOEING XB-29 (Photo shows #3)
Wright R-3350-13, 2200 hp at 25,000′
DIMENSIONS: Span 141′ 3″, Lg. 98′ 2″, Ht. 27′ 9″, Wing Area 1739 sq. ft.
WEIGHT: Empty 66,120 lb., Gross 105,000 lb., Max. 120,000 lb. Fuel 5155–7494 gal.
PERFORMANCE: Speed—Top 368 mph at 25,000′, Cruising 247 mph, Landing 105 mph. Service Ceiling 32,100′, Climb 25,000′/27 min. Range 4100 miles/16,000 lbs. bombs (120,000 lbs. gross), 5850 miles max.

SUPERFORTRESS OVER JAPAN

Had war ended on V-E Day there could have remained doubt as to the decisive effects of strategic bombardment. Postwar study revealed that German production actually increased during 1944, and had the Nazi jet fighter program not foundered, defeat of Hitler might have depended entirely on Allied ground forces.

But war against Japan demonstrated air power's full weight. Japan, whose armed forces suffered 760,000 combat casualties in the entire war, sustained in nine months 806,000 civilian casualties, including 330,000 dead. All were victims of the Boeing B-29 Superfortress, which had proved itself a weapon of war without equal in the history of mankind.

The bomber which accomplished this feat, making the Kaiser's Gothas, Hitler's Heinkels, and our own B-17s seem rather primitive, had been ordered as a prototype in September 1940. By the time the XB-29 flew on September 21, 1942, 1644 had been programed for a three billion dollar effort that finally produced 4221 B-29s from four different plants.

So that the B-17 program would not be obstructed, a new plant was built at Wichita, Kansas, utilizing Midwestern labor reserves. An order for fourteen YB-29s placed in May 1941 had been followed on September 6 by a contract for 250 B-29s, and 500 more were added on January 31, 1942. Later, Bell Aircraft was enlisted to build others at a Marietta, Georgia, facility, first aircraft plant in the old South. A Renton, Washington, plant built for Boeing flying boats was released by the Navy for B-29A production in exchange for Mitchell medium bombers. Finally, Martin's Omaha factory then building B-26Cs was also, after a short reservation for 400 stillborn B-33As, assigned to B-29s.

Three XB-29s were built at Seattle, using four Wright R-3350-13 Cyclones, each with double turbo-superchargers and 2200 hp at 25,000 ft. These prototypes could be distinguished from succeeding models by their three-bladed propellers, tear-drop blisters, and olive-drab paint. The second soon crashed, killing everyone aboard, and there was momentary doubt of the gamble committing so much industrial effort to one airplane.

The first YB-29-BW was delivered in July 1943 with the R-3350-21 and four-bladed propellers. One modified with Allison V-3420-11 inline engines became the XB-39, designed March 1942, ordered in September, and delivered March 1944.

Wichita delivered its first production B-29-1-BW in September 1943 and completed 1570 by September 1945. The first 240 (blocks 1 to 20) had R-3350-23 engines, ten .50-caliber guns with 5000 rounds, and 60 rounds for a 20-mm. gun. Later blocks (25 to 90) had twelve .50-caliber guns with 11,500 rounds, 100 rounds of 20-mm. ammunition, more fuel, and usually had later Cyclone models (R-3350-41 or -57). The Renton plant began deliveries in January 1944, and the first 20 ships had the original armament, but 1098

B-29A-BNs built there by May 1946 had the later modifications. Martin and Bell began delivery on 536 B-29-MO and 668 B-29-BA in February 1944, and 311 B-29B-BAs were accepted from January to September 1945. The latter model had APG-15 radar, two or three .50-caliber tail guns, but no turrets.

All Superfortresses were similar in appearance, with an unbroken nose, crew of eleven in pressurized compartments connected by a tunnel through double bomb bays, and double wheels for the retractable tricycle gear. Distinguishing armament feature was an elaborate General Electric fire-control system with computing sights in the nose and in rear top and side blisters directing four remote-controlled turrets with 360° arcs. Each had two .50-caliber guns, but the upper front turret soon got four. On night raids late in the war, range and speed were improved by dispensing with all four turrets. A tail gunner remained, whose two .50-caliber and one 20-mm. gun turned 30° around center. The heavy gun was later omitted, and sometimes replaced by a third .50-caliber gun. Up to 20,000 lbs. of bombs could be carried.

AF

BOEING B-29 (Photo shows B-29-90-BW)
Wright R-3350-23, 2200 hp take-off, 2430 hp WE (also -47 and -57).
DIMENSIONS: Span 141' 3", Lg. 99', Ht. 29' 7", Wing Area 1736 sq. ft.
WEIGHT: Empty 70,140 lb., Gross 110,000 lb., Max. 124,000 lb. Fuel 5638–8198 gal.
PERFORMANCE: Speed—Top 358 mph at 25,000', Cruising 230 mph, Landing 105 mph. Service Ceiling 31,850', Climb 20,000'/38 min. Range 3250 miles/20,000 lbs. bombs, 5600 miles max.

MFR

The bombardier sat in the nose with his bombsight and gunsight, with panels of armor and bulletproof glass behind him protecting pilot and co-pilot. Behind them was more armor, then the flight engineer, radio operator, and navigator, then armor, and the bomb bays. The rear compartment contained three gunners and the radar man, all protected by an armor bulkhead. The radar protruded below between the bomb doors, while the tail gunners' compartment was also protected and, like the main cabins, was pressurized to maintain an internal altitude of 8000 ft. up to an actual altitude of 30,000 ft.

PMB

BOEING B-29A
Wright R-3350-23, -41, or -57, 2200 hp
DIMENSIONS: As B-29
WEIGHT: Empty 71,360 lb., Gross 138,500 lb., Max. 141,100 lb. Fuel 6988–9548 gal.
PERFORMANCE: As B-29, except range 4100 miles/16,000 lbs. bombs, 6000 miles max.

BOEING B-29B-BA (Bell)
Wright R-3350-23, 2200 hp
DIMENSIONS: As B-29
WEIGHT: Empty 69,000 lb., Gross 110,000 lb., Max. 137,500 lb. Fuel 6988–9548 gal.
PERFORMANCE: Speed—Top 364 mph at 25,000′, Cruising 228 mph, Landing 105 mph. Service Ceiling 32,000′, Climb 20,000′/38 min. Range 4200 miles/18,000 lbs. bombs.

PMB

BOEING XB-39
Allison V-3420-11, 3000 hp take-off, 2600 hp at 25,000′
DIMENSIONS: Span 141′ 3″, Lg. 98′ 2″, Ht. 27′ 9″, Wing Area 1739 sq. ft.
WEIGHT: Empty 75,037 lb., Gross 105,000 lb., Max. 135,000 lb. Fuel 3333 gal.
PERFORMANCE: Speed—Top 405 mph at 25,000′, 312 mph at s. l., Cruising 282 mph. Service Ceiling 35,000′, Climb 1300′/1 min., 30,000′/29.3 min. Range 2840 miles/4000 lbs. bombs, 6290 miles max.

PMB

Big bases were needed for take-offs with heavy loads, 2900 ft. of concrete runway at 60 tons gross, and 3700 ft. for a 65-ton condition. Stalling speed at that weight was 114 mph with full flaps, and 140 mph without flaps, so it was fortunate that engine failures were few and that the big bomber was not considered difficult to fly.

Superfortresses began bombing Japan in June 1944. When Chinese bases proved too difficult to supply and defend, the B-29s shifted to the newly captured Mariana Islands. From there, in November 1944, they began the 177,000 ton bombing of the main Japanese islands which eventually inflicted the casualties mentioned before. Japanese weather frustrated the precision bombing technique used in Europe, and General Curtis E. LeMay shifted his method to night incendiary attacks on Japanese cities. The first of these on Tokyo, March 9, 1945, caused more casualties than either of the atomic bombs. On March 27 the B-29s added to their effort Operation Starvation, eventually dropping 12,035 mines in coastal waters to destroy Japanese shipping. Even without the atomic bomb, these fire bomb and mining attacks crippled Japan.

In his letter to President Roosevelt on August 2, 1939, suggesting the atomic bomb, Albert Einstein had feared "such bombs might very well prove too heavy for transport by air." The weapon completed at Los Alamos under the direction of J. Robert Oppenheimer, however, was well within the capacity of the B-29, which in September 1943 was selected as its carrier. Minor modifications were made to the bomb bay, but "the atom bomb was tailored to fit the plane rather than the reverse." A specially trained squadron received their modified B-29s (fifteen had been ordered) in May 1945, and flew to Tinian in the Marianas in June. There they awaited test-firing of the first bomb on July 16 in New Mexico, and the rush of the next two bombs to Tinian by cruiser in time for the August 6 strike on Hiroshima.

By war's end, 40 groups, including 21 already at Pacific combat bases, had 2132 B-29s. But their service career wasn't over, for B-29A production at Renton continued until May 1946, and when the Korean War began in 1950, Superfortresses were still the most numerous type in the USAF bomber inventory. So many modifications were made during a long service life that variations in weight and performances makes selection of "typical" characteristics difficult. The data accompanying this text is for early wartime models. Early sets of engines were replaced eventually with modernized R-3350-79 or -81s and cruise control experience improved range capabilities.

Superfortress success made redundant the parallel heavy bomber development by Convair. The first XB-32, flown on September 7, 1942, had the same engines, unbroken nose, and pressurization as the XB-29, but was smaller and had the high wing and twin tails of its B-24 ancestors. The first crashed after thirty flights, but the second, flown on July 2, 1943, had an indented nose, while the third flew on November 9 with the high single tail adopted for production copies. Armament on the prototype included 20,000 lbs. of bombs, fourteen .50-caliber guns, and two 20-mm. guns.

Pacific war tacticians, now thinking of attacks from lower altitudes, eliminated weighty pressurization and remote-controlled turrets from production models. Ten .50-caliber guns were paired in power-operated turrets like the B-24s: one in the nose, two on top, one in the tail, and a retractable belly turret.

When delivery began in November 1944 on B-32 Dominators, official opinion was that B-32s were no longer needed as "insurance against failure of the B-29," and that they were overweight, and had poor bombardier's vision. By the following summer it was decided to cut back orders and equip but one combat group. When the war's end halted production, only 114 of 1213 ordered had been finished at Fort Worth and just one of 500 more ordered from Convair's San Diego plant. A few entered skirmishes in the war's last few days, but the B-29 had already defeated Japan.

CONVAIR XB-32 (with single tail)

MFR

THE A-BOMB AND THE COLD WAR

While American occupation troops thoughtfully examined the burned-out heart of Tokyo and the flattened wasteland at Hiroshima, United States policymakers considered the postwar military establishment. Adherence to the United Nations implied a world security system in which armed forces might be dis-

CONVAIR XB-32
Wright R-3350-13, 2200 hp at 25,000′
DIMENSIONS: Span 135′, Lg. 83′, Ht. 20′ 10″, Wing Area 1422 sq. ft.
WEIGHT: Empty 64,960 lb., Gross 101,662 lb., Max. 113,500 lb. Fuel 5226 gal.
PERFORMANCE: Speed—Top 376 mph at 25,000′, Landing 96 mph. Service Ceiling 30,700′, Climb 25,000′/22.6 min. Range 4450 miles/2000 lbs. bombs.

MFR

MFR

CONVAIR B-32

Wright R-3350-23, 2200 hp at 25,000′

DIMENSIONS: Span 135′, Lg. 82′ 1″, Ht. 33′, Wing Area 1422 sq. ft.

WEIGHT: Empty 60,278 lb., Gross 100,000 lb., Max. 111,500 lb. Fuel 5460–6960 gal.

PERFORMANCE: Speed—Top 357 mph at 30,000′, Cruising 290 mph, Landing 96 mph. Service Ceiling 30,700′, Climb 25,000′/38 min. Range 2500 miles/8000 lbs. bombs, 4200 miles max.

patched anywhere. Continental defense, center of prewar plans, became secondary to offensive capabilities of global range.

As the U.S. had the world's only atomic weapons and in its B-29 fleet, by far the world's best agency to deliver them, it appeared that the nation was well able to fill the role of world policeman, with little aid from other nations, or even from its own land armies. Long-range nuclear bombing was seen by many as a magic weapon which had ended the war with Japan, could deter any future aggression, and established American leadership in world affairs.

In the years following World War II, the world polarized into two camps as hostility and tension increased between the United States and Russia, and U.S. bombardment capacity was a major weight in the balance of power between them. Air power had achieved equal status with the Army and Navy through creation of the National Military Establishment on September 18, 1947, with Secretaries of Air, Army, and Navy under a Secretary of Defense. On July 18, 1947, President Truman appointed an Air Policy Commission headed by Thomas K. Finletter to formulate "an integrated national aviation policy."

The Commission's report submitted on December 30 called for a 70 group Air Force to be ready by 1950. Heart of this fleet was to be five B-36 groups and sixteen groups of "medium bombers" (as the B-29 and its improvement, the B-50, were now called), all under the Strategic Air Command. The expense of such a force, however, was so tremendous that by 1950 appropriated funds—although higher than in any prewar year including 1941—were enough for only 48 groups (now called wings). The Air Force then looked hungrily at funds going to the Army and Navy, and concentrated its own buying on long-range bombers.

Many developments of this period are concealed by security censorship, but enough is known to give a brief account of the present status of bomber development. The story of Rainbow Five in 1941 makes it improbable that a war plan has not been framed including lists of Soviet targets (a task made difficult by Russian secrecy) and bomber numbers and types needed to attack them—presumably with nuclear weapons making unnecessary fleets of the size used in the last war.

However rapidly ground armies were dispersed, and Fortresses and Liberators retired to long, rusting rows in desert and fields, awaiting sale or scrapping, the strategic bombing force had not been dissolved at war's end. Production on the atomic bomb continued and grew, and a few B-29s continued to roll out of Renton. Over 2700 Superfortresses were carefully "mothballed," and like the bombs, stockpiled for future use. Meanwhile, Boeing continued production on improved versions, while the U.S.S.R. utilized a B-29 forced landing in Siberia as a pattern for a Soviet version. (This provided an interim strategic bomber without expensive development costs, so that Russian effort could be concentrated on advanced jet types.)

The new Strategic Air Command had inherited a wide program of bomber development from World War II, with a propeller-driven phase of Boeing, Northrop, and Consolidated projects built around the Pratt & Whitney R-4360 Wasp Major, and a jet-propelled phase with several projects using General Electric J-35 engine.

In July 1944 a B-29A had been ordered fitted with 3000 hp R-4360-33s by Pratt & Whitney, and the ship was designated XB-44 and flown in May 1945. It became the prototype for next Boeing series, originally designated B-29D, but relabeled B-50. First flown on

BOEING XB-44

Pratt & Whitney R-4360-33, 3000 hp take-off, 2500 hp at 25,000′

DIMENSIONS: Span 141′ 3″, Lg. 99′, Ht. 29′ 7″, Wing Area 1728 sq. ft.

WEIGHT: Empty 75,035 lb., Gross 105,000 lb., Max. 140,000 lb.

PERFORMANCE: Speed—Top 392 mph at 25,400′, Cruising 282 mph. Range 2400 miles normal.

MFR

PMB

BOEING B-50A
Pratt & Whitney R-4360-35, 3500 hp
DIMENSIONS: Span 141′ 3″, Lg. 99′, Ht. 32′ 8″, Wing Area 1720 sq. ft.
WEIGHT: Empty 81,050 lb., Max. 168,480 lb. Fuel 7195–10,772 gal.
PERFORMANCE: (At 121,700 lbs., combat weight) Speed—Top 385 mph at 25,000′, Cruising 235 mph, Landing 136 mph. Service Ceiling 37,000′, Climb 2225′/1 min. Range 4650 miles/10,000 lbs. bombs, 5270 miles max.

June 25, 1947, they had 3500 hp R-4360-35s, thirteen .50-caliber guns, and could be distinguished from B-29s by their modified nacelles and tall tail, which folded for hangar storage. Seventy-nine B-50As were completed by January 1949 and followed by 45 B-50Bs with strengthened wings. The latter were modified to RB-50Bs and issued to strategic reconnaissance units. One B-50A flew entirely around the world in February 1949 on a nonstop flight demonstrating in-flight refueling from tanker planes converted from B-29s.

A B-50C was proposed with Pratt & Whitney R-4360-51 compound VDT engines, but this change required complete redesign of the airframe. Forty-three were ordered as the 207,000 lbs. gross Boeing B-54A, but on April 5, 1949, they were canceled in favor of the B-36. Production continued on R-3350-35 powered B-50Ds, carrying more fuel and underwing fixtures for a pair of 700 gallon drop tanks. Range with 5 tons of bombs was about 4900 miles, but up to 14 tons could be carried for short distances. Between May 1949 and February 1953, 222 B-50Ds and 24 TB-50H trainers were built. Many were eventually converted into WB weather reconnaissance and KB tanker versions, while RB-50E, RB-50F, and RB-50G were RB-50B conversions.

Boeing's Superfortress series had survived competition from the unique Northrop "flying wing." First American plane of this style had been the twin-engined experimental Northrop N1M flown in July 1940, which demonstrated the possibilities of aircraft carrying all loads and controls within the wing, and dispensing with fuselage and tail sections. In September 1941, the results of this experiment were given to the Air Force with proposals for a four-engined long-range bomber. Two XB-35 prototypes were ordered in November 1941, and followed later by a contract for 13 service test articles. There was a wartime plan to build 200 at Martin's Omaha plant, but this program was dropped.

After testing four one-third scale flying models, construction began on prototypes, the first flying on June 25, 1946. Power plants were Pratt & Whitney Wasp Majors (two R-4360-17 and two R-4360-21) with double turbo-superchargers and co-axial counter-rotating four-bladed pusher propellers. Crew consisted of nine in the pressurized center section (two pilots, bombardier, engineer, navigator, radioman, and three gunners), plus accommodations for six relief men. The bomb bays held up to 51,200 pounds of bombs, and twenty .50-caliber guns were provided for, but not installed on the prototype. Seven remote-controlled turrets were aimed from central sighting stations behind the pilot and on top of a cone protruding from the trailing edge. Four-gun turrets were spotted above and below the center section, two-gun turrets were visible outboard of the engines, one pair on top, another below, and four guns could be placed in the cone.

The first three flying wings had Wasp Majors, but a June 1, 1945, order had the next two finished with Allison J35-A-5 jets. First flown on October 21, 1947, the YB-49 fed eight 4000-lb. thrust engines through intakes in the leading edge, eliminated turrets except for the cone guns, and added four vertical stabilizing fins. The jet version had a bomb capacity of 36,760 lbs., and a normal 10,000 lb. load could be carried an estimated 4000 miles on 16,700 gallons of fuel. This was less than half B-35 range, and shows the thirst of jet engines, but preliminary estimates promised a 100 mph increase in speed. Contracts were placed for 30 RB-49s and conversion of the remaining ten B-35 airframes to YRB-49A strategic reconnaissance types.

BOEING B-50D
Pratt & Whitney R-4360-35, 3500 hp take-off
DIMENSIONS: As B-50A
WEIGHT: Empty 80,609 lb., Max. 173,000 lb. Fuel 11,685 gal.
PERFORMANCE: (At 123,100 lbs., combat weight) Speed—Top 380 mph at 25,000′, Cruising 277 mph, Landing 137 mph. Service Ceiling 36,700′, Climb 2165′/1 min. Range 4900 miles/10,000 lbs. bombs, 7750 miles max.

MFR

Results of YB-49 flight tests are not available, but an average of 511 mph on a 2258-mile hop was announced. Stability difficulties hurt the flying wing's usefulness as a bombing platform, and range was insufficient for long-distance reconnaissance. Cancellations ended the RB-49 contract in April 1949 and hit the YRB-49A in October. Only one YRB-49A was completed, and first flew on May 4, 1950. Four 5000-lb. thrust Allison J-35-A-19 engines were in the wing, two more in pods below it, and photographic equipment was installed in a bulge below the center section.

MFR

NORTHROP XB-35
Pratt & Whitney R-3350-17 and -21, 3000 hp
DIMENSIONS: Span 172′, Lg. 53′ 1″, Ht. 20′ 1″, Wing Area 4000 sq. ft.
WEIGHT: (Estimated) Empty 89,560 lb., Gross 180,000 lb., Max. 209,000 lb. Fuel 10,000–18,000 gal.
PERFORMANCE: (Estimated) Speed—Top 391 mph at 35,000′, Cruising 183 mph. Service Ceiling 39,700′, Climb 35,600′/57 min. Range 8150 miles at 183 mph with 16,000 lbs. bombs, 720 miles at 240 mph with 51,070 lbs. bombs.

AF

AF

NORTHROP YB-49
Allison J35-A-5, 4000 lbs.
DIMENSIONS: Span 172′, Lg. 53′ 1″, Ht. 20′, Wing Area 4000 sq. ft.
WEIGHT: Empty 86,000 lb., Gross 160,000 lb., Max. 168,000 lb. Fuel 13,540–17,545 gal.
PERFORMANCE: (Estimated) Speed—Top 495 mph at 20,000′, Cruising 430 mph. Service Ceiling 42,000′, Climb 40,000′/37 min. Range 4000 miles/16,700 gal. with 10,000 lbs. bombs, 1150 miles/36,760 lbs. bombs, 4450 miles ferry.

MFR

NORTHROP YRB-49A
Allison J35-A-19, 5000 lbs.
DIMENSIONS: As YB-49
WEIGHT: Empty 88,500 lb., Gross 117,500 lb., Max. 206,000 lb.
PERFORMANCE: Not available

THE INTERCONTINENTAL BOMBER

The aircraft which symbolized American bombers during the cold war and became the most controversial native combat type since the DH-4, began its career before the attack on Pearl Harbor. We have mentioned before that an order for two XB-36 prototypes was placed with Consolidated Aircraft on November 15. 1941.

Heavy demands on that firm's B-24 program delayed any real effort on the B-36 until June 1943, when General Arnold saw that it might be needed for attacking Japan if bases near enough for B-29 strikes were not secured by surface forces. To his interest was added the complaint of Thomas Girdler, president of the Consolidated-Vultee combination, that "it was difficult to get subcontractors to work on an experimental order for two planes, whereas they would be interested if the plane had some promise of large-scale production." The situation was met by giving Convair on

MFR

July 23, 1943, a "letter of intent" for 100 planes to be built at Fort Worth.

On August 19, 1944, the letter of intent was replaced by a cost-plus-fixed-fee contract, but no priority was included, for U.S. capture of the Mariana Islands opened bases within B-29 range of Japan. Convair was ordered to concentrate on the B-32, counterpart of the B-29. An air staff conference on August 9, 1945, recommended that four groups of B-36s be included in the proposed 70 group post-war Air Force, and with Japan defeated and the B-32 unnecessary, Convair's Fort Worth plant went ahead with the larger plane.

The original XB-36 made its first flight nearly five years after it had been ordered, instead of the 30 months originally planned. Powered by six 3000 hp R-4360-25 radials with pusher propellers, it took off on August 8, 1946, weighing 100 tons; heaviest and largest plane ever to fly up to that time, even in Texas.

On August 30, 1947, the first B-36A completed was flown to Wright Field for static tests. In December, flight tests began on the YB-36A, actually the second prototype, but the first completely equipped model. Both of these had a new landing gear and nose; the pilots now sat high above the hull with all-around visibility. The original XB-36s weight bore down on a single 110 in. wheel on each side, necessitating special runways, but subsequent models had four 56 in. wheels on each side, while the dual nose wheels remained. This modification saved weight and eliminated the need for special runways. (In April 1950 the large wheels on the prototype were replaced by track-type gear.)

Twenty-one more B-36As followed in 1948, as Convair began weekly delivery. Two pressurized compartments contained the crew: two pilots, radar-bombardier, navigator, flight engineer (a second was added on the B-36H), two radiomen, and three gunners forward were separated by an 85 ft. bomb bay from five gunners in the rear compartment. Four rest bunks were provided for reliefs, and personnel shifted between compartments by rolling on a little dolly in a tunnel through the bomb cells. Thirty-hour missions

CONVAIR XB-36

Pratt & Whitney R-4360-25, 3000 hp

DIMENSIONS: Span 230′, Lg. 163′, Ht. 46′ 10″, Wing Area 4772 sq. ft.

WEIGHT: (Estimated) Empty 131,740 lb., Gross 276,506 lb., Fuel 19,976 gal.

PERFORMANCE: (Estimated) Speed—Top 346 mph at 35,000′, Cruising 216 mph. Service Ceiling 36,000′, Absolute Ceiling 38,000′, Climb 25,000′/42 min. Range 9500 miles/10,000 lbs. bombs, 3850 miles/77,784 lbs. bombs.

MFR

CONVAIR B-36A

through the thin air and 100° below zero temperature of high altitudes required pressurization and heating.

The armament on the XB-36 was to include five 37-mm. and ten .50-caliber guns, with up to 72 1000-lb. bombs, but no guns were actually installed on the prototype. Production models had the most formidable armament of any warplane, sixteen 20-mm. guns paired in eight General Electric remote-controlled turrets. Computing sights at blisters in the nose, and six side spots aimed the front turret and six retractable turrets which disappeared behind sliding panels, and radar aimed the tail guns. The bomb bay accommodated 84,000 lbs. of bombs, or 12,000 gallons of fuel in auxiliary tanks could augment over 21,000 gallons in regular tanks.

Early flight tests were disappointing, for fuel consumption was greater than expected, and engine overheating at high altitudes curtailed speed and ceiling. Strategic Air Force Commander, General George C. Kenney, in December 1946 proposed cutting back the B-36 contract and using the remainder as aerial

MFR

CONVAIR B-36B
Pratt & Whitney R-4360-41, 3500 hp
DIMENSIONS: Span 230′, Lg. 162′ 1″, Ht. 46′ 8″, Wing Area 4772 sq. ft.
WEIGHT: Empty 140,640 lb., Max. 328,000 lb. Fuel 21,010–33,010 gal.
PERFORMANCE: (At 227,700 lbs., combat weight) Speed—Top 381 mph at 34,500′, 354 mph at 25,000′, Cruising 202 mph, Landing 115 mph. Service Ceiling 42,500′, Climb 1510′/1 min. Range 8175 miles/10,000 lbs. bombs, 8770 miles max.

tankers or antisubmarine search. He was overruled by USAF Chief of Staff, General Carl Spaatz.

Convair proposed in March 1947 a means of increasing speed; install Pratt & Whitney's new experimental VDT engines with tractor propellers. This project was designated B-36C and approved in October 1947. The last 34 bombers on order were to get the VDT engines. Top speed might be increased to 410 mph, and increased costs were met by reduction of the total program from 100 to 95 planes.

These engines, however, did not reach anticipated levels of development, so the B-36C was abandoned on May 21, 1948, and the projected ships were completed as B-36Bs.

On June 25, 1948, the Air Staff finally decided to go ahead with the full order of 22 B-36As and 73 B-36Bs because B-36A flight tests indicated engine problems were overcome and performance was better than expected. Altitude tests, for example, on the YB-36A eventually reached 46,100 ft. compared to 38,000 ft. for the XB-36. World tension over the Berlin blockade increased the desire to have an intercontinental bomber force in being, rather than await future technical advances.

On July 8, 1948, the first B-36B was flown, powered by 3500 hp R-4360-41 instead of the R-4360-25s used on earlier models. Gross weight of 328,000 lbs. was reduced by fuel consumption to a combat weight over the target of 227,700 lbs., when the B-36B had a top speed of 381 mph at 34,500 ft. Two 42,000 lb. bombs were dropped halfway on a 2900 mile flight, and a five-ton bomb was carried halfway on flights of 8200 miles made in 1948. Attacks could be made in any weather, for a radome bulging below the fuselage was part of the elaborate K-1 radar bombing system, which "weighs 1700 lbs., contains 365 vacuum tubes, costs $200,000 . . . permits high speed bombing at night through the overcast with greater accuracy than former daylight methods at half the altitudes and speeds."

Intercontinental atomic bombing was entirely practical for these aircraft, and in January 1949 the USAF ordered 39 more B-36s for strategic reconnaissance—targets had to be located before they could be bombed. On March 12, 1949, a modified B-36B was flown with four Allison J-35 turbojets, slung in pairs under each wing. Enthusiastic officials bought 36 additional B-36s in April 1949 and specified that all ships on hand or on order be fitted with four 5200-lb. thrust J-47 jets. These gave short bursts of speed for emergencies, at a moderate cost in range. Money for the additions was obtained by canceling contracts for 327 smaller planes.

With Soviet-American relations deteriorating, the B-36 assumed great importance in world strategy. If the B-29 held the atomic bomb threat over any industrial center within 1500 miles of a United States air base, the B-36 could threaten any point within 4000 miles of these bases; virtually the entire inhabited world.

Key to any estimate of the big bomber's value was its ability to escape destruction by hostile fighters. Supporters of the B-36 argued that current jet fighters could not climb to high altitudes in time to intercept the bomber. Once in position, the fighter's limited speed advantage might permit only slow tail-cone passes in the face of heavy defensive gunfire.

Others challenged B-36 ability to penetrate an effective defense system. Critics insisted that radar would detect the big ship soon after it began its approach, and that latest jet fighters could indeed reach high altitudes quickly enough to stop it. A British engineer attacking "piston-engined giantism," wrote that British jets could reach B-36 height in less than eight minutes, were far faster at high altitudes, and would find the B-36 "practically a sitting duck."

On May Day in 1949, the Russians first displayed formations of a jet interceptor eventually known as the MIG-15. Large numbers were built, and its capabilities would make daylight flying over Russia dangerous for

MFR

CONVAIR B-36D
Pratt & Whitney R-4360-41, 3500 hp, and J47-GE-19, 5200 lbs.
DIMENSIONS: As B-36B
WEIGHT: Empty 158,843 lb., Max 357,500 lb. Fuel 32,910 gal.
PERFORMANCE: (At 243,600 lbs., combat weight) Speed—Top 439 mph at 32,120′, 426 mph at 25,000′ (383 mph at 34,750′, no jets), Cruising 225 mph, Landing 121 mph. Service Ceiling 45,200′, Climb 1740′/1 min. Range 7500 miles/10,000 lbs. bombs, 8800 miles ferry.

hostile bombers. Soviet capabilities in bad weather were less apparent, but the deterrent value of large long-range bombers was in question.

Official controversy suddenly exploded into the open with a Congressional investigation of charges that political favoritism had influenced procurement of a costly sitting duck.

Expensive the B-36 was. The original 95 production models cost $266,792,000 for airframes and $326,833,000 for government-furnished equipment, including later modifications; a total of nearly $594,000,000, or more precisely, $6,248,686 per airplane. The 75 additional bombers ordered in 1949 would reflect production savings; $130,000,000 for airframes, $225,000,000 for equipment, $4,732,939 per airplane. These costs do not include over $39,000,000 for the prototypes.

Reflecting that "the more cost, the more plus" on this type of contract, unfriendly critics rose. A Republican congressman spoke on the House floor of "ugly, disturbing reports" about the political influence of Secretary of Defense Louis A. Johnson (a former director of Convair), and Floyd B. Odlum, president of a holding company controlling Convair; influence which led to B-36 procurement after they "had been found unsatisfactory."

The House Armed Services Committee voted an investigation in June 1949. Odlum defended himself from the charges. "There is not one rivet of politics in the B-36; there is not one ounce of special favoritism in its more than 300,000 pounds of loaded weight . . .

CONVAIR RB-36F

PMB

CONVAIR B-36H

PMB

MFR

CONVAIR GRB-36J (with F-84F parasite)

MFR

CONVAIR NB-36H
Testbed for the first airborne nuclear reactor

These planes were ordered on the basis of merit . . . It is not wrong to be a contributing Democrat."

More serious were the technical issues raised. The Navy "made a formal request to USAF for use of a B-36 in making tests of the defensive capabilities" of the Navy's F4U-5 and F2H-1 fighters, both of which, the Navy believed, could successfully attack big ships at high altitudes. Behind the challenge lay resentment over Defense Secretary Johnson's cancellation, on April 23, 1949, of a 65,000 ton supercarrier ordered the year before by his predecessor Secretary James V. Forrestal. This ship had been proposed as a means of giving the carrier striking force capability of delivering atomic attacks "on the capitol [sic] and industrial centers of the enemy." But Air Force partisans depreciated the offensive possibilities of carriers against a power like the Soviet Union, and insisted that strategic bombing was primarily an Air Force function with the Navy's role limited to control of the seas.

Air Force leaders strongly defended the B-36 program, which survived the Congressional investigation and was further expanded. The speed added by outboard jet units on the B-36D improved its possibilities of evading interception. On July 11, 1949, the first B-36D was flown with four 5200-lb. thrust General Electric J47-GE-19 jets and six R-4360-53 engines. Eighty-six B-36Ds and 24 RB-36Ds were accepted, including 71 modified from B-36Bs by Convair's San Diego division. All 22 RB-36Es were modified from B-36As, and the first flew on December 18, 1949. The RB-36D and RB-36E reconnaissance versions had a crew of 22 and a bay with 14 cameras, one with a 48 in. lens.

On November 18, 1950, the first of the B-36Fs ordered in April 1949 was flown with R-4360-53s of 3800 hp and the J-47s now standard on all models. Twenty-eight B-36F and 24 RB-36F models were followed by 81 B-36H and 73 RB-36H ships. First flown on April 5, 1952, the B-36H was similar to early models but for control and instrument changes. Final service type in the series was the B-36J, whose increased fuel capacity increased overload weight to a possible 205 tons. Last of 22 built was delivered in August 1954, and the B-36 remained in service until retired in May 1958.

Two jet-propelled B-36Gs ordered were delivered as the YB-60s described later. Most remarkable example of this series was the unarmed NB-36H which tests the world's first airborne nuclear reactor. Special shielding protects the crew of five from radiation on flights that began September 17, 1955.

In December 1950, the Air Force authorized new studies of the concept of a parasite single-seater carried by B-36s for scouting or defense. The first parasite project had been the XF-85 described later in this book; all its tests had been made from a modified B-29. Republic F-84Es were launched from a modified B-36F in June 1952, and an RF-84F was launched in May 1953. About a dozen RB-36Ds became GRB-36Js when the bomb bays contained a retractable frame on which a YRF-84F could be lifted. Known as FICON, this system enabled the jet to be carried thousands of miles, released for a high-speed camera run over a target too dangerous for direct B-36 approach, and recovered for the return home. Presumably, a small-size atomic weapon might be delivered by the parasite, if required.

In 1958 the last B-36 was retired from active Air Force inventory. In the opinion of many top-level military and civilian experts the Air Force's B-36 fleet had kept the peace in a turbulent decade, with the unique record of having won a war without having to fight.

JET BOMBERS

Adapting jet propulsion to bombers was no easy task. The first gas turbine units made in America were centrifugal-flow units with wide diameter and a fuel consumption too great to allow the endurance needed for bomber missions.

By April 1944, however, General Electric's J-35 (then called TG-180) had made its bench run, providing an axial-flow turbojet engine whose narrow diameter and smaller fuel thirst recommended it for bomber use. The first American bomber to use jet engines then became the Douglas XB-43, a development of the pusher propellered XB-42, ordered on March 31, 1944.

First flown on May 17, 1946, the XB-43 replaced

the Allisons of its predecessor with two J-35s fed by air intakes behind the pilots and delivering 4000 lbs. thrust each from jet exhausts in the tail. Like the XB-42 it was a three-place, high-wing monoplane with an 8000-lb. bomb capacity, but no guns were used.

Early in the study of bomber jet propulsion it became apparent that more than two engines would be required for the capabilities needed. As early as January 1944, Boeing offered its model 413 photoreconnaissance design to the Air Force. Basically a B-29 powered by four turbojets paired in nacelles slung under the wings, the 413 was not accepted. Shortly after the J-35 engine was satisfactorily tested in April, the Air Force invited bids on a jet-powered bomber capable of a speed of 500 mph, a service ceiling of 40,000 ft., and a thousand mile tactical radius. In December 1944, four manufacturers responded with proposals, all of which were accepted, and by March 1945, ordered as design studies.

All types then ordered were three-place high-wing monoplanes powered by the 4000-lb. thrust J-35 engine, which was transferred from General Electric to Allison in September 1946. The North American XB-45 and Consolidated XB-46 had four J-35s, while Boeing XB-47 and Martin XB-48 had six. (In June 1945, Northrop was given the designation YB-49 for two flying wings fitted with eight jets.) Since it was necessary to minimize drag by suppressing protrusions, and since it was believed that the bomber's high speed would permit enemy fighters only tail-cone passes, armament was limited to a pair of .50-caliber tail guns, trained by radar and fired by the co-pilot. With gunners unnecessary and endurance short, the crew was kept small and weight saved for fuel. Normal bomb load was 8000 lbs. but a single 22,000 lb. bomb could be carried by all types.

NORTH AMERICAN B-45A
General Electric J47-GE-7, -9, 5200 lbs.
DIMENSIONS: Span 89′, Lg. 75′ 4″, Ht. 25′ 2″, Wing Area 1175 sq. ft.
WEIGHT: Empty 45,206 lb., Gross 81,418 lb., Max. 95,558 lb. Fuel 3366–5746 gal.
PERFORMANCE: (At 60,900 lbs. combat weight) Speed—Top 580 mph at s. l., 510 mph at 35,000′, Cruising 458 mph, Landing 123 mph. Service Ceiling 46,250′, Climb 6900′/1 min. Range 1220 miles/10,000 lbs. bombs, 1000 miles/22,000 lbs. bombs, 2234 miles max.

PMB

PMB

DOUGLAS XB-43
General Electric J35-GE, 4000 lbs.
DIMENSIONS: Span 71′ 2″, Lg. 51′ 5″, Ht. 24′ 3″, Wing Area 563 sq. ft.
WEIGHT: Empty 22,890 lb., Gross 40,000 lb. Fuel 1209–2309 gal.
PERFORMANCE: Speed—Top 503 mph at s. l. Service Ceiling 38,200′, Absolute Ceiling 41,800′, Climb 2470′/1 min. Range 1100 miles, 1765 gals., with 8000 lbs.

MFR

NORTH AMERICAN XB-45
Allison J35-A-11, 4000 lbs.
DIMENSIONS: Span 89′ 6″, Lg. 74′, Ht. 25′ 2″, Wing Area 1175 sq. ft.
WEIGHT: Empty 41,876 lb., Gross 66,820 lb., Max. 82,600 lb. Fuel 3400–4477 gal. (5684 gal. max.).
PERFORMANCE: (Estimated) Speed—Top 506 mph at s. l., Cruising 419 mph. Service Ceiling 38,500′, Climb 35,000′/21.5 min. Range 2236 miles/8350 lbs. bombs, 1700 miles/14,000 lbs. bombs, 2921 miles max.

NORTH AMERICAN B-45C
General Electric J47-GE-13, -15, 5200 lbs.
DIMENSIONS: As B-45A, except span 96′ with tip tanks.
WEIGHT: Empty 48,903 lb., Max. 112,952 lb. Fuel 3366–7996 gal.
PERFORMANCE: Speed—Top 579 mph at s. l., 507 mph at 35,000′, Cruising 456 mph, Landing 141 mph. Service Ceiling 43,200′, Climb 5800′/1 min. Range 1910 miles/10,000 lbs. bombs, 2610 miles ferry.

MFR

MFR

CONSOLIDATED-VULTEE XB-46
General Electric J35-C-3
DIMENSIONS: Span 113′, Lg. 105′ 9″, Ht. 27′ 11″, Wing Area 1285 sq. ft.
WEIGHT: Empty 48,018 lb., Gross 91,000 lb., Max. 95,600 lb. Fuel 4280–6682 gal.
PERFORMANCE: Speed—Top 491 mph at s. l., Cruising 439 mph at 35,000′. Service Ceiling 40,000′, Climb 35,000′/19 min. Range 2870 miles/8000 lbs. bombs.

All of these prototypes first flew in 1947; the XB-45 on St. Patrick's Day, XB-46 on April 2, XB-48 on June 14, YB-49 on October 21, and XB-47 on December 17. The first two had a pair of J-35s in a nacelle under each wing and landed on tricycle gear. Three XB-45s and one example of Convair's larger XB-46 were built. The torpedo-shaped XB-46 carried more fuel and up to 16 1000-lb. bombs, but was slower than the smaller North American XB-45s which became the first U.S. jet bomber to go into production.

MARTIN XB-48
Allison J35-A-5, 4000 lbs.
DIMENSIONS: Span 108′ 4″, Lg. 85′ 8″, Ht. 26′ 6″, Wing Area 1330 sq. ft.
WEIGHT: Empty 58,260 lb., Gross 102,600 lb. Fuel 4968 gal.
PERFORMANCE: (Estimated) Speed—Top 552 mph at s. l., Cruising 437 mph. Service Ceiling 43,000′, Climb 35,000′/13.3 min. Range 2400 miles/8000 lbs. bombs.

AF

Ninety-six B-45A Tornados were delivered in 1948–49. Since the radar gun-laying device provided for on the prototype had not yet been perfected, these ships had a cockpit for a tail gunner and his twin Brownings. Powered by four 5200-lb. thrust General Electric J-47-GE-3s developed from the J-35, the B-45A carried from 10,000 to 22,000 lbs. of bombs.

On May 3, 1949, North American flew the first of ten B-45Cs with a 1200 gallon drop tank on each wing tip. Fifty others were canceled to provide B-36 funds, but 33 RB-45Cs were completed with cameras in the nose for photoreconnaissance.

Martin's XB-48, third to appear, had six J35s in individual nacelles under the wings. As on the previous ships, crew consisted of a bombardier in the nose enclosure, followed by pilot and co-pilot seated in tandem under a canopy. Fourteen 1000-lb. or one 22,000-lb. bomb could be accommodated. Most unusual feature was the retractable landing gear; a pair of large wheels forward, another pair aft, and a smaller outrigger wheel under each wing; this tandem gear had been tested two years before on a converted Marauder

SOLDIER OF FORTUNE
MAGAZINE

NO POSTAGE
NECESSARY
IF MAILED
IN THE
UNITED STATES

BUSINESS REPLY MAIL

FIRST-CLASS MAIL PERMIT NO. 8 MT. MORRIS, IL

POSTAGE WILL BE PAID BY ADDRESSEE

SOLDIER OF FORTUNE
PO BOX 348
MT MORRIS IL 61054-9817

MFR

called the XB-26H. Only two XB-48 prototypes were built, for the design was outclassed by the XB-47.

Boeing's XB-47 Stratojet also had six J35-A-15 engines and the tandem landing gear, but its construction had been delayed so that captured German research data on the high-speed advantages of swept-back wings could be verified and incorporated in the layout. The December 1944 proposal was Boeing's Model 432, with a straight wing and power units buried within the fuselage. In September 1945 Model 448 with a swept-back wing was substituted, but the enclosed engines were unsatisfactory. Model 450 replaced this project in October, with four engines paired in pods below and forward of the wing, where interference with airflow over the wing would be minimized. The other two engines were in individual pods at the wing tips.

By November 1945, Model 450 was finalized with a sweep back of 35°, an aspect ratio of 9.6, and outboard engines mounted below the wings. The mockup was approved in April 1946, and completed wind tunnel tests promised a 635 mph top speed and a 2245-mile range with 8000 lbs. of bombs. Construction of two XB-47 prototypes begun in June 1946 cost $8,000,000, in addition to $2,000,000 already expended on engineering. A bombardier-navigator in the nose had a K radar bombing system whose antenna bulged below in a plastic fairing, and the pilot and co-pilot sat in tandem under a bubble canopy. Up to 16 1000-lb. or one 22,000-lb. bomb could be accommodated, and two .50s mounted in the tail cone were aimed by an Emerson radar system. Flight tests on the XB-47 began on December 17, 1947, and on February 8,

BOEING XB-47

General Electric J35-GE-7, 4000 lbs.

DIMENSIONS: Span 116′, Lg. 107′ 6″, Ht. 27′ 8″, Wing Area 1427 sq. ft.

WEIGHT: Empty 74,623 lb., Max. 162,500 lb. Fuel 11,550 gal. max.

PERFORMANCE: Speed—Top 578 mph at 15,000′, Cruising 466 mph, Landing 149 mph. Service Ceiling 37,500′. Range 2650 miles/10,000 lbs. bombs.

BOEING B-47A-BW

General Electric J47-GE-11, 5200 lbs.

DIMENSIONS: Span 116′, Lg. 106′ 9″, Ht. 28′, Wing Area 1428 sq. ft.

WEIGHT:* Empty 73,149 lb., Gross 150,500 lb., Max. 162,500 lb. Fuel 9789 gal.

PERFORMANCE:* (At 104,143 lbs., combat weight) Speed—Top 617 mph at 10,500′, 564 mph at 35,000′, Cruising 486 mph, Landing 144 mph. Service Ceiling 46,100′, Climb 7080′/1 min. Range 3050 miles/10,000 lbs. bombs.

* Estimates made on Oct. '49 Characteristics Chart, actual test data still classified.

MFR

MFR

BOEING B-47B

General Electric J47-GE-23, 5800 lbs.

DIMENSIONS: Span 116′, Lg. 107′ 2″, Ht. 27′ 11″, Wing Area 1428 sq. ft.

WEIGHT: (Approx.) Empty 78,000 lb., Gross 122,000 lb., Max. 185,000 lb. Fuel 10,000–17,000 gal.

PERFORMANCE: (Approx.) Speed—Top Over 630 mph at s. l., 560 mph at 35,000′, Cruising 500 mph, Landing 150 mph. Service Ceiling 45,000′. Range 3870 miles/10,000 lbs. bombs.

MFR

BOEING B-47E (With Bell GAM-63 Rascal missile)

AF

1949, it flew 2289 miles between 32- and 37,000 ft. at an average speed of 608 mph, without armament.

Cautiously, the USAF put the Stratojet into production, while reserving its main funds for the B-36. On October 28, 1948, ten B-47As were ordered at a cost of $37,000,000. New 5200-lb. thrust General Electric J47-GE-11s tested on the prototype in October 1949 were installed in the B-47A, which made its first flight on March 1, 1950. It was similar to the prototype except for elimination of wing slots.

The new weapon received a stimulus from both events and technical development. The North Atlantic Pact provided the U.S. with bases abroad encircling its presumptive enemy, the Korean crisis opened the national purse, and ways were found to extend the Stratojet's range. Production began on 398 B-47B-BWs, which had a pair of huge 1780 gallon drop tanks under the wings, ejection seats, minor changes in the nose and tail, and equipment with which the bomber could be refueled in flight from fat KC-97A Boeing flying tankers. Engines were 5800-lb. thrust J47-GE-23s. The estimated range with 10,000 lbs. of bombs was increased from the about 3000 miles in the B-47A to over 3800 miles.

The first B-47B was flown on April 26, 1952, at the Wichita plant where the B-47As had been built. In order to meet Korean War expansion requirements, plants at Tulsa, Oklahoma, and Marietta, Georgia, were opened under the management of Douglas and Lockheed, and the first Stratojets from these sources were flown in December 1952. Production was slow and expensive getting started, for the Stratojet's construction required machine tools of a size and weight unique even in American production. The wing skin, for example, varied in thickness "from five-eighths of an inch at the butt to three-sixteenths at the tip. . . . The thickest section of B-29 skin by contrast was three-sixteenth of an inch and ran down to only .032 inches."

A four-jet version of the Stratojet originally designated YB-56 was redesignated YB-47C. January 1950 estimates anticipated Allison J35-A-23s of 9700-lb. thrust, a top speed of 633 mph at sea level to 560 mph at 35,000 ft. and a 4800-mile range. Allison J71s were used in later proposals, but the project was not completed.

The XB-47D, a research ship with two 10,000 hp Wright YT49-W-1 turboprops inboard, and two J47 turbojets outboard, was completed in January 1955.

On January 30, 1953, the first B-47E flew with 6000-lb. thrust J47-GE-25 engines and two 20-mm. guns in a General Electric radar tail turret. Hundreds have been built by all three plants in Stratojet production, along with the RB-47E, photoreconnaissance version with a long camera nose. By October 1954, Wichita alone had delivered a thousand B-47s, and this plant completed its contracts in December 1956. The Stratojet was then the standard USAF medium bomber, replacing B-29 and B-50 types. Attacking its targets from altitudes of 40,000 ft., and over ranges extended by flying tankers, its high speed posed a difficult defense problem to any potential opponent.

LIGHT BOMBERS REVIVED

When the Korean War began in 1950, the majority of USAF bombers were B-29 mediums, with three groups of B-50s serving as an interim type until B-47 production got under way. Intercontinental B-36s being delivered added long-range punch to SAC, but for short-range light bombing the only type available was the Douglas B-26 Invader from World War II. Tactical Air Command had no jet bomber for direct support.

Two such projects had been started under the old "Attack" category: Convair's XA-44 and Martin's XA-45. Redesignated XB-53 in 1948, the former was an odd canard design with three J35 jets and a swept forward wing, which was canceled before completion. Two Martin ships were ordered in June 1946, redesignated XB-51, and began flight tests on October 28, 1949. Unique features included variable-incidence on a 35° swept-back drooped wing, a T tail, and tandem dual main wheels with little wingtip stabilizing wells. Two J47-GE-13 jets mounted on pylons below the fuselage were aided by a third in the tail. The pilot sat under a bubble canopy and the navigator was behind him within the fuselage. Eight 20-mm. nose guns with 160 rpg and up to 10,400 lbs. of bombs comprised the armament.

Another two-seat jet bomber of very different design philosophy, the English Electric Canberra, had been flown in Britain on May 13, 1949, and put into production for the Royal Air Force. Although not as fast or well-armed as the XB-51, it had advantages in range and maneuverability, especially at high altitudes. To the surprise of American aviation in general, Martin received in March 1951 a letter of intent ordering the firm into production on the Canberra, designated B-57 in the U.S.

On July 20, 1953, the first Martin B-57A Canberra was flown, powered by two 7200-lb. thrust Wright J65 Sapphires. Like the British original, it had short, wide wings, a pilot's canopy and bomb aimer's nose window, and no guns. Eight B-57A and 67 RB-57A were followed by the B-57B which had both crew members under a single canopy, eight .50-caliber wing guns, and up to sixteen rockets. Martin Canberras had a rotary bomb bay, tested on the XB-51, and drop tanks.

These B-57B night intruders, first flown June 28, 1954, comprised most of the 403 Martin Model 272s built, but the RB-57A reconnaissance variants, and some B-57C trainers, RB-57D high-altitude reconnaissance single seaters (with a new 103 ft. 6 in. wing and J57-P-5s), and B-57E target tugs were included.

The next Air Force tactical bomber was also adopted from another organization. Douglas' A3D Skywarrior was designed as a carrier-based twin-jet bomber, but on February 15, 1952, the Air Force decided to purchase the type, designating it as the B-66. By May 1953 a TAC version with different engines and equipment had an engineering release for production at Long Beach. First flown on June 28, 1954, the RB-66A is a three-place high-wing monoplane with two Allison J71-A-11s beneath swept 36° wings. The first five ships were RB-66A-DLs, followed by the B-66B-DL flown January 4, 1955. Tulsa's Douglas plant flew its first RB-66C on October 28, 1955, and the five-place B-66D on May 27, 1957. By June 1958 production was completed, and 209 Destroyers of all versions had been delivered.

A radar bombing system was installed in the nose, and radar aimed the two 20-mm. guns in the General

MARTIN XB-51
General Electric J47-GE-13, 5200 lbs.
DIMENSIONS: Span 53′ 1″, Lg. 85′ 1″, Ht. 17′ 4″, Wing Area 548 sq. ft.
WEIGHT: Empty 29,584 lb., Gross 55,923 lb., Max. 62,457 lb. Fuel 2835–3535 gal.
PERFORMANCE: (At 41,457 lbs., combat weight) Speed—Top 645 mph at s. l., Cruising 532 mph. Landing 153 mph. Service Ceiling 40,500′, Climb 6980′/1 min. Range 1075 miles normal, 1613 miles max.

AF

MARTIN B-57A
Wright J65-W-5, 7200 lbs.
DIMENSIONS: Span 64′, Lg. 65′ 6″, Ht. 15′ 7″, Wing Area 960 sq. ft.
WEIGHT: Gross 47,000 lb., Max. 51,000 lb.
PERFORMANCE: Speed—Top 582 mph at 40,000′, 520 mph at s. l. Service Ceiling 48,000′, Climb 3500′/1 min. Range 2300 miles normal, 2650 miles max.

MFR

MFR

Electric tail turret. Since this turret is similar to those used in the B-47 and B-36, a description of its function by the General Electric Company is of interest. Things have changed since the days when the bomber gunner used brute strength to swing Lewis guns against the slip stream, and guessed at leading his target, or peered through the night for the glow of enemy exhaust pipes. Today, the gunner sits comfortably within the fuselage aiming power operated guns with electronics. When the bomber enters a danger area,

> . . . the gunner switches the radar to "search" and adjusts the system control panel to provide the computer with air temperature, altitude and air speed information.
>
> When the radar picks up an attacking plane, a bright spot shows on the screen. By means of a control handle, the gunner easily moves the radar antenna until it is centered on the target. Once the target is "acquired" and the radar is "locked on," the target is tracked automatically.
>
> Radar then supplies the computer with the position and range of the attacking plane. Necessary gun deflections and corrections are computed automatically. When the hostile aircraft enters gun range, the gunner presses a trigger which fires the guns electrically.

MARTIN B-57B
Wright J65-W-5, 7200 lbs.
DIMENSIONS: As B-57A
WEIGHT: Gross 49,000 lb., Max. 55,000 lb.
PERFORMANCE: As B-57A.

DOUGLAS B-66B
Allison J71-A-11, 10,000 lbs.
DIMENSIONS: Span 72′ 6″, Lg. 75′ 2″, Ht. 23′ 7″, Wing Area 780 sq. ft.
WEIGHT: Empty 42,086 lb., Gross 78,000 lb., Max. 83,000 lb. Fuel 4650 gal.
PERFORMANCE: Classified.

PMB

AF

H-BOMBERS

"The most formidable expression of air power in the history of military aviation" said Air Force Secretary Donald A. Quarles of the B-52. "Its range, which can be augmented by refueling techniques, its bomb load, its highly skilled crews, coupled with electronic equipment which makes it possible to find and hit any target

BOEING XB-52 (below) and YB-52 (above)
Pratt & Whitney J57-P-3, 9000 lbs.
DIMENSIONS: Span 185′, Lg. 153′, Ht. 48′ 4″, Wing Area 4000 sq. ft.
WEIGHT: (Approx.) Empty 155,000 lb., Max. 390,000 lb. Fuel 38,270 gal.
PERFORMANCE: (Approx., at 256,000 lbs., combat weight) Speed—Top Over 600 mph, Cruising 525 mph, Landing 145 mph. Service Ceiling 50,000′, Climb 2400′/1 min. Range 7000 miles/10,000 lbs. bombs.

MFR

anywhere in the world in any weather, constitute a weapons system which no other nation can match."

This estimate was made of the bomber which is the center of contemporary American air strategy, and whose development was accompanied by appearance of one of the most significant weapons to appear in man's history: the hydrogen bomb. The world's first thermonuclear explosion was at Eniwetok on November 2, 1952, the first bombs were exploded on August 12, 1953, by Russia and on March 1, 1954, by the United States, and the hydrogen bomb was mated with the airplane when one was dropped from a B-52 in May 1956.

The plane had a history longer than that of the bomb, for it began with a specification issued by the Air Force in January 1946 for an intercontinental bomber. Boeing answered with a 180-ton project incorporating six 5500 hp Wright T-35 turboprops on a straight wing. A design contract was awarded in June 1946, and engineers began another struggle to combine long range with speed. Two XB-52 prototypes were ordered in July 1948, with the turboprops and 20° sweep back, but, in September, Pratt & Whitney's XJ-57 engine seemed to offer a new chance at higher speeds. The present B-52 configuration with eight J-57s suspended on pods below a wing swept back 35° was accepted October 27, 1948. After mockup approval in April 1949, construction of the prototypes proceeded at a cost that finally reached $53,000,000.

MFR

BOEING B-52A
Pratt & Whitney J57-P-3
DIMENSIONS: Span 185′, Lg. 152′ 7″, Ht. 48′ 3″, Wing Area 4000 sq. ft.
WEIGHT & PERFORMANCE: Classified.

BOEING B-52B
Pratt & Whitney J57-P-19W
DIMENSIONS: Span 185′, Lg. 157′ 7″, Wing Area 4000 sq. ft.
WEIGHT: Max. 400,000 lb.
PERFORMANCE: Classified.

MFR

Meanwhile, Boeing studied other bomber projects, including the XB-55 of 1949 with four Westinghouse J-40 jets and four Allison T-40 turboprops, and an XB-59 jet stillborn in 1953. But the B-52 required most of Boeing's engineering effort. The first flight on April 15, 1952, at Seattle was actually made by the second prototype, YB-52, which was similar in appearance to the XB-52 flown October 2, 1952. Eight J57-P-3s of 9700-lb. thrust, eight main wheels retracting into the fuselage, small outrigger wheels at wingtips, and a tall fin folding for storage were featured. A canopy over tandem pilot and co-pilot, and the tail turret for gunner and two .50-caliber guns distinguished the prototypes from production models.

Production models ordered from Seattle in February 1951 were first flown on August 5, 1954, just as the last B-36 was being completed. They had the pilot and co-pilot side by side in the nose, a socket to receive aerial refueling, and 10,000-lb. thrust J57-P-9Ws. Three B-52As were followed by the RB-52B, whose bomb bay could hold exchangeable capsules with camera or radar countermeasures equipment. Some 500 Stratofortresses were ordered, and in 1956 the B-52C-BO and B-52D-BW were delivered from Boeing's Seattle and Wichita plants, respectively. These models had larger external drop tanks and four .50-caliber guns in an Arma tail turret utilized both optical and radar tracking, as well as an additional radar for search.

The crew of six guided their bomber to the target aided by a 1457-lb., $300,000, MA-2 BRANE (Bombing Radar Navigation Equipment) produced by International Business Machines Corporation, which replaced the Sperry K system used on early models. More than half of the Stratofortress' 200 tons of take-off weight consists of fuel. Over 60 tons of this fuel may be consumed before the B-52 reaches the target area, and the decrease in weight causes an improvement in speed and ceiling capabilities. Even without air refueling, the range is high enough to make the B-52 a satisfactory B-36 replacement.

With the B-52C-BO, appearing in March 1956, the Seattle contract was completed. Production began at Wichita with the similar B-52D-BW of September 1956, followed by the B-52E in October 1957 with improved electronics and the B-52F in June 1958 with the J57-P-43.

Even the most advanced bomber is endangered by surface-to-air missiles and interceptors, and the most likely new method of attack seems to be the "stand-off bomb"; an air-to-surface missile that could be launched by the bomber at a distance from the target. A 32 ft., rocket-propelled radar-command missile, the Bell GAM-63 could be launched from a B-47 over 75 miles away from the target. A range of "several hundred miles" was promised for North American GAM-77, Hound Dog, a 40 ft., turbo-jet propelled missile with guidance.

First USAF bomber designed to use air-to-surface missiles as its primary armament, the Boeing B-52G carried two GAM-77s on under-wing pylons, in addition to bombs in the internal weapons bays. Powered by J57-P-43W jets of 11,200–13,750 lbs. thrust, the B-52G first flew on October 26, 1958, and on April 23, 1959, Hound Dog was successfully launched. The B-52G also differed from the preceding 358 Stratofortresses by a shorter tailfin, more internal fuel, and a remote-controlled tail turret, the gunner having been moved forward.

Yet another version of this type was prepared in the B-52H, which is to have Pratt & Whitney TF-33-P-1 turbo-fan engines. Orders for this type brought B-52 contract totals by 1960 to 704 aircraft, with 14 SAC wings scheduled to receive the type.

Convair tried to lengthen the life of its own big ship with the B-36G proposal, having eight J57-P-3s, swept-wings and tail, modified landing gear, reduced armament and increased fuel. Since about 72 per cent of the parts were identical with those in the B-36, early and economical production was likely, and on March 15, 1951, in the tension induced by the Korean conflicts, two prototypes were ordered. They were redesignated YB-60 and flight tests began on April 18, 1952. Comparative flight tests showed performance to be inferior to that of the B-52, and relaxation of the international situation made authorities willing to await production deliveries of the Boeing ship. The YB-60 prototypes were used only for research and had a needle nose with test instruments replacing the bombardier's windows.

Convair engineers concentrated their efforts on the Air Force's first supersonic bomber, the B-58 Hustler. Planned at Fort Worth as a complete weapons system, the project has had an uncertain status since it was begun in 1951. On October 13, 1954, the AAF ordered thirteen B-58 prototypes, but debates continued at high level until high priority was given. First flown on November 11, 1956, the three-place medium bomber featured conical-cambered delta wings, area-ruled geometry, and four J79 turbo-jets in pods below the wings. Afterburners were fitted to increase thrust per engine from a reported 12,000- to 16,000-lbs. thrust (exact figures classified at this writing). A high stilted landing gear gave clearance for any one of a choice of exchangeable pods containing fuel, bombing, photo-reconnaissance, missile or bomber defense systems.

Navigation and bombing from a 1000 mph aircraft presents unusual problems, which on the B-58 are solved by a Sperry (AN/ASQ-42) system which used active radar navigation during a mission's approach phase, with inertial and star-tracking methods while over enemy territory. Weighing 1948 lbs., the system uses an analog computer receiving data from search radar in the nose, an astro-star-tracker amidships, a doppler radar in the tail, inertial sensors, and radio altimeter. Sitting at his console behind the pilot, the bombardier-navigator is provided with continuous and precise information on aircraft position, heading, ground speed, altitude, steering data, and distance to target, as well as ballistic computations for weapons release.

Third crewman is the defense systems operator, who is seated behind the navigator with controls for the warning radar and 20 mm. T-171 Vulcan (radar-

BOEING B-52C

MFR

CONVAIR YB-60
Pratt & Whitney J57-P-3, 9000 lbs.
DIMENSIONS: Span 206′, Lg. 171′, Ht. 60′ 9″
WEIGHT & PERFORMANCE: Classified.

MFR

CONVAIR XB-58
General Electric J79-GE-1, 10,500 lbs. (16,000 lbs. AB)
DIMENSIONS: Span 56′ 10″, Lg. 96′ 9″, Ht. 31′ 5″, Wing Area 1542 sq. ft.
WEIGHT & PERFORMANCE: Classified.

MFR

aimed and firing some 6000 rounds per minute) in the tail, and a choice of electronic countermeasures for enemy radar and missiles.

The first 30 Hustlers were built as test ships, but 13 were to be modified to the B-58A tactical configuration. The first of 36 B-58As purchased with fiscal 1959 funds was flown in September 1959.

Despite the very advanced 1000 mph-plus performance of the Hustler, only 86 were on order at the time this is being written. Hesitancy in putting the B-58 into production was due less to the plane itself than to uncertainty about the extent to which guided missiles can replace bombers as the striking force of future airpower. Should future production funds be allotted to aircraft or to missiles?

In 1951, bomber designations were given to five guided missiles then at various stages of development: the Martin B-61 Matador short-range tactical missile, Northrop B-62 Snark long-range strategic missile, Bell B-63 Rascal air-to-surface parasite (carried on a bomber to within 100 miles of target), North American B-64 Navaho long-range supersonic missile, and the Convair B-65 Atlas intercontinental ballistics missile, a multistage rocket. All of the projects were redesignated according to a standardized missile nomenclature system, fortunately, so as not to be confused with piloted aircraft.

Pilotless aircraft are outside the scope of this study, and security considerations rule out any meaningful history of their development, but their appearance does suggest that a decline in the importance of piloted combat aircraft is in sight. Perfection of efficient guidance systems may mean that air crews will be unnecessary for future air bombardment of fixed targets.

At this writing only one new bomber project is under construction, and that was limited to a prototype contract. North American's B-70 will have six General Electric J93-GE-3 jets in the rear mounted in a pack under a delta wing, a canard horizontal control surface, and a crew of four. Performance may include Mach 3 speeds.

Chapter 13: Summary

The bomber has compressed into the last forty years a history of great importance to America. It began as an imitation of a fabric-covered biplane pattern established in Europe, and its limited capabilities were disdained by conservative national policymakers. In biplane form, bombers could not supplant warships as an influence on international power struggles, and their unrealized potential threatened a form of war unacceptable to that period's chivalry. The bomber's most outspoken advocate was dismissed for criticizing elder military leadership.

A technical revolution in aircraft design, after some hesitancy, replaced the older bombers with all-metal monoplanes offering much greater performance. Their appearance coincided with rising fascist aggression, but the B-17, most advanced example of the new weapon, was at first thought too expensive for mass production.

The Munich crisis convinced American leadership of the importance of the air weapon, and an air force was begun and continued until the American Air Force became the largest in history. A war plan was prepared that centered on the long-range bomber as the major weapon, and equipment to accomplish this strategy was produced.

The growing expense and difficulty of producing aircraft of the required performance, temporarily seemed to give superiority with offensive air weapons an exclusive, national character; it appeared that only the United States had the financial reserves, industrial capacity, and scientific knowledge to build an air fleet of the size and power required to defeat major nations by strategic bombardment. Geography so sheltered the nation itself that no hostile bomber ever crossed U.S. continental territory.

Advances in technique gave bombers a growing range, and atomic weapons multiplied the effect of their blows. At war's end, it appeared that offensive air weapons could be the power behind a national policy which assumed that U.S. world leadership was upheld by the ability to deliver atomic bombs to any place in the world. Although moral objection to aerial bombardment had vanished as an element of U.S. policy, the high cost of air weapons tended to delay full acceptance of the recommended air program. Criticism of U.S. policies was frequently combined with skepticism of the omnipotence of the air offensive.

Today, development of the hydrogen bomb has added new fears of air warfare and Soviet technical progress now suggests that strategic bombing may be as much of a threat to America as to her enemies. Attention must now be given to air defense capabilities of stopping a fatal bomber attack.

The next section of this book deals with fighters, the best weapons until now for meeting an airborne offensive. In this field, America had not always maintained the superiority displayed by her bombers, perhaps because geography hasn't made interception the necessity it was for Britain. But air defense is now a vital national requirement, and will continue to be.

Since the 94 mph speed and 7400 ft. ceiling of the Handley-Page, the piloted bomber has increased its speed and altitude more than tenfold and the 550-mile range has been multiplied by more than twelvefold. Today's bombs and guns are aimed by electronics, and the ton of TNT released in 1918 is puny compared to today's thermonuclear weapon. Forty years of piloted bomber progress has changed the entire picture of international relations.

Development of electronic controls may some day enable guided missiles to replace piloted aircraft for attacks on large fixed targets, but until that time, strategic bombing capabilities are the decisive weight in the balance of military power.

Part 4 Fighters for the Air Force

Chapter 14: The First Fighter Planes 1915–18

THE GUN AND THE PLANE

In the beginning, aerial warfare was leisurely and unspectacular. A routine of trips across the lines for scouting and artillery spotting was only occasionally interrupted by picayune bombing raids. The first attack by one aircraft upon another has not been definitely recorded, but there were awkward engagements between reconnaissance pilots who fired pistols, rifles, and crudely mounted machine guns. A French authority claims the first aerial victory was that of a Voisin over a German Taube on October 14, 1914.

In any case, machine guns were difficult to mount effectively, especially on the more efficient tractor planes,[1] and fighting was limited. In December 1914, a Frenchman fired his machine gun forward through the propeller of his Morane scout. Metal deflector plates on the wooden propeller threw off the tenth of the bullets that struck the blades. The device worked to some extent, but ruined propeller efficiency and tossed ricochets in all directions.

After five victories, engine failure caused capture of the Morane by Germans. They invited Dutch designer Anthony Fokker to suggest improvements. Fokker, working for Germany because the Allies had refused his price, took only 48 hours to invent a satisfactory synchronization gear. A synchronized gun was fitted on a Fokker monoplane which the Germans asked Fokker to demonstrate by shooting down a French plane. Protesting neutrality, Fokker was persuaded into a uniform, and took off in one of his planes. He actually swooped down on a defenseless French pusher's tail, lined up his sights and abruptly changed his mind. "Suddenly I decided that the whole job could go to hell. It was too much like 'cold meat' . . . Let them do their own killing!"

In July 1915, Oswald Boelcke took the Fokker up and began a massacre of Allied planes. As a short-range single-seater, it was lighter and therefore faster than the two-seater scouts. The Fokker's agility and its gun soon turned 72 mph scout planes like the BE-2c, "a delightful touring machine," into "Fokker Fodder." Pursuit, or fighter aviation had been born.

Eventually, of course, answers to this weapon were made, even before the Allies got synchronization gear. The Scarff ring enabled the two-seater observer to turn his Lewis gun in any direction not obstructed by his own aircraft. Pusher fighters like the DH-2 could carry a Lewis gun in the bow, although they did not match the Fokker's speed. The first really successful Allied pursuit was the Nieuport 11 of 1915, a tractor biplane single-seater with a Lewis gun on the upper wing, firing above the propeller. In the summer of 1916 appeared Nieuport, Spad, and Sopwith fighters with a single synchronized gun. By 1917, two-gun armament was standard, and remained so for nearly two decades.

Thus, long before America's entrance into the First World War, mating synchronized guns with fast single-seaters had produced fighters, upon whose success also rested the possibility of using both the reconnaissance and bombardment capabilities of air power. The fighter was the essential and only possible weapon to win control of the air.

Nevertheless, no American-built fighter existed when the A.E.F. went to France, so our first fighter squadrons had to use French and British machines. All of these reflected conventional design ideas, being single-seat tractor biplanes of wood and fabric construction generously braced with struts and wires. Although both monoplane and triplane designs also saw much action during the war, none were used by the A.E.F.

The first fighters flown into battle by Americans were the Nieuport 11s of the Lafayette Escadrille's volunteers, who had preceded to France both the A.E.F. and U.S. declaration of war. On April 20, 1916,

[1] Tractor planes have their propellers facing frontward while pusher propellers face rearward.

the Escadrille flew its first sorties in the Nieuports, which had already become famous as the first Allied "*chasse*" plane to meet the challenge of the Fokker's synchronized gun.

Because of this plane's historical significance as the first designed-for-the-purpose Allied fighter, we quote its specifications as a starting point for measurement of fighter progress. For after all, although it was never owned or operated by a U.S. organization, it was the mount of the first American fighting pilots.

The Nieuport 11 biplane had only an 80 hp Le Rhone rotary, and was small enough to achieve a 97 mph top speed! Armament was a Lewis gun mounted on the top wing with 47 rounds of ammunition to fire over the propeller. In August 1916, the Escadrille was re-equipped with the slightly larger Nieuport 17 which had a synchronized Vickers cowl gun, a 110 hp Le Rhone, and a 107 mph top speed. Having no throttle, Nieuports hardly had a "cruising speed," but ran on full throttle, unless ignition in some cylinders was suppressed. Nieuport fighters of this period were characterized by a narrow lower wing supporting with Vee struts a larger high wing. Models 21, 23, 24, and 27 were similar to the 17 but for minor changes in the tail, wingtips, and engine.

PMB

NIEUPORT 11
Gnome "A", 80 hp
DIMENSIONS: Span 24′ 6″, Lg. 19′, Ht. 8′, Wing Area 140 sq. ft.
WEIGHT: Empty 759 lb., Gross 1210 lb. Fuel 21 gal.
PERFORMANCE: Speed—Top 97 mph at s. l., Landing 30 mph. Service Ceiling 15,000′, Climb 3300′/5 min. Endurance 2 hrs.

FIGHTERS OF THE A.E.F.

After the A.E.F. arrived in France, it trained its fighter pilots on the Nieuports 17, 21, 23, 24, and 27, but fortunately never had to use these underpowered models in combat. When Army fliers shot down their first enemy Albatros on April 14, 1918, a year after we came into the war, they used the heavier Nieuport 28. The U.S. received 297 of these biplanes with the 170 hp Gnome 9N, two Vickers guns on the cowl's left side, and a pair of vertical struts on each wing.

Four A.E.F. squadrons used Nieuports until July 1918, when they were replaced by the famous Spads, which did not shed their wings as easily as did their predecessors. The Spad was a husky, double-bay biplane[2] with good lines from the nose radiator to the scalloped tail. It had been first flown by the French in July 1916 as the Spad 7 with a 180 hp Hispano-Suiza 8Aa and one synchronized Vickers. From December 1917 on, the A.E.F. received 189 Spad 7s, but did not use them in combat because the more powerful Spad 13 had appeared at the front in August 1917 and was chosen for American fliers.

Fifteen of the 16 A.E.F. pursuit squadrons by war's end used Spad 13s, which had a 235 hp Hispano 8BEc and two Vickers or Marlin guns. Strong and heavy, it was the best diver of the war, and among the fastest

[2] A single-bay biplane has one set of struts on each side; a double-bay biplane has two.

ARC

NIEUPORT 17
LeRhone 9J, 110 hp
DIMENSIONS: Span 27′, Lg. 19′ 6″, Ht. 7′, Wing Area 159 sq. ft.
WEIGHT: Empty 825 lb., Gross 1233 lb. Fuel 21 gal.
PERFORMANCE: Speed—Top 107 mph at 6500′. Service Ceiling 17,400′, Climb 6500′/5.5 min. Endurance 2 hrs.

AF—PMB

NIEUPORT 28
Gnome 9N, 155 hp
DIMENSIONS: Span 26′ 9″, Lg. 21′, Ht. 8′ 1″, Wing Area 172 sq. ft.
WEIGHT: Empty 961 lb., Gross 1539 lb. Fuel 53 gal.
PERFORMANCE: Speed—Top 128 mph at s. l. Service Ceiling 19,685′. Endurance 2 hrs.

AF

SPAD 13
Hispano-Suiza 8BEc, 235 hp. (Wright-Hispano 8Ba, 220 hp on U.S.A. test)
DIMENSIONS: Span 26′ 4″, Lg. 20′ 4″, Ht. 7′ 6″, Wing Area 227 sq. ft.
WEIGHT: Empty 1255 lb. (1464 lb.), Gross 1811 lb. (2036 lb.). Fuel 30 gal.
PERFORMANCE: Speed—Top 138.5 (131.5) mph at s. l., 135 (128) mph at 6500′, Cruising (124.5 mph), Landing 59 mph. Service Ceiling 22,300′ (18,400′), Climb 6500′/4.7 min. (6.5 min.). Endurance 2.5 hrs.

AF—PMB

SOPWITH CAMEL F-1
Clerget 9-Bc, 130 hp
DIMENSIONS: Span 28′, Lg. 18′ 8″, Ht. 8′ 6″, Wing Area 231 sq. ft.
WEIGHT: Empty 929 lb., Gross 1453 lb. Fuel 31.5 gal.
PERFORMANCE: Speed—Top 113 mph at 6500′, 106.5 mph at 10,000′. Service Ceiling 19,000′, Climb 6500′/6 min. Range 300 miles. Endurance 2.5 hrs.

types. Of 893 acquired after February 1918, 435 were shipped to the U.S. after the Armistice, and often re-engined with the U.S.-built Wright-Hispano of 220 hp.

At the same time the French had introduced the Spad 13, they had tested in small quantities the similar Spad 12, incorporating the first cannon on a single-seat fighter. Armament consisted of one Vickers .303 machine gun, and a 37-mm. cannon mounted to fire through the propeller shaft of a geared 220 hp Hispano 8C. Fourteen rounds of ammunition were carried for the single-shot, hand-loaded cannon. The French ace Captain René Fonck downed seven Germans with the experimental weapon, but felt hand-loading an inconvenient distraction. A single example of the Spad 12 went to the Americans in July 1918.

In addition to these French planes, three types were purchased from the British government. Introduced in July 1917, the Sopwith Camel ran up the highest score of enemy planes downed of any wartime type. This maneuverable single-bay biplane was powered by a

PMB

SOPWITH DOLPHIN
Hispano 8-B, 210 hp
DIMENSIONS: Span 32′ 6″, Lg. 22′ 3″, Ht. 8′ 6″, Wing Area 262 sq. ft.
WEIGHT: Empty 1391 lb., Gross 2000 lb. Fuel 27 gal.
PERFORMANCE: Speed—Top 131.5 mph at 6500′, 128.5 mph at 10,000′, Landing 40 mph. Service Ceiling 21,000′, Climb 6500′/6.4 min. Range 230 miles. Endurance 2¼ hrs.

130 hp Clerget 9B rotary, had two Vickers guns, and was tricky and dangerous to fly. An A.E.F. squadron often assigned to night work got Camel pilots who had survived the training course, and 143 Camels were received after June 1918.

Less tricky was the Royal Aircraft Factory's S.E.5, appearing at the front in April 1917 with a 15 hp Hispano. A 210 hp Hispano 8B powered 38 S.E.5As issued to an A.E.F. squadron in August 1918. They were single-bay biplanes with a nose radiator, two Vickers, or one cowl Vickers and one Lewis gun on the upper wing.

Five Sopwith Dolphins went to the Air Service in October 1918. Used by the British since January, they were double-bay biplanes with back stagger and a cut-out in the upper wing for the pilot's head. Two Lewis guns were attached to the front spar there, in addition to twin Vickers on the cowl. Radiators on each side behind the cockpit cooled the 210 hp Hispano.

NATIVE SINGLE-SEATERS

No American-designed single-seat fighters were delivered during the nineteen months of war. Although several low-powered single-seaters were produced, such as the Curtiss S-3, Standard E-1, Heinrich "Pursuit," Thomas-Morse S-4, and Orenco C, all were unarmed trainers. American design of fighters was officially foregone in favor of tested foreign types.

Attempts to produce foreign-designed fighters also failed. A sample Spad was received from France in September 1917, and a contract for 3000 copies was placed with Curtiss. The contract was canceled the following month, as the airframe seemed inadequate for the more powerful Liberty engine then planned for Army standardization. Several months were lost searching for a Liberty-powered fighter. When it failed to materialize by April 1918, Curtiss was again asked to build fighters; this time 1000 S.E.5As. By then it was too late for any to be delivered in time for action.

Part of this delay was due to inability to decide which foreign type to produce here, and a story told by Grover Loening illustrates the rivalry of Allied air missions on behalf of their own designs. One day at Dayton, when a British general stood before a sample S.E.5 telling of its merits, the captain of the French mission swaggered up with his walking stick asking, "Have you heard of that prehistoric bird, the pterodactyl?" Then, shrugging his shoulders at the squarish S.E.5, "Must have been of British design." His own Spad was then rolled out to show its more graceful lines.

Rivalry among airplane designs continues, with favorites being chosen on the basis of esthetic appeal, performance characteristics, the "feel" of the type to its pilots, economy, and just plain prejudice.

Only one Curtiss S.E.5A was finished. Delivered in August 1918, it used the 180 hp Wright-Hispano E, although by then machines at the front had 210 hp. Fifty-six other S.E.5s were assembled from British parts by Curtiss, who built enough spare parts for Eberhardt in 1922 to assemble 50 more. All used the 180 hp engine.

Not until after the Armistice did completed fighters of U.S. design appear. First was the Orenco D of January 1919. Four were built by the Ordnance Engineering Corporation from an Army Engineering Division design. Powered by a 300 hp Wright-Hispano H,

AMC

ROYAL AIRCRAFT FACTORY S.E.5A
Hispano 8-B, 210 hp
DIMENSIONS: Span 26′ 8″, Lg. 20′ 11″, Ht. 9′ 6″, Wing Area 247 sq. ft.
WEIGHT: Empty 1531 lb., Gross 2048 lb. Fuel 35 gal.
PERFORMANCE: Speed—Top 128 mph at 6800′, 113.4 mph at 10,000′. Absolute Ceiling 19,500′, Climb 1175′/1 min. Endurance 2.5 hrs.

PMB

CURTISS S.E.5 (U.S. markings)
Wright-Hispano E, 180 hp
DIMENSIONS: Span 26′ 9″, Lg. 20′ 10″, Ht. 10′, Wing Area 247 sq. ft.
WEIGHT: Empty 1486 lb., Gross 2060 lb. Fuel 35 gal.
PERFORMANCE: Speed—Top 122 mph at s. l., 120 mph at 6500′. Service Ceiling 20,400′, Climb 6500′/8 min. Range 280 miles at top speed.

AMC

ORENCO D PROTOTYPE
Hispano-Suiza H, 300 hp
DIMENSIONS: Span 30′, Lg. 21′ 6″, Ht. 7′ 9″, Wing Area 261 sq. ft.
WEIGHT: Empty 1776 lb., Gross 2432 lb. Fuel 55 gal.
PERFORMANCE: Speed—Top 147 mph at s. l., 143 mph at 5000′, Cruising 139 mph, Landing 56 mph. Service Ceiling 22,000′, Absolute Ceiling 23,600′, Climb 6500′/5.2 min. Endurance 2.5 hrs. at 139 mph.

this double-bay biplane somewhat resembled the Spad. Fifty heavier production models were ordered from Curtiss and delivery began in August 1921.

On February 21, 1919, the Thomas-Morse MB-3 with a 340 hp Wright-Hispano made its first flight. Four prototypes were followed in 1920 by fifty production models of good performance. At that time, military designs were Army property, and bidding on a further contract was open to all firms. Boeing far underbid Aero Marine, Curtiss, Dayton-Wright, LWF, and Thomas-Morse itself in February 1922 and won $1,448,000 for 200 MB-3As, largest pursuit contract awarded until 1937.

AMC

CURTISS-ORENCO D
Wright H, 330 hp
DIMENSIONS: Span 33′, Lg. 21′ 5½″, Ht. 8′ 4″, Wing Area 273 sq. ft.
WEIGHT: Empty 1908 lb., Gross 2820 lb. Fuel 53 gal.
PERFORMANCE: Speed—Top 139.5 mph at s. l., 136 mph at 6500′, Cruising 133.5 mph, Landing 64.5 mph. Service Ceiling 18,450′, Absolute Ceiling 20,250′, Climb 1140′/1 min., 6500′/6.9 min. Endurance 2.5 hrs.

Delivered between July and December 1922, the MB-3A differed from the original in many details. Its radiator was moved from the upper wing, split, and placed on each side of the fuselage. The vertical fin was redesigned. While the MB-3s two .30-caliber guns had been exposed, the MB-3As Brownings were under a fairing. One of the .30s could be replaced by a .50-caliber gun when desired, an arrangement standard on Army fighters up to the Second World War. Although performance of the MB-3A was good, visibility was hampered by the upper wing. In March 1923, one was fitted with a 37-gallon belly fuel tank, the first in the U.S., which extended the range to 400 miles. The MB-3A remained the standard Army fighter until replaced by Curtiss Hawks about five years later.

Two other single-seat fighters of 1919 failed to win production contracts. The Pomilo Bros. FVL-8 was a single-bay biplane based on an Italian design with the lower wing hung below the fuselage. Six were built and first delivered in February. A four-bladed propeller was driven by a 290 hp Liberty 8, smaller edition of the more famous Liberty 12. First of four Lewis and Vought VE-8 fighters appeared in July 1919. This was a conventional-looking double-bay biplane powered by a 300 hp Wright-Hispano H. Few FVL-8 or VE-8 details are available.

TWO-SEAT FIGHTERS

Actually, the American aircraft industry had more luck during the First World War with two-seat fighter designs than with single-seaters. Several prototypes were flown in 1918.

These designs found their main inspiration in England's Bristol Fighter, a double-bay biplane with a

AMC

THOMAS-MORSE MB-3 (2nd prototype)
Hispano H, 300 hp
DIMENSIONS: Span 26′, Lg. 20′, Ht. 8′ 6″, Wing Area 250.5 sq. ft.
WEIGHT: Empty 1506 lb., Gross 2094 lb. Fuel 41 gal.
PERFORMANCE: Speed—Top 152 mph at s. l., 148 mph at 6500′, Cruising 144 mph, Landing 58 mph. Service Ceiling 23,700′, Absolute Ceiling 24,900′, Climb 1930′/1 min., 6500′/3.9 min. Range 288 miles.

275 hp Rolls-Royce engine, pilot and gunner back to back, and fuselage suspended between the wings. It went to war in April 1917 with two fixed Vickers guns and two flexible Lewis guns, and had excellent maneuverability which made the Bristol quite successful against enemy fighters. The combination of the front guns with the rear guns for tail protection helped Canadian ace Major Andrew E. McKeever win thirty victories and established the two-seater biplane as a standard fighter type.

A sample Bristol was shipped to the U.S. in August 1917, and 2000 were ordered in September from Curtiss. The Curtiss-Bristol appeared in April 1918 with

AMC

THOMAS-MORSE MB-3 (2nd prototype)

a 400 hp Liberty 12. One crash followed another, for this engine proved too much for the airframe, and the contract was canceled in July after 27 were built. The Curtiss-Bristol weighed 3600 lbs., over a thousand pounds heavier than its British prototype.

On the Fourth of July 1918, the Army's Engineering Division began tests on a Bristol known as the USB-1 with the lighter 300 hp Hispano H, and weighing 2910 lbs. Two Marlin nose guns and two Lewis rear guns were carried. Another Bristol was finished the following month with a 290 hp Liberty 8, known as

BOEING MB-3A
Wright H-3, 300 hp
DIMENSIONS: Span 26′, Lg. 20′, Ht. 8′ 7″, Wing Area 229 sq. ft.
WEIGHT: Empty 1716 lb., Gross 2539 lb. Fuel 45 gal.
PERFORMANCE: Speed—Top 141 mph at s. l., 138 mph at 6500′, Cruising 125 mph, Landing 55 mph. Service Ceiling 19,500′, Absolute Ceiling 21,200′, Climb 1235′/1 min., 6500′/6.7 min. Endurance 2 hrs. 15 min.

AF

AMC

POMILIO FVL-8
Liberty 8, 290 hp
DIMENSIONS: Span 26′ 8″, Lg. 21′ 8″, Ht. 8′ 2″, Wing Area 284 sq. ft.
WEIGHT: Empty 1726 lb., Gross 2284 lb. Fuel 40 gal.
PERFORMANCE: Speed—Top 133 mph at s. l.

AMC

VOUGHT VE-8
Wright-Hispano H, 300 hp
DIMENSIONS: Span 31′, Lg. 21′ 4″, Ht. 8′ 8″, Wing Area 307 sq. ft.
WEIGHT: Empty 1638 lb., Gross 2435 lb.
PERFORMANCE: Speed—Top 137 mph at s. l. (est.). Service Ceiling 23,800′, Climb 6500′/4.2 min.

MFR

CURTISS-BRISTOL FIGHTER (LIBERTY 12)

ENGINEERING DIV. USB-1 [*Photo unavailable*]
Hispano H, 300 hp
DIMENSIONS: Span 39′ 4″, Lg. 25′ 5″, Ht. 8′ 3″, Wing Area 403 sq. ft.
WEIGHT: Empty 1842 lb., Gross 2910 lb. Fuel 53 gal.
PERFORMANCE: Speed—Top 114.5 mph at s. l. "Theoretical Ceiling" 25,000′, Climb 6500′/3.5 min.

AMC

ENGINEERING DIV. XB-1A
Wright-Hispano H, 300 hp
DIMENSIONS: Span 39′ 4″, Lg. 25′ 6″, Ht. 9′ 9″, Wing Area 406 sq. ft.
WEIGHT: Empty 2010 lb., Gross 2994 lb. Fuel 54 gal.
PERFORMANCE: Speed—Top 124 mph at s. l., 121 mph at 6500′, Cruising 118 mph, Landing 59 mph. Service Ceiling 20,900′, Climb 6500′/7.8 min. Endurance 2.4 hrs.

AMC

DAYTON-WRIGHT XB-1A
Wright-Hispano H, 330 hp
DIMENSIONS: Span 39′ 4″, Lg. 25′ 6″, Ht. 9′ 10″, Wing Area 406 sq. ft.
WEIGHT: Empty 2155 lb., Gross 3791 lb.
PERFORMANCE: Speed—Top 130 mph, Cruising 101 mph. Service Ceiling 18,900′, Absolute Ceiling 21,000′, Climb 6500′/7.5 min. Range 495 miles at 125 mph.

the USB-2. The USB-1 proved workable and was followed in July 1919 by four similar Engineering Division XB-1A models. Forty more, with added fuel, equipment, and leakproof tanks, were ordered in June 1920 from Dayton-Wright. They were delivered in 1921 with the 330 hp Hispano, and finally rated as observation types. One was tested with a 350 hp Packard 1A-1237.

LePere, a French engineer loaned by his government, designed around the 425 hp Liberty 12 an excellent fighter which appeared in September 1918. Thirty Packard-LePere LUSAC-11s were built, followed in January 1919 by three similar LUSAC-21 models with the 420 hp Bugatti 16. Two of the former were shipped to the A.E.F., and orders for thousands were canceled by the war's end. Armament was the customary two fixed Marlin and two flexible Lewis .30-caliber guns.

A 300 hp Wright-Hispano H powered the remarkable Loening M-8, the first American monoplane

AMC

PACKARD-LEPERE LUSAC-11
(with first U.S. turbo-supercharger)
Liberty 12, 425 hp
DIMENSIONS: Span 41′ 7″, Lg. 25′ 3″, Ht. 10′ 7″, Wing Area 415 sq. ft.
WEIGHT: Empty 2561 lb., Gross 3746 lb. Fuel 65 gal.
PERFORMANCE: Speed—Top 133 mph at s. l., 130 mph at 6500′, Cruising 118 mph, Landing 50 mph. Service Ceiling 20,200′, Absolute Ceiling 21,500′, Climb 6500′/6 min. Range 320 miles.

MFR

THOMAS-MORSE MB-1
Liberty 12, 400 hp
DIMENSIONS: Span 37′, Lg. 22′.
WEIGHT: Gross 2375 lb.
PERFORMANCE: Never flown.

THOMAS-MORSE MB-2
Liberty 12, 400 hp
DIMENSIONS: Span 31′, Lg. 24′, Ht. 8′, Wing Area 323 sq. ft.
WEIGHT: Empty 2047 lb., Gross 2773 lb. Fuel 50 gal.
PERFORMANCE: Not available.

AMC

AF

PACKARD-LEPERE LUSAC-11

fighter. The wings were joined to the top of a narrow fuselage and braced by struts underneath, leaving the upper field of fire clear for the observer's Lewis guns. Two Marlin guns were mounted at the engine's sides, above a neat tunnel radiator. Careful design reduced the time required to produce the type. Ordered in March 1918, the M-8 was first flown in August. Two went to the Army, before the Armistice ended plans to put the Loening into production, but six were ordered as observation planes by the Navy in June 1919.

Three other two-seaters were built in 1918, powered by the 400 hp Liberty 12, but little is known about them. The Engineering Division's USAC-1 of October 1918 was a large overweight biplane, while the Thomas-Morse MB-1 was a light high-wing monoplane braced by a wide strut. Efforts to keep the MB-1 light were a bit overdone, for the machine collapsed while being taxied out for flight trials. The Ithaca, New York, firm tried again with the MB-2 biplane of November 1918, but there is no evidence that this ship completed flight tests either. It should be mentioned,

LOENING M-8
Wright-Hispano H, 300 hp
DIMENSIONS: Span 32′ 9″, Lg. 24′, Ht. 8′ 4″, Wing Area 215 sq. ft.
WEIGHT: Empty 1663 lb., Gross 2639 lb. Fuel 55 gal.
PERFORMANCE: Speed—Top 143.5 mph at s. l., 138 mph at 6500′, Landing 58 mph. Service Ceiling 18,600′, Absolute Ceiling 19,900′, Climb 6500′/5.2 min., 10,000′/9.2 min. Endurance 2 hrs. at top speed.

AMC

MFR

CURTISS 18-T
Kirkham K-12, 340 hp
DIMENSIONS: Span 31′ 11″, Lg. 23′ 4″, Ht. 9′ 10″, Wing Area 309 sq. ft.
WEIGHT: Empty 1724 lb., Gross 2901 lb.
PERFORMANCE: Speed—Top 151 mph at s. l., 145 mph at 10,000′, Landing 58 mph. Service Ceiling 22,000′, Climb 10,000′/6.9 min. Endurance 1¾ hrs.

MFR

CURTISS 18-B
Kirkham K-12, 350 hp
DIMENSIONS: Span 37′ 6″, Lg. 23′ 4″, Wing Area 306 sq. ft.
WEIGHT: Empty 1690 lb., Gross 2867 lb. Fuel 53 gal.
PERFORMANCE: Not Available.

however, that Thomas-Morse was more successful with its MB-3 single-seater.

Curtiss designed a neat two-seater fighter with the 350 hp Curtiss Kirkham K-12. It first appeared in February 1919 as the 18-T, a triplane, and in June 1919 the 18-B biplane version was completed; two of each were built. The triplane 18-T set a new U.S. altitude record in August 1919 of 32,450 ft.

The First World War had provided American fighter pilots with a pattern for future development. The well-liked Spad was superseded in the postwar period by the MB-3A, which followed the same general arrangement. The two-seater fighter, however, was not incorporated into the postwar air service, in spite of the success of the wartime Bristol and the promising Loening monoplane. The dozen years following the war produced a great variety of types, for the fighter is cheaper and easier to build than the bomber, but there was only a small advance from the wartime tradition.

Chapter 15: The Biplane Period 1919-32

POSTWAR EXPERIMENTS

Between 1921 and 1923 a great variety of single-seaters was tested by the Air Service to explore the directions future fighter design might take. None were ordered in quantity, but several supplied data of value for later machines.

Some of these prototypes were developed as unarmed racers, and as such can get only passing mention in a history limited to combat types. These include the Thomas-Morse MB-6, which was an MB-3 with clipped wings and the 400 hp Wright H-3, and the MB-7, which was also similar to the MB-3 but built as a high-wing monoplane. There were a whole series of "R" ships, which were flown with more or less success to secure data on "hi-speed" flight. The fastest of these was the Curtiss R-6 biplane with a 460 hp Curtiss D-12, which in 1922 did 236 mph. Most unique was the Dayton-Wright XPS-1 which was a high-wing parasol monoplane (wing above the fuselage), with a 200 hp Lawrence J-1 radial and one of the first retractable wheel arrangements. The wheels folded up into the fuselage, as on the Grummans a decade later.

By September 1920, the Army adopted a system of aircraft designation to replace the previous confusion of builders' letters and numbers. The new system provided for PW, PA, and PN types (pursuit, water-cooled; pursuit, air-cooled; and pursuit, night). The heavy PG-1 (pursuit ground) is discussed in Part 2 on attack planes, p. 56.

The only example of the specialized night fighter was the Curtiss PN-1 biplane with a 220 hp Liberty L-825 (six cylinder) engine and an overhanging upper wing with balanced ailerons. The theory behind this design seems to have been to get a low wing loading for easy operation out of small blacked-out wartime fields. Since the top speed was barely above that of the bombers it was supposed to stop, only two such planes were built in 1921.

An air-cooled 350 hp Wright R-1454 powered the Loening PA-1 biplane. The pair built in 1922 had their gas tank in the thick upper wing, enabling a shorter fuselage for quick turns. The only other air-cooled fighter tested was the imported British Aerial Transport F.K.23 "Bantam," a very light little job with a monocoque fuselage and a 184 hp A.B.C. Wasp A radial. It was a double-bay biplane, in contrast to the single set of struts possessed by the U.S. fighters mentioned in this section.

The first fighter under the "Pursuit, water-cooled" designation was the biplane designed by Alfred Verville for the Engineering Division. The first two appeared in August 1919 as the VCP-1 with a 300 hp Hispano H. One rebuilt later became the VCP-R racer (R-1), and the other, modified to VCP-1A, was tested in June 1920. Another pair, labeled VCP-2, with the 350 hp Packard 1A-1237, became the PW-1 when tested in November 1921. Construction included "I" struts between the wooden wings, welded steel tubing in the fuselage, and a droppable fuel tank inside the fuselage. One PW-1 was converted with Fokker wings to the PW-1A.

Wing flutter was little known when Loening built his first monoplanes, but as the designer wryly remarked after the first flights, "we knew all we wanted to know about it." Since early monoplanes tended to shed their wings, the government preferred biplanes, but in September 1921 the Loening PW-2 high-wing monoplane with a 300 hp Wright was tested. Two twin-tailed PW-2s were to be followed by ten PW-2As with revised single tails, but on October 20, 1922, a PW-2A lost its wings and gave Lieutenant Harold R. Harris the unwanted distinction of being the first American pilot to save himself by parachute. The PW-2A contract was cut back to four, one becoming the PW-2B with a Packard 1A-1237.

The PW-3 biplane began as the Orenco D-2 with odd struts and a 320 hp Wright H. Three built in 1921 were condemned as unsafe because of unsatisfactory

AMC

CURTISS PN-1
Liberty 6, L-825, 220 hp
DIMENSIONS: Span 30′ 10″, Lg. 23′ 6″, Ht. 10′ 3″, Wing Area 300 sq. ft.
WEIGHT: Empty 1631 lb., Gross 2311 lb. Fuel 53 gal.
PERFORMANCE: Speed—Top 108 mph. Service Ceiling 23,900′, Absolute Ceiling 25,600′, Climb 6500′/5.5 min. Range 255 miles at top speed.

AMC

LOENING PA-1
Wright R-1 (R-1454), 350 hp
DIMENSIONS: Span 28′, Lg. 19′ 9″, Ht. 8′ 8″, Wing Area 283 sq. ft.
WEIGHT: Empty 1536 lb., Gross 2463 lb. Fuel 69 gal.
PERFORMANCE: Speed—Top 130 mph at s. l., 124 mph at 10,000′. Service Ceiling 19,200′, Absolute Ceiling 21,000′, Climb 6500′/7 min.

VERVILLE VCP-1A (VCP-1)
Wright-Hispano H, 300 hp
DIMENSIONS: Span 32′, Lg. 22′ 4″, Ht. 8′ 4″, Wing Area 269 sq. ft.
WEIGHT: Empty 2014 lb., Gross 2669 lb. Fuel 41 gal.
PERFORMANCE: Speed—Top 154 mph at s. l., 152 mph at 6500′, Cruising 149 mph, Landing 61.5 mph. Service Ceiling 25,400′, Absolute Ceiling 27,000′, Climb 1690′/1 min., 6500′/4.4 min. Range 298 miles.

AMC

AMC

B.A.T. F.K.23
A.B.C. Wasp A, 184 hp
DIMENSIONS: Span 25′, Lg. 18′ 5″, Ht. 6′ 4″.
WEIGHT: Empty 683 lb., Gross 1128 lb.
PERFORMANCE: Speed—Top 135 mph, Cruising 127 mph, Landing 50 mph. Climb 5000′/3.7 min. Range 445 miles.

AMC

ENGINEERING DIV. PW-1
Packard 1A-1237, 350 hp
DIMENSIONS: Span 32′, Lg. 22′ 6″, Ht. 8′ 4″, Wing Area 269 sq. ft.
WEIGHT: Empty 2069 lb., Gross 3005 lb. Fuel 61.5 gal.
PERFORMANCE: Speed—Top 146 mph at s. l., 144 mph at 6500′, Cruising 131.5 mph, Landing 65 mph. Service Ceiling 19,300′, Absolute Ceiling 21,000′, Climb 10,000′/11 min. Endurance 2.5 hrs. at 131.5 mph.

AMC

ENGINEERING DIV. PW-1A
Packard 1A-1237, 350 hp
DIMENSIONS: Span 31′ 2″, Lg. 22′ 6″, Ht. 8′ 10″, Wing Area 288 sq. ft.
WEIGHT: Empty 2139 lb., Gross 3075 lb. Fuel 61.5 gal.
PERFORMANCE: Speed—Top 134 mph at s. l., 133 mph at 6500′, Cruising 115.5 mph. Service Ceiling 17,200′, Absolute Ceiling 18,800′, Climb 10,000′/12.3 min. Endurance 2.5 hrs. at 115.5 mph.

AMC

LOENING PW-2 (Original prototype shown)
Wright H, 320 hp
DIMENSIONS: Span 39′ 8″, Lg. 24′ 2″, Ht. 9′, Wing Area 287 sq. ft.
WEIGHT: Empty 1876 lb., Gross 2788 lb. Fuel 59 gal.
PERFORMANCE: Speed—Top 132 mph at s. l., 131 mph at 6500′, 127.5 mph at 10,000′, Cruising 120.5 mph, Landing 61 mph. Service Ceiling 20,000′, Absolute Ceiling 21,800′, Climb 6500′/6.2 min., 10,000′/10.6 min. Range 301 miles.

AF

LOENING PW-2A
Wright H, 322 hp
DIMENSIONS: Span 39′ 9″, Lg. 26′ ½″, Ht. 8′ 1″, Wing Area 299 sq. ft.
WEIGHT: Empty 1876 lb., Gross 2799 lb. Fuel 61 gal.
PERFORMANCE: Speed—Top 136 mph at s. l., 133.5 mph at 6500′, 131 mph at 10,000′, Cruising 125 mph, Landing 63 mph. Service Ceiling 21,400′, Absolute Ceiling 23,000′, Climb 1340′/1 min., 10,000′/9.8 min. Endurance 2.5 hrs.

AMC

LOENING PW-2B
Packard 1A-1237, 352 hp
DIMENSIONS: Span 34′ 1″, Lg. 23′ 4″, Ht. 8′ 1″, Wing Area 225 sq. ft.
WEIGHT: Empty 2040 lb., Gross 2976 lb. Fuel 61 gal.
PERFORMANCE: Speed—Top 140 mph at s. l., 137 mph at 6500′, Cruising 134 mph, Landing 71 mph. Service Ceiling 17,150′, Absolute Ceiling 18,600′, Climb 6500′/6.1 min., 10,000′/11 min. Endurance 2¾ hrs.

workmanship. Gallaudet's PW-4 of 1922 wasn't flown either, but was used for static tests. First all-metal fighter built, the PW-4 had bullet lines, "I" struts, and a 350 hp Packard IA-1237.

Anthony Fokker had built many successful fighters for the Kaiser's Air Force during World War I, the most famous being the D-7. After the Armistice he moved his factory to the Netherlands and began selling planes to his erstwhile adversaries. The Air Service had brought back 142 D-7s captured from Germany, actually used them in service, and had great respect for Fokker's sturdy cantilever structures. Fokker sent to the U.S. a development of his wartime D-8 high-wing monoplane, the V-40 with a 334 hp Wright H. During a mock dogfight with a Loening PW-2 on March 13, 1922, the V-40s wings failed, and the pilot was killed.

ORENCO PW-3
Wright H, 320 hp
DIMENSIONS: Span 27′ 9″, Lg. 23′ 10″, Ht. 8′ 1″, Wing Area 240 sq. ft.
WEIGHT: Empty 1870 lb., Gross 2669 lb. Fuel 50 gal.
PERFORMANCE: Never Flown.

AMC

GALLAUDET PW-4 [*Photo unavailable*]
Packard 1A-1237, 350 hp
DIMENSIONS: Span 29′ 10″, Lg. 22′ 8″, Ht. 8′, Wing Area 245 sq. ft.
WEIGHT: Empty 2203 lb., Gross 3040 lb. Fuel 60 gal.
PERFORMANCE: Speed—Top (Estimated 145 mph) Not Flown.

FOKKER D-7 (Packard, 1923 test)
Packard 1A-1237, 352 hp
DIMENSIONS: Span 27′ 6″, Lg. 23′, Ht. 9′ 3″, Wing Area 236 sq. ft.
WEIGHT: Empty 1867 lb., Gross 2462 lb. Fuel 51 gal.
PERFORMANCE: Speed—Top 151 mph at s. l., 147 mph at 6500′, Cruising 144 mph, Landing 63 mph. Service Ceiling 19,750′, Absolute Ceiling 21,000′, Climb 6500′/4.6 min., 10,000′/8.9 min. Endurance 2.2 hrs.

AMC

AMC

FOKKER V-40
Wright H, 334 hp
DIMENSIONS: Span 39′ 5″, Lg. 26′ 1″, Ht. 9′, Wing Area 247 sq. ft.
WEIGHT: Empty 1935 lb., Gross 2686 lb. Fuel 51 gal.
PERFORMANCE: Speed—Top 144.5 mph at s. l., 141 mph at 10,000′, Landing 62 mph. Service Ceiling 23,750′, Absolute Ceiling 25,400′, Climb 1585′/1 min., 10,000′/8 min. Endurance 2 hrs. at top speed.

Nevertheless, ten heavier examples designated PW-5 were purchased.

Fokker also sent a D-IX biplane for tests in September 1922 as the PW-6. The metal fuselage had a nose radiator for the Wright H-2, and "N" struts between the wings became common on later American biplanes. In February 1924 the Army began tests on three Fokker D-XI sesquiplanes. Known here as the PW-7, they had a 440 hp Curtiss D-12 engine and plywood upper wings much larger than the lower wings.

All-metal construction and cantilever monoplanes were audacious experiments in those days, but some German designers combined both in fighter design. One was the all-metal "Falke" single-seater with a high wing built in Switzerland by Dornier. Inspected at McCook Field in Dayton, Ohio, in April 1923, its clean

AF

FOKKER PW-5
Wright H-2, 300 hp
DIMENSIONS: Span 39′ 5″, Lg. 27′ 2″, Ht. 9′, Wing Area 246 sq. ft.
WEIGHT: Empty 2170 lb., Gross 3015 lb. Fuel 61 gal.
PERFORMANCE: Speed—Top 138 mph at s. l.

AMC

FOKKER PW-6 (D-IX)
Wright H-2, 315 hp
DIMENSIONS: Span 29′ 6″, Lg. 23′ 3″, Ht. 9′, Wing Area 238 sq. ft.
WEIGHT: Empty 1926 lb., Gross 2763 lb. Fuel 58 gal.
PERFORMANCE: Speed—Top 138.5 mph at s. l., 129 mph at 10,000′, Cruising 117 mph, Landing 62 mph. Service Ceiling 16,750′, Absolute Ceiling 18,200′, Climb 6500′/6.3 min., 10,000′/11.4 min. Range 293 miles.

AMC

FOKKER PW-7 (D-XI)
Curtiss D-12, 440 hp
DIMENSIONS: Span 38′ 4″, Lg. 23′ 11″, Ht. 9′ 4″, Wing Area 250 sq. ft.
WEIGHT: Empty 2271 lb., Gross 3176 lb. Fuel 65 gal.
PERFORMANCE: Speed—Top 151 mph at s. l., Cruising 145 mph, Landing 63 mph. Service Ceiling 20,700′, Absolute Ceiling 22,000′, Climb 1690′/1 min. Range 338 miles.

WRIGHT-DORNIER "FALKE"
Wright H-3, 320 hp
DIMENSIONS: Span 32′ 10″, Lg. 24′ 5″, Ht. 8′ 9″, Wing Area 215 sq. ft.
WEIGHT: Empty 1819 lb., Gross 2674 lb. Fuel 72 gal.
PERFORMANCE: Speed—Top 162 mph, Landing 60 mph. Climb 10,000′/6.75 min. Range 217 miles.

PMB

CURTISS XPW-8 (First prototype)
Curtiss D-12, 440 hp
DIMENSIONS: Span 32′, Lg. 22′ 6″, Ht. 8′ 8″, Wing Area 265 sq. ft.
WEIGHT: Empty 1879 lb., Gross 2784 lb.
PERFORMANCE: Speed—Top 169 mph at s. l., 160 mph at 10,000′, Landing 70 mph. Service Ceiling 27,150′, Absolute Ceiling 28,600′, Climb 2500′/1 min. Endurance 2 hrs. 48 min.

MFR

AMC

CURTISS PW-8 (2nd prototype)
Curtiss D-12 (Low-Compression), 438 hp
DIMENSIONS: Span 32′, Lg. 22′ 6″, Ht. 8′ 10″, Wing Area 287 sq. ft.
WEIGHT: Empty 2191 lb., Gross 3151 lb. Fuel 75 gal.
PERFORMANCE: Speed—Top 168 mph at s. l., 163 mph at 6500′, Cruising 159 mph, Landing 63 mph. Service Ceiling 20,350′, Absolute Ceiling 21,500′, Climb 1830′/1 min., 10,000′/7.4 min. Endurance 2.75 hrs. at 159 mph.

lines were defeated by high costs and the fear the wing might come off. Powered by a Wright H-3, the Dornier Falke was credited with 162 mph, and carried the usual two synchronized guns.

CURTISS ARMY HAWKS VERSUS BOEING BIPLANES

For nearly ten years, the Curtiss Hawk was the dominant Army fighter type, until vigorous competition from Boeing elbowed these single-seaters aside. Streamlining developed in the Curtiss racer series resulted in neater lines and the "eversharp pencil" nose characteristic of the fighter design begun in May 1922. The Curtiss PW-8 was flown first in January 1923 and was sold to the Army on April 27, 1923, with two more prototypes. It became the XPW-8 when the Air Service adopted the X prefix on May 14, 1924, as the symbol for experimental planes.

The second prototype was more streamlined and heavier, accommodating more equipment, and was followed by 25 production copies ordered September 14, 1923, and delivered from June to August 1924. Made famous by Lieutenant Russell L. Maughan's

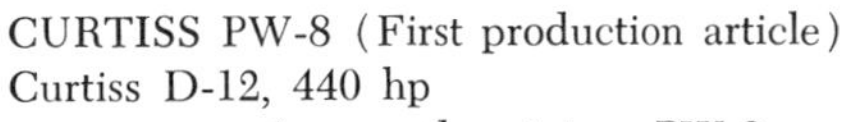

CURTISS PW-8 (First production article)
Curtiss D-12, 440 hp
DIMENSIONS: As second prototype PW-9
WEIGHT: As second prototype PW-9
PERFORMANCE: Speed—Top 165 mph at s. l., 162 mph at 6500′, Cruising 160 mph, Landing 61 mph. Service Ceiling 21,700′, Absolute Ceiling 23,300′, Climb 10,000′/9 min. Range 440 miles.

AMC

CURTISS PW-8A
Curtiss D-12, 440 hp (Tunnel Radiator)
DIMENSIONS: Span 30′, Lg. 22′ 6″, Ht. 8′, Wing Area 255 sq. ft.
WEIGHT: Empty 2007 lb., Gross 2820 lb. Fuel 53 gal.
PERFORMANCE: Speed—Top 178 mph at s. l., 171.5 mph at 6500′, Cruising 169 mph, Landing 68 mph. Service Ceiling 22,250′, Absolute Ceiling 23,400′, Climb 10,000′/6.91 min. Range 338 miles.

AMC

AMC

CURTISS XPW-8B
Curtiss D-12, 435 hp
DIMENSIONS: Span 31′ 6″, Lg. 22′ 2″, Ht. 8′ 6″, Wing Area 250 sq. ft.
WEIGHT: Empty 2032 lb., Gross 2802 lb., Max. 2926 lb. Fuel 50–100 gal.
PERFORMANCE: Speed—Top 167 mph at s. l. (162 mph with drop tank), 163 mph at 5000′, Landing 61 mph. Service Ceiling 21,400′, Absolute Ceiling 22,600′, Climb 1800′/1 min., 10,000′/7.3 min. Endurance 1 hr. 35 min.

transcontinental flight, the PW-8 was the last double-bay biplane fighter, with two pairs of "N" struts, wing radiators, and a 440 hp Curtiss D-12. Two .30-caliber guns with 600 rounds each were carried, unless one was replaced by a .50-caliber gun with 200 rounds. The wing radiators were the least desirable feature, for a puncture in their vulnerable area might subject the pilot to a stream of hot water.

This problem was eliminated in the third prototype (XPW-8A) delivered February 1924 with a tunnel radiator below the high-compression D-12 engine, and short, single-bay wings. Essentially, the XPW-8A was a racer, but in December 1924 it was ordered converted to the XPW-8B with a low-compression D-12 engine and new wings for greater maneuverability. This new tapered wing became standard on future Curtiss Hawks from the P-1 to P-23.

Boeing's Model 15, first flown April 29, 1923, to compete with the Curtiss ships, always had single-bay tapered wings and a tunnel radiator. Otherwise, they were very similar to the Hawks in appearance. The first, designated XPW-9, was powered by a D-12 engine and weighed 2971 lbs., but the second prototype weighed 3015 lbs. when it arrived at McCook

AF

BOEING XPW-9
Curtiss D-12, 440 hp
DIMENSIONS: Span 32′ 1″, Lg. 22′ 10″, Ht. 8′ 9″, Wing Area 248 sq. ft.
WEIGHT: Empty 2011 lb., Gross 2971 lb. Fuel 75 gal.
PERFORMANCE: Speed—Top 161 mph at s. l., 154 mph at 6500′, Cruising 150 mph, Landing 64 mph. Service Ceiling 22,000′, Absolute Ceiling 22,850′, Climb 2055′/1 min., 10,000′/6.7 min. Endurance 2.83 hrs. at 150 mph.

AMC

BOEING XPW-9 (2nd prototype)
Curtiss D-12, 448 hp
DIMENSIONS: As first XPW-9
WEIGHT: Empty 2052 lb., Gross 3015 lb. Fuel 75 gal.
PERFORMANCE: Speed—Top 163 mph at s. l., 159 mph at 6500′, Cruising 156 mph, Landing 64 mph. Service Ceiling 21,000′, Absolute Ceiling 22,600′, Climb 10,000′/9.1 min. Endurance 2.6 hrs. at 156 mph.

Field in June 1924. The three prototypes' performance varied on different tests with changes in propeller and weight, but the Army had bought them on September 9, 1923, and a September 19, 1924, order for 12 ships was increased to 30 in December of that year.

Deliveries of the PW-9, which had split-axle landing gear, began in October 1925, when the Army bought 25 PW-9As with the D-12-C engine. The last of these became the PW-9B when fitted with a D-12-D, which also powered 39 strengthened PW-9Cs ordered in June and August of 1926. A year later, 16 PW-9Ds were ordered and the first was tested in June 1928. Additional weight, such as wheel brakes, reduced performance below that of earlier models and required a balanced rudder, but still the Boeing fighters were usually considered a bit more maneuverable than the Curtiss types.

Although most fighters of this period were either Curtiss or Boeing types, there were experiments by other builders. The last combat type built by the Army itself was the Engineering Division's conventional looking TP-1, powered by a Liberty engine. One of the two built was tested in November 1924, and showed a top speed of 129 mph at sea level, hardly an improvement on 1918 types, but another fitted with an experimental supercharger did 125 mph at sea level and 150 mph after climbing to 20,300 ft. The first two-seat fighter attempted since the war, it was armed with two Brownings in the nose, two Lewis guns on the rear cockpit's ring, and another Lewis in the floor.

The only two-seat fighter offered by a private firm was the Thomas-Morse TM-24 tested February 1925 with a 440 hp Curtiss D-12. This biplane's upper wing

BOEING PW-9 (First production model)
Curtiss D-12, 430 hp
DIMENSIONS: Span 32′ 1″, Lg. 22′ 10″, Ht. 8′ 8″, Wing Area 242 sq. ft.
WEIGHT: Empty 2166 lb., Gross 3030 lb. Fuel 63 gal.
PERFORMANCE: Speed—Top 165 mph at s. l., 160 mph at 10,000′, Landing 65 mph. Service Ceiling 20,175′, Absolute Ceiling 21,400′, Climb 1710′/1 min., 10,000′/7.9′. Endurance 2 hrs. 35 min. at top speed.

AF

BOEING PW-9D
Curtiss D-12D, 435 hp
DIMENSIONS: Span 32′, Lg. 24′ 2″, Ht. 8′ 8″, Wing Area 241 sq. ft.
WEIGHT: Empty 2328 lb., Gross 3234 lb. Fuel 63 gal.
PERFORMANCE: Speed—Top 155 mph at s. l., 152 mph at 5000′, Cruising 124 mph, Landing 63 mph. Service Ceiling 18,230′, Absolute Ceiling 19,600′, Climb 5000′/4 min. Endurance 2.87 hrs.

AMC

AMC

ENGINEERING DIV. TP-1
(Photo shows supercharged version)
Liberty 12, 423 hp
DIMENSIONS: Span 36′, Lg. 25′ 1″, Ht. 10′, Wing Area 375 sq. ft.
WEIGHT: Empty 2748 lb., Gross 4363 lb. Fuel 93 gal.
PERFORMANCE: Speed—Top 129 mph at s. l., 123 mph at 6500′, Cruising 117 mph, Landing 63 mph. Service Ceiling 13,450′, Absolute Ceiling 15,200′, Climb 495′/1 min., 6500′/9.2 min. Endurance 3.6 hrs.

ARC

THOMAS-MORSE TM-24
Curtiss D-12, 440 hp
DIMENSIONS: Span 30′, Lg. 20′ 5″, Wing Area 237 sq. ft.
WEIGHT: Empty 1969 lb., Gross 3470 lb. Fuel 84 gal.
PERFORMANCE: Speed—Top 143 mph at s. l., 138 mph at 15,000′, Cruising 114 mph, Landing 63 mph. Service Ceiling 15,600′, Absolute Ceiling 17,050′, Climb 1178′/1 min., 5000′/5.1 min. Endurance 2¾ hrs. at 114 mph/15,000′.

was smaller than the lower wing, and was supported by an ugly arrangement of "V" and "N" struts. Other unconventional features were the short metal fuselage and biplane tail. No Army contract or designation was given, but the firm tried again with the Thomas-Morse TM-23 single-seat biplane with a Curtiss D-12 and small wings joined by "I" struts. Official performance tests on March 9, 1926, brought complaints that the TM-23 flew badly and had too high a landing speed.

As Boeing's PW-9 series made progress, and Thomas-Morse tried unsuccessfully to get some fighter business, Curtiss went into production on the popular P-1 Hawks. Ten P-1s ordered March 7, 1925, began the fighter designation series that continues today. Essentially a refined PW-8B with a 435 hp V-1150-1 (the new Curtiss D-12 engine designation), the P-1 was tested at McCook Field on August 17, 1925, and had fabric covering over wooden wing spars and a steel-tubed fuselage and tail. A 50-gallon main tank could be supplemented by a 50-gallon auxiliary tank attached behind the tunnel radiator, increasing endurance from two to four hours.

Twenty-five similar P-1As ordered September 9, 1925, were delivered in 1926, and 25 P-1Bs were purchased August 17, 1926. Tested July 1927, the P-1B had a V-1150-3, larger wheels and minor changes. A V-1150-5 and wheel brakes distinguished 33 P-1Cs ordered October 3, 1928. March 1929 tests indicated that continuous increments of weight had depressed the Hawk's performance. Cost of the P-1C, $9862 each, was very low compared to today's fighters. Navy Hawks of this type were F6C-3s, while one P-1A was sold

THOMAS-MORSE TM-23
Curtiss D-12, 440 hp
DIMENSIONS: Span 23′, Lg. 16′ 8″, Wing Area 200 sq. ft.
WEIGHT: Empty 1918.5 lb., Gross 2706.5 lb. Fuel 50–61 gal.
PERFORMANCE: Speed—Top 167 mph at s. l., 150.6 mph at 15,000′, Cruising 125 mph, Landing 80 mph. Service Ceiling 20,150′, Absolute Ceiling 21,275′, Climb 10,000′/7.3 min. Endurance 2¼ hrs. at 125 mph.

AMC

CURTISS P-1
Curtiss V-1150-1, 435 hp
DIMENSIONS: Span 31′ 7″, Lg. 22′ 10″, Ht. 8′ 7″, Wing Area 250 sq. ft.
WEIGHT: Empty 2058 lb., Gross 2846 lb., Max. 3238 lb. Fuel 50–100 gal.
PERFORMANCE: Speed—Top 163 mph at s. l., 159 mph at 5000′, Cruising 136 mph, Landing 59 mph. Service Ceiling 22,500′, Absolute Ceiling 23,800′, Climb 1810′/1 min., 5000′/3.1 min. Range 325 miles at top speed.

MFR

AF

CURTISS P-1B
Curtiss V-1150-3, 435 hp
DIMENSIONS: Span 31′ 7″, Lg. 22′ 8″, Ht. 8′ 11″, Wing Area 250 sq. ft.
WEIGHT: Empty 2105 lb., Gross 2932 lb., Max. 3562 lb. Fuel 50–100 gal.
PERFORMANCE: Speed—Top 159.6 mph at s. l., 157 mph at 5000′, Cruising 127 mph, Landing 57 mph. Service Ceiling 21,400′, Absolute Ceiling 22,900′, Climb 1540′/1 min.

AF

CURTISS P-1B (Modified radiator and flare racks)

CURTISS P-1A [*Photo unavailable*]
Curtiss V-1150-1, 435 hp
DIMENSIONS: As P-1
WEIGHT: Empty 2041 lb., Gross 2866 lb. Fuel 50–100 gal.
PERFORMANCE: Speed—Top 160 mph at s. l., 155 mph at 10,000′, Cruising 128 mph, Service Ceiling 20,200′, Absolute Ceiling 21,350′, Climb 2170′/1 min., 5000′/2.6 min.

to Japan, and Chile bought eight P-1As and eight P-1Bs. In addition, 52 of 71 Hawks built as AT-4 and AT-5 advanced trainers were converted in 1929 to P-1D, P-1E, and P-1F fighters generally similar to those in service.

While these Hawks went into service, the same basic airframe tested other engine arrangements. Five Curtiss P-2s bought on the first P-1 contract and flown in December 1925 had the 505 hp Curtiss V-1400. Like most previous types, this was a water-cooled inline engine, but the Curtiss XP-3 was a P-1A fitted with a 400 hp air-cooled Curtiss R-1454 radial. When this powerplant failed, a 410 hp Pratt & Whitney R-1340-9 radial was substituted for April 1928 tests. Five P-3As with the R-1340-3 had been ordered December 1927 and delivery began in September 1928. Early flights showed that the naked ring of cylinders handicapped performance, but in June 1930 one was flown with an SR-1340-C, a streamlined cowl, spinner, and side fairings, and top speed increased

AF

CURTISS P-1C
Curtiss V-1150-5, 435 hp
DIMENSIONS: Span 31′ 6″, Lg. 23′ 3″, Ht. 8′ 6″, Wing Area 252 sq. ft.
WEIGHT: Empty 2136 lb., Gross 2973 lb. Fuel 50–100 gal.
PERFORMANCE: Speed—Top 154 mph at s. l., 148 mph at 10,000′, 153 mph at 5000′, Cruising 124 mph, Landing 58 mph. Service Ceiling 20,800′, Absolute Ceiling 22,300′, Climb 1460′/1 min., 5000′/3.9 min., 10,000′/9.1 min. Range 554–650 miles.

AMC

CURTISS P-2 (Photo shows supercharger added)
Curtiss V-1400, 505 hp
DIMENSIONS: Span 31′ 7″, Lg. 22′ 10″, Ht. 8′ 7″, Wing Area 250 sq. ft.
WEIGHT: Empty 2081 lb., Gross 2869 lb., Max. 3255 lb. Fuel 50–100 gal.
PERFORMANCE: Speed—Top 172 mph at s. l., 151 mph at 15,000′, Cruising 138 mph, Landing 65 mph. Service Ceiling 22,950′, Absolute Ceiling 24,000′, Climb 2170′/1 min., 6500′/3.5 min. Range 400 miles at top speed.

from 153 to 190 mph at sea level. Other P-3As got standard ring cowls, and two became trainers with 300 hp R-985-1s, but were rather misleadingly labeled XP-21.

Another path of engine development was the turbo-supercharger developed by Dr. Moss of General Electric. After static tests at Pikes Peak in September 1918, flight trials had been made on a LePere fighter in February 1920, and further tests had been made on an MB-2 bomber, TP-1, PW-8, and the first P-2. Boeing also built a turbo-supercharged high-altitude fighter, the XP-4. Actually a reworked PW-9 with a 510 hp Packard, four-bladed propeller, and enlarged

AF—MFR

CURTISS P-3A
(Data applies to uncowled, standard version)
Pratt & Whitney R-1340-3, 410 hp
DIMENSIONS: Span 31′ 7″, Lg. 22′ 5″, Ht. 8′ 9″, Wing Area 252 sq. ft.
WEIGHT: Empty 1956 lb., Gross 2788 lb. Fuel 50–100 gal.
PERFORMANCE: Speed—Top 153 mph at s. l., 151 mph at 5000′, 148 mph at 10,000′, Cruising 122 mph, Landing 58 mph. Service Ceiling 23,000′, Absolute Ceiling 24,400′, Climb 1742′/1 min., 5000′/3.2 min.

PMB

CURTISS P-3A

MFR

CURTISS XP-3A
(Designation also applied to second aircraft, a P-3A with Cowl and Spinner)
Pratt & Whitney R-1340-3, 410 hp (R-1340-7, 450 hp)
DIMENSIONS: Span 31′ 7″, Lg. 22′ 6″, Ht. 8′ 7″, Wing Area 250 sq. ft.
WEIGHT: Empty 1864 lb. (2107 lb.), Gross 2689 lb. (2939 lb). Fuel 50 gal.
PERFORMANCE: Speed—Top 154 mph at s. l. (190 mph at s. l.), 153 mph at 5000′ (188 mph at 5000′), Cruising 123 mph (152 mph), Landing 57 mph (60 mph). Service Ceiling 22,400′ (28,100′), Absolute Ceiling 23,650′ (29,400′), Climb 5000′/2.9 min. (2290′/1 min., 10,000′/5.34 min.). Range 390 miles at top speed.

AMC

BOEING XP-4
Packard 1A-1500, 510 hp
DIMENSIONS: Span 32′, Lg. 23′ 11″, Ht. 8′ 10″, Wing Area 308 sq. ft.
WEIGHT: Gross 3603 lb. Fuel 100 gal.
PERFORMANCE: Speed—Top 161 mph. Service Ceiling 22,000′, Absolute Ceiling 22,850′, Climb 2055′/1 min. Range 375 miles.

lower wing, the overweight XP-4 was grounded August 1929 after only 4½ flying hours.

A contract placed May 14, 1927, called for five Curtiss P-5 Hawks to be built with turbo-superchargers on V-1150-3 engines. Except for cockpit heater, longer wheel struts, and enlarged propellers, the P-5 was similar to the P-1. The supercharger's weight reduced sea level speed to 146 mph, but at 25,000 ft., 173 mph was attained in a July 1929 test. Since these superchargers were driven by hot exhaust gases, and compressed frigid high-altitude air, they required metals able to withstand great extremes of temperature. It was to take another decade of work before turbo-superchargers would be reliable enough for production and service.

When the 600 hp Curtiss V-1570-1 Conqueror became available, two Hawks were rebuilt to try it out

CURTISS P-5
Curtiss V-1150-3, 435 hp
DIMENSIONS: Span 31′ 6″, Lg. 23′ 8″, Ht. 9′ 3″, Wing Area 252 sq. ft.
WEIGHT: Empty 2520 lb., Gross 3349 lb. Fuel 50–100 gal.
PERFORMANCE: Speed—Top 146 mph at s. l., 173.5 mph at 25,000′, Cruising 117 mph, Landing 62 mph. Service Ceiling 31,900′, Absolute Ceiling 32,500′, Climb 1110′/1 min., 10,000′/8.4 min., 15,000′/12.4 min. Endurance 1.31 hrs. at s. l./top speed.

MFR

MFR

CURTISS XP-6
Curtiss V-1570-1, 600 hp
DIMENSIONS: Span 31′ 7″, Lg. 22′ 8″, Ht. 8′ 11″, Wing Area 250 sq. ft.
WEIGHT: Empty 2204 lb., Gross 3037 lb. Fuel 50 gal.
PERFORMANCE: Speed—Top 176 mph at s. l., 168 mph at 10,000′, 143 mph at 20,000′, Cruising 141 mph, Landing 61 mph. Service Ceiling 23,110′, Absolute Ceiling 24,200′, Climb 2271′/1 min., 10,000′/5.7 min.

at the September 1927 air races. The XP-6 was a P-2 with a Conqueror installed, while the XP-6A had a high-compression Conqueror, P-1A body, XPW-8A wings, and wing radiators. At the races, the XP-6A came first with a speed of 201 mph, leaving the XP-6 second place, but it should be remembered that the XP-6A was strictly a racer whose wing radiators had already been found unsuitable for service. Another conversion was the XP-6B, a P-1C rebuilt with the Conqueror and a 250 gallon fuel capacity for a July 1929 flight to Alaska.

Eighteen P-6s were ordered with the P-1C on October 3, 1928, and deliveries began a year later. Like previous Hawks, the first ten P-6s had water-cooling for their V-1570-17, but the last eight P-6A had V-1570-23s cooled by ethylene glycol (commercially sold as Prestone). Chemical cooling permitted smaller radiators, and had been tried on modified P-1B and P-1Cs before the P-6A was flown in November 1930.

Eight more P-6s were built for the Dutch East Indies, while one was purchased by Mitsubishi in 1930. Incidentally, the Japanese firm's inspector at Curtiss

CURTISS XP-6A RACER

MFR

AMC

CURTISS P-6
Curtiss V-1570-17, 600 hp
DIMENSIONS: Span 31′ 6″, Lg. 23′ 7″, Wing Area 252 sq. ft.
WEIGHT: Gross 3150 lb., Max. 3310 lb. Fuel 50–100 gal.
PERFORMANCE: Speed—Top 178 mph at s. l., 171 mph at 10,000′, 144 mph at 20,000′. Service Ceiling 22,700′, Absolute Ceiling 24,000′, Climb 2140′/1 min., 10,000′/6.6 min. Range 260 miles normal, 520 max.

then was Jiro Horikoshi, who later became chief designer of the Zero and earlier Japanese fighters on the basis of his knowledge gained by contact with American technique. Cuba also received some Hawks about this time, but they were powered by a 450 hp Pratt & Whitney air-cooled radial.

No P-6C appeared, but the XP-6D was a P-6A modified by an F-2 turbo-supercharger on a V-1570-23. This ship had a two-bladed propeller like most biplanes, but a dozen P-6Ds converted February 1932 from P-6 and P-6As had three-bladed propellers whose bite would take better advantage of the turbo-supercharger's high-altitude capabilities.

Boeing continued to give Curtiss stiff competition for fighter contracts during this period. Like every other firm, they had failures as well as successes. In November 1928, tests were made on an XP-7, actually the last PW-9 with a V-1570-1 Conqueror and new

CURTISS P-6A
Curtiss V-1570-23, 600 hp
DIMENSIONS: Span 31′ 6″, Lg. 23′ 7″, Ht. 8′ 7″, Wing Area 252 sq. ft.
WEIGHT: Empty 2389 lb., Gross 3172 lb. Fuel 50 gal.
PERFORMANCE: Speed—Top 178 mph at s. l., 177 mph at 5000′, 173.5 mph at 10,000′, 160 mph at 20,000′, Cruising 154 mph, Landing 60 mph. Service Ceiling 27,200′, Absolute Ceiling 28,400′, Climb 10,000′/5.8 min.

AMC

MFR

CURTISS XP-6B
Curtiss V-1570-1, 600 hp
DIMENSIONS: Span 31′ 6″, Lg. 23′ 7″, Ht. 8′ 9″, Wing Area 252 sq. ft.
WEIGHT: Empty 2545 lb., Gross 3269 lb. Fuel 250 gal.
PERFORMANCE: Speed—Top 178 mph at s. l., 175 mph at 5000′, Cruising 142 mph, Landing 62.4 mph. Service Ceiling 22,600′, Absolute Ceiling 23,800′, Climb 5000′/2.7 min. Endurance 1.9 hrs. normal, 3.8 hrs. max.

MFR

CURTISS CUBAN HAWK
Pratt & Whitney R-1340, 450 hp
DIMENSIONS: Not Available
WEIGHT: Gross 2910 lb. Fuel 100 gal.
PERFORMANCE: Speed—Top 157 mph at s. l. Service Ceiling 21,800′, Climb 1820′/1 min., 12,500′/10 min. Endurance 2.54 hrs. at top speed.

CURTISS P-6D
Curtiss V-1570-23, 600 hp
DIMENSIONS: Span 31′ 6″, Lg. 23′ 7″, Ht. 8′ 7″, Wing Area 252 sq. ft.
WEIGHT: Gross 3483 lb. Fuel 50–100 gal.
PERFORMANCE: Speed—Top 197 mph at 13,000′, 190 mph at 10,000′, 172 mph at s. l., Landing 63 mph. Service Ceiling 32,000′, Climb 1720′/1 min., 15,000′/8.7 min.

PMB

BOEING XP-7
Curtiss V-1570-1, 600 hp
DIMENSIONS: Span 32′, Lg. 24′, Ht. 9′, Wing Area 241 sq. ft.
WEIGHT: Empty 2323 lb., Gross 3157 lb. Fuel 50 gal.
PERFORMANCE: Speed—Top 167.5 mph at s. l., 163.5 mph at 5000′, Cruising 134 mph, Landing 62 mph. Service Ceiling 21,120′, Absolute Ceiling 22,300′, Climb 1867′/1 min., 10,000′/7.1 min. Endurance 92 hr. at s. l./top speed.

AMC

BOEING XP-8
Packard 2A-1530, 600 hp
DIMENSIONS: Span 30′ 1″, Lg. 23′ 4″, Ht. 8′ 4″, Wing Area 237 sq. ft.
WEIGHT: Empty 2390 lb., Gross 3421 lb. Fuel 90 gal.
PERFORMANCE: Speed—Top 170 mph at s. l., 166 mph at 5000′, Cruising 136 mph, Landing 64 mph. Service Ceiling 20,950′, Absolute Ceiling 22,500′, Climb 1800′/1 min., 5000′/3.1 min.

AMC

AMC

BOEING XP-9
Curtiss V-1570-15, 600 hp (583 hp actual)
DIMENSIONS: Span 36′ 7″, Lg. 25′ 8″, Ht. 7′ 9‴, Wing Area 214 sq. ft.
WEIGHT: Empty 2694 lb., Gross 3604 lb. Fuel 81–135 gal.
PERFORMANCE: Speed—Top 181 mph at s. l., 179.5 mph at 5000′, Cruising 144 mph, Landing 70 mph. Service Ceiling 25,300′, Absolute Ceiling 26,400′, Climb 2430′/1 min., 5000′/2.3 min. Endurance 1.5 hrs. at top speed.

tail. Boeing's Model 66, tested by the Army in January 1928 as the XP-8, had an inverted 600 hp Packard 2A-1530 cooled by a radiator built into the juncture of lower wing and fuselage. The final report in May 1929 described the design as good (it was similar to the Navy's F2B), but handicapped by an unsatisfactory engine.

Although biplanes dominated the aviation picture, the Army and Boeing signed a $60,000 contract in June 1928 for an XP-9 monoplane with a V-1570-15 engine, and strut-braced gull wings attached to the top of an all-metal stressed skin fuselage, the first since 1922. When the XP-9 was flown in November 1930, the pilot called it "a menace" due to exceedingly poor vision and dangerous flying qualities.

On June 18, 1928, the Army had ordered the Curtiss XP-10. Designed for good maneuverability, pilot visibility, and high speeds at 13,000 ft., the XP-10 had a V-1570-15, plywood wings gulled into the fuselage, and wing skin radiators; a cooling system too vulnerable to bullet damage and not used again. Tests were stopped in October 1930 due to trouble with these coolers.

The next Curtiss design was a development of the familiar Hawk layout. The Curtiss XP-11 was to be a P-6 with the experimental 600 hp Curtiss H-1640-1. This engine, flight-tested on the Thomas-Morse XP-13, was a failure, and the XP-11 project, together with a more advanced Curtiss XP-14 designed around this engine, was abandoned. Two of three P-11 airframes

CURTISS XP-10
Curtiss V-1710-15, 600 hp
DIMENSIONS: Span 33′, Lg. 24′ 6″.
WEIGHT: Gross 3700 lb.
PERFORMANCE: Speed—Top 173 mph.

MFR

BOEING P-12
Pratt & Whitney R-1340-7 (SR-1340C), 450 hp at 5000′
DIMENSIONS: Span 30′, Lg. 20′ 1″, Ht. 9′ 7″, Wing Area 227.5 sq. ft.
WEIGHT: Empty 1758 lb., Gross 2536 lb. Fuel 52–99 gal.
PERFORMANCE: Speed—Top 171 mph at 5000′, 158 mph at s. l., Cruising 135 mph, Landing 60 mph. Service Ceiling 28,200′, Absolute Ceiling 29,600′, Climb 2080′/1 min., 10,000′/5.77 min.

MFR
MFR

BOEING XP-12A

ordered in January 1929 were completed as P-6s, while the third became the YP-20.

The most successful Boeing fighter family began in June 1928 with the Model 83 biplane, a private venture powered by a 400 hp Pratt & Whitney R-1340C Wasp. Together with the later Model 89, it was submitted to the Navy and became the XF4B-1. Impressed by Navy reports, the Army on November 7, 1928, ordered nine P-12s and one XP-12A for service trials. First flown on April 11, 1929, the P-12 had a 450 hp R-1340-7 with cylinder fairings and the usual two guns in front of the pilot. The XP-12A displayed a deep NACA cowl, new Frieze ailerons, and shorter landing gear, but was destroyed four days after its first flight on May 10, 1929.

Ninety P-12Bs purchased on June 10, 1929, and first delivered in February 1930 had the As ailerons and landing gear. At first, they had cylinder fairings on their R-1340-7s, but cooling difficulties forced their removal. Some P-12Bs later received ring cowls.

Meanwhile, Boeing turned out four Model 100s, in 1929, commercial P-12s powered by 525 hp SR-1340Ds. One tested at Wright Field showed a top speed with ring cowl of 192 mph, and 177.5 mph without cowl. Another was sold to Japan.

A monoplane development of the P-12 series was Boeing's 202, built with a 525 hp SR-1340D, a high braced wing, and metal fuselage. Designated XP-15, it did 185 mph with a ring cowl on May 3, 1930, and 178 mph when flown with bare cylinders. An XF5B-1

BOEING P-12B
Pratt & Whitney R-1340-7 (SR-1340C), 450 hp at 5000′
DIMENSIONS: Span 30′, Lg. 20′ 3″, Ht. 8′ 10″, Wing Area 227.5 sq. ft.
WEIGHT: Empty 1945 lb., Gross 2638 lb. Fuel 50–99 gal.
PERFORMANCE: Speed—Top 166.5 mph at 5000′, 157 mph at s. l., Cruising 135 mph, Landing 59 mph. Service Ceiling 27,450′, Absolute Ceiling 28,800′, Climb 2040′/1 min., 10,000′/5.9 min. Range 540 miles normal, 622 miles max.

AF

BOEING MODEL 100
Pratt & Whitney SR-1340D, 525 hp
DIMENSIONS: Span 30′, Lg. 20′ 1″, Ht. 9′ 3″, Wing Area 227.5 sq. ft.
WEIGHT: Empty 1815 lb., Gross 2597 lb. Fuel 50 gal.
PERFORMANCE: Speed—Top 192 mph at 8000′, 168 mph at s. l., Cruising 155 mph, Landing 60 mph. Service Ceiling 29,900′, Absolute Ceiling 31,000′, Climb 2010′/1 min., 10,000′/5.9 min.

MFR

PMB

BOEING P-12C
Pratt & Whitney R-1340-9, 450 hp at 8,000′
DIMENSIONS: Span 30′, Lg. 20′ 1″, Ht. 8′ 8″, Wing Area 227.5 sq. ft.
WEIGHT: Empty 1938 lb., Gross 2630 lb. Fuel 50–110 gal.
PERFORMANCE: Speed—Top 178 mph at 8000′, Cruising 141 mph, Landing 58 mph. Service Ceiling 26,200′, Absolute Ceiling 27,600′, Climb 1410′/1 min., 10,000′/6.1 min. Range 580 miles normal, 668 miles max.

AMC

BOEING XP-15

Pratt & Whitney SR-1340D, 525 hp at 8000′

DIMENSIONS: Span 30′ 6″, Lg. 21′, Ht. 9′, Wing Area 157 sq. ft.

WEIGHT: Empty 2050 lb., Gross 2790 lb. Fuel 50–128 gal.

PERFORMANCE: Speed—Top 185 mph at 8000′, 163.5 mph at s. l., Cruising 150 mph, Landing 71 mph. Service Ceiling 26,550′, Absolute Ceiling 27,650′, Climb 1860′/1 min.

AMC

BOEING XP-15

Navy version had a curved rudder later installed on the XP-15.

Although the XP-15s performance was good, the Army on June 2, 1930, ordered 96 P-12C and 35 P-12D biplanes. Tested in November 1930, the P-12C had a 450 hp R-1340-9 under a ring cowl and introduced split-axle landing gear, instead of the older crossed axle style. The P-12Ds of early 1931 were similar but for a 500 hp R-1340-17 and different auxiliary tank.

An all-metal monocoupe fuselage was introduced in December 1930 on Boeing Model 218. Sometimes seen with wheel pants, it became the XP-925A in August 1931 when the 450 hp SR-1340C was replaced by a 500 hp R-1340F. Sent to China for demonstration, it became the first American fighter to shoot down Japanese planes in combat, before it was itself destroyed in a dogfight near Shanghai. The 218s metal fuselage was specified for the P-12Es bought for $9100 each on March 20, 1931, with the largest pursuit contract in a decade.

Instead of the traditional tail skid, a tail wheel was used on the P-12E, which appeared in October 1931 with an R-1340-17, 55 gallons of internal fuel, and a belly tank of equal capacity. Twenty-five P-12Fs with the 550 hp R-1340-19 followed 110 P-12s into service after April 1932 tests.

A number of P-12 models were converted by engine changes. They include the XP-12G, a P-12B with a turbo-supercharger and three-bladed propeller. The XP-12H was a D with a geared Wasp, and the P-12J was an E testing the H Wasp. Seven Es with Q-2 fuel systems, and one with an F-7 supercharger became the YP-12K and XP-12L. Navy counterparts of the P-12s were the F4B series.

Two smaller firms tried to win some pursuit business, with little success. Thomas-Morse, luckless since the MB-3, built the XP-13 purchased in June 1929 during flight tests. An all-metal biplane with "I" struts and a corrugated metal fuselage, the Viper had an experimental air-cooled 600 hp Curtiss H-1640-1. A twin-row radial with the second row of six cylinders directly behind the first row of six, the engine had cooling difficulties, which were not solved until later twin-row radials were introduced with a staggered arrangement.

When the XP-13 failed to win a contract, the Thomas-Morse firm was absorbed by Consolidated

PMB

BOEING P-12D
Pratt & Whitney R-1340-17, 500 hp at 7000′
DIMENSIONS: As P-12C
WEIGHT: Empty 1956 lb., Gross 2648 lb.
PERFORMANCE: Speed—Top 188 mph at 7000′, Cruising 163 mph, Landing 58 mph. Service Ceiling 25,400′, Climb 10,000′/5.8 min. Range 475 miles normal, 622 miles max.

PMB

BOEING P-12E
Pratt & Whitney R-1340-17 (SR-1340E), 500 hp at 7000′
DIMENSIONS: Span 30′, Lg. 20′ 3″, Ht. 9′, Wing Area 227.5 sq. ft.
WEIGHT: Empty 1999 lb., Gross 2690 lb. Fuel 55–110 gal.
PERFORMANCE: Speed—Top 189 mph at 7000′, Cruising 160 mph, Landing 60 mph. Service Ceiling 26,300′, Absolute Ceiling 27,400′, Climb 10,000′/5.8 min.

MFR

BOEING 218 (later XP-925)
Pratt & Whitney SR-1340C, 450 hp
DIMENSIONS: Span 30′, Lg. 20′ 5″, Ht. 9′ 1″, Wing Area 227.5 sq. ft.
WEIGHT: Empty 1976 lb., Gross 2667 lb. Fuel 50 gal.
PERFORMANCE: Speed—Top 190 mph at 5000′, Cruising 157 mph, Landing 58 mph. Service Ceiling 29,000′, Absolute Ceiling 30,000′, Climb 10,000′/2.3 min.

AMC

BOEING P-12F
(Showing experimental canopy on last ship)
Pratt & Whitney R-1340-19, 600 hp take-off, 500 hp at 10,000′.
DIMENSIONS: As P-12E
WEIGHT: Empty 2035 lb., Gross 2726 lb. Fuel 55–110 gal.
PERFORMANCE: Speed—Top 194.5 mph at 10,000′, Cruising 166 mph, Landing 59 mph. Service Ceiling 31,400′, Absolute Ceiling 32,400′, Climb 2595′/1 min., 10,000′/4.2 min.

USN

BOEING XP-925A (Modified 218)
Pratt & Whitney SR-1340F, 500 hp at 10,000′
DIMENSIONS: Span 30′, Lg. 23′, Ht. 8′ 10″, Wing Area 227.5 sq. ft.
WEIGHT: Empty 1981 lb., Gross 2673 lb. Fuel 50 gal.
PERFORMANCE: Speed—Top 205 mph at 10,000′, 176 mph at s. l., Landing 58 mph. Service Ceiling 31,925′, Absolute Ceiling 33,000′, Climb 2310′/1 min., 10,000′/4.8 min.

in August 1929. A Pratt & Whitney Wasp and a new tail were installed on the aircraft by the Army in September 1930, and the fighter redesignated XP-13A.

A design competition for two-seat fighters was held in April 1929, and Berliner-Joyce was chosen over Boeing and Curtiss proposals for a prototype contract in June. First two-seat fighter since the TM-24, the Berliner-Joyce XP-16 appeared in October 1929. A 600 hp Curtiss V-1570-25 Conqueror turned a two-bladed prop above the tunnel radiator, and biplane wings were gulled into the fuselage. Armament included two nose guns, a flexible .30-caliber rear gun, and 244 lbs. of bombs.

A three-bladed propeller distinguished 25 YP-16s first ordered March 31, 1931, and tested April 1932. Later redesignated PB-1 (pursuit-biplace), they had better endurance than contemporary single-seaters,

AMC

THOMAS-MORSE XP-13
Curtiss H-1640-1, 600 hp
DIMENSIONS: Span 28′, Lg. 23′ 6″, Ht. 8′ 5″, Wing Area 189 sq. ft.
WEIGHT: Empty 2262 lb., Gross 3256 lb. Fuel 80 gal.
PERFORMANCE: Speed—Top 173 mph at s. l., 170 mph at 5000′, Cruising 138 mph, Landing 67 mph. Service Ceiling 20,775′, Absolute Ceiling 22,000′, Climb 5000′/3 min.

AF

BERLINER-JOYCE XP-16
Curtiss V-1570A, 600 hp
DIMENSIONS: Span 34′, Lg. 28′ 5″, Ht. 8′ 11″, Wing Area 279 sq. ft.
WEIGHT: Empty 2756 lb., Gross 3927 lb. Fuel 78 gal.
PERFORMANCE: Speed—Top 186 mph at 5000′, 176 mph at s. l., Cruising 148 mph, Landing 68 mph. Service Ceiling 26,200′, Absolute Ceiling 28,000′, Climb 2260/1 min., 5000′/2.6 min.

AMC

THOMAS-MORSE XP-13A
Pratt & Whitney SR-1340C, 450 hp
DIMENSIONS: As XP-13
WEIGHT: Empty 2224 lb., Gross 3194 lb. Fuel 74 gal.
PERFORMANCE: Speed—Top 188.5 mph at 5000′, Cruising 150 mph, Landing 67 mph. Service Ceiling 24,150′, Absolute Ceiling 25,600′, Climb 5000′/3.5 min.

AF

BERLINER-JOYCE Y1P-16
Curtiss V-1570-25, 600 hp
DIMENSIONS: Span 34′, Lg. 28′ 2″, Ht. 9′, Wing Area 279 sq. ft.
WEIGHT: Empty 2803 lb., Gross 3996 lb. Fuel 85–160 gal.
PERFORMANCE: Speed—Top 175 mph at s. l., 172 mph at 5000′, Cruising 151 mph, Landing 66 mph. Service Ceiling 21,600′, Absolute Ceiling 22,800′, Climb 1970′/1 min., 5000′/2.9 min. Range 650 miles.

but were handicapped by low speed and poor visibility. Without their prototype's supercharger, performance at altitude was poor.

EBB TIDE FOR BIPLANES

Boeing had been doing well in the fight for pursuit contracts, but Curtiss did not let their West Coast competitor capture the field entirely. New versions of the Hawk appeared sporting the latest wrinkles in design.

The Curtiss XP-17 was actually the first P-1 airframe modified by Army engineers to test in June 1930 the 480 hp air-cooled inverted inline Wright V-1460-3 Tornado. A pair of Curtiss designs, the XP-18 biplane and the XP-19 low-wing monoplane, were planned for the 600 hp Wright V-1560-1, but both were discarded on the drawing board.

AMC

CURTISS XP-17
Wright V-1460-3, 480 hp
DIMENSIONS: Span 31′ 7″, Lg. 22′ 10″, Ht. 8′ 7″, Wing Area 250 sq. ft.
WEIGHT: Empty 2204 lb., Gross 2994 lb. Fuel 43 gal.
PERFORMANCE: Speed—Top 165 mph at s. l., 161 mph at 5000′, Cruising 130 mph, Landing 62 mph. Service Ceiling 21,400′, Absolute Ceiling 22,800′, Climb 10,000′/8 min.

MFR

CURTISS YP-20
Wright R-1820-9, 575 hp
DIMENSIONS: Span 31′ 6″, Lg. 23′ 9″, Ht. 9′ 2″, Wing Area 252 sq. ft.
WEIGHT: Empty 2477 lb., Gross 3233 lb. Fuel 50–103 gal.
PERFORMANCE: Speed—Top 187 mph at s. l., 184 mph at 5000′, Cruising 149 mph, Landing 61 mph. Service Ceiling 26,700′, Absolute Ceiling 27,800′, Climb 2400′/1 min., 5000′/2.3 min. Endurance 1.1 hrs. at top speed.

The next Curtiss Hawk also had an air-cooled power plant, in this case the Wright R-1820-9 Cyclone. The YP-20 was actually a P-11 completed with this new radial, an NACA cowl, and wheel pants. It was first flown in November 1930. This was a very busy year in pursuit aviation at Wright Field; what with the P-6A, XP-9, P-12B, P-12C, XP-13A, XP-15, XP-16, XP-17, Model 100, and the YP-20.

A Curtiss P-6A was rebuilt with a new radiator, single-strut panted landing gear, three-bladed propeller, more streamlined appearance and designated XP-22. After trying odd elliptical and circular cowls containing the radiator, the XP-22 settled for a neat Prestone cooler between the legs of the landing gear, and behind the V-1570-23.

AMC

CURTISS XP-22
Curtiss V-1570-23, 600 hp
DIMENSIONS: Span 31′ 6″, Lg. 23′ 7″, Ht. 8′ 9″, Wing Area 252 sq. ft.
WEIGHT: Empty 2597 lb., Gross 3354 lb. Fuel 50–100 gal.
PERFORMANCE: Speed—Top 202 mph at s. l., 200 mph at 5000′, 195.5 mph at 10,000′, Cruising 172 mph, Landing 61 mph. Service Ceiling 26,500′, Absolute Ceiling 27,700′, Climb 2400′/1 min., 5000′/2.3 min., 10,000′/5.2 min.

In June 1931, an Army board met to consider the respective merits of the best fighters then available: the turbo-supercharged P-6D, the air-cooled P-12D and YP-20, and the liquid-cooled XP-22. The supercharger still seemed unready for squadron service, and the YP-20, while slightly superior in speed and climb to 5000 ft., was inferior to the P-12D in maneuver-

CURTISS P-6E
Curtiss V-1570-23, 600 hp
DIMENSIONS: Span 31′ 6″, Lg. 23′ 2″, Ht. 8′ 10″, Wing Area 252 sq. ft.
WEIGHT: Empty 2699 lb., Gross 3392 lb. Fuel 50–100 gal.
PERFORMANCE: Speed—Top 198 mph at s. l., 194.5 mph at 5000′, 189.5 mph at 10,000′, Cruising 175 mph, Landing 61 mph. Service Ceiling 24,700′, Absolute Ceiling 25,800′, Climb 2400′/1 min., 5000′/2.3 min., 10,000′/5.3 min. Range 285 miles normal, 572 miles max.

AF

CURTISS XP-6F
Curtiss V-1570-55, 600 hp at 15,000′
DIMENSIONS: As P-6E
WEIGHT: Empty 3149 lb., Gross 3842 lb. Fuel 50 gal.
PERFORMANCE: Speed—Top 225 mph at 18,000′, 183 mph at s. l., 212 mph at 10,000′. Service Ceiling not determined. Climb 1400′/1 min., 10,000′/6.1 min. Range 200 miles at top speed.

PMB

PMB

CURTISS XP-6H
Curtiss V-1570-51, 600 hp
DIMENSIONS: As P-6E
WEIGHT: Gross 3854 lb.
PERFORMANCE: Speed—Top 190 mph at s. l. Service Ceiling 22,800′, Absolute Ceiling 24,000′, Climb 2000′/1 min., 13,400′/10 min. Range 256 miles.

ability and visibility. On June 30, 1931, however, the XP-22 showed itself to be the fastest, with a speed of 202 mph; apparently the first true combat type in America to pass the 200 mark. A contract was placed with Curtiss on July 10, 1931, for 46 at a unit cost of $12,211. The designation was then changed from P-22 to P-6E.

A prototype P-6E was assembled by installing the XP-22s engine, nose, and landing gear to the YP-20s airframe. A more shallow fuselage, a larger headrest, and a tail wheel distinguished it from the XP-22. During January 1932 tests, this ship did 198 mph at sea level with a gross weight of 3392 lbs., but the regular P-6E production ship, tested in May, weighed 3436 lbs. Fifty gallons of fuel were carried behind the V-1570-23 engine, and a 50-gallon belly drop tank or 244 lbs. of bombs in wing racks could be added.

Two of these ships were modified with turbo-supercharged V-1570-55s, a cockpit canopy and open-sided wheel pants. Top speed of the XP-6F increased with altitude from 183 mph at sea level to 225 mph at 18,000 ft.; but engine overheating prevented higher flights, and tests were discontinued on August 1, 1933.

A temporary installation of a V-1570-51 on a P-6E was represented by the XP-6G designation, but more significant was the XP-6H, first Army multi-gun single-seater. Two .30-caliber synchronized guns, with 600 rpg, had been standard on pursuit ships since 1918, the only difference on the P-6E being that the guns were lowered from their usual position on the cowl, to fire through troughs below the exhaust stacks. But the need for more firepower was felt, and a P-1B with another pair of .30-caliber guns in the upper wing had been tested in December 1931. Conversion of a P-6E into a six-gun XP-6H, with an additional pair of .30-caliber guns in the upper wing with 600 rounds each, and one with 450 rounds in each lower wing, was approved on September 11, 1932. Opinion seems to have been that wing guns were not feasible on P-6s and the project was dropped.

The last and finest of the Army's biplane fighters was converted from the final P-6E. A metal monocoupe fuselage and wings, a 600 hp V-1570-23 Conqueror with a turbo-supercharger on the side, and a finely streamlined nose pointed by a three-bladed prop characterized the XP-23. This good-looking Curtiss resembled Britain's Hawker Fury, and it is too bad that new monoplanes elbowed it out of the way. A

AMC

CURTISS XP-23
Curtiss V-1570-23, 600 hp
DIMENSIONS: Span 31′ 6″, Lg. 23′ 10″, Ht. 9′ 6″, Wing Area 252 sq. ft.
WEIGHT: Empty 3274 lb., Gross 4124 lb. Fuel 78–128 gal.
PERFORMANCE: Speed—Top 223 mph at 15,000′, Cruising 190 mph, Landing 70 mph. Service Ceiling 33,000′, Climb 1370′/1 min. Range 435 miles normal, 703 miles max.

company report in April 1932 credited the XP-23 with 223 mph at 15,000 ft. Later the prototype was refitted with the geared 600 hp V-1570-27 minus the turbo, and with a two-bladed prop. Redesignated YP-23, this version had a more prosaic performance. Armament is reported at two .30-caliber and one .50-caliber gun, plus a bomb load of 488 lbs.

AMC

CURTISS YP-23

Chapter 16: Monoplanes 1932-39

Since World War I dogfighting had left pursuit pilots more conscious of twisting and turning with enemy fighters than of chasing bombers, pilots preferred sturdy, maneuverable biplanes to untried monoplanes; not a bad choice so long as bombers were slow biplanes of the traditional pattern. But new all-metal monoplanes like the Martin XB-10 with retractable wheels sharply reduced interception capabilities of biplane pursuit planes. The XB-10s 207 mph speed was faster than any 1931 Army biplane, and pressed fighter designers to use monoplane layouts.

The P-12E and P-6E types on order were simply not fast enough to catch the Martin bomber, and the Army abruptly turned to the monoplane pattern for its fighters. The switch was sooner than that of the Navy, which persisted with the Grumman biplanes, and was far ahead of most foreign powers, who as late as 1940 were still using in battle biplanes like the British Gladiator, Italian Fiat, and Soviet I-15.

The first low-wing monoplane to begin the new trend in Army fighters was the XP-900, designed by the Lockheed company, which was then a subsidiary of an ill-fated combine called Detroit Aircraft. This two-seater was developed from a series of commercial monoplanes culminating in the Altair, a low-wing monoplane with internally braced wings, retractable landing gear, and enclosed cockpits. These features were incorporated in the XP-900, which was powered by a 600 hp Curtiss V-1570-23, was plywood covered, and had a gunner seated back-to-back with the pilot. Armament included two fixed and one flexible .30 caliber gun.

After inspection of the mockup at Detroit in March 1931, the Air Corps considered the type as a P-16 replacement, and on September 29, 1931, the prototype and four further examples were purchased, and assigned the designation YP-24 and Y1P-24. Four Y1A-9 attack versions were added to the contract.

During tests at Wright Field in October 1931, however, the YP-24 crashed, and a few months later the Detroit organization was disrupted financially and defaulted on the contract. Fortunately, the YP-24s young designer, Robert Wood, had joined Consolidated Aircraft, then in Buffalo, and was able to plan a new two-seater of similar layout, but of all-metal construction. Air Corps funds from the former project were allotted in March 1932 to the Consolidated Y1P-25, Wood's new design.

The Y1P-25 was built with a turbo-supercharged V-1570-57 in a streamlined nose. A second prototype was completed without a supercharger as the XA-11. Wood also projected in May 1932 two air-cooled versions with Pratt & Whitney radials: a YP-27 with a 550 hp R-1340-21, and the YP-28 with a 600 hp R-1340-19. Both projects were canceled, however.

Consolidated's Y1P-25 got 247 mph at 15,000 ft. out of its turbo-supercharger during the December 1932 tests. Although the Y1P-25 crashed on January 13, 1933, followed a week later by another unlucky accident to the XA-11, an Army board impressed with the plane's performance recommended purchase of an improved Y1P-25 which became the P-30. Before the P-30 appeared, the Army purchased a more conservative single-seater.

BOEING P-26

Previously, most Army monoplanes had been high-wing, usually parasol, types with a variety of struts and bracing wire canceling out much of the speed which should have been gained by eliminating lower wings. In spite of Fokker's success with cantilever wings, the Matériel Division had felt the internally braced wing not secure enough to delete outside struts, and engineering technique had yet to prevent the tendency of wings to break when pulling out of a dive.

Outside bracing wires were still visible on three Model 248 mid-wing monoplanes built by Boeing as

MFR

LOCKHEED YP-24 (XP-900)
Curtiss V-1570-23, 600 hp at s. l.
DIMENSIONS: Span 42′ 9″, Lg. 28′ 9″, Ht. 8′ 6″, Wing Area 292 sq. ft.
WEIGHT: Empty 3193 lb., Gross 4360 lb. Fuel 75 gal.
PERFORMANCE: Speed—Top 214.5 mph at s. l., 210.5 mph at 5000′, Cruising 186 mph, Landing 73 mph. Service Ceiling 26,400′, Absolute Ceiling 28,000′, Climb 1800′/1 min., 5000′/3.1 min. Range 556 miles.

BOEING P-26A
Pratt & Whitney R-1340-27, 600 hp at 6,000′
DIMENSIONS: Span 27′ 11½″, Lg. 23′ 10″, Ht. 10′ 5″, Wing Area 149.5 sq. ft.
WEIGHT: Empty 2271 lb., Gross 3012 lb. Fuel 52–107 gal.
PERFORMANCE: Speed—Top 234 mph at 7500′, 211 mph at s. l., Cruising 199 mph, Landing 82.5 mph (74 mph with flaps). Service Ceiling 27,400′, Absolute Ceiling 28,300′, Climb 2360′/1 min., 6000′/3 min. Range 360 miles normal, 570 miles max.

MFR

CONSOLIDATED Y1P-25
Curtiss V-1570-27, 600 hp
DIMENSIONS: Span 43′ 10″, Lg. 29′ 4″, Ht. 8′ 7″, Wing Area 296 sq. ft.
WEIGHT: Empty 3887 lb., Gross 5110 lb. Fuel 90–173 gal.
PERFORMANCE: Speed—Top 247 mph at 15,000′, 205 mph at s. l. Climb 10,000′/6.7 min.

a private venture and first flown on March 20, 1932. Bought by the Army in June 1932 as the Y1P-26 (formerly XP-936), they had excellent visibility for the pilot seated high behind a 550 hp R-1340-21. A lower set of wires connected the wings to neat wheel pants, while the upper set tied the wings to the top of the metal fuselage.

On January 11, 1933, the Army ordered 111 P-26As (Model 266), and they were delivered between January and June 1934 with a 600 hp R-1340-27

AF

PMB

BOEING Y1P-26 (XP-936)
Pratt & Whitney R-1340-21 (SR-1340G), 525 hp at 6000′
DIMENSIONS: Span 27′ 5″, Lg. 23′ 9″, Ht. 7′ 6″, Wing Area 150 sq. ft.
WEIGHT: Empty 2120 lb., Gross 2789 lb. Fuel 50–106 gal.
PERFORMANCE: Speed—Top 227 mph at 6000′, Cruising 193 mph, Landing 73.5 mph. Service Ceiling 27,800′, Absolute Ceiling 28,900′, Climb 2230′/1 min.

and wing flaps. An export model (Boeing 281) was built: one for Spain, and ten for the Cantonese provincial government in China. A repeat order for 25 P-26Bs, similar but for an R-1340-33, was completed in March 1936. All but two reverted to -27 engines and became known as P-26Cs. Armament included two guns and two 116-lb. bombs. Some Boeings fought Japan in August 1937 in China, and in December 1941 in the Philippines.

MFR

BOEING 281
Pratt & Whitney R-1340-33, 600 hp
DIMENSIONS: Span 27′ 11½″, Lg. 23′ 7¼″, Ht. 7′ 10½″, Wing Area 149.5 sq. ft.
WEIGHT: Empty 2354 lb., Gross 3039 lb., Max. 3390 lb. Fuel 55–107 gal.
PERFORMANCE: Speed—Top 235 mph at 6000′, 215 mph at s. l., Cruising 210 mph, Landing 68 mph. Service Ceiling 28,200′, Climb 2210′/1 min. Range 386 miles normal, 745 miles max.

CURTISS XP-31 (XP-934)
Curtiss V-1570-53, 600 hp at s. l.
DIMENSIONS: Span 36′, Lg. 26′ 3″, Ht. 7′ 9″, Wing Area 203 sq. ft.
WEIGHT: Empty 3334 lb., Gross 4143 lb. Fuel 75–125 gal.
PERFORMANCE: Speed—Top 208 mph at s. l., 202.5 mph at 5000′, Cruising 184 mph, Landing 80.5 mph. Service Ceiling 24,400′, Absolute Ceiling 25,600′, Climb 2130′/1 min., 5000′/2.6 min. Range 370 miles.

AF

MFR

CURTISS XP-31 (XP-934 with radial engine)

MFR

BOEING XP-940 (XP-29)
Pratt & Whitney R-1340-31, 475 hp
DIMENSIONS: Span 29′ 5″, Lg. 23′ 10″, Wing Area 177 sq. ft.
WEIGHT: Empty 2447 lb., Gross 3332 lb. (Design 3267 lb.).
PERFORMANCE: Speed—Top 220 mph.

Curtiss offered competition with the XP-934 Swift, tested in December 1932. Later designated XP-31, the Swift resembled the A-8 attack and was an all-metal monoplane with an enclosed cockpit, 600 hp Curtiss V-1570-53 inline engine, wing slots, and flaps. It was the last U.S. fighter with nonretractable wheels, which were in wheel-pants connected by Vee struts to the low-wing. The normal two nose guns could be supplemented by another pair in fairings on each side of the cockpit. The XP-31 was too heavy for the fast low-altitude speeds desired, even after modification by a radial engine.

On January 18, 1934, Boeing flew a development of the P-26 called XP-940 (later XP-29), a cantilever low-wing minus any external bracing, and powered by a 475 hp R-1340-31 Wasp. The cockpit was enclosed, and the wheels retracted backwards about halfway into the wings. After tests, three examples were ordered in June 1934, designated YP-29, YP-29A, and YP-29B.

Delivered in September, the YP-29A was actually the prototype rebuilt with an open cockpit (the former enclosure seemed too cramped), P-26A headrest and tail wheel, and a 575 hp R-1340-35. Fitted with the R-1340-27 standard on the P-26A, the plane was designated P-29A.

MFR

BOEING YP-29A (P-29A)
Pratt & Whitney R-1340-35 (or -27), 570 hp at 7500′
DIMENSIONS: Span 29′ 5″, Lg. 25′ 1″, Ht. 7′ 8″, Wing Area 177 sq. ft.
WEIGHT: Empty 2502 lb., Gross 3270 lb. (Design 3267 lb.). Fuel 73–110 gal.
PERFORMANCE: Speed—Top 242 mph at 7500′, Cruising 206 mph, Landing 82 mph. Climb 1840′/1 min.

In October 1934, Boeing delivered the YP-29B, which also had an open cockpit and R-1340-35 but added a single flap between the wheels and a different type tail wheel. Last of three to be delivered was the YP-29 which had new, roomy pilot's canopy, flaps, YP-29B tail wheel, and wing dihedral of 6°, instead of 7° on the earlier ships. Tested at Wright in June 1935, the YP-29 had two guns and 327 lbs. of bombs.

Boeing planned another version as the YP-32, with a 700 hp twin-row R-1535-1, but this project was not carried through. The XF7B fighter built for the Navy was also similar to the P-29 layout. Neither type was successful, and Boeing went out of the fighter business to concentrate on bombers.

TWO-SEATERS

Purchase of four Consolidated P-30s had been recommended by an Air Corps Board in January 1933, and these two-seaters were built like the Y1P-25 but for a turbo-supercharged, 675 hp V-1710-57, simplified landing gear, and omission of the nose spinner. During August 1934 tests, Wright Field pilots complained that the rear gunner became valueless if even the simplest maneuvers were performed. Nevertheless, the Air Corps made a $1,996,700 contract on December 6, 1934, for 50 P-30As.

CONSOLIDATED P-30
Curtiss V-1570-57, 675 hp at 15,000′
DIMENSIONS: Span 43′ 11″, Lg. 29′ 4″, Ht. 8′ 4″, Wing Area 297 sq. ft.
WEIGHT: Empty 3832 lb., Gross 5092 lb. Fuel 90–130 gal.
PERFORMANCE: Speed—Top 239 mph at 15,000′, 194 mph at s. l., Cruising 201.5 mph, Landing 77 mph. Climb 10,000′/7.6 min., 15,000′/10.9 min. Range 495 miles.

MFR

BOEING YP-29B (P-29B)

AF

BOEING YP-29 (P-29)

Pratt & Whitney R-1340-31 (or -39), 550 hp at 10,000′

DIMENSIONS: Span 29′ 5″, Lg. 25′ 2″, Ht. 7′ 8″, Wing Area 177 sq. ft.

WEIGHT: Empty 2573 lb., Gross 3572 lb. Fuel 73–110 gal.

PERFORMANCE: Speed—Top 244 mph at 10,000′, Cruising 208 mph, Landing 81 mph. Service Ceiling 24,200′, Climb 1570′/1 min., 10,000′/6.8 min. Range 520 miles normal, 707 miles max.

MFR

MFR

CONSOLIDATED PB-2A
Curtiss V-1570-61, 700 hp at 15,000′
DIMENSIONS: Span 43′ 11″, Lg. 30′, Ht. 8′ 3″, Wing Area 297 sq. ft.
WEIGHT: Empty 4306 lb., Gross 5643 lb. Fuel 90–180 gal.
PERFORMANCE: Speed—Top 274.5 mph at 25,000′, 255.5 mph at 15,000′, 214 mph at s. l., Cruising 215 mph, Landing 62 mph. Service Ceiling 28,000′, Climb 15,000′/7.78 min. Range 508 miles.

SI—MFR

BELLANCA 28-90
Pratt & Whitney R-1830 Wasp, 900 hp at 6200′
DIMENSIONS: Span 46′ 2″, Lg. 26′ 6″, Ht. 7′, Wing Area 279 sq. ft.
WEIGHT: Empty 4450 lb., Gross 6755 lb., Max. 7849 lb. Fuel 150 gal.
PERFORMANCE: Speed—Top 280 mph at 6500′, Cruising 250 mph, Landing 68 mph. Service Ceiling 30,500′, Climb 2800′/1 min., 15,000′/7.5 min. Range 800 miles.

Consolidated moved from Buffalo to San Diego, and these ships were the first built in the new plant. Powered by a 700 hp V-1710-61, the P-30A was redesignated PB-2A, and P-30s became PB-2s. Effects of the General Electric F-3 turbo-supercharger on speed was revealed in April 1936 trials when a PB-2A did 214 mph at sea level, 255 mph at 15,000 ft., and 274 mph at 25,000 ft. There, however, engine overheating interfered with performance, and the actual ceiling was not obtained. Armament included the usual two fixed and one flexible .30-caliber gun.

An air-cooled version, the Consolidated P-33, was planned with an 800 hp Pratt & Whitney R-1830-1. This project was canceled, and the PB-2A was the only two-place fighter monoplane in American service before World War II. Valuable mainly for experience with turbo-supercharging, the PB-2A was the last two-seater of the tradition begun by the Bristol fighter. The rear gun's firepower was insufficient compensation for lost speed and maneuverability, and future two-seaters were built only for special night or long-range missions in which the second crewman's role was that of direction, rather than gunnery.

While considering two-seat fighters, we might mention here another design developed as a private venture for the export trade. The Bellanca 28-70 was built in 1936 as a transatlantic racer for a private pilot. It had a 700 hp Pratt & Whitney Wasp, enclosed cockpits, retractable wheels, and mixed metal and fabric construction. Wings were externally braced by wires, and steel supporting struts protruded below the fuselage, an unfortunate disturbance of otherwise good lines.

A military development of the machine became known in 1937 when 20 of the 28-90 model (using a 900 hp Wasp) built for French airmail operations were purchased for use in the Spanish Civil War. This particular shipment was halted by the State Department, but it was reported in August 1938 that more had been purchased by the Chinese government, of the 28-110 model with the 1000 hp R-1830 Wasp.

Armament included five .30-caliber guns, and up to 1600 lbs. of bombs if desired. Two fixed guns with 360 rounds each were located in the side of the fuselage, two more with 500 rounds each were in the wings, and a flexible gun was in the rear pit. Normal fuel load of 150 gallons could be doubled if no bombs were carried.

PURSUIT COMPETITIONS, 1935–36

Up to 1932, it looked as if future fighters would be the same open cockpit biplanes that had prevailed in World War I, but by 1936 it became evident that the whole layout of fighters had been altered to the pattern familiar in World War II: all-metal low-wing monoplanes with enclosed cockpits, and retractable landing gear.

A series of design competitions, held in an international atmosphere charged with the menace of aggressive fascism, demonstrated what designers had learned about streamlining aircraft. All entries in these contests followed the general form that was fast becoming a world-wide fighter style. All were low-wing, single-seat all-metal monoplanes with retracting wheels, enclosed cockpit, and a three-bladed, controllable-pitch propeller. Armament, however, showed persistence of 1917 habits, for two synchronized guns mounted on the cowling were considered sufficient. Caliber of both was still .30, unless an alternative installation of one .50 and one .30 was made.

Wedell-Williams, a Louisiana builder of racers, had considered offering a fighter design to the Air Corps. In February 1934 inquiries indicated the Matériel Division would not be interested in anything as light as their famous racer, but on May 6, 1935, a proposal was submitted which won a September design competition, and a design study contract on October 1, 1935, for a 4250 lb. fighter powered by a Pratt & Whitney R-1535 and capable of 286 mph at 10,000 ft. Since the April 1936 fighter competition indicated superior performance in aircraft already tested, the design was revised in June to use a 900 hp R-1830 which was to produce a speed of 308 mph. Although the designation XP-34 was assigned, the Wedell-Williams type was not actually built.

Looking for a P-26 replacement, the Matériel Division called for bids to be opened in May 1935 on single-seat pursuits. Only the Curtiss Design 75 was ready at that time, so a second competition was held in August, at which the Seversky Sev-1 also appeared. Still another competition had to be held in April 1936 before settling which ships would equip Air Corps fighter squadrons on the eve of World War II. Prototypes built by Consolidated and Vought joined the Curtiss and Seversky ships to establish low-wing fighter styles familiar in the approaching war and prevailing until the advent of jet propulsion.

Powered by a 900 hp twin-row Wright R-1670, Curtiss Design 75 was begun in November 1934 and was submitted May 27, 1935, with a unique landing gear whose wheels rotated as they folded back within the wings. Seversky's pursuit was damaged and delayed on the way to Wright Field, and arrived on June 18, 1935. Originally a two-seater with panted landing-gear, it was returned to the Long Island factory to be reworked into a single-seater with wheels retracting back into underwing fairings. Powered by a single-row Wright R-1820-G5 Cyclone rated at 850 hp, the Sev-1 came back to Wright Field on August 15, 1935. Favored by the Army, it would have received a contract in November had not Curtiss protested that unfair advantage had been given by allowing the Seversky's late arrival. When the third bid opening was held on April 15, 1936, Consolidated and Vought single-seaters were ready. Curtiss was low bidder on the contract: $29,412 each in lots of 25, and $14,150 each in lots of 200. Other bids on these lots were Vought, $34,148—$16,051; Seversky, $34,900—$15,800; and Consolidated, $44,000—$24,260.

Consolidated offered a single-seat modification of the seventh PB-2A, with a Curtiss V-1710-61 of 700 hp at 15,000 ft. The only entry with a liquid-cooled inline engine, it was larger, heavier, and more expensive than the other types, and was disqualified due to destruction in a fatal crash.

From experience with the Navy XFT-1, Northrop had prepared a design known as the XP-948, or Northrop 3A. On July 30, 1935, the prototype took off for its initial flight, headed out over the Pacific, and completely disappeared! Powered by a Pratt & Whitney Twin Wasp, the XP-948 had wheels retracting into the wing roots as on the A-17A.

Chance Vought then purchased the design and built the plane anew as the V-141 with a 750 hp Pratt &

VOUGHT V-141
Pratt & Whitney R-1535-A5G, 750 hp at 8000′
DIMENSIONS: Span 33′ 6″, Lg. 22′ 10″, Ht. 9′ 8″, Wing Area 187 sq. ft.
WEIGHT: Empty 3515 lb., Gross 4430 lb. Fuel 75–112 gal.
PERFORMANCE: Speed—Top 274 mph at 10,000′, Cruising 249.5 mph, Landing 73 mph. Service Ceiling 28,300′, Climb 10,000′/3.86 min. Range 704 miles.

AF

NORTHROP 3A (XP-948)

MFR

CONSOLIDATED SINGLE-SEATER (P-30A #7)
Curtiss V-1710-61, 700 hp at 15,000′
DIMENSIONS: As PB-2A
WEIGHT: Empty 4315 lb., Gross 5602 lb. Fuel 90–180 gal.
PERFORMANCE: Speed—Top 275 mph at 25,000′, 250 mph at 15,000′, Cruising 220 mph. Service Ceiling 30,000′, Climb 10,000′/5 min. Range 1012 miles max.

MFR

SEVERSKY SEV-7
(SEV-1 with Pratt & Whitney R-1830-9)

MFR

SEVERSKY SEV-1
Wright R-1820-G-5, 850 hp at 10,000′
DIMENSIONS: Span 36′, Lg. 25′, Wing Area 220 sq. ft.
WEIGHT: Empty 3706 lb., Gross 5014 lb.
PERFORMANCE: Speed—Top 300 mph at 10,000′ (285 mph on test), Cruising 265 mph. Service Ceiling 30,000′, Climb 10,000′/3 min. Range 1192 miles.

AF

SEVERSKY P-35 (First production article)

AMC

Whitney R-1535-A5G. The V-141 was the smallest type in the 1936 competition, but suffered from tail vibrations. Offered for export sale as the V-143, it had an R-1535-32 of 600 hp for take-off and 525 hp at 8000 ft., and carried two .30-caliber guns, 1000 rounds of ammunition, and up to 300 lbs. of bombs. Japan purchased the prototype in 1937, and during the war there were comments on the resemblance between Mitsubishi's Zero and the American design. The Japanese ship's designer has stated that the Zero's system of wheel retraction was based on the V-143, but points out that, apart from the general similarity in appearance of most radial-engined low-wing fighters, each fighter type is built in response to particular needs and experiences.

In April 1936, the Curtiss Design 75 had reappeared for the final contest with a modified cockpit canopy and the original twin-row engine replaced by a single-row Wright XR-1820-39 (G-5) giving 850 hp, as on Seversky's ship. Actually, the Matériel Division was undecided about this Cyclone radial, and asked each aircraft builder for alternate performance estimates based on Pratt & Whitney's twin-row R-1830 Wasp, whose smaller diameter promised more visibility and a bit less drag.

Troubles with the Cyclone engine bothered both the Curtiss and Seversky ships. The Curtiss 75 required four engine changes during tests, and achieved but 285 of the 294 mph guaranteed by the builder. Seversky's Sev-1 tested at 289 mph instead of the 300 mph promised. During the trials, the Seversky's R-1820 was replaced by an R-1830 rated at 850 hp. In this case, only 277 mph was achieved, for the power plant seemed to yield only 738 hp. Nevertheless, the R-1830 was specified for both Seversky and Curtiss ships when production orders were placed. Wright R-1820 Cyclones, however, were used on B-17, B-18, and A-18 types ordered that same year, and gave very satisfactory service on the multiengined ships.

Seventy-seven Seversky P-35s were ordered June 16, 1936, and delivered between July 1937 and August 1938. They differed from the Sev-1 prototype in having an R-1830-9 Wasp, modified canopy and wheel fairings, and the air intake was moved from the fuselage's side to its bottom. Up to 300 lbs. of bombs or as much as 200 gallons of fuel could be carried. The first production P-35 had fully enclosed wheels and no dihedral, but successors had open wheel fairings and dihedral.

Seversky continued P-35 development in the following years. Several built for private pilots were used in the National Air Races. The last aircraft of the P-35 contract was completed as the XP-41. Changes included installation of a 1200 hp R-1830-19 with a two-stage supercharger, wheels retracting flat into the center section, and the intake placed on top of the cowl.

Meanwhile, the first export version was built as a two-seater with a single-row 1000 hp R-1820 Cyclone

SEVERSKY P-35

Pratt & Whitney R-1830-9, 950 hp take-off, 850 hp at 8000′

DIMENSIONS: Span 36′, Lg. 25′ 2″, Ht. 9′ 1″, Wing Area 220 sq. ft.

WEIGHT: Empty 4315 lb., Gross 5599 lb., Max. 6295 lb. Fuel 110–200 gal.

PERFORMANCE: Speed—Top 281.5 mph at 10,000′, Cruising 259.5 mph, Landing 79 mph. Service Ceiling 30,600′, Absolute Ceiling 31,750′, Climb 2440′/1 min., 5000′/2.05 min., 15,000′/6.9 min. Range 1150 miles/200 gal. at 259.5 mph, 800 miles/134 gal. at 200 mph.

AF

instead of the twin-row Wasp. This two-seater Seversky 2PA-L was known as the "Convoy Fighter." A pair were sold to the U.S.S.R. late in 1937 with the manufacturing rights, although it is not known whether any Soviet editions were actually built. Twenty more "Convoy Fighters" were built in 1938 for the Japanese Navy, and (as the A8V1) were the only American planes used operationally by a Japanese squadron. Armament on the 2PA-L included a .30-caliber flexible gun, two fixed guns, and up to 600 lbs. of bombs.

Sweden ordered in 1939 over a hundred of an improved P-35 known as the EP-1. Those built up to May 1940 were delivered, but 60 completed from July 1940 to January 1941 were requisitioned by the U. S. Army as the Republic[1] P-35A. Powered by a 1050 hp R-1830-45 Wasp, the P-35A had the intake atop the cowl, and to the original pair of .30-caliber guns added a .50-caliber gun in each wing, and 350 lbs. of bombs. The P-35As went to the Philippines, where they found themselves in December 1941 during the opening of the war with Japan.

A two-seater version of the P-35A was the Republic Guardsman, which used the same engine but could carry up to 1350 lbs. of bombs, and had two .50-caliber fixed and one .30-caliber flexible gun. Fifty built in

[1] Seversky left the firm and the name was changed to Republic in 1939.

MFR

SEVERSKY 2PA-L
Wright R-1820, 1000 hp take-off
DIMENSIONS: Span 36′, Lg. 25′ 5″, Ht. 9′ 6″, Wing Area 220 sq. ft.
WEIGHT: Empty 4034 lb., Gross 5952 lb. Fuel 200 gal.
PERFORMANCE: Speed—Top 290 mph at 16,500′, Cruising 270 mph, Landing 65 mph. Service Ceiling 30,000′, Climb 3150′/1 min.

MFR

REPUBLIC P-35A
Pratt & Whitney R-1830-45, 1050 hp take-off, 1000 hp at 11,500′, 900 hp at 12,000′
DIMENSIONS: Span 36′, Lg. 26′ 10″, Ht. 9′ 9″, Wing Area 220 sq. ft.
WEIGHT: Empty 4575 lb., Gross 6118 lb., Max. 6723 lb. Fuel 130–200 gal.
PERFORMANCE: (6118 lb.) Speed—Top 290 mph at 12,000′, Cruising 260 mph, Landing 80 mph. Service Ceiling 31,400′, Absolute Ceiling 32,300′, Climb 1920′/1 min. Range 600 miles/130 gal. at 260 mph, 950 miles/200 gal. at 220 mph with 350 lbs. bombs.

PMB

REPUBLIC GUARDSMAN (AT-12)

Pratt & Whitney R-1830-45, 1050 hp
DIMENSIONS: Span 41′, Lg. 27′ 8″, Ht. 9′ 10″, Wing Area 250 sq. ft.
WEIGHT: Empty 5146 lb., Gross 7480 lb., Max. 8360 lb. Fuel 130 gal.
PERFORMANCE: Speed—Top 285 mph at 11,500′, Cruising 250 mph, Landing 86 mph. Service Ceiling 28,000′, Climb 2050′/1 min. Range 580 miles.

1940 for Sweden were taken over by the U.S. as AT-12 advanced trainers.

CURTISS P-36 AND SUCCESSORS

Although the Seversky P-35 had won the first competition, three service test examples of the Curtiss YP-36 ordered in July 1936 were delivered February 1937, with a modified cockpit, retractable tail wheel, and a 1050 hp twin-row Pratt & Whitney R-1830-13. On July 7, 1937, the Army ordered 210[2] similar production models for $4,113,550, the largest fighter order since 1918. Delivery of the P-36A began in April 1938, and after 177 were finished, the last 31 were completed by May 1939 as the P-36C, with a 1200 hp R-1830-17 and a pair of .30-caliber wing guns added to the usual two on the cowl by a January 26, 1939,

[2] One aircraft on this order was completed as the XP-40, another as the XP-42.

CURTISS YP-36
Pratt & Whitney R-1830-13, 1050 hp take-off, 900 hp at 12,000′
DIMENSIONS: Span 37′ 4″, Lg. 28′ 2″, Ht. 9′, Wing Area 236 sq. ft.
WEIGHT: Empty 4389 lb., Gross 5437 lb., Max. 5960 lb. Fuel 100–151 gal.
PERFORMANCE: Speed—Top 294.5 mph at 10,000′, Cruising 256 mph, Landing 65 mph. Service Ceiling 35,100′, Absolute Ceiling, 36,150′, Climb 3145′/1 min., 10,000′/3.44 min. Range 752 miles/150 gal.

MFR

CURTISS DESIGN 75 (Prototype P-36 with R-1670)

MFR

CURTISS DESIGN 75B
Wright XR-1820-39, 850 hp at 10,000′
DIMENSIONS: Span 37′ 4″, Lg. 28′ 1″, Ht. 9′, Wing Area 236 sq. ft.
WEIGHT: Empty 4049 lb., Gross 5075 lb. Fuel 133–151 gal.
PERFORMANCE: Speed—Top 285 mph at 10,000′, Cruising 260 mph, Landing 66 mph. Service Ceiling 32,500′, Climb 10,000′/3.87 min. Range 730 miles.

AF

PMB

CURTISS P-36A
Pratt & Whitney R-1830-13, 1050 hp take-off, 900 hp at 10,000′
DIMENSIONS: Span 37′ 4″, Lg. 28′ 6″, Ht. 12′ 2″, Wing Area 236 sq. ft.
WEIGHT: Empty 4567 lb., Gross 5650 lb., Max. 6010 lb. Fuel 105–162 gal.
PERFORMANCE: Speed—Top 300 mph at 10,000′, Cruising 270 mph, Landing 75 mph. Service Ceiling 33,000′, Absolute Ceiling 34,000′, Climb 3400′/1 min. Range 825 miles max.

PMB

CURTISS P-36C
Pratt & Whitney R-1830-17, 1200 hp take-off, 1050 hp at 10,000′
DIMENSIONS: As P-36A
WEIGHT: Empty 4620 lb., Gross 5800 lb., Max. 6150 lb. Fuel 105–162 gal.
PERFORMANCE: Speed—Top 311 mph at 10,000′, Cruising 270 mph, Landing 75 mph. Service Ceiling 33,700′, Climb 15,000′/4.9 min. Range 820 miles at 200 mph, 600 miles at 270 mph.

order. This model could be recognized by retainer boxes for wing gun cartridges, required so that empty shells wouldn't rain down on peacetime taxpayers.

A number of P-36As were modified to try engine and armament innovations. One with a 1100 hp R-1830-25 became the 313 mph P-36B of November 1938. Another, fitted by the company with a turbo-supercharger was called the 75-R. On September 6, 1939, the Air Corps approved tests of heavier firepower, and an XP-36D was armed with two .50-caliber guns on the cowl and four .30-caliber wing guns. Other P-36A conversions made that month were the XP-36E, with eight .30-caliber guns in the wings and one .50-caliber cowl gun, and the XP-36F, which had a 23-mm. Madsen attached below each wing as well as a .50-caliber and a .30-caliber gun on the cowl.

Many of these Curtiss monoplanes were also built for export, beginning with the Hawk 75. This type differed from the P-36 in having a Wright R-1820-G3 Cyclone giving 840 hp at 8700 ft., and fixed, panted wheels. Armament included two cowl guns (one .30-caliber with 600 rounds and one .50-caliber with 200 rounds), two .30-caliber wing guns, and racks for 300 lbs. of bombs.

The demonstration model was purchased by China in the summer of 1937 and used as a command plane by General Claire L. Chennault, then leading their air force. A production lot of 112 sent to China in 1938 suffered more losses to inexperienced piloting than to Japanese action. The Hawk 75 was also sold to Siam and to Argentina, where 200 were built under license.

Before the outbreak of the Second World War, France bought 200 Hawk 75A-1 fighters. First flown in December 1938, the 75A-1 had four .30-caliber guns, bomb racks, and the first pilot armor on a modern U.S. fighter. With the retractable wheels of the P-36, it was otherwise similar to the Army ship but for a 900 hp Wright R-1820-G105.

CURTISS XP-36F
Pratt & Whitney R-1830-13, 1050 hp
DIMENSIONS: As P-36A
WEIGHT: Max. 6850 lb.
PERFORMANCE: Speed—Top 265 mph.

AMC

CURTISS 75R
Pratt & Whitney R-1830-SC2-G
DIMENSIONS: As P-36A
WEIGHT: Empty 5074 lb., Gross 6163 lb.
PERFORMANCE: Speed—Top 330 mph at 15,000′, Cruising 302 mph, Climb 15,000′/4.75 min. Range 600 miles.

MFR

MFR

CURTISS HAWK 75
Wright GR-1820-G3, 840 hp at 8700′
DIMENSIONS: Span 37′ 4″, Lg. 28′ 7″, Ht. 9′ 4″, Wing Area 236 sq. ft.
WEIGHT: Empty 3975 lb., Gross 5172 lb., Max. 6418 lb. Fuel 107–220 gal.
PERFORMANCE: Speed—Top 280 mph at 10,700′, Cruising 240 mph, Landing 68 mph. Service Ceiling 31,800′, Climb 2340′/1 min. Range 547 miles normal, 1210 miles max.

SI—MFR

CURTISS HAWK 75A-1
Wright R-1820-G105, 900 hp.
DIMENSIONS: Span 37′ 4″, Lg. 28′ 7″, Ht. 9′ 4″, Wing Area 236 sq. ft.
WEIGHT: Empty 4483 lb., Gross 5692 lb. Fuel 105–163 gal.
PERFORMANCE: Speed—Top 303 mph at 19,000′, 259 mph at s. l., Cruising 260 mph, Landing 68.5 mph. Service Ceiling 32,800′, Absolute Ceiling 34,120′, Climb 2340′/1 min. Range 677 miles normal, 1040 miles max.

After successful tests, including a 575 mph power dive, and shooting down in September 1939 the first Nazi plane from French skies, orders for 430 additional Hawks were placed by France on October 5, 1939, followed by orders from Iran, Norway, and the Dutch East Indies. These ships appeared with six .30-caliber guns and both the R-1830-S1C3G Pratt & Whitney Wasp of 1050 hp at 7500 ft. (Hawk 75A-2) and the Wright R-1820-95 Cyclone giving 1000 hp at 15,000 ft. (Hawk 75A-4). Although 465 Hawks were delivered between February and August 1940, and 46 added from December 1940 to March 1941, most were not flown by their original buyers. Instead, 44 captured by the Germans were sold to Finland, 227 absorbed by the British from French contracts were named "Mohawk" and sent to Africa, and 30 Cyclone-powered 75A-4s for Norway were used in Canada for training, sold to the U. S. Army in April 1942, designated P-36G, and later given to Peru.

The first American fighter used in the Second World War, the Curtiss Hawk fought on many fronts, beginning with the lost defense of France. Arriving in Africa in December 1940, Mohawks hit Italy in East Africa and were then retired to South Africa and India for training. In India they were at one time the sole remaining defense against Japan, and were not retired until December 1942. In the meantime, Americans flew them against the attackers of Pearl Harbor, and fought those flown by Vichy pilots in North Africa, while Dutchmen flew them defending Java. A good all-around design, the Hawk 75 was soon surpassed in speed by more advanced types.

CURTISS HAWK 75A-4 (P-36G)
Wright R-1820-95, 1200 hp take-off, 1000 hp at 15,000′
DIMENSIONS: Span 37′ 4″, Lg. 28′ 10″, Ht. 9′ 6″, Wing Area 236 sq. ft.
WEIGHT: Empty 4541 lb., Gross 5750 lb. Fuel 105–163 gal.
PERFORMANCE: Speed—Top 323 mph at 15,100′, Cruising 262 mph, Landing 69 mph. Service Ceiling 32,700′, Absolute Ceiling 33,600′. Range 1003 miles max.

SI—MFR

Even before P-36As went into service, several foreign fighters with more firepower and speed stepped ahead of American fighter progress. Germany had selected Messerschmitt's Bf109 as the Luftwaffe's standard single-seater at an October 1935 competition, and this type went into service in 1937, although early versions didn't have the power and armament of wartime models.

The best fighters of this period were the *eight*-gun monoplanes belonging to Britain. On June 3, 1936, two weeks before the Army bought 77 two-gun, 281 mph P-35s, the Royal Air Force ordered 600 Hurricanes and 310 Spitfires, which went into service in 1938. Rolls-Royce Merlin engines in smoothly pointed noses gave speeds of 325 mph to the Hurricane and 362 mph to the Spitfire, reminding American engineers that air-cooled radials used on American fighters had built-in drag.

Since American failure to match such speeds seemed due to lack of a high-powered inline engine, development was pushed on the liquid-cooled power plant built by the Allison division of General Motors. The first plane designed around the Allison was the Curtiss XP-37, whose V-1710-11 was cooled by side radiators, and used a General Electric turbo-supercharger to get a rating of 1000 hp at 20,000 ft. Based on the P-36,

AMC

CURTISS XP-37
Allison V-1710-11, 1150 hp take-off, 1000 hp at 20,000′
DIMENSIONS: Span 37′ 4″, Lg. 31′, Ht. 9′ 6″, Wing Area 236 sq. ft.
WEIGHT: Empty 5272 lb., Gross 6350 lb., Max. 6643 lb. Fuel 104–148 gal.
PERFORMANCE: Speed—Top 340 mph at 20,000′, Cruising 304 mph, Landing 75 mph. Service Ceiling 35,000′, Climb 20,000′/7.1 min. Range 485 miles normal, 625 miles max.

AF

CURTISS YP-37
Allison V-1710-21, 1000 hp take-off, 880 hp at 25,000′
DIMENSIONS: Span 37′ 4″, Lg. 32′ 10″, Ht. 9′ 6″, Wing Area 236 sq. ft.
WEIGHT: Empty 5723 lb., Gross 6889 lb., Max. 7178 lb. Fuel 108–164 gal.
PERFORMANCE: Speed—Top 331 mph at 20,000′, Cruising 305 mph, Landing 85 mph. Service Ceiling 34,000′, Climb 2920′/1 min., 20,000′/8.5 min. Range 570 miles normal, 870 miles max.

but with a longer fuselage, the XP-37 had its cockpit moved rearward to improve streamlining. Visibility, however, wasn't helped by this change. Submitted to the Air Corps on April 1, 1937, the XP-37 was the *first* American fighter to surpass *300* mph, but was armed only with the usual two cowl guns.

Thirteen heavier service test YP-37s were bought on December 11, 1937, but when the first was completed in June 1939 it fell short of the guaranteed 340 mph, partially because the V-1710-21 did not yield the power expected. A longer fuselage, modified radiator, and different supercharger distinguished the YP-37 from its prototype.

This design was replaced in Air Corps thinking by the Curtiss XP-40, which was a standard P-36 modified to use an Allison engine supercharged for medium altitudes. Critical altitude was 12,000, instead of 20,000 ft., which fitted current Army strategy viewing low-level flying as more important than high-altitude performance. This type requires a separate account of its history, given later.

Another P-36A, converted to the XP-42 specification, attempted to give a radial engine the streamlining of its inline competitors. The XP-42 arrived at Dayton on March 5, 1939, with its R-1830-31 enclosed in a special cowl with a long nose and an air scoop below the large prop spinner. Since this ship was intended only to try cowling arrangements, no armament was fitted. Top speed was 315 mph at first, but the XP-42 later did 343 mph when rebuilt and flown with a "short-nose," more conventional-looking cowl on the same engine.

CURTISS XP-42
Pratt & Whitney R-1830-31, 1050 hp take-off, 1000 hp at 14,500′
DIMENSIONS: Span 37′ 4″, Lg. 30′ 7″, Ht. 12′, Wing Area 236 sq. ft.
WEIGHT: Empty 4818 lb., Gross 5919 lb., Max. 6260 lb. Fuel 105–161 gal.
PERFORMANCE: Speed—Top 315 mph at 15,000′, Cruising 286 mph. Range 730 miles normal, 1200 miles max.

AF

THE AIRACUDA

The most unusual prewar combat type was the only twin-engined pusher fighter ever built in the U.S. First flown on September 1, 1937, the five-place low-wing Bell XFM-1 was a heavily armed, long-range answer to four-engined bombers, and was the first

CURTISS XP-42 (Short-nose version)

NACA

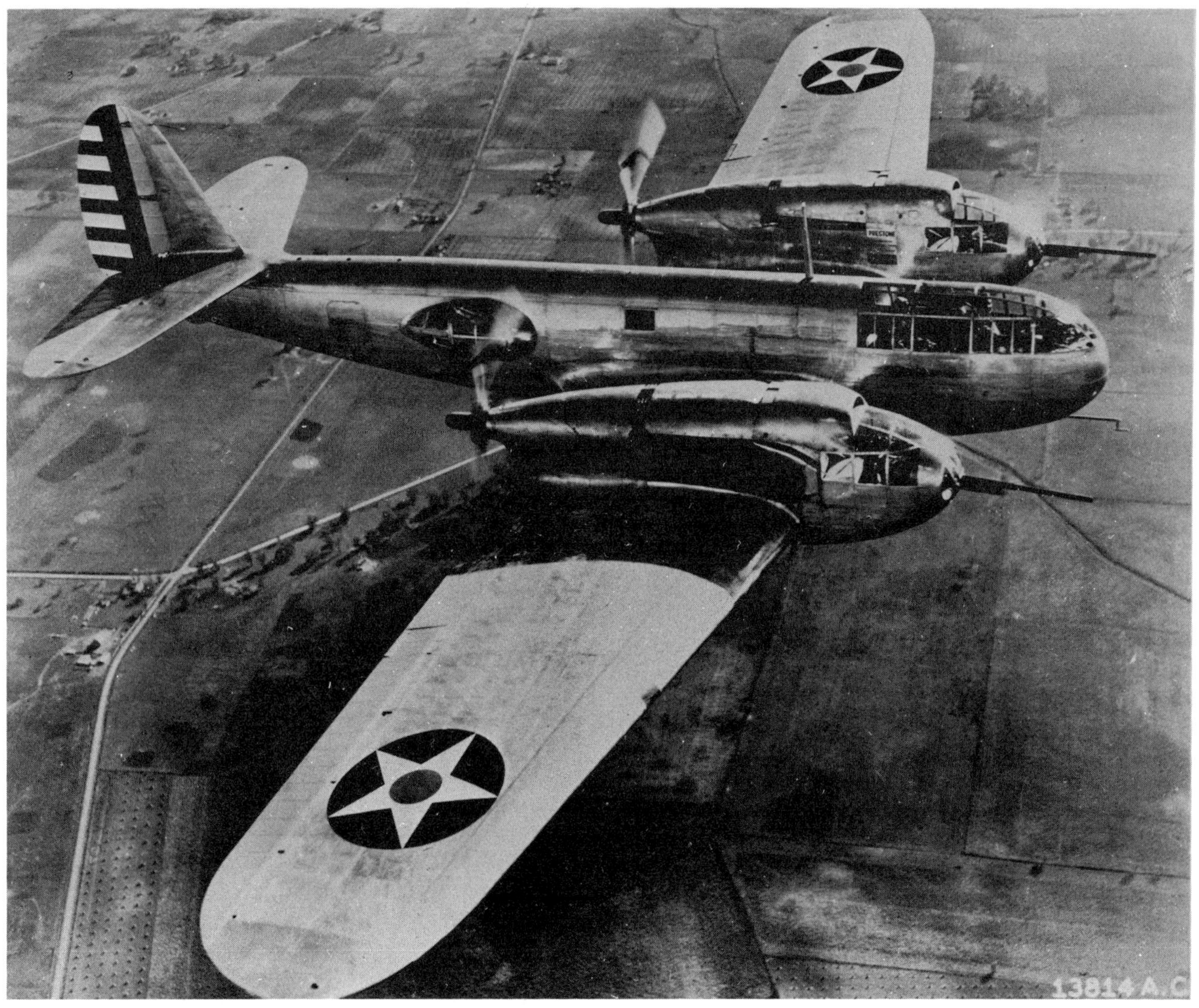

AF

BELL XFM-1

Allison V-1710-13, 1150 hp take-off, 1000 hp at 20,000′

DIMENSIONS: Span 69′ 10″, Lg. 44′ 10″, Ht. 13′ 7″, Wing Area 684 sq. ft.

WEIGHT: Empty 13,376 lb., Gross 17,333 lb. Fuel 400–800 gal.

PERFORMANCE: Speed—Top 271 mph at 20,000′, Cruising 244 mph, Landing 77 mph. Service Ceiling 30,500′, Climb 15,000′/10 min. Range 800 miles normal, 2600 miles max.

twin-engined American plane intended solely for fighting.

Outstanding feature of the Airacuda, as the new Buffalo company's first type was named, was the nacelle on each wing containing in front a gunner and in back a turbo-supercharged Allison V-1710-13 turning a pusher propeller. The wing gunners were to have 37-mm. guns, but since this caliber was not yet available, only dummies were installed on the XFM-1 (Experimental Fighter Multi-place). To the rear of the pilot and co-pilot, seated tandem in the nose of the main fuselage, was a rear gunner who fired a .50-caliber gun from a tear-drop blister on each side. A pair of .30-caliber guns were also carried, one above each nacelle cannon.

Service test models ordered on May 20, 1938, for $3,168,265 (nearly six times the cost of the YP-37s) were designed originally to have turbo-superchargers like the prototype and expected to do 305 mph at 20,000 ft. Altitude-rated Allisons limiting top speed to 270 mph at 12,600 ft. were substituted because of an explosion of the turbo on the YFM-1's first flight on September 28, 1939. Other YFM-1 features were radiator placement in the wings, rather than atop the nacelle, and improvement of the rear defense, which included two .50- and two .30-caliber guns. The lighter guns fired through side openings while the heavies were placed in a retractable top turret and a ventral post. Underwing racks could accommodate up to 340 lbs. of bombs and 110 37-mm., 500 .50-caliber, and 600 .30-caliber rounds of ammunition were carried.

Landing gear on nine YFM-1s delivered in 1940 consisted of conventional main wheels retracting backward halfway into the nacelles, as on the XFM-1. Three YFM-1As introduced in October 1940 were identical to the YFM-1, but for addition of a retracting

BELL YFM-1
Allison V-1710-23, 1150 hp take-off
DIMENSIONS: Span 70′, Lg. 46′, Ht. 12′ 9″, Wing Area 600 sq. ft.
WEIGHT: Empty 13,630 lb., Gross 18,000 lb., Max. 19,000 lb. Fuel 400–800 gal.
PERFORMANCE: Speed—Top 270 mph at 12,600′, Landing 77 mph. Service Ceiling 30,500′, Climb 15,000′/10.3 min. Range 940 miles normal, 1800 miles max.

MFR

BELL YFM-1A
Allison V-1710-23, 1150 hp
DIMENSIONS: As YFM-1
WEIGHT: Empty 13,962 lb., Gross 18,431 lb., Max. 19,301 lb. Fuel 400–800 gal.
PERFORMANCE: As YFM-1

PMB

BELL YFM-1B
Allison V-1710-41, 1090 hp at 13,200′
DIMENSIONS: Span 70′, Lg. 46′, Ht. 12′ 5″, Wing Area 600 sq. ft.
WEIGHT: Empty 13,023 lb., Gross 18,373 lb., Max. 21,150 lb. Fuel 400–800 gal.
PERFORMANCE: Speed—Top 268 mph at 12,600′, Cruising 240 mph, Landing 77 mph. Service Ceiling 30,000′, Climb 15,000′/10.6 min. Range 650 miles normal, 1675 miles max.

PMB

nose wheel for the tricycle gear becoming popular on bombers. On this version, the main wheels folded inward to fit flat within the wings. A pair of YFM-1s fitted with V-1710-41s became YFM-1B types.

Although the Airacuda aroused much excitement on its appearance, it proved a disappointment as a bomber interceptor. Comparison of XFM-1 performance with the contemporary XP-37 shows the multi-seater far behind in speed, climb, and ceiling, while the single-seater was far less expensive to build and operate. Not only was the Airacuda's speed insufficiently greater than the bombers it had to catch, but the big fighter's lack of maneuverability would have made it easy prey for single-seat escorts attacking from the rear. Nor did the unwieldy arrangement recommend itself for protecting bombers against light interceptors.

EXPORT FIGHTERS

An entirely different approach to antibomber weapons was the lightweight fighter designed by the St. Louis subsidiary of the parent Curtiss-Wright combination. The Curtiss-Wright CW-21 was intended for export as a fast-climbing interceptor, and was developed from earlier trainer designs. Emphasizing light weight, the CW-21 had a Wright Cyclone giving 750 hp at 15,200 ft., and wheels retracting backward into fairings below the wing. First flown in January 1939, it had one .30- and one .50-caliber nose gun and pilot armor.

The production model had the wheels folding inward completely into the wing, and armament included two .30- and two .50-caliber guns under the cowl.

MFR

CURTISS-WRIGHT CW-21
Wright R-1820-G5, 850 hp at 6000′, 750 hp at 15,200′
DIMENSIONS: Span 35′, Lg. 26′ 6″, Ht. 8′ 8″, Wing Area 174 sq. ft.
WEIGHT: Empty 3050 lb., Gross 4250 lb. Fuel 96 gal.
PERFORMANCE: Speed—Top 304 mph, Cruising 275 mph, Landing 68 mph. Service Ceiling 35,000′, Climb 4800′/1 min.

MFR

CURTISS-WRIGHT CW-21B
Wright R-1820-G5, 1000 hp take-off, 750 hp at 15,200′
DIMENSIONS: Span 35′, Lg. 27′ 2″, Ht. 8′ 11″, Wing Area 174 sq. ft.
WEIGHT: Empty 3382 lb., Gross 4500 lb. Fuel 100 gal.
PERFORMANCE: Speed—Top 314 mph at 12,200′, Cruising 282 mph, Landing 68 mph. Service Ceiling 34,300′, Absolute Ceiling 35,000′, Climb 13,120′/4 min. Range 630 miles.

PMB

NORTH AMERICAN P-64 (NA-68)
Wright R-1820-77, 840 hp at 8700′
DIMENSIONS: Span 37′ 3″, Lg. 27′, Ht. 9′, Wing Area 227.5 sq. ft.
WEIGHT: Empty 4660 lb., Gross 5990 lb., Max. 6800 lb. Fuel 120–170 gal.
PERFORMANCE: Speed—Top 270 mph at 8700′, Cruising 235 mph, Landing 70 mph. Service Ceiling 27,500′. Range 630 miles normal, 965 miles max.

Twenty-seven completed for the Dutch East Indies between June and December 1940 were used in the battle for Java.

Two other single-seaters were built in 1939 for export, the North American NA-50 and Vultee V-48. Although they found foreign buyers, few were used in battle. Both received U. S. Army designations, due to circumstances of war. These designations were quite high in the fighter catalog, since intervening numbers had been issued to the many projects already in progress.

Built for Peru in March 1939, the North American NA-50s were seven low-wing single-seaters developed from that firm's famous AT-6 trainer. Powered with a Wright Cyclone R-1820-77 giving 840 hp at 8700 ft., they had two .30-caliber guns on the cowl and were intended as a low-cost fighter for smaller nations. Originally they also had provisions for 550 lbs. of bombs and 20-mm. wing guns. Six more (NA-68) were completed in November 1940 for Siam, but the U.S. became aware of Japanese influence there and confiscated them. Designated P-64, they were used for advanced training, and after the war at least one passed into private hands to be fitted with a "rain-maker" device in California!

In September 1939, Vultee completed its more ambitious Vanguard 48, with a narrow wing and the 1200 hp Pratt & Whitney Wasp enclosed in a special cowl resembling that on the XP-42. Retractable cooling ducts below and above the large prop spinner were the only breaks in a nose that was as streamlined as that on an inline engine, but which must have added

WL

VULTEE VANGUARD (Prototype)
Pratt & Whitney R-1830-S4C4-G, 1200 hp take-off, 900 hp at 15,400′
DIMENSIONS: Span 36′, Lg. 29′ 2″, Ht. 9′ 5″, Wing Area 197 sq. ft.
WEIGHT: Empty 4657 lb., Gross 6029 lb. Fuel 240 gal.
PERFORMANCE: Speed—Top 358 mph at 15,600′, Cruising 316 mph, Landing 73 mph. Service Ceiling 34,300′, Climb 3300′/1 min. Range 738 miles normal.

to the weight. Eventually, that fancy nose was abandoned for a conventional cowl. Armament offered included up to ten .30-caliber guns, one pair aimed by mirrors to fire to the rear. This idea didn't work out either, and was dropped.

The Vanguard arrived late on an overcrowded market,[3] failed to get the nod from the Army or Britain, but did get an order for 144 from Sweden on February 6, 1940. Production deliveries were made between September 1941 and April 1942, but Sweden had been barred from U.S. planes by the State Department in October 1940, and the Vanguards were given British serial numbers. Canada was allotted the contract in December 1940 for training purposes, but by June 1941 the type was transferred to Chinese lend-lease schedules and received the designation P-66. It is reported that 129 Vanguards actually went to China, and the remainder to the Army Air Forces.

Using the R-1830-33, the P-66 had two .50-caliber nose guns, four .30-caliber wing guns, and pilot armor.

MFR

VULTEE VANGUARD (Short-nose modification)

MFR

VULTEE P-66
Pratt & Whitney R-1830-33 (S3C4-G), 1200 hp take-off, 1050 hp at 13,100′
DIMENSIONS: Span 36′, Lg. 28′ 5″, Ht. 9′ 5″, Wing Area 197 sq. ft.
WEIGHT: Empty 5237 lb., Gross 7100 lb., Max. 7384 lb. Fuel 124–185 gal.
PERFORMANCE: Speed—Top 340 mph at 15,100′, Cruising 290 mph, Landing 82 mph. Service Ceiling 28,200′, Absolute Ceiling 29,750′, Climb 2520′/1 min., 19,700′/9.2 min. Range 850 miles normal, 950 miles at 240 mph.

[3] Other single-seat fighters introduced in 1939 were the CW-21, XP-38, NA-50, XP-39, XP-42, and XP-43, in that order.

Chapter 17: World War II Fighters

SHAPING THE WEAPONS

When Congress appropriated in 1939 funds to begin the Air Corps expansion that continued throughout the war, the fighter plane's general arrangement was almost standardized. Both the P-35 and P-36 types already in service were all-metal, single-seat low-wing monoplanes with the retractable landing gear, flaps, and enclosed cockpit standard on all American wartime planes. Both were radial-powered types quite inferior in speed and firepower to the Hurricanes and Spitfires in service with Britain's Fighter Command.

The P-37 development demonstrated the value of inline engines and turbo-superchargers, although the latter's weight led to its omission on the XP-40, not intended for high altitudes. Increased armament was also on the agenda, although engineers were reluctant to depress performance by adding more and heavier guns.

Additional armament required a heavier and more powerful aircraft, but the unmaneuverable Airacuda's limitations left unsolved the problem of stopping the fast, heavily armed bombers coming into the picture. Searching for a combination of speed and firepower beyond that offered by contemporary single-engined, two-gun styles, the Air Corps discarded a Lockheed XFM-2 multiplace project and ordered prototypes of the twin-engined Lockheed XP-38 and single-engined Bell XP-39. Both were single-seater interceptors powered by Allisons turbo-supercharged to yield 1000 hp at 20,000 ft., and were the first fighters with tricycle gear, permitting faster landings than were safe for older types. Both preliminary specifications promised a heavy-caliber gun and speeds of 400 mph at 20,000 ft., suggesting that Britain fighter superiority could be overcome.

When the Air Corps invited bids to be submitted January 25, 1939, for production ships to expand the fighter groups, a more modest specification was issued, calling for a minimum top speed of 310 mph at 15,000 ft., climb to that altitude in six minutes, and an endurance of two hours at 280 mph. Desired performance included a top speed of 370 mph at 15,000 ft., reached in 4.5 minutes, and 335 mph cruising with the same endurance. These requirements show that the Army still thought of fighters as short-range, low-altitude weapons, and did not anticipate World War II air battles fought above 20,000 ft. at distances much greater than an hour's flight from home bases.

On April 27, 1939, the Air Corps placed its largest peacetime pursuit contract yet, for 524 medium-altitude Curtiss P-40s at $12,872,898. On the same day 13 Lockheed YP-38s and 13 Bell YP-39s were ordered; like 13 radial-powered Republic YP-43s bought two weeks later, they were originally planned for pursuit-interceptor service with turbo-superchargers. The contracts showed the cost of advanced weapons: where the same number of YP-37s were $531,000 in 1937, the YP-43s cost the government $974,324, the YP-39s $1,073,000, and the twin-engined YP-38s $2,181,000.

Each of the fighter types ordered that day began a lengthy wartime type development that may be told best by taking one type at a time, beginning with the one first available for combat service.

THE LONG LINE OF P-40s

The original Curtiss XP-40, ordered July 1937 and flown October 1938, was converted from the tenth P-36A by replacing the radial engine with a V-1710-19 (Allison C-13). Cooling was by a radiator under the rear fuselage, but the prototype was later modified by moving the radiator forward to below the engine. Armament consisted of one .30- and one .50-caliber nose gun.

Although the P-40 was less capable than more advanced types, it was more quickly available and less

AMC

CURTISS XP-40

Allison V-1710-19, 1160 hp take-off, 1000 hp at 10,000′

DIMENSIONS: Span 37′ 4″, Lg. 31′ 1″, Ht. 12′ 4″, Wing Area 236 sq. ft.

WEIGHT: Empty 5417 lb., Gross 6260 lb., Max. 6870 lb. Fuel 100–158 gal.

PERFORMANCE: Speed—Top 342 mph at 12,200′, Cruising 299 mph, Landing 72 mph. Range 460 miles normal, 1180 miles at 200 mph with full load.

AMC

CURTISS XP-40

expensive. Neither Lockheed nor Bell could reach quantity production until 1941, and although the P-43 was based on a more familiar airframe, it must await enlargement of Republic's factory. But the Curtiss plant had been expanded to fill French orders and was to produce the bulk of American fighters during 1940–42. The P-40 was based on a tried airframe already in production and offered low cost and early delivery. Five hundred could and would be delivered before five of any of the others. The Lockheed fighter, on the other hand, was a weapon far in advance of its contemporaries, even the Spitfire, but four years were to elapse before it could undertake a really large share of combat operations. In the meantime, the P-40 would be the main combat type available in the United States.

Production ships ordered April 27, 1939, and appearing in May 1940 had a V-1710-33 (Allison C-15) and could be distinguished from the XP-40 by a long carburetor intake above the nose and changes about the exhausts, radiator, and landing gear. Two hundred Curtiss P-40s built first for the Air Corps had only two .50-caliber synchronized guns, and a speed of 357 mph at 15,000 ft.

Delivery on 324 planes remaining on this contract was deferred in April 1940 to expedite production on the similar Curtiss H-81A purchased by France and taken by Britain as the Tomahawk. When rescheduled in September, the 324 Army ships were to incorporate wing guns, pilot armor, and the fuel tank protection found so necessary for wartime planes.

The first of 140 H-81A-1 (Tomahawk I) models appeared September 1940, and were similar to the P-40 except for instrumentation and accessories. Training work in the United Kingdom accounted for most of their use. They were followed by 110 H-81A-2s (Tomahawk IIA) with pilot armor, armor-glass windscreen, and self-sealing tanks, which prevent leaking through bullet punctures. Two .30-caliber guns were added in the wings. The Army's version was 131 P-40Bs that began arriving at Air Corps fields in February 1941.

Final Tomahawk type to appear was the H-81A-3, with two .50-caliber nose guns, four .30-caliber guns, different self-sealing tanks, and attachments for a 52-gallon belly tank. Britain was allotted 930 as the Tomahawk IIB, and 193 more went to the Air Corps as P-40C. Performance on later P-40 models, of course, suffered from the added weight of wartime modifications.

British Tomahawks fought their early actions in the Middle East, their first reported victims, ironically, being several Martin Marylands flown by Syrian-based Vichy French forces in June 1941. Hundreds of other Tomahawks waited in England, but when the expected German invasion failed to materialize, they were made

CURTISS P-40-B

Allison V-1710-33, 1040 hp at 15,000′

DIMENSIONS: As P-40

WEIGHT: Empty 5590 lb., Gross 7325 lb., Max. 7600 lb. Fuel 120–160 gal.

PERFORMANCE: (6835 lb.) Speed—Top 352 mph at 15,000′, Cruising 280 mph, Landing 80 mph. Service Ceiling 32,400′, Climb 15,000′/5.1 min. Range 730 miles normal, 940–1230 miles max.

PMB

AF

CURTISS P-40
Allison V-1710-33, 1040 hp at 15,000′
DIMENSIONS: Span 37′ 4″, Lg. 31′ 9″, Ht. 12′ 4″, Wing Area 236 sq. ft.
WEIGHT: Empty 5376 lb., Gross 6787 lb., Max. 7215 lb. Fuel 120–181 gal.
PERFORMANCE: Speed—Top 357 mph at 15,000′, Cruising 277 mph, Landing 80 mph. Service Ceiling 32,750′, Absolute Ceiling 33,800′, Climb 3080′/1 min., 15,000′/5.3 min. Range 650 miles normal, 950 miles at 250 mph, 1400 miles max. at 188 mph.

available for other places. Some went to Turkey in November 1941, while 195 became the first American planes in action on the Russian front. One hundred P-40Cs transferred from Britain to China were sent to Burma and used by the Flying Tigers against Japan with more success than Army counterparts fighting at the same time in the Philippines. Most of Hawaii's fighters on December 7, 1941, were P-40Bs, and a few got in the air in the face of the surprise attack to down the first Japanese planes destroyed by the Army Air Forces.

Meanwhile, development of the 1150 hp Allison F model (V-1710-39) gave a new opportunity to improve the fighter situation. This engine was specified for the Curtiss XP-46 ordered September 29, 1939, a single-seater more compact and smaller than the P-40, with wheels retracting inward instead of backward, and the radiator back below the small slotted wings. Original specifications included a top speed of 410 mph at 15,000 ft. at a weight of 5471 lbs. empty and 6849 lbs. gross, but later increases in weight were to produce disappointing results. By October 19, the design provided two .50-caliber nose guns, eight .30-caliber wing guns, 65 lbs. of pilot armor, and self-sealing tanks, apparently the first to be required by an Air Corps specification. Two prototypes were ordered, one (XP-46A) being delivered without armament to expedite tests and insure against an accident like the one that curtailed XP-38 studies.

By the time the XP-46 flew on February 15, 1941, a development of the P-40 had replaced it in procurement planning. Interrupting Curtiss production lines for an entirely new airframe seemed unwise in that crucial period, and adapting the P-46s engine to the P-40 airframe, together with internal protection and increased armament, was the most feasible alternative. Substitution of a modified P-40 for the P-46 was proposed by the Matériel Division on June 10, 1940. Curtiss had already received a British contract in May for the H-87A Kittyhawk with the V-1710-39 engine, and this type was ordered by the Army as the P-40D in September 1940.

On May 22, 1941, flight tests began on the first Kittyhawk I, which differed from the Tomahawk by a modified fuselage with radiator and top intakes moved forward on a nose given a new shape by the V-1710-39. About 175 lbs. of armor was carried with 148 gallons in self-sealing internal fuel tanks, and fittings for a 52-gallon drop tank or 500 lb. bomb. Nose guns were omitted in favor of four .50-caliber wing guns. Twenty Kittyhawk Is were followed by 540 Kittyhawk IAs, which had six .50-caliber wing guns.

Concurrently, United States contracts for the same type produced twenty-two P-40Ds, with four wing guns. An order of February 18, 1941, increased the

CURTISS TOMAHAWK IIA

MFR

CURTISS P-40C (Tomahawk IIB)
Allison V-1710-33, 1040 hp at 15,000′
DIMENSIONS: As P-40
WEIGHT: Empty 5812 lb., Gross 7549 lb., Max. 8058 lb. Fuel 134–186 gal.
PERFORMANCE: (7327 lb.) Speed—Top 345 mph at 15,000′, Cruising 270 mph, Landing 86 mph. Service Ceiling 29,500′, Absolute Ceiling 30,500′, Climb 2690′/1 min.

PMB

PMB

CURTISS XP-46
Allison V-1710-39, 1150 hp at 11,800′
DIMENSIONS: Span 34′ 4″, Lg. 30′ 2″, Ht. 13′, Wing Area 208 sq. ft.
WEIGHT: Empty 5625 lb., Gross 7322 lb., Max. 7665 lb. Fuel 103–156 gal.
PERFORMANCE: Speed—Top 355 mph at 12,200′, Landing 79 mph. Service Ceiling 29,500′, Climb 12,300′/5 min. Range 325 miles at 332 mph.

MFR

CURTISS H-87A-1
(Photo shows Kittyhawk I, data is for P-40D)
Allison V-1710-39, 1150 hp at 11,800′
DIMENSIONS: Span 37′ 4″, Lg. 31′ 2″, Ht. 12′ 4″, Wing Area 236 sq. ft.
WEIGHT: Empty 5970 lb., Gross 7740 lb., Max. 8810 lb. Fuel 148–200 gal.
PERFORMANCE: Speed—Top 359 mph at 15,000′, Cruising 258 mph, Landing 85 mph. Service Ceiling 30,600′, Absolute Ceiling 31,600′, Climb 2580′/1 min., 15,000′/6.4 min. Range 800 miles normal, 1150 miles max. at 195 mph.

armament to six .50-caliber wing guns with 281 rpg, and remaining ships on the contract were designated P-40E. Of 2320 P-40Es built, 420 P-40E-1s ordered May 7, 1941, and 1080 added June 30, 1941, were purchased with lend-lease funds and allotted to Great Britain. Kittyhawks operating in Russia early in 1942 were transferred from this or the preivous R.A.F. order.

Without turbo-supercharging, the Allison's poor high-altitude performance limited P-40 capabilities, so American manufacture of the Rolls-Royce Merlin with a two-speed integral supercharger offered a new opportunity. The P-40F, powered by a Packard-built V-1650-1 Merlin, was ordered February 5, 1941, and an XP-40F prototype, converted from a P-40D with an imported Merlin, flew on November 25. Labeled Warhawk in the U.S., and Kittyhawk II by the R.A.F., Merlin-powered types could be recognized by absence of the top intake. Actually, all Army Air Force P-40s were called Warhawks, and the R.A.F. got none of the 250 P-40Fs allotted, since 100 were transferred to Russia, some went to the Free French, and others were lost at sea. Curtiss built 1311 P-40Fs in 1942 and 700 similar P-40Ls in 1943 before V-1650 output was taken by North American Mustangs. Merlin engines became so scarce that 300 F and L models in service were refitted with Allison V-1710-81s when the original power plants wore out, and relabeled P-40R.

Effort continued to make the best of the Allisons which powered most Warhawks. Experimental conversions included a YP-40F which had a deep belly radiator moved back behind the V-1650-1, and an XP-40G (a P-40 with E type wings), but no H or J model was completed. The XP-40K had a neat pencil nose and a radiator built into the thickened wing, but what that proved hasn't been reported.

CURTISS P-40E
Allison V-1710-39, 1150 hp at 11,800′
DIMENSIONS: As P-40D
WEIGHT: Empty 6350 lb., Gross 8280 lb., Max. 9200 lb. Fuel 148–200 gal.
PERFORMANCE: Speed—Top 354 mph at 15,000′. Service Ceiling 29,000′.

PMB

CURTISS KITTYHAWK 1A(H-87A-2)

MFR

PMB

CURTISS P-40F
Packard V-1650-1, 1300 hp at 12,000′, 1120 hp at 18,500′
DIMENSIONS: Span 37′ 4″, Lg. 33′ 4″, Ht. 12′ 4″, Wing Area 236 sq. ft.
WEIGHT: Empty 6590 lb., Gross 8500 lb., Max. 9350 lb. (10,000 lb. ferry). Fuel 157 gal. (327 gal. ferry).
PERFORMANCE: Speed—Top 364 mph at 20,000′, Cruising 290 mph, Landing 82 mph. Service Ceiling 34,400′, Climb 15,000′/7.6 min. Range 375 miles/500 lb. bomb.

Six hundred P-40Ks ordered October 28, 1941, and intended for lend-lease to China might have been the last of this series, had the P-60 replaced the P-40 as originally planned. Fearing to interrupt production for an unproven type, authorities substituted 2000 more P-40s (K, L, and M types) on June 11, 1942, for P-60As originally scheduled. The P-40K and P-40M had the P-40Ds nose and the lengthened fuselage. First appearing August 1942, the 1300 P-40Ks had the improved V-1710-73, and 600 P-40Ms for Britain introduced in November had a V-1710-81. The 700 Merlin-powered P-40Ls built on these contracts were delivered concurrently through 1943, but some had two guns, armor, and some fuel and equipment removed to lighten the aircraft.

CURTISS P-40K
Allison V-1710-73, 1325 hp take-off, 1150 hp 11,800′
DIMENSIONS: As P-40F
WEIGHT: Empty 6400 lb., Gross 8400 lb., Max. 10,000 lb. Fuel 120–157 gal. (327 gal. ferry).
PERFORMANCE: Speed—Top 362 mph at 15,000′, Cruising 290 mph, Landing 82 mph. Service Ceiling 28,000′, Climb 15,000′/7.5 min. Range 350 miles/500 lb. bomb, 1600 miles max.

PMB

MFR

CURTISS YP-40F

In March 1944 the P-40N series introduced a lightweight structure, cockpit canopy with improved visibility, and four wing guns. The first 400 (P-40N-1) were stripped down for high-altitude combat and were the fastest production Warhawks. Like 1577 normally loaded, six-gun ships in blocks P-40N-5 to N-15, they had the P-40Ms Allison V-1710-81. Blocks P-40N-20 to P-40N-35, 3022 ships in all, had a V-1710-99 and were the most prolific model of this series. A thousand P-40N-40s with a V-1710-115 were ordered, but this contract was terminated after 220 ships. Lend-lease deliveries to Great Britain included 21 P-40K and 595, or nearly all, of the P-40Ms, which became the Kittyhawk III. Some were used in the Mediterranean theater, but most went to Australian, New Zealand, and R.A.F. pilots in the Far East, which also employed the Kittyhawk IV, 586 P-40Ns.

An effort at more basic improvement was made in April 1944 with the XP-40Q, featuring a 1425 hp V-1710-121, four-bladed propeller, four .50-caliber guns in clipped wings, wing radiators, longer fuselage and "bubble" canopy for all-around pilot vision. Several modifications were made on this ship, but it was not equal to the P-47 and P-51, and did not reach production.

CURTISS P-40L

PMB

PMB

CURTISS P-40M
Allison V-1710-81, 1200 hp take-off, 1360 hp WE, 1125 hp at 14,600′
DIMENSIONS: As P-40F
WEIGHT: Empty 6464 lb., Gross 8400 lb., Max. 9100 lb. Fuel 120–157 gal. (327 gal. ferry).
PERFORMANCE: Speed—Top 360 mph at 20,000′, Cruising 272 mph, Landing 82 mph. Service Ceiling 30,000′, Climb 15,000′/7.2 min. Range 350 miles/500 lb. bomb, 1600 miles max.

AF

CURTISS P-40N-1
Allison V-1710-81, 1360 hp max. WE
DIMENSIONS: As P-40F
WEIGHT: Empty 6000 lb., Gross 7400 lb., Max. 8850 lb. Fuel 122–292 gal.
PERFORMANCE: Speed—Top 378 mph at 10,500′, Cruising 288 mph, Landing 82 mph. Service Ceiling 38,000′, Climb 15,000′/6.7 min. Range 240 miles/500 lb. bomb, 1400 miles ferry.

AF

CURTISS P-40N-20
Allison V-1710-99, 1200 hp take-off, 1125 hp at 17,300′
DIMENSIONS: As P-40F
WEIGHT: Empty 6200 lb., Gross 8350 lb., Max. 11,400 lb. Fuel 159–609 gal.
PERFORMANCE: Speed—Top 350 mph at 16,400′, Cruising 290 mph, Landing 82 mph. Service Ceiling 31,000′, Climb 14,000′/7.3 min. Range 340 miles/500 lb. bomb, 3100 miles at 198 mph ferry load.

MFR

CURTISS XP-40Q (Showing 2nd version)
Allison V-1710-121, 1425 hp take-off, 1100 hp at 25,000′
DIMENSIONS: Span 35′ 3″, Lg. 35′ 4″.
WEIGHT: Max. 9000 lb.
PERFORMANCE: Speed—Top 422 mph at 20,500′. Service Ceiling 39,000′, Climb 20,000′/4.8 min.

When the weary P-40 assembly line reached its end in December 1944, 13,738 had been completed. Peak AAF inventory was 2499 in April 1944. "As other planes became available a continuing equipment of P-40s was an unfailing mark of low priority." One unfortunate group had P-40s to the end of the war. Why was this design kept in production so long after it had fallen behind its competitors, and been officially pronounced as "of more limited value than fighters produced by other American companies"? This question has not been satisfactorily answered. At first, the P-40 was a necessary stopgap until more advanced types were available in quantity, but by 1942 plans to use the Curtiss plant for something better were underway. Somehow, nothing came of them; the P-60 program was discontinued and only a token quantity of P-47 Thunderbolts were substituted. Instead the P-40s continued on, and when they finally did stop, so did all pursuit production at the facility which once produced most of the nation's fighters.

As a second-choice fighter that became for many units the only choice, the P-40 fought on many fronts.

Warhawks operated in North Africa through 1942 and 1943, while others fought Japanese over Alaska, Australia, China, Java, Hawaii, New Guinea and the Solomons. Chinese and Russian pilots also flew P-40s, although Joseph Stalin complained that they did not stand the fight against the Germans as well as the Bell Airacobra. Some American pilots, however, preferred the Curtiss ship's lower wing loading.

LOCKHEED LIGHTNING

The fastest American fighter available when World War II began, the Lockheed Lightning was one of the most unusual single-seat fighters ever in mass production. Originating as Lockheed Model 22, it became the XP-38 when the prototype was ordered June 23, 1937, but took over five years to enter combat.

There were two engines, the same Allison C-9s used on the XP-37, but one had its propeller rotation reversed, so that both propellers turned inward and counteracted each other's torque. Designated V-1710-11 and V-1710-15, the Allisons were rated at 1150 hp for take-off and 1000 hp at 20,000 ft., and had General Electric turbo-superchargers in the twin booms that extended back to twin rudders. A short central nacelle held the pilot and armament of one 23-mm. Madsen and four .50-caliber Browning guns, which shot a concentrated stream of bullets from the nose without interruption by synchronization. The first tricycle gear on a fighter permitted faster landings than were safe for older types, although an elaborate system of extended flaps was needed to keep stalling speed within reason.

Europe already had twin-engined fighters in 1936, when the Messerschmitt Bf 110 and Fokker G-1 two-seaters appeared, the G-1 even anticipating the Lightning's tail booms, but these ships were long-range two-seaters. Lockheed's XP-38 was a single-seat pursuit-interceptor far outdoing the comparable Westland Whirlwind built in 1938 by the British. The original XP-38 specification called for a 417 mph top speed at 20,000 ft., which was to be reached in 4½ minutes, a service ceiling of 39,100 ft. and an endurance of 1.75 hours at 393 mph. This was promised at weights of 7802 lbs. empty and 10,500 lbs. gross.

By time of the XP-38s first flight on January 27, 1939, 3700 lbs. had been added to that weight, and Lockheed had spent $761,000 on a $163,000 contract. It was a good investment, for despite flap trouble on its first flight, the XP-38 was clearly the most advanced antibomber weapon available in the world.

The secrecy that had surrounded the project was lifted for a transcontinental speed dash on February 11, 1939. Although the flight ended in a crash that destroyed the prototype and inspired doubts that one man could handle the big fighter, thirteen YP-38s were ordered on April 27. On August 10, a production contract for 66 more was placed.

These ships were powered by Allison F-2s (V-1710-27/-29) yielding 1150 hp at 25,000 ft., to outward turning propellers, and could be distinguished from the prototype by new cooling intakes under a raised thrust line. Armament on the YP-38 consisted of a 37-mm. gun mounted below two .50-caliber and two .30-caliber guns. An order on August 5, 1940, changed all four machine guns on later P-38 models to .50-caliber, with 200 rounds per gun, and provided armor plate for the pilot.

Britain was allowed to buy 667 export versions (Lockheed 322-61) on June 5, 1940, but they were to be powered by 1090 hp V-1710-C15s turning both propellers in the same direction. These were the same engines used by the P-40, and had no turbo-supercharger. On paper, the threat to the type's performance was not fully realized. Guaranteed YP-38 performance at design weight of 11,171 lbs. empty and 13,500 lbs. gross promised 353 mph at 5000 ft. and 405 mph at 20,000 ft., and a climb to 20,000 ft. in six minutes, while the 322-61 without turbos was expected to do 361 at 5000 ft. and 404 at 16,000 ft., and climb to 16,000 ft. in 5.6 minutes. Addition of armor and leakproof tanks, however, was to increase the Lightning Is weight to 11,945 lbs. empty and 14,467 lbs. gross, and performance with the C-15 engines was very disappointing.

British Lightnings (the name was also adopted by the U.S.) were to get a 20-mm. gun with 50 rounds instead of the 15 round, 37-mm. gun installed on the YP-38 and P-38. Attracted by the higher rate of fire and increased ammunition supply, the Army followed suit in September 1940 by authorizing the 20-mm. gun for 607 P-38E and P-38F types ordered even before the YP-38s completion.

Shortly after Spitfires and Hurricanes broke the back of the German bomber offensive in the Battle of Britain, the first YP-38 was flown on September 18, 1940. It is fortunate that this victory could be won without recourse to U.S. fighter production, which that month was limited to one each of the YP-38, YP-39, and YP-43, with some P-40s. Only the first ship outperformed the British types.

Production of the Lockheeds grew very slowly, for not until June 1941 was the YP-38 service test lot complete and delivery of the P-38 begun. These production models were similar to the YP-38 but for pilot armor and the change to .50-caliber on all four machine guns over the 37-mm. weapon. Thirty P-38s were delivered by August, and the remaining 36 on that contract were completed as P-38Ds, which added the leakproof tanks standard on all following models. One P-38 fitted with a pressurized cabin became the XP-38A (Lockheed Model 622), but no B or C model ever appeared.

MFR

LOCKHEED XP-38

Allison V-1710-11, -15, 1150 hp take-off, 1000 hp at 20,000′
DIMENSIONS: Span 52′, Lg. 37′ 10″, Ht. 12′ 10″, Wing Area 327.5 sq. ft.
WEIGHT: Empty 11,507 lb., Gross 13,500 lb., Max. 15,416 lb. Fuel 230–400 gal.
PERFORMANCE: Speed—Top 413 mph at 20,000′, Landing 80 mph. Service Ceiling 38,000′, Climb 20,000′/6.5 min. Endurance 1 hr. at top speed.

Standard Lightning armament of one 20-mm. and four .50-caliber guns was introduced in October 1941 on the P-38E, which followed the P-38D in other details. Although 210 P-38Es were built, 99 were reworked in 1942 by substituting four K-17 cameras for the guns. Known as the F-4, they were the Air Force's first high-speed photoreconnaissance planes. The Lightning was still not combat-ready, however, for a tail flutter had developed at high speeds, due to the fact that the P-38 was the first Army fighter fast enough to encounter compressibility. Although some 350 P-38s were in service by April 1942, they were limited to 350 mph to avoid tail troubles and awaited refinements before commitment to battle.

British Lightning Is began to appear in December 1941 and were similar to the P-38E but for British equipment and turbo-less C-15 engines. Performance was so poor that few of 143 "castrated Lightnings" went to the R.A.F. Most remained in the U.S., where Air Corps pilots found them nose-heavy and unable to keep formation over 12,000 ft. with regular P-38s, so as "P-322s" they were limited to training. The 524 ships remaining on the British contract were to be Lightning IIs with the standard turbo-supercharged Allison F-2, but were absorbed into AAF contracts, 150 as P-38Fs, and the rest as P-38Gs.

Wartime Lightning development centered on turning a good interceptor into the good offensive fighter needed by the United States at that stage of the war. The next version, the P-38F appeared in February 1942 with a pair of drop tanks to increase range and new Allison F-5s (V-1710-49/-53) giving 1325 hp for take-off. After 527 P-38Fs were delivered, the P-38G followed in June with larger drop tanks and Allison F-10s. A total of 1082 were built.

More power became available with the Allison F-15,

LOCKHEED YP-38

Allison V-1710-27, -29, 1150 hp take-off
DIMENSIONS: Span 52′, Lg. 37′ 10″, Ht. 9′ 10″, Wing Area 327.5 sq. ft.
WEIGHT: Empty 11,171 lb., Gross 13,500 lb., Max. 14,348 lb. Fuel 230–410 gal.
PERFORMANCE: Speed—Top 405 mph at 20,000′, 353 mph at 5000′, Cruising 330 mph, Landing 80 mph. Service Ceiling 38,000′, Climb 3333′/1 min. 20,000′/6 min. Range 650 miles normal, 1150 miles max.

PMB

LOCKHEED YP-38

MFR

PMB

LOCKHEED P-38
Allison V-1710-27, -29, 1150 hp
DIMENSIONS: As YP-38
WEIGHT: Empty 11,672 lb., Gross 14,178 lb., Max. 15,340 lb. Fuel 230–410 gal.
PERFORMANCE: Speed—Top 390 mph at 20,000′, Cruising 310 mph, Landing 80 mph, Climb 3200′/1 min. Range 825 miles normal, 1490 miles max.

yielding 1425 hp for take-off, and 1600 "war emergency" hp for short bursts when needed. This power plant was tested on a pre-production P-38H prototype in September 1942, and 600 more P-38Hs were accepted beginning in March 1943. The same engines (V-1710-89/-91) were used in the P-38J, which appeared in August 1943, but was distinguished from older models by a new chin intake below the engine, with core-type intercoolers, and added a 55-gallon leading edge fuel tank in each wing, which with two 300-gallon external tanks, increased Lightning ferry range to 2600 miles at 198 mph. On actual combat missions, two 165 gallon drop tanks gave the P-38J a radius of 795 miles for fighter sweeps or medium bomber escort. Two 1000 lb. bombs instead of tanks could be carried out to a radius of 375 miles. For short-range bombing, two 1600 lb. bombs could be carried. Late blocks of 2970 P-38Js had small dive flaps and power-boosted controls. One modified with V-1710-75/-77 Allisons and 12 ft. 6 in. propellers, instead of the usual 11 ft. 6 in. diameter, became the XP-38K.

In June 1944, the P-38L appeared with Allison F-30 engines of 1475 hp at take-off, and fittings under the wing for ten 5 in. rockets. Before war's end halted Lightning production in August 1945, 3810 P-38L-LOs had been built. Two thousand P-38L-VNs had been ordered from Consolidated-Vultee's Nashville plant, but this contract was canceled after 113 were accepted between January and June 1945.

The final Lightning model was the P-38M, a black-painted night fighter with a radome under the nose and a radar operator seated behind and above the pilot. Seventy-five were converted from P-38Ls.

A total of 9923 Lightnings were built, and many postdelivery modifications were made. Most useful auxiliary role of the Lightning was as a photo-reconnaissance type, and after the 99 F-4s mentioned before, 20 P-38F, 381 P-38G, 128 P-38H, and 705 P-38J and Ls became camera jobs designated F-4A, and F-5A to E. Two torpedoes were carried on the racks of a P-38F, while a P-38J tried retractable skis. A desire to introduce new pilots to the P-38 gradually led to awkward efforts to provide a second seat by building a cockpit on the port boom, or more often, by removing the radio behind the pilot's seat so a second man could crouch there. Glass-nosed "Droop-snoots" guided dive-bomber missions in 1944, with a bombardier replacing nose armament. The "Pathfinder" modification had a radar nose.

LOCKHEED P-38D
Allison V-1710-27, -29, 1150 hp
DIMENSIONS: As YP-38
WEIGHT: Empty 11,780 lb., Gross 14,456 lb., Max. 15,500 lb. Fuel 230–300 gal.
PERFORMANCE: Speed—Top 390 mph at 25,000′, Cruising 300 mph, Landing 85 mph. Service Ceiling 39,000′, Climb 20,000′/8 min. Range 400 miles normal, 975 miles at 200 mph max.

PMB

LOCKHEED P-38E
Allison V-1710-27, -29, 1150 hp
DIMENSIONS: As YP-38
WEIGHT: Empty 11,880 lb., Gross 14,424 lb., Max. 15,482 lb. Fuel 230–310 gal.
PERFORMANCE: Speed—Top 395 mph. Service Ceiling 39,000′. Range 500 miles.

PMB

MFR

LOCKHEED 322-61 (LIGHTNING I)
Allison V-1710-C15, 1040 hp at 15,000′
DIMENSIONS: As YP-38
WEIGHT: Empty 11,945 lb., Gross 14,467 lb.
PERFORMANCE: Speed—Top 357 mph. Service Ceiling 40,000′, Climb 2850′/1 min.

AF

LOCKHEED P-38F
Allison V-1710-49, -53, 1325 hp take-off, 1150 hp at 25,000′
DIMENSIONS: As YP-38
WEIGHT: Empty 12,264 lb., Gross 15,900 lb., Max. 18,000 lb. Fuel 230–300 gal. (600 gal max.)
PERFORMANCE: Speed—Top 395 mph at 25,000′, Cruising 305 mph, Landing 85 mph. Service Ceiling 39,000′, Climb 20,000′/8.8 min. Range 350 miles/230 gal. at 305 mph, 425 miles/300 gal. at 290 mph, 1925 miles/600 gal. at 195 mph.

LOCKHEED P-38H
Allison V-1710-89, -91, 1425 hp take-off, 1240 hp at 27,000′
DIMENSIONS: As YP-38
WEIGHT: Empty 12,380 lb., Gross 16,300 lb., Max. 20,300 lb. Fuel 230–900 gal.
PERFORMANCE: Speed—Top 402 mph at 25,000′, Cruising 300 mph, Landing 88 mph. Climb 2650′/1 min. Range 300 miles normal, 2400 miles ferry at 215 mph.

MFR

MFR

LOCKHEED P-38G
Allison V-1710-51, -55, 1325 hp take-off, 1150 hp at 25,000′
DIMENSIONS: As YP-38
WEIGHT: Empty 12,200 lb., Gross 15,800 lb., Max. 19,800 lb. Fuel 230–300 gal. (900 gal. max.)
PERFORMANCE: Speed—Top 400 mph at 25,000′, Cruising 340 mph, Landing 89 mph. Service Ceiling 39,000′, Climb 20,000′/8.5 min. Range 275 miles normal, 350 miles at 310 mph, 2400 miles at 203 mph.

PMB

LOCKHEED P-38L
Allison V-1710-111, -173, 1475 hp take-off, 1600 hp WE at 28,700′
DIMENSIONS: As YP-38
WEIGHT: Empty 12,800 lb., Gross 17,500 lb., Max. 21,600 lb. Fuel 410–1010 gal.
PERFORMANCE: Speed—Top 414 mph at 25,000′, Landing 105 mph. Service Ceiling 44,000′, Climb 20,000′/7 min. Range 450 miles with 3200 lbs. bombs, 2600 miles ferry.

LOCKHEED P-38J
Allison V-1710-89, -91, 1425 hp take-off, 1600 hp at 27,000′
DIMENSIONS: As YP-38
WEIGHT: Empty 12,780 lb., Gross 17,500 lb., Max. 21,600 lb. Fuel 410–1010 gal.
PERFORMANCE: Speed—Top 414 mph at 25,000′, Cruising 290 mph, Landing 105 mph. Service Ceiling 44,000′, Climb 20,000′/7 min. Range 450 miles/3200 lbs. bombs, 2600 miles max. at 198 mph.

AF

PMB

LOCKHEED P-38L (Droop-snoot version)

MFR

LOCKHEED XP-49

Continental XIV-1430-13-15, 1350 hp take-off

DIMENSIONS: Span 52′, Lg. 40′ 1″, Ht. 9′ 10″, Wing Area 327.5 sq. ft.

WEIGHT: Empty 15,410 lb., Gross 18,750 lb. Fuel 300–600 gal.

PERFORMANCE: (18,500 lb.) Speed—Top 406 mph at 15,000′, 361 mph at 5000′, 347 mph at s. l. Climb 3075′/1 min., 20,000′/8.7 min. Range 679 miles.

The Lockheed Lightning had a successful combat career, for in the early part of the war it was the fastest and most heavily armed Army fighter. After the short range of the early models was increased, the P-38 was the first fighter useful for long range escort. Its main limitation was the relatively awkward maneuverability inherent in the machine's bulk, but it was especially fast in a dive, and the added safety of the second engine was appreciated.

The first Lightnings to go overseas were some F-4 photo jobs sent to the Southwest Pacific early in 1942. The first fighter P-38s went into combat there in November 1942, although the first all P-38 group was not on hand until the following May. Three such groups were in the Southwest Pacific Theater by 1944. Major Richard Bong, who downed 40 Japanese planes, was the greatest P-38 ace.

First actual combat sorties by P-38s were flown in defense of Iceland in August 1942, an Iceland-based pilot downing the Army's first Nazi plane (a Focke-Wulf Kurier). P-38s flew directly across the Atlantic to England and made their first offensive sortie on September 1, but no enemy was encountered. They saw action in North Africa by November 1942. By 1944, 13 AAF groups used P-38s in European and Pacific areas.

Lockheed attempted to make a basic improvement on the P-38 by using more advanced engines. This project, known as the XP-49 (Lockheed Model 522), began with a company proposal to the Air Corps in August 1939. Purchase of a prototype was ordered in October and a contract readied by November 30, but it was not finally approved until January 8, 1940.

The first specification called for the proposed Pratt & Whitney X-1800 (H-2600) 24-cylinder engine, and a speed of 473 mph at 20,000 ft. was anticipated. When this engine failed to materialize, Continental XIV-1430s were substituted in September 1940, and the new specification estimated top speed to be 458 mph at 25,000 ft., where 1600 hp per engine was expected, and 372 mph at 5000 ft.

MFR

LOCKHEED P-38M (night fighter)

Flight tests began on November 11, 1942, and continued until the following June, with discouraging results. Top speed at 18,500 lbs. gross was only 361 mph at 5000 ft. and 406 mph at 15,000 ft. In appearance, the XP-49 was like the P-38s but armament included two 20-mm. guns with 120 rounds and four .50-caliber guns with 1200 rounds.

BELL AIRACOBRA

Placing the engine behind the pilot has become common since jet propulsion, but this arrangement was first introduced to American fighters by Bell's Airacobra. Previously, it had been seen abroad in Westland and Koolhoven fighters, but the P-39 was the first such design in mass production.

Several advantages became apparent when the

engine was moved back to the center of gravity. A slimmer nose allowed better streamlining and visibility, and had room for heavier armament and the retracted nose wheel of a tricycle landing gear. This undercarriage offered better ground handling and permitted higher landing speeds, which in turn led to smaller wings; not an unmixed blessing since the higher wing loadings handicapped climb and maneuverability at high altitudes.

The Airacobra layout was offered to the Army in a Bell specification dated May 18, 1937, and an XP-39 prototype was ordered on October 7. A turbo-supercharged Allison V-1710-17 of 1150 hp at take-off and 1000 hp at 20,000 ft. turned the propeller through a ten-foot extension shaft. Specifications called for top speeds of 330 mph at sea level and 400 mph at 20,000 ft., climbing to that altitude in five minutes, but this was at 3995 lbs. empty and 5550 lbs. gross, weights far exceeded by future evolution. Provision was made for two synchronized .50-caliber guns with 400 rounds, above a 25-mm. gun with 50 rounds, whose barrel pointed through the propeller hub; but that was replaced by a 37-mm. T-9 cannon with 20 rounds on December 2, 1938. (Actually, no weapons seem to have been installed on the prototype during flight tests.)

The first test flights were made at Dayton in April 1939, and on April 27, a service test contract was made for 12 YP-39s and one YP-39A. After initial trials, the prototype was studied by the NACA and shipped back to the Buffalo factory for modifications. These changed the machine considerably. Radiators, which on the XP-39 were behind the engine on each side of the fuselage, were placed within the modified wing roots with intakes at the leading edge. The cockpit enclosure was lowered and the main wheels covered for smoother streamlining. A carburetor air scoop was placed behind the cockpit, the turbo-supercharger was removed, and the original engine replaced by a V-1710-37 rated at 1090 hp at 13,300 ft.

First flown on November 25, 1939, the revised prototype was designated XP-39B and proved satisfactory enough for its features to be incorporated into the YP-39s on order. Originally, the YP-39 was to have a turbo-supercharger like the prototype, and do 375 mph at 20,000 ft., climb to that altitude in six minutes, and have a 41,300 ft. service ceiling, while the YP-39A would have no turbo, and reach 360 mph at 10,000 ft. Instead of the V-1710-17 and V-1710-19 engines planned, the V-1710-37 without turbo-supercharger was chosen in January 1940 for all thirteen service test aircraft.

This decision to omit the turbo-supercharger was a crucial one in Airacobra development, for while it made the type less expensive and handier at low altitudes, high-altitude performance was seriously crippled; a handicap shared by earlier P-40s and the British version of the P-38. The first YP-39 (Bell Model 12) appeared in September 1940 and had a top speed of 368 mph at 13,600 ft. Armament consisted of one 37-mm. gun with 15 rounds, two .50-caliber guns with 400 rounds, and two .30-caliber guns with 1000 rounds, all mounted in the nose. The pilot's cockpit was protected by armor and entered by an auto-style side door, instead of the common sliding canopy.

Generous production orders for the Airacobra began August 10, 1939, with 80 Model 13s for the Army, temporarily with a P-45 designation. On April 13, 1940, Bell Model 14 was ordered for the British government, and Model 15 was purchased by the Army on September 13. The next day, the first contract was changed so that the last 60 ships could get the leakproof tanks and wing guns specified for the planes ordered in 1940.

Wearing camouflage paint and powered by V-1710-35s of 1150 hp at 12,000 ft., production machines began appearing in January 1941. The first 20 were P-39Cs (ex P-45), identical to the YP-39s but for engine. Sixty planes remaining on that contract became P-39Ds (Model 15), the fully militarized Airacobra with leakproof tanks and four .30-caliber guns in the wings with 4000 rounds. Two synchronized .50s with 400 rounds were in the nose above the 37-mm. gun with 30 rounds. Since tank protection reduced internal fuel capacity from 170 to 120 gallons, the P-39D had provision for a 75-gallon belly drop tank, or a 500-lb. bomb. All this weight, including 184 lbs. of armor and 61 lbs. of armor-glass windshield, had a depressing effect on climb.

The first 60 P-39Ds were followed by 344 more delivered on the 1940 contract along with 229 P-39Fs, similar but for changed propeller (Aeroproducts instead of Curtiss) and exhausts. Allison V-1710-59 engines were installed in the last 25 ships of this contract, which were designated P-39J. All these aircraft were known as Model 15 on company records and had the same characteristics.

British Model 14s began to appear in April 1941 concurrently with Army P-39Ds, and had the same V-1710-35 engine and armament, except for replacement of the 37-mm. gun by the more rapid-firing 20-mm. gun with 60 rounds. These planes were called Airacobra I by the R.A.F. and P-400 in U.S. records. Although 675 were scheduled to go to Britain, at least 212 were transferred to Russia, 54 were lost at sea, and 179 were repossessed by the Army Air Forces in December 1941 for emergency use in the South Pacific and on home training fields.

Lend-lease funds were used in June 1941 to purchase 494 Bell 14As, which had 20-mm. guns and were delivered in 1942. The first ships were designated P-39D-1 and were like the P-39D, but the last 158 had V-1710-63s and were P-39D-2s. For long-range

AF

BELL XP-39

Allison V-1710-17, 1150 hp take-off, 1000 hp at 20,000′

DIMENSIONS: Span 35′ 10″, Lg. 28′ 8″, Ht. 11′, Wing Area 200 sq. ft.

WEIGHT: Empty 3995 lb., Gross 5550 lb., Max. 6204 lb. Fuel 115–200 gal.

PERFORMANCE: Speed—Top 390 mph at 20,000′, Landing 80 mph. Service Ceiling 32,000′, Climb 20,000′/5 min. Endurance 1 hr. at top speed.

ferry flights, a flush belly tank could increase fuel capacity to 265 gallons.

A new, square-cut, laminar-flow wing was designed for the XP-39E, and two prototypes were ordered April 10, 1941, with a third added later. Armed with a 37-mm. nose gun with 30 rounds, two .50-caliber guns in the nose, and four in the wings with 300 rpg, the XP-39E was to use a Continental IV-1430-1. This power plant was unready when flight tests began in February 1942, and was replaced by an Allison V-1710-47 of 1325 hp for take-off, 1150 hp at 21,300 ft. Each of the three examples tested a different vertical tail surface, and engineering studies made on this project contributed to the development of the Bell Kingcobra. Four thousand production models, designated P-76, were ordered on February 24, 1942, from a new Bell facility at Marietta, Georgia, but this contract was canceled on May 20 so that this plant would be free for B-29 production, and Bell engineers could concentrate on the P-63.

The next Airacobra production batch was externally like the P-39D, and began with a contract made August 21, 1941, for 1800 P-39Gs. Changes in engine model led to different designations upon their delivery in 1942. Using a V-1710-63 of 1325 hp for take-off, the first 210 were P-39Ks with an Aeroproducts 10 ft. 4 in. propeller, while 250 P-39Ls built at the same time had Curtiss propellers. In November 1942, the P-39M appeared with an 11 ft. 1 in. propeller and a V-1710-83 of 1200 hp for take-off and 1420 hp at 9500 ft. After 240 P-39Ms had ben accepted, Bell rolled out 2095 P-39Ns. This Airacobra had internal fuel capacity reduced to 87

BELL XP-39B

Allison V-1710-37, 1090 hp at 13,300′

DIMENSIONS: Span 34′, Lg. 29′ 9″, Ht. 11′ 10″, Wing Area 213 sq. ft.

WEIGHT: Empty 4530 lb., Gross 5834 lb., Max. 6450 lb. Fuel 115–200 gal.

PERFORMANCE: Speed—Top 375 mph at 15,000′, Cruising 310 mph, Landing 103 mph. Service Ceiling 36,000′, Climb 20,000′/7.5 min. Range 600 miles normal, 1400 miles/200 gal. at 190 mph.

MFR

BELL XP-39B (with wide fin, and cannon)

MFR

BELL YP-39
Allison V-1710-37, 1090 hp at 13,300′
DIMENSIONS: Span 34′, Lg. 30′ 2″, Ht. 11′ 10″, Wing Area 213 sq. ft.
WEIGHT: Empty 5042 lb., Gross 7000 lb., Max. 7235 lb. Fuel 104–170 gal.
PERFORMANCE: Speed—Top 368 mph at 13,600′, Cruising 257 mph, Landing 80 mph. Service Ceiling 33,300′, Absolute Ceiling 34,500′, Climb 20,000′/7.3 min. Range 600 miles normal, 1000 miles max.

MFR

MFR

BELL P-39C
Allison V-1710-35, 1150 hp at 12,000′
DIMENSIONS: As YP-39
WEIGHT: Empty 5070 lb., Gross 7075 lb. Fuel 104–170 gal.
PERFORMANCE: Speed—Top 379 mph at 13,000′, Cruising 274 mph, Landing 80 mph. Service Ceiling 33,200′, Climb 13,000′/3.6 min. Range 500 miles normal, 900 miles max.

MFR

BELL P-39D
Allison V-1710-35, 1150 hp at 13,800′
WEIGHT: Empty 5462 lb., Gross 7500 lb., Max. 8200 lb. Fuel 120–195 gal.
PERFORMANCE: Speed—Top 368 mph at 13,800′, Cruising 213 mph, Landing 82 mph. Service Ceiling 32,100′, Absolute Ceiling 33,200′, Climb 2720′/1 min., 15,000′/5.7 min. Range 800 miles/500 lb. bomb, 1545 miles ferry at 195 mph.

AF

BELL P-39D

PMB

BELL P-39F (data as P-39D)

MFR

BELL P-400 (AIRACOBRA I)

MFR

BELL XP-39E
Allison V-1710-47, 1325 hp take-off, 1150 hp at 21,300′
DIMENSIONS: Span 35′ 10″, Lg. 31′ 11″, Ht. 11′ 10″, Wing Area 236 sq. ft.
WEIGHT: Empty 6936 lb., Gross 8918 lb. Fuel 100–150 gal.
PERFORMANCE: Speed—Top 386 mph at 21,680′, Cruising 205 mph, Landing 88 mph. Service Ceiling 35,200′, Climb 20,000′/9.3 min. Range 500 miles normal, 800 miles max.

PMB

BELL P-39K
Allison V-1710-63, 1325 hp take-off, 1150 hp at 11,800′
DIMENSIONS: As YP-39
WEIGHT: Empty 5658 lb., Gross 7600 lb., Max. 8400 lb. Fuel 104–295 gal.
PERFORMANCE: Speed—Top 368 mph at 13,800′, Cruising 213 mph, Landing 82 mph. Service Ceiling 32,000′, Climb 15,000′/5.7 min. Range 750 miles normal, 800 miles/500 lb. bomb with 120 gal., 1500 miles max.

MFR

BELL P-39Q

DIMENSIONS: As P-39N

WEIGHT: Empty 5645 lb., Gross 7700 lb., Max. 8300 lb. Fuel 104–295 gal.

PERFORMANCE: Speed—Top 385 mph at 11,000′, Landing 88 mph. Service Ceiling 35,000′, Climb 15,000′/4.5 min. Range 650 miles/500 lb. bomb, 1250 miles max. ferry.

gallons, and a V-1710-85 of 1420 hp at 9700 ft. for war emergency power. Armor weight on the last 695 (block P-39N-5) was reduced from 231 to 193 lbs. All the aircraft in these lots are known as Model 26 on company records, and are so alike in appearance that they can be told apart only by serial numbers. (Note that no P-39G, H or P was ever finished, and that I and O are not used for designation letters since they might be confused with numbers.)

On September 17, 1942, the Airacobra's wing gun installation was ordered changed from four .30-caliber to two .50-caliber guns with 600 rounds, and these underslung weapons distinguished the 4905 P-39Qs that began appearing in March 1943 with a V-1710-85. Internal arrangements varied; the first 150 (P-39Q-1) had 87 gallons of fuel and 231 lbs. or armor, the next 950 (Q-5) had 110 gallons and 193 lbs., and the remainder (Q-10 to Q-30) had 120 gallons and 227 lbs. armor weight. Blocks Q-21 to Q-30 could be recognized by a four-bladed propeller.

By the time Airacobra production was completed in August 1944, 9558 had been built, of which 4773 were allotted to the Soviet Union. The first Airacobra's to go into action were the R.A.F. Model 14s that were used on sweeps in October 1941, but the British withdrew the type from action because of its inadequate performance at high altitudes. Army Air Force P-39Ds and P-400s were rushed to the Pacific after Japan's

BELL P-39M [*Photo unavailable*]

Allison V-1710-83, 1200 hp take-off, 1420 hp at 9500′

DIMENSIONS: As YP-39

WEIGHT: Empty 5610 lb., Gross 7500 lb., Max. 8400 lb. Fuel 104–295 gal.

PERFORMANCE: Speed—Top 386 mph at 9500′, Cruising 200 mph, Landing 84 mph. Service Ceiling 36,000′, Climb 15,000′/4.4 min. Range 650 miles/500 lb. bomb, 1500 miles max.

BELL P-39N

Allison V-1710-85, 1200 hp take-off, 1420 hp at 9700′

DIMENSIONS: Span 34′, Lg. 30′ 2″, Ht. 12′ 5″, Wing Area 213 sq. ft.

WEIGHT: Empty 5657 lb., Gross 7600 lb., Max. 8200 lb. Fuel 87–295 gal.

PERFORMANCE: Speed—Top 399 mph at 9700′, Landing 85 mph. Service Ceiling 38,500′, Climb 15,000′/3.8 min. Range 750 miles/500 lb. bomb with 120 gal., 1250 miles max.

PMB

attack. Some squadrons were scattered from Alaska to Hawaii, Panama, and the South Pacific, while two groups defending Australia flew the first AAF Airacobra sorties from Port Moresby on April 30, 1942. Three P-39 groups went to North Africa, and some were lend-leased to Portugal. Up to September 1943, in fact, most AAF fighter groups overseas were either P-39s or P-40s. Peak AAF Airacobra inventory was 2150 on hand in February 1944, but by August, all P-39 groups had converted to more advanced equipment.

The Airacobra was a disappointment to the Army, for it was outclimbed by the Zero and seemed "practically useless over 17,000 ft." The P-40 was thought "much better" because a lower wing loading made it climb better. In North Africa the P-39s internal armor and high sea-level speed made it useful for ground strafing, and "unusually resistant" to enemy flak, it had the lowest rate of losses per sortie of any AAF fighter in the ETO. In Russia, where air operations were usually at low altitudes in support of ground armies, the P-39 was better liked than the P-40. Wing guns were sometimes removed to lighten the weight.

It is probable that the wing was too small; 213 square feet of area may have been adequate for the prototype's weight, but production models were over a third heavier. High altitude performance was further crippled by removal of the prototype's turbo-supercharger, a mistake that was made on the British version of the otherwise successful P-38.

REPUBLIC THUNDERBOLT

Contrasting sharply with the pointed noses of inline-engine types was the barrel-shaped P-47 Thunderbolt, largest single-engined fighter used in the war. The last successful air-cooled, radial-powered single-seat type, it represented the only radial fighter series to survive the Army's 1939 selection of liquid-cooled Allisons as the primary power plant for pursuits.

During the bidding early in 1939 on pursuit types, Seversky Aircraft had offered two main proposals: the XP-41, last P-35 finished with flush retracting wheels and an R-1830-19 with an integral medium-altitude supercharger; and a new cleaned-up prototype called AP-4, which had a turbo-supercharger in the belly, fed air through an orifice ahead of the port wing fillet.

On May 12, 1939, 13 service test examples of the turbo-supercharged project were ordered and designated YP-43. Since Alexander Seversky had left the firm he founded and named, the company reorganized in October 1939 as Republic Aviation and began work on the Republic YP-43 Lancer. Powered by a Pratt & Whitney R-1830-35 Wasp of 1100 hp at 20,000 ft., they were designed to do 351 mph at that altitude and were armed with two synchronized .50-caliber guns on the cowl and two .30-caliber guns in the wings. Delivery of the YP-43 began in September 1940 and was completed in April 1941.

In the meantime, Republic engineers tried to improve this type so that the speeds of its liquid-cooled competitors could be excelled. The company AP-4J proposal used a 1400 hp Pratt & Whitney R-2180-1, and was estimated to do 386 mph; 80 were ordered September 13, 1939, as the P-44. Another proposal, AP-4L, suggested a big 2000 hp Pratt & Whitney R-2800-7 to lift P-44 speed to 406 mph. On July 12, 1940, an Air Corps letter of intent promised a contract for 225 of the new aircraft and a September 9, 1940, order scheduled 602 more.

In contrast to the chunky P-44 design, Republic engineers had also offered on August 1, 1939, the AP-10 with a liquid-cooled 1150 hp Allison V-1710-39, two synchronized guns, and a small (115 square foot) wing. Weighing only 4900 lbs., it was supposed to do 415 mph and climb to 15,000 ft. in only 3½ minutes. Air Corps engineers requested an enlarged 6570-lb. design, increasing armament to two .50-caliber and four .30-caliber guns and reducing speed to 400 mph,

AMC

SEVERSKY XP-41

Pratt & Whitney R-1830-19, 1200 hp take-off, 1050 hp at 17,500′

DIMENSIONS: Span 36′, Lg. 27′, Ht. 12′ 6″, Wing Area 220 sq. ft.

WEIGHT: Empty 5390 lb., Gross 6600 lb., Max. 7200 lb. Fuel 150–230 gal.

PERFORMANCE: Speed—Top 323 mph at 15,000′, Cruising 292 mph. Range 730 miles normal, 1860 miles max.

and in November two prototypes, an XP-47 and a stripped-down XP-47A, were ordered.

Neither the P-44 nor the XP-47 were ever flown, for war in Europe demonstrated the need for more fire power and internal protection on future fighters. Republic's Russian-born Chief Engineer Alexander Karteveli offered a new specification dated June 12, 1940, calling for an eight gun, 11,500 lb. fighter built around an XR-2800 Double Wasp turbo-supercharged to deliver 2000 hp at 27,800 ft. Top speed was over 400 mph and climb to 15,000 ft. took five minutes. Evaluation by Wright Field engineers led to abandonment of

AF

SEVERSKY AP-4 (XP-43)

AF

REPUBLIC YP-43

Pratt & Whitney R-1830-35, 1200 hp take-off, 1100 hp at 20,000′

DIMENSIONS: Span 36′, Lg. 28′ 6″, Ht. 14′, Wing Area 223 sq. ft.

WEIGHT: Empty 5730 lb., Gross 7300 lb., Max. 7880 lb. Fuel 145–218 gal.

PERFORMANCE: Speed—Top 351 mph at 20,000′, Landing 78 mph. Service Ceiling 38,000′, Climb 15,000′/6 min. Range 800 miles normal, 1300 miles max.

the earlier projects, in spite of nearly a million dollars' worth of engineering study and a P-44 mockup. On September 6, 1940, the XP-47 prototype contract was changed to call for an XP-47B with the Double Wasp, and on September 13, 1940, the P-44 contracts negotiated during the previous two months were replaced by a $56,000,000 contract for 171 P-47B and 602 P-47Cs, plus 54 P-43s to fill the delivery gap until the P-47 and Double Wasp were available. The eighty P-44s ordered in 1939 were to be finished as P-43As for the same reason; since the P-43 and P-44 were similar but for engines, the change wasn't too costly.

The production P-43 Lancers began to appear in May 1941 and were like the YP-43. Eighty P-43As began to arrive in September and were followed by 125 P-43A-1s ordered on June 28, 1941, with lend-lease funds for China. Actually built to assure continuity in fighter production at Republic, the P-43A-1s had an R-2800-57 Wasp and an additional pair of .50-caliber wing guns. Lancer deliveries were completed March 1942, but 150 were converted to P-43B photoreconnaissance jobs, while 108 P-43A-1s went to China. Essentially an interim pursuit while the P-47 was prepared for service, the P-43 was the first air-cooled fighter with a turbo-supercharger, and suffered from faulty self-sealing fuel tanks.

On May 6, 1941, the XP-47B made its first flight. Largest single-engined fighter then built, it had a four-bladed propeller, pilot armor, leakproof tanks, and a low cockpit entered from the port side by a door. Tests were incomplete when the prototype was destroyed on August 8, 1942, but the XP-47B did achieve 412 mph at 25,800 ft. when 1960 hp was available. Eight .50-caliber guns were placed in the wings.

In March 1942, the first production P-47B appeared with a sliding cockpit canopy and metal-covered control surfaces instead of the prototype's door and fabric-covered surfaces. A 2000 hp R-2800-21 gave the Thunderbolt speeds of from 340 mph at 5000 ft. to 429 mph at 27,800 ft. It was the best interceptor in production anywhere, but was handicapped in maneuverability by size and weight, and sluggish at low altitudes.

MFR

REPUBLIC P-43
Pratt & Whitney R-1830-47, 1200 hp at 25,000′
DIMENSIONS: As YP-43
WEIGHT: Empty 5654 lb., Gross 7810 lb., Max. 7935 lb. Fuel 145–218 gal.
PERFORMANCE: Speed—Top 349 mph at 25,000′, Cruising 280 mph, Landing 78 mph. Service Ceiling 38,000′, Climb 2850′/1 min., 15,000′/5.5 min. Range 800 miles normal, 1300 miles max.

MFR

REPUBLIC P-43

Two years after the production order, 602 P-47Cs began to appear in September 1942. They were longer than the P-47B, eliminated the sloping radio mast, and could carry beneath the fuselage a 500-lb. bomb or a droppable fuel tank to extend range. The first P-47Ds, ordered October 13, 1941, were very similar to the P-47C, but later blocks added attachments for wing tanks or bombs. These models used R-2800-21 Wasps at first, but then adopted the R-2800-59 providing 2300 hp for emergencies, and permitting 433 mph at 30,000 ft. A new Republic plant in Evansville, Indiana, also built the P-47D. In addition Curtiss delivered between December 1942 and March 1944, 354 Thunderbolts designated P-47G, which were identical to early P-47Ds.

More Thunderbolts were delivered from those three sources in 1943 than any other U.S. fighter type, and thousands were shipped to the various fronts. Until then the Army had to depend on low-altitude P-40s and P-39s, and only a limited quantity of P-38s, so two American groups in the ETO had to use British Supermarine Spitfire Vs, until the high-performance P-47s arrived. In April 1943, Britain-based Thunderbolts went into action. There were three groups there at that time, one of them replacing Spitfires, while P-47s began to replace the P-40 in the Mediterranean in November 1943. The Southwest Pacific debut of the Thunderbolts was in June 1943, while others arrived in China the next April, and at Saipan via CVE in June 1944.

Although designed primarily as a destroyer of bombers, the Thunderbolt arrived on the scene at a time when bomber escort was the Air Force fighter's chief work, and the 305 gallons of fuel provided in the fuselage of early models was insufficient. By July 1943, P-47s used a 108 gallon drop tank to extend the combat radius to 350 miles. A few months later, two such tanks boosted combat radius to 445 miles. Meanwhile, the

AF

REPUBLIC P-43A-1
Pratt & Whitney R-1830-57, 1200 hp at 25,000′
DIMENSIONS: As YP-43
WEIGHT: Empty 5996 lb., Gross 7435 lb., Max. 8480 lb. Fuel 145–268 gal.
PERFORMANCE: Speed—Top 356 mph at 20,000′, Cruising 280 mph, Landing 78 mph. Service Ceiling 36,000′, Climb 15,000′/6 min. Range 650 miles/200 lb. bomb, 1450 miles max.

AF

REPUBLIC P-47B
Pratt & Whitney R-2800-21, 2000 hp at 27,800′
DIMENSIONS: As XP-47B
WEIGHT: Empty 9346 lb., Gross 12,245 lb., Max. 13,360 lb. Fuel 205–305 gal.
PERFORMANCE: Speed—Top 429 mph at 27,800′, 340 mph at 5000′, Cruising 335 mph, Landing 100 mph. Service Ceiling 42,000′ Climb 2560′/1 min., 15,000′/6.7 min. Range 550 miles normal, 1100 miles ferry.

Republic plant tried various innovations on standard P-47 airframes.

The last P-47B off the line became the XP-47E when it was fitted with a pressure cabin, while the XP-47F was another B model testing a laminar-flow wing. The next variation was the XP-47H of 1943, which was a D airframe mated with an experimental 2300 hp Chrysler 16-cylinder XIV-2220-1 inverted inline engine, making it the only pencil-nosed Thunderbolt flown.

AF

REPUBLIC XP-47B
Pratt & Whitney XR-2800-21, 2000 hp at 27,800′
DIMENSIONS: Span 40′ 9″, Lg. 35′, Ht. 12′ 8″, Wing Area 300 sq. ft.
WEIGHT: Empty 9189 lb., Gross 12,086 lb., Max. 12,700 lb. Fuel 205–305 gal.
PERFORMANCE: Speed—Top 412 mph at 25,800′ on test. Service Ceiling 38,000′, Climb 15,000′/5 min. Range 575 miles normal, 1150 miles max.

MFR

REPUBLIC P-47C
Pratt & Whitney R-2800-21, 2000 hp at 27,800′ (2300 hp WE)
DIMENSIONS: Span 40′ 9″, Lg. 36′ 1″, Ht. 14′ 2″, Wing Area 300 sq. ft.
WEIGHT: Empty 9900 lb., Gross 13,500 lb., Max. 14,925 lb. Fuel 305–505 gal.
PERFORMANCE: Speed—Top 433 mph at 30,000′, Cruising 350 mph, Landing 100 mph. Service Ceiling 42,000′, Climb 20,000′/11 min.

The engine did not go into production, and so neither did this particular plane.

By November 1942, an XP-47J project was planned to reduce Thunderbolt weight and explore the speed limits of propeller-driven aircraft. Powered by an R-2800-57 giving 2800 hp for war emergencies, this type had a fan behind a prop spinner to suck cooling air over the cylinders, exhaust ejection to boost speed, and lightweight wing construction with ordnance reduced to six .50-caliber guns and 1602 rounds. The contract was approved June 18, 1943 and the XP-47J first flown November 26. On August 5, 1944, the XP-47J did 504 mph, fastest speed for a propeller-driven aircraft ever officially announced here or abroad (which does not mean, however, that faster prop flights haven't been made). Plans to produce more P-47Js were canceled August 1943 in favor of the P-72.

The next Thunderbolt models tested features more readily put on production planes. Converted from D

PMB

REPUBLIC P-47D-4 (Similar to P-47C)

airframes the XP-47K was completed July 1943 with an R-2800-21 and a bubble canopy affording all-around vision, while the XP-47L had internal fuel capacity increased from 305 to 370 gallons and an R-2800-59 offering water injection for short bursts of speed.

Both bubble canopy and larger fuel tanks were incorporated into 1944 production line Ds, together with -59 or -63 engines. The first 3962 P-47D-1 to P-47D-22-RE produced at Farmingdale had the old style cockpit, while the last 2547, with block numbers from P-47D-25 on, had the bubble canopy. At Evansville, the first 1461 P-47D-2 to P-47D-23-RA were old style, the last 4632 (Blocks 26–40) were new.

Characteristics of the P-47D-25 are typical of the line. Fuel load could include up to 370 gallons internally plus 330 in drop tanks, which could extend the radius of action to 690 miles for fighter sweeps. Radius with one 165 gallon drop tank and one 1000 lb. bomb was 518 miles; with two 1000 lb. bombs 320 miles. In this latter role, as a low-altitude fighter bomber, the heavily armed Thunderbolt was outstanding through the last year of the European war. Leading Thunderbolt aces included Lieutenant Colonel Francis S. Gabreski, with 31 victories, and Major Robert S. Johnson with 28.

Improvement of the type continued. Three D airframes were fitted with 2100 hp R-2800-57 engines, dive-brakes under the wing, and designated as YP-47M. During 1944, 130 more were built as P-47Ms and sent to the ETO to met the threat of V-1 "buzz bombs."

Last of these Thunderbolt variations was the XP-47N of September 1944, which had an R-2800-57, larger wing, and weighed a hefty 20,450 lbs. In production as a long-range escort fighter for Pacific air forces, P-47N deliveries from Farmingdale totaled 1667 from December 1944, to December 1945. The Evansville plant added 149 more before V-J cancellations eliminated almost 6000 others.

Heaviest single-engined fighter used in action, the P-47N could carry up to 1156 gallons in internal and drop tanks. A radius of action up to 1000 miles was possible, provided the pilot's physical condition permitted a solo flight of nine or more hours. Alternately, ten 5 in. rockets or three 1000 lb. bombs could augment the eight .50-caliber guns with 2136 rounds, in attacks on surface targets.

The Thunderbolt total of 15,660 is the largest in American fighter plane history. The AAF had 31 groups on hand before the end of 1944, and a peak inventory of 5595 in May 1945. Britain was allocated

MFR

REPUBLIC P-47D-30
Pratt & Whitney R-2800-59, 2300 hp at 31,000′
DIMENSIONS: Span 40′ 9″, Lg. 36′ 1″, Ht. 14′ 2″, Wing Area 300 sq. ft.
WEIGHT: Empty 10,000 lb., Gross 14,500 lb., Max. 19,400 lb. Fuel 370–700 gal.
PERFORMANCE: Speed—Top 428 mph at 30,000′, 350 mph at s. l., Landing 100 mph. Service Ceiling 42,000′, Climb 20,000′/9 min. Range 475 miles/500 lb. bomb, 1700 miles max.

PMB

REPUBLIC P-47D-30

MFR

REPUBLIC XP-47H
Chrysler XIV-2220-1, 2300 hp
DIMENSIONS: Span 40′ 9″, Lg. 39′ 2″, Wing Area 300 sq. ft.
WEIGHT: Gross 13,750 lb.
PERFORMANCE: Speed—Top 490 mph.

MFR

REPUBLIC XP-47J

Pratt & Whitney R-2800-57, 2100 hp take-off, 2800 hp at 30,000′

DIMENSIONS: Span 40′ 11″ Lg. 33′ 3″, Ht. 17′ 3″, Wing Area 300 sq. ft.

WEIGHT: Empty 9663 lb., Gross 12,400 lb., Max. 16,780 lb. Fuel 287 gal.

PERFORMANCE: Speed—Top 507 mph at 34,300′, Cruising 400 mph, Landing 92 mph. Service Ceiling 45,000′, Climb 15,000′/4.5 min. Range 765 miles/210 gal., 1070 miles max.

MFR

REPUBLIC XP-47K

REPUBLIC P-47M [*Photo unavailable*]

Pratt & Whitney R-2800-57, 2800 hp WE at 32,500′

DIMENSIONS: Span 40′ 9″, Lg. 36′ 4″, Ht. 14′ 9″, Wing Area 308 sq. ft.

WEIGHT: Empty 10,423 lb., Gross 13,275 lb., Max. 15,500 lb. Fuel 370–480 gal.

PERFORMANCE: Speed—Top 473 mph at 32,000′, Landing 99 mph. Service Ceiling 41,000′, Climb 32,000′/13.4 min. Range 530 miles normal.

MFR

REPUBLIC P-47N

Pratt & Whitney R-2800-57, -73, or -77, 2800 hp at 32,500′

DIMENSIONS: Span 42′ 7″, Lg. 36′ 1″, Ht. 14′ 8″, Wing Area 322 sq. ft.

WEIGHT: Empty 11,000 lb., Gross 16,300 lb., Max. 20,700 lb. Fuel 556–1156 gal.

PERFORMANCE: Speed—Top 467 mph at 32,500′, Cruising 300 mph, Landing 98 mph. Service Ceiling 43,000′, Climb 25,000′/14.2 min. Range 800 miles/2000 lbs. bombs, 2200 miles at 281 mph.

240 P-47Ds with the old cockpit (Thunderbolt I), and 590 with the new canopy (Thunderbolt II). They were used operationally in the Southeast Asia Theater. Many were also lend-leased to Russia (203) and Brazil (88), and after the war served with the Air National Guard, the air forces of France, Italy, Turkey, Iran, and several Latin American powers. Their last combat mission was during the Guatemalan revolution in 1953.

NORTH AMERICAN MUSTANG

The most effective American fighter of the Second World War had no radical layout or major departure from conventional patterns. An untrained observer, seeing the Mustang at a distance, might be hard put to tell it from the P-40, Messerschmitt, Spitfire, Yak, or any of the numerous low-wing single-seaters powered by an inline engine. North American's highly successful fighter was good because it represented the highest refinement of a fighter layout which could be seen in America as far back as the old P-24; the long, pointed opposite of the barrel-shaped radial-engined jobs.

The Mustang's story began in April 1940, when British officials asked the North American firm to produce the Curtiss H-87 (P-40D) in quantity for the R.A.F. Company officials countered with a proposal to design a superior machine around the same 1150 hp Allison V-1710-39 engine, which was accepted by the British on condition that the prototype be available in 120 days. On May 4, 1940, the Army released the NA-73, as the new design was labeled, for sale to Britain provided that two of the initial lot be transferred to the Air Corps for tests. After the NA-73 had been ordered in quantity for the R.A.F., an Air Corps contract approved on September 20, 1940, scheduled two XP-51s, actually the fifth and tenth NA-73s.

A prototype was finished within the time alloted, but a wait for the engine delayed the first flight to October 26, 1940. Designed by Raymond Rice and Edgar Schmued, formerly with Germany's Messerschmitt group, the NA-73 had a low square-cut wing whose laminar-flow airfoil reduced drag, and a radiator scoop streamlined into the fuselage's underside aft of the pilot. Delivery of 620 production models named Mustang I began in August 1941. Equipment included armor, leakproof tanks, two .50-caliber guns with 400 rpg low in the nose, and two more in the wings inboard of four .30-caliber guns with 500 rpg. American government data on the XP-51 samples indicated a top speed of 382 mph at 13,000 ft., and British fliers reported the type to be one of the handiest fighters available in both maneuverability and speed at low altitudes.

Lend-lease funds were used in September 1940 to order 150 P-51s similar to the XP-51, but appearing in July 1942 with four 20-mm. wing guns and 500 rounds. Fifty-five fitted with two K-24 cameras in the rear fuselage became F-6A tactical reconaissance ships, 93 went to Britain as Mustang IAs, and the last two were assigned to the XP-78 project.

In September 1942 delivery began on A-36A dive bomber versions. Described more fully in Part 2 of this book, they had dive-brakes and six .50-caliber guns. Five hundred were followed, beginning in March 1943, by 310 P-51As which had a 1200 hp V-1710-81, four .50-caliber wing guns with 1260 rounds, and racks for two 500 lb. bombs or drop tanks. Fifty went to the R.A.F. as Mustang IIs, and 35 became F-6B photo-reconnaissance aircraft for the Army Air Forces.

Although the first Allison-powered Mustangs were not used in action by the R.A.F. until July 1942, they quickly acquired a good reputation, and in the Tunisian campaign next winter, the U.S. successfully operated two squadrons of P-51s (F-6As) as tactical reconnaissance planes. Wisely, the Army had decided not to enter its first battle with Germany with prewar observation types, and the fast, well-armed, single-seater had definitely replaced the conventional two-place types used for Army Co-operation since the First World War. Artillery spotting from a single-seater was first tried by an R.A.F. Mustang at Salerno on September 18,1943, and the scheme worked many times. In most cases, however, our air supremacy permitted more precise correction of artillery fire by observers in light planes.

Meanwhile, the U.S. military attaché in London, Major Thomas Hitchcock, advised developing the Mustang into a high-altitude fighter by "cross-breeding" the excellent airframe with the Rolls-Royce Merlin engine. Rolls-Royce received four Mustang Is for conversion, and had successful installations airborne in six weeks, the converted ships being called Mustang Xs in England. Data obtained in this work was transmitted to the United States, where production of Merlin-powered Mustangs was scheduled, and two P-51s converted to XP-78s in August 1942 by installation of a U.S.-built Packard Merlin V-1650-3 with a two-stage supercharger, carburetor intake below the four-bladed propeller's hub, 1380 hp for take-off, and 1595 hp with water injection for emergencies. In September these aircraft were redesignated XP-51B, although their speed of 441 mph at 29,800 ft. was phenomenal enough to warrant their own designation.

By summer 1943, the P-51B was in full production at Inglewood, California, and 1988 were built. Production models used the V-1650-3, had more fuel, four .50-caliber wing guns with 1260 rounds, and racks below the wings for two 1000 lb. bombs or 150 gallon drop

NACA

NORTH AMERICAN XP-51 (MUSTANG I)
Allison V-1710-39, 1150 hp at 11,800′
DIMENSIONS: Span 37′, Lg. 32′ 3″, Ht. 12′ 2″, Wing Area 233 sq. ft.
WEIGHT: Empty 6278 lb., Gross 7965 lb., Max. 8400 lb. Fuel 105–170 gal.
PERFORMANCE: Speed—Top 382 mph at 13,000′, Cruising 300 mph, Landing 83 mph. Service Ceiling 30,800′, Climb 20,000′/10.9 min. Range 625 miles normal, 1040 miles max.

tanks. In August 1943, the new North American plant at Dallas, Texas, began delivery of 1750 P-51Cs identical to the B. A bulged sliding cockpit hood was fitted to 274 P-51B and 636 P-51Cs that went to the R.A.F. as the Mustang III, and 71 Bs and 20 Cs became F-6C reconnaissance models.

The P-51D appeared in 1944 with a plastic canopy affording all-around vision, six .50-caliber wing guns with 1880 rounds and a Packard V-1650-7. This was the most widely used Mustang, with 6502 built at Inglewood and 1454 at Dallas. The 1337 P-51Ks built in 1945 at Dallas were identical to the D but for a new propeller. Mustang IV was British nomenclature for 281 P-51D and 594 P-51Ks received by lend-lease. Reconnaissance variants were 136 F-6D and 163 F-6Ks.

When Merlin-powered Mustangs arrived in Britain, the major U.S. fighter assignment was escorting U.S. heavy bombers on raids into Germany. The Mustang's combination of speed and maneuverability was the best of U.S. fighters, and its range made possible the deepest penetrations of enemy territory. The P-51B fought its first battle on December 1, 1943, and by the following summer Mustangs dominated the air over the very center of Germany. Other Mustang groups operated in the Mediterranean and the Pacific. As a fighter bomber, the P-51D did not match the P-47s blows. But P-51D radius of action was 475 miles on internal tanks alone, 650 with two 75 gallon drop tanks added, and 850 with two 108 gallon tanks, the latter being more than enough to cover the farthest B-17 strikes. As Table 8 shows, the Mustang was the most efficient destroyer of enemy aircraft in the air, and thus became the most popular U.S. fighter in Europe.

Despite such success, engineers planned further improvements, and built a number of prototypes involv-

MFR

NORTH AMERICAN P-51A
Allison V-1710-81, 1200 hp take-off, 1470 hp WE at 11,800′
DIMENSIONS: Span 37′, Lg. 32′ 3″, Ht. 12′ 2″, Wing Area 233 sq. ft.
WEIGHT: Empty 6433 lb., Gross 8600 lb., Max. 9000 lb. Fuel 105–180 gal. (480 gal. max.).
PERFORMANCE: Speed—Top 390 mph at 20,000′, Cruising 307 mph, Landing 90 mph. Service Ceiling 31,350′, Climb 25,000′/16 min. Range 350 miles normal, 450 miles/180 gal., 2550 miles/480 gal.

ing similar layouts but new lightweight airframes, so that weight saved in structure could permit better speeds. The first three lightweight Mustangs were the XP-51Fs, appearing in June 1944, with smaller wheels, three-bladed propeller, reduced fuel capacity, only four .50-caliber guns, and a new wing section. The next pair of experimental Mustangs were the XP-51Gs, of September 1944, similar in appearance but with an imported 1665 hp Rolls-Royce Merlin 145, a unique five-bladed prop, and six .50-caliber guns. The final pair of experimental Mustangs appeared in March 1945 with the Allison V-1710-119 and were known as the XP-51J. They had four wing guns, a three-bladed propeller, and a top speed of 491 mph.

The lessons learned from these machines were incorporated in the last production model, the P-51H, which made its first flight on February 3, 1945. Only 555 of 2000 ordered were built at Inglewood before the end of the war with Japan. The remainder were canceled, with all but one of over 1600 identical P-51Ms expected from the Dallas plant. A P-51L order (V-1650-11) was also eliminated. With 700 lbs. saved in structural weight, a sharper nose cowl over the Packard V-1650-9, and new tail and wing sections, the P-51H was probably the fastest prop-driven plane actually used in wartime.

Top speed was 487 mph at 25,000 ft. when used as an interceptor, 450 mph when carrying two 500 lb. bombs and added fuel. Range with two 110 gallon drop tanks could be extended to 2400 miles at 241 mph, or 850 miles when carrying two 1000 lb. bombs. Armament was six .50-caliber guns, plus optional external loads of the two bombs or ten 5 in. rockets. Ammunition supply included 400 rounds for each inner wing gun, and 270 rounds for each of the others. Armor included $\frac{7}{16}$ in. behind the pilot's head, $\frac{5}{16}$ in. behind his back, and $\frac{1}{4}$ in. at the front fire wall.

Long after the end of the war, the Mustang continued in service with the Air Force (14,819 were built, and 5541 were on hand at war's end). Surplus machines were sold or given to Australia (where 80 were built under license), Canada, China, Cuba, Denmark, the Dominican Republic, France, Indonesia, Israel, Italy, Korea, Sweden, and Switzerland. In July 1950, the Mustang again went to war in Korea. Although

NORTH AMERICAN P-51
Allison V-1710-39, 1150 hp at 11,800′
DIMENSIONS: As XP-51
WEIGHT: Empty 6550 lb., Gross 7850 lb., Max. 8800 lb. Fuel 105–180 gal.
PERFORMANCE: (8800 lb.) Speed—Top 387 mph at 15,000′, Cruising 307 mph, Landing 90 mph. Service Ceiling 31,350′, Climb 25,000′/16 min. Range 350 miles normal, 540–1175 miles max.

MFR

NORTH AMERICAN XP-51B
Packard V-1650-3, 1380 hp take-off, 1595 hp WE
DIMENSIONS: Span 37′, Lg. 32′ 3″, Ht. 13′ 8″, Wing Area 233 sq. ft.
WEIGHT: Empty 7030 lb., Gross 8350 lb., Max. 8880 lb. Fuel 105–180 gal.
PERFORMANCE: Speed—Top 441 mph at 29,800′. Service Ceiling 42,000′, Climb 20,000′/5.9 min.

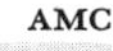
AMC

such generalizations are difficult to prove, there is good reason to believe the Mustang the best of World War II fighters.

AN EVALUATION

Now that the major fighter types with which the Army Air Forces fought the war have been described, it may be helpful to summarize their role. Table 8 shows what fighters were used by the AAF in the European Theater of Operations from 1942 to 1945. The planes are given in order of number of sorties, as an indication of each type's relative importance, including Spitfires and Beaufighters obtained on reverse lend-lease, and P-61 night fighters to be discussed later. Unfortunately, we do not have this data for the Pacific theaters.

Table 8

AAF FIGHTERS IN THE EUROPEAN WAR, 1942–45

	No. of Sorties	Bomb Tonnage	U. S. A/C Lost in Combat	Enemy A/C Claimed Destroyed in Air	Enemy A/C Claimed Destroyed on Ground	Combat Missions Loss Rate Per Sortie
P-47	423,435	113,963	3,077	3,082	3,202	0.7%
P-51	213,873	5,668	2,520	4,950	4,131	1.2%
P-38	129,849	20,139	1,758	1,771	749	1.4%
P-40	67,059	11,014	553	481	40	0.8%
P-39	30,547	121	107	14	18	0.4%
Spitfire	28,981	212	191	256	3	0.7%
A-36	23,373	8,014	177	84	17	0.8%
Beaufighter	6,706	—	63	24	—	0.9%
P-61	3,637	141	25	58	—	0.7%
Total	927,460	159,272	8,471	10,720	8,160	0.9%

MFR

The first two columns give the number of sorties and show the decisive role in Europe of the Thunderbolt, Mustang, and Lightning. The next column indicates the extent that fighters were used for tactical bombing, and shows the P-47 delivering over ⅔ of the bombs dropped by fighters, although the A-36, dive-bomber version of the P-51A, dropped the heaviest weight of bombs per sortie. Columns four and seven list total losses of each type on combat missions and per cent of aircraft loss per sortie. The reader should remember that loss-rate reflects not only the type's vulnerability, but also the relative risk taken on its particular missions. With this in mind, Lightnings seem to have suffered the heaviest losses, 1.4 per cent, and Airacobras the lowest, with only 0.4 per cent per sortie. The lower losses of the night fighters and fighter bombers probably indicate that attacking enemy bombers or ground targets is less risky than tackling enemy fighters.

Column five indicates how many enemy aircraft were believed destroyed in the air by each type, while the sixth column tells the number of enemy aircraft destroyed when caught on the ground. This data gives only a rough index of each fighter design's relative efficiency in the job which is its *raison d'être,* destroying enemy aircraft. The effect of ground-fire and the uneven risks of interception and offensive missions, of course, limits this index's value. Nevertheless, the Mustang accounted for almost half the enemy aircraft destroyed in Europe by U.S. fighters and emerges clearly as the most effective type, especially when we remember that Mustangs did relatively little bombing, and almost no interception, but were used for long-distance penetration of enemy fighter territory. Column six indicates Mustang success at strafing planes at their home fields, this largely in the war's last weeks.

The reader may draw his own conclusions from these figures. Why did Lightnings suffer losses greater than Airacobras when the former had a much better record in destroying the enemy? Possibly because the P-39s low-level maneuverability and extensive armor reduced the effects of hostile fire, while the P-38s speed and ceiling enabled it to close with an enemy that wished to avoid combat more often than to join it; but no doubt the where and when of each type's mission was also important here.

It would be highly interesting to have comparable data for the fighter types of other countries, but until then what we do have is a record of Air Force success in building fighters. The relative quality of fighter pilots is not constant, so it may not really be possible to make precise comparison of each type's efficiency, but quality of aircraft remains a significant factor, if not always the decisive one.

NORTH AMERICAN P-51B
Packard V-1650-3, 1380 hp take-off, 1595 hp WE at 17,000′, 1295 hp at 28,750′
DIMENSIONS: As XP-51B
WEIGHT: Empty 6985 lb., Gross 9800 lb., Max. 11,800 lb. Fuel 105–269 gal. (569 gal. max.).
PERFORMANCE: Speed—Top 440 mph at 30,000′, Cruising 362 mph, Landing 100 mph. Service Ceiling 41,800′, Climb 30,000′/12.5 min. Range 400 miles normal, 900 miles at 362 mph, 2900 miles max.

MFR

NORTH AMERICAN P-51C
Packard V-1650-7, 1490 hp take-off, 1720 hp at 17,000′, 1505 hp at 19,300′
DIMENSIONS: As XP-51B
WEIGHT: Empty 6985 lb., Gross 9800 lb., Max. 11,800 lb. Fuel 105–269 gal. (569 gal. max.).
PERFORMANCE: Speed—Top 439 mph at 25,000′, Cruising 362 mph, Landing 100 mph. Service Ceiling 41,900′, Climb 30,000′/12.1 min. Range 400 miles normal, 950 miles/269 gal., 2700 miles max.

CRISIS-BORN PROJECTS

Now that the five types that did most Air Force fighter work in World War II have been discussed, attention can be given the numerous experimental projects begun by the Matériel Division. In the two years between the outbreak of war in Europe and the attack on Pearl Harbor, an extraordinary variety of designs received pursuit designations XP-46 to XP-72. Nevertheless, only three of over two dozen projects reached production in time to join the P-38, P-39, and P-40 types already on order when Germany's invasion of Poland began the war.

The first flurry of designs were the XP-46 to XP-50 prototypes ordered in October–November 1939. None passed the prototype stage, since the Curtiss XP-46, Republic XP-47, and Lockheed XP-49 were submerged by P-40, P-47B, and P-38 developments. Douglas made its only attempt at a land-based fighter with their XP-48 (Model 312), but it never was built.

The Grumman XP-50 was a twin-engined single-seat interceptor based on the Navy's XF5F-1. Ordered November 25, 1939, the XP-50 began flight tests in March 1941 powered by turbo-supercharged Wright Cyclones. Like its naval counterpart, it had short,

WL

NORTH AMERICAN P-51D
Packard V-1650-7, 1490 hp take-off, 1720 hp at 6200′, 1505 hp at 19,300′
DIMENSIONS: As XP-51B
WEIGHT: Empty 7125 lb., Gross 10,100 lb., Max. 11,600 lb. Fuel 269–489 gal.
PERFORMANCE: Speed—Top 437 mph at 25,000′, 413 mph at 15,000′, 395 mph at 5000′, Cruising 362 mph, Landing 100 mph. Service Ceiling 41,900′, Climb 3475′/1 min., 30,000′/13 min. Range 950 miles/269 gal., 2300 miles/489 gal.

squared-off wing, stubby fuselage, and twin rudders, but the nose was lengthened to accommodate tricycle landing gear. Armament included two 20-mm. guns with 120 rounds and two .50-caliber guns with 1000 rounds in the nose, and two 100 lb. bombs below the fuselage.

A turbo-supercharger explosion on May 14, 1941, destroyed the prototype and despite expenditures of $353,828 the XP-50 was abandoned. An improved version with 1700 hp Wright R-2600-10s was designated XP-65, but was canceled on August 4, 1941, before a prototype was begun.

NORTH AMERICAN P-51H
Packard V-1650-9, 1380 hp take-off, 2220 hp at 10,200′, 1800 hp WE at 25,000′
DIMENSIONS: Span 37′, Lg. 33′ 4″, Ht. 13′ 8″, Wing Area 233 sq. ft.
WEIGHT: Empty 6585 lb., Gross 9500 lb., Max. 11,054 lb. Fuel 255–475 gal.
PERFORMANCE: Speed—Top 487 mph at 25,000′, Cruising 380 mph, Landing 96 mph. Service Ceiling 41,600′, Climb 30,000′/12.5 min. Range 850 miles/1000 lb. bombs, 940 miles normal, 2400 miles at 241 mph.

MFR

PMB

NORTH AMERICAN P-51K

By June 1940, France was crumbling before the Nazi onslaught, and Congress was providing funds for expansion and development of combat aviation. New designations from XP-51 to XP-60 were begun that year by the Matériel Division, exploring new possibilities of advancing fighter performance. Ironically, the most successful was the XP-51, which was not adopted by the Air Force until 1942, after it had been operated by Britain. Republic's XP-47B, which replaced two earlier projects, was the most fruitful of Army developments that summer. But the Matérial Division also backed the Bell XP-52 and XP-59, which like the radical XP-54, XP-55, and XP-56 had pusher propellers, as well as the conventional Curtiss XP-53 and XP-60, the lightweight XP-57 and the giant XP-58.

Of eleven new projects begun that year, four were canceled before prototypes were made. The first to drop out was the XP-57, which had been proposed to General Arnold in May 1940 by Tucker Aviation of Detroit. A light (3400 lb.) fighter armed with two .50-caliber and one 20-mm. gun, the wooden-winged Tucker was to get 308 mph from a 720 hp Miller L-510

NORTH AMERICAN P-51J
Allison V-1710-119, 1500 hp take-off, 1720 hp WE at 20,700′
DIMENSIONS: Span 37′, Lg. 32′ 11″, Ht. 13′ 8″, Wing Area 233 sq. ft.
WEIGHT: Empty 6030 lb., Gross 7550 lb., Max. 9140 lb. Fuel 105–180 gal. (330 gal. max.).
PERFORMANCE: Speed—Top 491 mph at 27,400′, Landing 84 mph. Service Ceiling 43,700′, Climb 20,000′/5 min.

MFR

MFR

NORTH AMERICAN XP-51F
Packard V-1650-7, 1490 hp take-off
DIMENSIONS: As XP-51B
WEIGHT: Empty 5635 lb., Gross 7610 lb., Max. 9060 lb. Fuel 105–180 gal. (330 gal. max.).
PERFORMANCE: Speed—Top 466 mph at 29,000′, Cruising 379 mph, Landing 100 mph. Service Ceiling 42,500′, Climb 19,500′/4.9 min. Range 650 miles normal, 2100 miles max.

MFR

NORTH AMERICAN XP-51G
Rolls-Royce Merlin 145, 1675 hp take-off, 1910 hp at 15,400′, 2080 hp at 20,000′
DIMENSIONS: As XP-51B
WEIGHT: Empty 5750 lb., Gross 7265 lb., Max. 8885 lb. Fuel 105–180 gal. (330 gal. max.).
PERFORMANCE: Speed—Top 472 mph at 20,750′, Cruising 315 mph, Landing 100 mph. Service Ceiling 45,700′, Climb 20,000′/3.4 min. Range 485 miles normal, 1865 miles max.

engine driving its propeller by an extended shaft like the P-39s. By February 1941, however, the little company was in financial difficulties, and since current fighter trends were to heavier and faster aircraft, the contract was allowed to lapse.

PUSHER PROTOTYPES

Among the most unusual American fighters were the group designed to explore effects of pusher propeller arrangements on fighter performance. Single-seaters with rearward facing propellers and engines behind the pilot had been built abroad as early as 1915, and offered a nose cleared for pilot visibility and heavy armament installations. Numerous complications of structure presented themselves, however, and the layout was untried in the United States until June 1940, when several prototypes were begun to test various approaches to the problem.

Bell Aircraft had used a pusher arrangement on its multiplace Airacuda, and their Model 16 single-seater was the first pusher type to receive an Air Corps pursuit designation. The XP-52 had tricycle landing gear, twin booms to support the tail assembly, and a new inline engine, the 1250 hp Continental XIV-1430-5, cooled by a nose radiator and turning contrarotating propellers. Specifications called for a 435 mph speed, 8200 lbs. gross, and an armament of two 20-mm. and six .50-caliber guns.

Another Bell pusher was the XP-59, which had a

GRUMMAN XP-50
Wright R-1820-67, -69, 1200 hp take-off, 1000 hp at 25,000′
DIMENSIONS: Span 42′, Lg. 31′ 11″, Ht. 12′, Wing Area 304 sq. ft.
WEIGHT: Empty 8307 lb., Gross 10,558 lb., Max. 13,060 lb. Fuel 217–450 gal.
PERFORMANCE: Speed—Top 424 mph at 25,000′, Cruising 317 mph. Service Ceiling 40,000′, Climb 20,000′/5 min. Range 585 miles normal.

MFR

VULTEE XP-54
Lycoming XH-2470-1, 2300 hp at 25,000′
DIMENSIONS: Span 53′ 10″, Lg. 54′ 9″, Ht. 13′, Wing Area 456 sq. ft.
WEIGHT: Empty 15,262 lb., Gross 18,233 lb., Max. 19,335 lb. Fuel 223–395 gal.
PERFORMANCE: Speed—Top 403 mph at 28,500′, Cruising 328 mph, Landing 110 mph. Service Ceiling 37,000′, Climb 26,000′/17 min. Range 500 miles normal, 850 miles max.

MFR

AF

CURTISS XP-55

Allison V-1710-95, 1275 hp take-off, 1125 hp at 15,500′

DIMENSIONS: Span 40′ 7″, Lg. 29′ 7″, Ht. 11′ 7″, Wing Area 209 sq. ft.

WEIGHT: Empty 5325 lb., Gross 6885 lb., Max. 7711 lb. Fuel 110–210 gal.

PERFORMANCE: Speed—Top 390 mph at 19,300′, Cruising 300 mph, Landing 80 mph. Service Ceiling 34,600′, Climb 20,000′/7.1 min. Range 635 miles at 296 mph, 1440 miles max.

AMC

CURTISS XP-55

2000 hp Pratt & Whitney R-2800-23 cooled by air from a nose intake, and an estimated 11,698 lbs. gross and 450 mph top. Neither Bell type was built, because the XP-59 was replaced by the XP-59A jet project, and the XP-52 was canceled November 25, 1941, to relieve the load on Bell's engineering staff.

Low priorities delayed completion of three other pusher prototypes, the first to appear being Vultee's XP-54 ordered June 22, 1940, and flown January 15, 1943. Only aircraft powered by a 2300 hp Lycoming XH-2470-1, the XP-54 (Vultee V-70) had twin rudders suspended on tail booms extending from the gulled wing. Largest single-seater offered the Air Force, its bullet-shaped fuselage stood so high on tricycle gear that the pilot was raised through the bottom up to the pressurized cockpit by an elevating seat. In emergencies, the seat dropped downward on a swinging arm to catapult the pilot clear of the four-bladed propeller. Built of welded magnesium, the XP-54 had excellent pilot's visibility and two 37-mm. guns with 120 rounds mounted in the nose below a pair of .50-caliber guns with 1000 rounds. Only two prototypes were built.

When originally purchased in June 1940, the Curtiss XP-55 was to have a Continental XIV-1430-3 and do 507 mph top, but this engine was replaced by an Allison V-1710-95, giving an actual speed of 390 mph. After studies in December 1941 on a full-scale wooden flying model with a 275 hp Menasco, three prototypes were built, and the first was flown on July 13, 1943.

This prototype was the only one to test a "canard" layout in which the tail assembly was eliminated, the elevators placed at the nose, and the vertical tail surface divided and placed near the tips of a sharply swept-back wing. Like the other pushers, it had tricycle wheels. A dorsal fin above and ventral fin below the engine contained air intakes for the supercharger and radiator, and the three-bladed prop could be jettisoned to make a pilot's bail-out safer. Armament consisted of four .50-caliber guns in the nose, and wing racks were provided for two drop tanks or bombs.

The most radical of the pusher fighters was the Northrop N2M, or XP-56, a tailless interceptor with short fuselage mounted on a swept-back wing. A Pratt & Whitney experimental X-1800 liquid-cooled engine (H-2600) was expected when XP-56 engineering studies were ordered on June 22, 1940, but the two prototypes purchased September 26 were changed in December to the air-cooled R-2800 Double Wasp.

Armed with two 20-mm. guns with 200 rounds and four .50-caliber guns with 1600 rounds, the Northrop XP-56 made its first official flight on September 30, 1943, and utilized welded magnesium construction. Cooled through wing-root intakes, the R-2800-29 turned contrarotating propellers behind dorsal and ventral fins. It had tricycle gear like the other pushers, but a unique wing had dropping tips with air-operated bellows rudders. The control surfaces were "elevons" of the type later seen on Northrop flying wings.

CURTISS PROTOTYPES

The XP-53 designation was applied to a Curtiss design planned as a P-40 replacement. The original specification called for a top speed of 450 mph with a 1250 hp Continental XIV-1430-3 and eight .50-caliber guns in a laminar-flow wing. Two prototypes were ordered October 1, 1940, but in January 1941 were redesignated XP-60 and a Packard V-1650-1 Merlin giving 1120 hp at 19,000 ft. was substituted for the Continental engine.

On September 18, 1941, the XP-60 was first flown, while the second prototype was used for static tests. A three-bladed propeller headed a neat nose, with the radiator ahead of the low tapered wing, and the wheels retracted inward of eight wing guns with 2000 rounds of .50-caliber ammunition. This prototype was later

MFR

NORTHROP XP-56
Pratt & Whitney R-2800-29, 2000 hp take-off, 1650 hp at 22,500′
DIMENSIONS: Span 42′ 6″, Lg. 27′ 6″, Ht. 11′, Wing Area 306 sq. ft.
WEIGHT: Empty 8700 lb., Gross 11,350 lb., Max. 12,145 lb. Fuel 215–314 gal.
PERFORMANCE: Speed—Top 465 mph at 25,000′, 417 mph at s. l., Cruising 396 mph. Service Ceiling 33,000′, Climb 3125′/1 min., 20,000′/7.2 min. Range 445 miles normal, 660 miles max.

rebuilt as the XP-60D with a V-1650-3 like the P-51B, a four-bladed propeller, and modified landing gear.

Instead of liquid-cooled Merlins, however, air-cooled Pratt & Whitney R-2800-10 Wasps were scheduled for 1950 P-60A production models ordered October 31, 1941, and it seemed that Curtiss would replace the P-40 with a type comparable to the P-47 Thunderbolt. But after the United States entered the war, production officials had second thoughts about the desirability of interrupting P-40 production at that crucial point. In January 1942 it was decided to drop the P-60A program in favor of a P-40K and P-40L contract and a try at building P-47s at Curtiss.

For developmental purposes three aircraft labeled

CURTISS XP-60A
Allison V-1710-75, 1425 hp at 25,000′
DIMENSIONS: Span 41′ 4″, Lg. 33′ 8″, Ht. 12′ 4″, Wing Area 275 sq. ft.
WEIGHT: Empty 7806 lb., Gross 9616 lb., Max. 10,160 lb. Fuel 116–200 gal.
PERFORMANCE: Speed—Top 420 mph at 29,000′, 324 mph at s. l., Cruising 300 mph. Service Ceiling 35,200′, Absolute Ceiling 36,000′, Climb 2560′/1 min., 10,000′/4.2 min.

MFR

MFR

CURTISS XP-60
Packard V-1650-1, 1300 hp take-off, 1120 hp at 19,000′
DIMENSIONS: Span 41′ 5″, Lg. 33′ 4″, Ht. 14′ 4″, Wing Area 275 sq. ft.
WEIGHT: Empty 7010 lb., Gross 9351 lb., Max. 9961 lb. Fuel 135–228 gal.
PERFORMANCE: Speed—Top 380 mph at 20,000′, 330 mph at 5150′, Landing 85 mph. Service Ceiling 29,000′, Climb 20,000′/7.3 min. Range 995 miles/228 gal.

XP-60A, XP-60B, and XP-60C were allowed to survive the cut. On November 1, 1942, the XP-60A was flown with a turbo-supercharged Allison V-1710-75, a four-bladed propeller, larger radiator and six .50-caliber wing guns with 1200 rounds. At first the P-60B was to be similar with a new supercharger, and the P-60C was to try a Chrysler XIV-2220 like the XP-47H. In September 1942, the P-60C changed to an R-2800-53 radial with contrarotating propellers and four .50-caliber wing guns with 1000 rounds. This version began flight tests on January 27, 1943. Meanwhile an R-2800-10 with an ordinary four-bladed propeller was substituted for the P-60Bs Allison by a December 2, 1942, order, and this aircraft was completed as the XP-60E, first flown on May 26, 1943, with four wing guns.

CURTISS XP-60C
Pratt & Whitney R-2800-53, 2000 hp at 20,000′
DIMENSIONS: Span 41′ 4″, Lg. 33′ 11″, Ht. 15′, Wing Area 275 sq. ft.
WEIGHT: Empty 8600 lb., Gross 10,525 lb., Max. 10,785 lb. Fuel 178/225 gal.
PERFORMANCE: Speed—Top 414 mph at 20,350′, Landing 89 mph. Service Ceiling 37,900′, Absolute Ceiling 38,400′, Climb 3890′/1 min.

MFR

MFR

CURTISS XP-60E
Pratt & Whitney R-2800-10, 2000 hp at 20,000′
DIMENSIONS: As XP-60C
WEIGHT: Empty 8574 lb., Gross 10,320 lb., Max. 10,667 lb. Fuel 178–225 gal.
PERFORMANCE: Speed—Top 410 mph at 20,200′, Cruising 348 mph. Service Ceiling 38,000′, Climb 4200′/1 min., 10,000′/2.5 min.

One more aircraft appeared in this series, the YP-60E accepted October 1944. Powered by an R-2800-18, it was similar to XP-60E but for an unbalanced rudder and a bubble canopy which made it look much like a P-47D-25. Armament included six .50-caliber wing guns, but performance was below Thunderbolt standards.

CURTISS YP-60E
Pratt & Whitney R-2800-18, 2100 hp
DIMENSIONS: As XP-60C
WEIGHT: Empty 8285 lb., Gross 10,270 lb., Max. 11,520 lb. Fuel 178–225 gal.
PERFORMANCE: Speed—Top 405 mph at 24,500′. Service Ceiling 34,000′, Climb 15,000′/4.8 min.

Another single-seat fighter was developed by Curtiss during this same period. Designated XP-62 and powered by a turbo-supercharged R-3350-17 with contra-rotating three-bladed propellers, this big low-wing monoplane was armed with four to eight 20-mm. guns in the wings with 150 rpg. The pressure cabin hatch opened upward, instead of sliding back, and a long dorsal fin led back to the rudder.

Authority for purchase of the XP-62 was dated May 16, 1941, a contract was made June 27, and the mockup was inspected in December. A letter contract dated May 20, 1942, scheduled 100 P-62As, but R-3350 engine production was so taken up supplying B-29 bombers that the P-62 could not supplant the P-40 in production. Without high priorities, the P-62A became just another fighter which never quite made it when the project was canceled July 18. Only the XP-62 was completed, making its first flight July 21, 1943.

LOCKHEED XP-58 "CHAIN LIGHTNING"

Last of 1940s fighter projects to be flown was the Lockheed XP-58, only two-seater begun that year, and the heaviest fighter built during the war. This type began with a Lockheed proposal in May 1940 for a twin-engined, two-place convoy fighter whose tactical role was comparable to the Messerschmitt Bf 110 then active in Europe.

On October 14 two XP-58 prototypes were ordered, scheduled to use Pratt & Whitney X-1800 (H-2600) liquid-cooled engines also planned for the XP-49. In December, the 2350 hp Wright R-2160s were substi-

AMC

tuted, since the earlier units did not materialize, and two remote-controlled turrets were added. By 1941, the specification called for a long-range fighter for escorting bombers, basically a bigger Lightning with 35,559 lbs. gross. Carrying two 20-mm. and eight .50-caliber guns, it was expected to do 450 mph.

An even larger fighter was the XP-71 offered by Curtiss in November 1941. This project was a two-place, 82 ft. span, 46,951 lb. monoplane with two 3450 hp turbo-supercharged R-4360-13 Wasp Majors turning contrarotating pusher propellers, and would carry one 75-mm. and two 37-mm. fixed guns. It was not built, and work on the more moderate XP-58 continued with low priority.

In September 1942, the XP-58s mission was changed to anti-shipping, instead of convoy work, and in April 1943, Allison V-3420s were substituted for the Wrights. Even so, no production was scheduled, and even the second prototype was canceled, leaving the XP-58 finally flown on June 6, 1944, the sole example of the type.

Looking much like an enlarged P-38 but for four-bladed propellers, double wheels on the tricycle gear, and a gunner at the rear of the center nacelle, the XP-58 had a remote-controlled turret above and below the crew's position. Two .50s were in each turret with 300 rpg, while the nose contained four 37-mm. fixed guns with 250 rpg. Four 1000 lb. bombs could be carried, or the nose armament replaced by one 75-mm. and two .50-caliber guns. Too heavy to maneuver against enemy fighters, the XP-58 might have been useful for attack missions.

MFR

CURTISS XP-62
Wright R-3350-17, 2300 hp take-off, 2250 hp at 25,000′
DIMENSIONS: Span 53′ 8″, Lg. 39′ 6″, Ht. 16′ 3″, Wing Area 420 sq. ft.
WEIGHT: Empty 11,773 lb., Gross 14,660 lb., Max. 16,651 lb. Fuel 245–384 gal.
PERFORMANCE: Speed—Top 448 mph at 27,000′, 358 mph at 5000′, Cruising 340 mph, Landing 85 mph. Service Ceiling 35,700′, Climb 15,000′/6.6 min. Range 900 miles normal, 1500 miles max.

LOCKHEED XP-58
Allison V-3420-11, -13, 2600 hp take-off, 3000 hp at 25,000′
DIMENSIONS: Span 70′, Lg. 49′ 5″, Ht. 13′ 7″, Wing Area 600 sq. ft.
WEIGHT: Empty 31,624 lb., Gross 39,192 lb., Max. 43,020 lb. Fuel 656–760 gal. (1690 gal. max.).
PERFORMANCE: Speed—Top 436 mph at 25,000′, Cruising 274 mph. Service Ceiling 38,400′, Absolute Ceiling 39,975′, Climb 2660′/1 min., 25,000′/12 min. Range 1150 miles/650 gal., 1250 miles/800 gal., 2650 miles max.

MFR

AF

DOUGLAS P-70
Wright R-2600-11, 1600 hp take-off, 1275 hp at 12,000′
DIMENSIONS: Span 61′ 4″, Lg. 47′ 7″, Ht. 17′ 7″, Wing Area 464 sq. ft.
WEIGHT: Empty 16,031 lb., Gross 21,264 lb. Fuel 600 gal.
PERFORMANCE: Speed—Top 329 mph at 14,000′, Cruising 270 mph, Landing 97 mph. Service Ceiling 28,250′, Climb 12,000′/8 min. Range 1060 miles normal, 1460 miles max.

THE NIGHT-FIGHTER PROBLEM

In spite of the common division of European offensive aircraft into day- and night-bomber categories, few night attacks were made in the early months of the Second World War. Far less accurate than daylight bombing, night bombing was unnecessary for the Germans when they had air supremacy, and considered impolitic for the Allies. As more vigorous air operations developed in 1940, heavy losses on daytime sorties led Britain's Bomber Command to concentrate on nocturnal raids. Their enemies began the Battle of Britain in the daytime, but when losses rose past a tolerable figure despite fighter escort, the Luftwaffe turned more and more to night work.

Precision was still lacking, but as unhappy Coventry was to learn, increasing tonnage volume could severely hurt industrial targets. And difficult to find at night as a factory might be, it was much less so than a moving airplane. The speedy interceptors which served London so well in sunshine groped about in darkness as Göring's bombers unloaded, and only occasional searchlight illumination gave opportunity for attack.

The perfection of radio-location equipment light enough to be airborne gave the fighter a better chance, and Britain developed a specialized night fighter large enough to carry the radar and its operator plus armament sufficient to destroy any bomber. While speed and climb could not match that of a single-seater, enough margin over bomber performance was required to insure successful interception. Other requirements included a moderate landing speed for safe operation from small, blacked-out fields, and endurance enough to permit persistence in ambush or pursuit.

Such weight and relatively low wing loading requirements would limit badly a single-engined aircraft's performance, and therefore the first successful plane for this work was a development of the Blenheim twin-engined bomber. First flown in July 1939, the Bristol Beaufighter was first used against the Germans in November 1940, and became the most important British night fighter. Powered by two Bristol Hercules radial engines, its pilot had good visibility forward, while the radar operator sat within the rear fuselage. Armament included four 20-mm. guns firing forward from the lower part of the nose and six .30-caliber guns in the wings.

DOUGLAS P-70

AF

The U. S. Army became interested in a Northrop design for a night fighter offered in November 1940, and on January 11, 1941, two XP-61 prototypes were ordered, followed by a service test order for 13 YP-61s on March 10. A Radiation Laboratory was established at Massachusetts Institute of Technology which undertook the construction of AI (airborne interception) radar.

During the time required for the Northrop design to enter service, another American plane was pressed into night-fighter duty. In 1940, the British were receiving Douglas Boston attack bombers whose admirable agility suggested a type that could function as a night fighter. The Boston's endurance and tricycle gear immediately made it a safer night operator than most, and when the nose enclosure was blocked in and replaced by twelve .30-caliber guns, and exhaust dampers and black paint added, it became the Havoc night fighter.

Other Havocs operated as night "intruders," which attempted to ambush enemy bombers over their home fields. Yet another modification was the "Turbinlight" of 1942; three dozen Havocs fitted with a 1400 amps. searchlight to be used after the Havoc closed within minimum range of its AI radar. A beam of 30° divergence illuminated 150 yards wide at one mile range, enabling accompanying conventional fighters to fire at the target. The powerful lamp was fitted behind a 3 ft. diameter armored glass disk and fed by a ton of batteries in the bomb bay.

After this R.A.F. experience, it is not surprising that the Army turned to Douglas when the first experimental MIT airborne radar was ready for installation in September 1941. Sixty of the A-20s were planned as high-altitude, attack bombers, but delivery of the supercharged engines had been delayed and low-altitude operations seemed the rule for light bombers. One was fitted with radar in the nose, four 20-mm. guns with 240 rounds on a tray below the bomb bay, and became known as the XP-70, with R-2600-7 Cyclones.

With Japan's sudden attack, the Havoc was the only available night fighter, and as soon as additional radar sets were available the remaining 59 A-20s were delivered as P-70s between April and September 1942. Using two 1600 hp R-2600-11 Cyclones, the P-70 had added internal protection. Night-fighter units awaiting P-61s, trained during 1943 on additional Havocs. These included 39 A-20C and 65 A-20Gs fitted with six .50-caliber nose guns and designated P-70A, while 105 A-20Gs fitted as night trainers were known as the P-70B.

The P-70 was used in the Pacific areas of war, but unfortunately Japanese bombers often attacked from 25,000 ft., an altitude difficult for the converted attack bombers to reach. While their pilots impatiently awaited the P-61 Black Widow, other Army night

AF

NORTHROP XP-61
Pratt & Whitney R-2800-10, 2000 hp
DIMENSIONS: Span 66′, Lg. 48′ 11″, Ht. 14′ 8″, Wing Area 663 sq. ft.
WEIGHT: Empty 19,245 lb., Gross 25,150 lb., Max. 28,870 lb. Fuel 540–640 gal.
PERFORMANCE: Speed—Top 370 mph at 20,900′, Cruising 200 mph, Landing 95 mph. Service Ceiling 33,100′, Climb 2900′/1 min., 20,000′/9 min. Range 1200 miles normal, 1450 miles max.

MFR

NORTHROP YP-61
Pratt & Whitney R-2800-10, 2000 hp
DIMENSIONS: As XP-61
WEIGHT: Empty 21,910 lb., Gross 27,950 lb., Max. 28,830 lb. Fuel 540–640 gal.
PERFORMANCE: As XP-61

fighter units in the Mediterranean used the British Beaufighter VI through 1943.

Back home, the Army rushed the P-61 project, ordering 150 on September 1, 1941, and 410 more on February 12, 1942, although the XP-61 wasn't flown until May 21, 1942. The prototypes were followed in August and September 1943 by 13 similar YP-61s, and the type became known as the "Black Widow" from its glossy finish.

The first American designed-for-the-purpose night fighter, the XP-61 was as big as a medium bomber, with two 2000 hp Pratt & Whitney R-2800-10 Wasps, twin rudders supported by tail booms, and tricycle gear. The central nacelle had radar in the nose, the pilot's cabin with a radar operator above and behind him, and finally a gunner's enclosure. Retractable ailerons permitted flaps the full length of the wing's trailing edge. Armament consisted of four 20-mm. fixed guns with 600 rounds in a bulge below the fuselage, and four .50-caliber with 1600 rounds in a top remote-controlled turret. The latter guns were usually fired forward like the cannon by the pilot, but could be unlocked and aimed by the gunner as flexible defense for the upper hemisphere.

NORTHROP P-61A-5
Pratt & Whitney R-2800-65, 2000 hp take-off, 2040 hp WE
DIMENSIONS: As XP-61
WEIGHT: Empty 20,965 lb., Gross 28,000 lb., Max. 32,400 lb. Fuel 550–640 gal.
PERFORMANCE: Speed—Top 369 mph at 20,000′, Cruising 322 mph, Landing 93 mph. Service Ceiling 33,100′, Climb 20,000′/10.3 min.

MFR

Production P-61As began to appear in October 1943, beginning with 45 P-61A-1, which had R-2800-10 Wasps like the test ships, but 155 (Blocks P-61A-5ff.) had R-2800-65s offering 2040 hp for war emergencies. Only the first 37 P-61A-1s had top turrets, for tail buffeting troubles caused their omission on later ships. In July 1944, acceptances of 450 P-61Bs began. This model had underwing fittings for four 1600 lb. bombs, or drop tanks of 165- or 300-gallon size. Turrets were omitted on the first 200 (P-61B-1 to P-61B-10), but were restored on the rest (P-61B-15 to P-61B-20), since the buffeting condition had been cured.

On July 7, 1944, Black Widows made their first kill in the South Pacific, where they had replaced P-70s, and by year's end were standard equipment for all Air Force night-fighter squadrons. They were considerably better than their predecessors, but better speed and ceiling was still needed, and faster ships like the P-38M and P-61C were scheduled.

The P-61C appeared in July 1945 with turbo-supercharged R-2800-73s offering 2800 hp for war emergencies. Forty-one were completed before V-J Day ended production. Two P-61As refitted with R-2800-77 engines became XP-61Ds, similar but for new turbo-superchargers.

Two XP-61E prototypes were converted earlier that year from P-61Bs with R-2800-65 Wasps. This was a long-range day fighter with radar and turret removed to enable a smaller, more streamlined fuselage. The two-man crew sat under a bubble canopy ahead of a fuselage fuel tank, while four .50-caliber nose guns

MFR

NORTHROP P-61B-15
Pratt & Whitney R-2800-65, 2000 hp take-off, 2040 hp WE
DIMENSIONS: Span 66′, Lg. 49′ 7″, Ht. 14′ 8″, Wing Area 664 sq. ft.
WEIGHT: Empty 22,000 lb., Gross 29,700 lb., Max. 38,000 lb. Fuel 550–1880 gal.
PERFORMANCE: Speed—Top 366 mph at 20,000′, Landing 93 mph. Service Ceiling 33,100′, Climb 20,000′/12 min. Range 3000 miles max. ferry.

MFR

NORTHROP P-61C
Pratt & Whitney R-2800-73, 2100 hp take-off, 2800 hp WE
DIMENSIONS: As P-61B
WEIGHT: Empty 24,000 lb., Gross 30,600 lb., Max. 40,300 lb. Fuel 640–1880 gal.
PERFORMANCE: Speed—Top 430 mph at 30,000′, Cruising 307 mph, Landing 87 mph. Service Ceiling 41,000′, Climb 30,000′/14.6 min. Range 330 miles at top speed, 415 miles/ 4000 lbs. bombs, 1725 miles at 195 mph.

MFR

NORTHROP XP-61D
Pratt & Whitney R-2800-77, 2100 hp take-off, 2800 hp at 30,000′
DIMENSIONS: As XP-61
WEIGHT: Empty 23,205 lb., Gross 29,850 lb., Max. 39,715 lb. Fuel 528–1880 gal.
PERFORMANCE: Speed—Top 430 mph at 30,000′, Landing 90 mph. Service Ceiling 43,000′, Climb 30,000′/13.5 min. Range 1050 miles/528 gal. at 197 mph, 3000 miles max.

MFR

NORTHROP XP-61E
Pratt & Whitney R-2800-65, 2000 hp take-off
DIMENSIONS: Span 66′, Lg. 49′ 7″, Ht. 13′ 5″, Wing Area 664 sq. ft.
WEIGHT: Empty 21,350 lb., Gross 31,425 lb., Max. 40,181 lb. Fuel 1158–2398 gal.
PERFORMANCE: Speed—Top 376 mph at 17,000′. Service Ceiling 30,000′, Climb 20,000′/13 min. Range 2250 miles normal, 3750 miles overload.

BELL XP-59A
General Electric I-A, 1400 lbs.
DIMENSIONS: Span 45′ 6″, Lg. 38′ 2″, Ht. 12′ 4″, Wing Area 385 sq. ft.
WEIGHT: Empty 7320 lb., Max. 12,562 lb. Fuel 570–850 gal.
PERFORMANCE: Speed—Top 404 mph at 25,000′. Absolute Ceiling 45,756′.

supplemented the usual four 20-mm. belly guns. This model didn't reach production in wartime, but 36 F-15A reconnaissance versions were built in 1946.

The Black Widow served adequately during the war's last year as the standard AAF night fighter. By then the Axis was on the defensive and no saturation raids were met. Generally, P-61s fought alone on their sorties, ambushing individual enemy raiders.

AMERICA'S FIRST JETS

While visiting England in April 1941, the U. S. Air Force Commanding General, Henry H. Arnold, saw the Gloster E28/39, which made the first British jet flight on May 15 of that year. He returned to the U.S. with details of its Whittle engine, and on September 4 asked General Electric, who had learned much from turbo-supercharger experience about the heat-resistant alloys necessary for whirling turbine blades, to build copies of the jet engine. The following day, Bell Aircraft, because of its proximity to GE's Schenectady plant, was assigned construction of three twin-jet prototypes. For security reasons, the first jet airframes were designated XP-59A and the engines the "I" series, in the hope of disguising them as the cancelled XP-59 pusher and General Electric superchargers.

The XP-59A contract was approved October 3, 1941,

AF

and work went ahead with great secrecy. Muroc Dry Lake, in California, was selected for the initial flights, for concealment's sake. This site later became Edwards Air Force Base, which has replaced Wright Field as the center of Air Force flight testing. The prototype was secretly shipped across the country from Buffalo by train, and on October 1, 1942, a company pilot made taxi runs that inadvertently became short hops. An Air Force pilot made the first official flight the next day.

America's first jet fighter was a single-seat, mid-wing monoplane sitting low on tricycle landing gear and was powered by a General Electric I-A unit of 1400-lb. thrust under each wing root. Two 37-mm. guns with 88 rounds were mounted in the nose. Top speed of 404 mph at 25,000 ft. was below expectations, but at least the principle of jet propulsion had been demonstrated.

Thirteen YP-59As had been ordered in March 1942, and the first example was flown August 1943 with an improved version of the General Electric engine, now called the I-16. The remaining YP-59As were accepted in May and June 1944, with two aircraft going to the Navy and one to Britain in trade for a Gloster Meteor. The first nine had the same armament as the prototypes, but the last four had the installation standard on later Airacomets, one 37-mm. with 44 rounds and three .50-caliber guns with 600 rounds.

Limitations in the Airacomet's performance, and a tendency to "snaking" made it a bad gun platform, and confined its use to orientation experience with jet flying. On October 30, 1943, the 100-plane production order was cut in half. The first 20 P-59As were delivered after August 1944 with jet units now designated J31-GE-3, and 30 P-59Bs were completed by May 1945. The latter model had J31-GE-5s and 66 gallons more of internal fuel.

Although not suitable as a weapon, the Airacomet gave useful training to future P-80 pilots, and it is notable that there were no test losses of XP or YP aircraft, in spite of the pioneering nature of these trials. Nevertheless, Air Force leaders would have been more uncomfortable had they known what they learned later—that Germany not only had developed jet planes, but had one of combat quality going into mass production.

The world's first jet flight, in fact, had been made on August 27, 1939, by the Heinkel He 178, and the He 280 twin-jet fighter flew on April 5, 1941. Messerschmitt's Me 262 flew with jets on July 27, 1942, and production deliveries of this 540 mph interceptor began in March 1944. Before long, it became the first jet fighter to be used in action, and the U.S. knew it had fallen behind again in fighter design.

BELL KINGCOBRA

Although nine new single-seat fighter types were flown in the two years following America's entry into the war, only the P-63, successor to the Bell Airacobra, reached mass production. Built mainly for lend-lease to the Soviet Union, the P-63 Kingcobra did not match the Mustang and Thunderbolt in high-altitude performance, but was considered good at low-level fighting.

The Kingcobra's design evolution began in February 1941 with the XP-39E project, proposing a laminar-flow wing for the Airacobra. Prototypes of the XP-39E ordered in April were flown early in 1942 with the laminar airfoil, square-cut tail, and Allison V-1710-47 engine later used on the XP-63. Two XP-63 prototypes were ordered on June 27, 1941, and the first flew on December 7, 1942. Damage ended tests next month,

BELL YP-59A
General Electric I-16 (J31), 1650 lbs.
DIMENSIONS: Span 45′ 6″, Lg. 38′ 2″, Ht. 12′, Wing Area 385 sq. ft.
WEIGHT: Empty 7626 lb., Gross 10,532 lb., Max. 12,562 lb. Fuel 290–590 gal.
PERFORMANCE: Speed—Top 409 mph at 35,000′, Cruising 314 mph, Landing 80 mph. Service Ceiling 43,200′, Absolute Ceiling 44,000′.

AF

BELL P-59A
General Electric J31-GE-5, 2000 lbs.
DIMENSIONS: Span 45′ 6″, Lg. 38′ 10″, Ht. 12′ 4″, Wing Area 385 sq. ft.
WEIGHT: Empty 7950 lb., Gross 10,822 lb., Max. 13,000 lb. Fuel 290–590 gal.
PERFORMANCE: Speed—Top 413 mph at 30,000′, 380 mph at 5,000′, Cruising 375 mph. Service Ceiling 46,200′, Climb 10,000′/3.2 min., 30,000′/15.5 min. Range 375 miles at 400 mph, 400 miles at 375 mph, 550 miles at 308 mph.

MFR

MFR

BELL P-59B

General Electric J31-GE-5, 2000 lbs.

DIMENSIONS: As P-59A

WEIGHT: Empty 8165 lb., Gross 11,040 lb., Max. 13,700 lb. Fuel 356–656 gal.

PERFORMANCE: As P-59A, but range 375 miles at 400 mph, 525 miles at 371 mph, 950 miles at 304 mph.

and a second prototype flown February 5, 1943, crashed the following May.

Fortunately a third prototype, the XP-63A, had been ordered in June 1942, and flew on April 26, 1943, with a V-1710-93 giving 1325 hp for take-off and 1150 hp at 22,400 ft. The Kingcobra's general arrangement was similar to the P-39s, with the Allison behind the pilot, tricycle gear, and a nose armament of one 37-mm. cannon and two .50-caliber guns, but the larger P-63 could be distinguished by its square-cut tail, wider wings, and four-bladed propeller. Load included 88 lbs. of armor, 100 gallons of internal fuel, and provisions for a 500-lb. bomb or 75-gallon drop tank beneath the fuselage.

Deliveries of production aircraft, ordered September 29, 1942, began in October 1943, and Blocks P-63A-1 to P-63A-10 introduced successive increases in armor and external loads. Besides the nose cannon and twin fifties, a .50-caliber gun was installed below each wing, with a total of 900 rounds for all four

BELL XP-63

Allison V-1710-47, 1325 hp take-off, 1150 hp at 22,140′

DIMENSIONS: Span 38′ 4″, Lg. 32′ 8″, Ht. 11′ 5″, Wing Area 248 sq. ft.

WEIGHT: Empty 6054 lb., Gross 7525 lb. Fuel 100–211 gal.

PERFORMANCE: Speed—Top 407 mph.

MFR

BELL XP-63A [*Photo unavailable*]
Allison V-1710-93, 1325 hp take-off, 1150 hp at 22,400′
DIMENSIONS: Span 38′ 4″, Lg. 32′ 8″, Ht. 12′, Wing Area 248 sq. ft.
WEIGHT: Empty 6185 lb., Gross 7705 lb, Max. 8400 lb. Fuel 100–211 gal.
PERFORMANCE: Speed—Top 421 mph at 24,100′, Cruising 341 mph, Landing 100 mph. Service Ceiling 45,500′, Absolute Ceiling 46,200′, Climb 3670′/1 min., 10,000′/2.64 min., 20,000′/5.8 min. Range 587 miles.

BELL P-63A
Allison V-1710-95, 1325 hp take-off, 1150 hp at 22,400′
DIMENSIONS: Span 38′ 4″, Lg. 32′ 8″, Ht. 12′ 7″, Wing Area 248 sq. ft.
WEIGHT: Empty 6375 lb., Gross 8800 lb., Max. 10,500 lb. Fuel 126–451 gal.
PERFORMANCE: Speed—Top 408 mph at 24,450′, Cruising 378 mph, Landing 100 mph. Service Ceiling 43,000′, Climb 25,000′/7.3 min. Range 390 miles/100 gal. at 378 mph, 450 miles/500 lb. bomb, 2575 miles ferry.

MFR

MFR

BELL P-63A

machine guns. Ammunition supply for the 37-mm. gun was increased from 30 rounds in early models to 58 in the P-63A-9. A 175-gallon ferry tank fitted flush under the belly could be replaced by a 500-lb. bomb or 75-gallon drop tank, while Kingcobras from P-63A-6 on had outboard wing racks for additional drop tanks, or two more 500-lb. bombs. Armor weight increased to 179 lbs. on the A-5, 189 lbs. on the A-8, 199 lbs. on the A-9, and 266 lbs. on the A-10.

After completion of 1725 P-63As, acceptances began in December 1944 on 1227 P-63Cs which had a V-1710-117, an extension fin under the tail, internal fuel capacity of 107 gallons, and 201 lbs. of armor. None of the early P-63As used by the AAF got overseas, but 2456 Kingcobras went to Russia, 300 P-63Cs went to France, and two P-63As were tested in England.

An improved version of the Kingcobra appeared in 1945 with a V-1710-109 and modified wings. The first, a single P-63D, sported a bubble canopy but 13 heavier P-63Es whose tests began in May, had the standard

BELL P-63C

Allison V-1710-117, 1510 hp take-off, 1100 hp at 27,000′

DIMENSIONS: As P-63A

WEIGHT: Empty 6800 lb., Gross 8800 lb., Max. 10,700 lb. Fuel 107–393 gal.

PERFORMANCE: Speed—Top 410 mph at 25,000′, Cruising 356 mph, Landing 115 mph. Service Ceiling 38,600′, Climb 25,000′/8.6 min. Range 320 miles/500 lb. bomb, 2100 miles ferry.

MFR

BELL P-63D

Allison V-1710-109, 1425 hp take-off, 1100 hp at 28,000′

DIMENSIONS: Span 39′ 2″, Lg. 32′ 8″, Ht. 11′ 2″, Wing Area 255 sq. ft.

WEIGHT: Empty 7076 lb., Gross 8740 lb., Max. 11,000 lb. Fuel 107–393 gal.

PERFORMANCE: Speed—Top 437 mph at 30,000′, Cruising 188 mph, Landing 91 mph. Service Ceiling 39,000′, Climb 28,000′/11.2 min. Range 700 miles/107 gal., 950 miles/500 lb. bomb, 2000 miles ferry.

MFR

MFR

BELL P-63E

Allison V-1710-109, 1425 hp take-off, 1100 hp at 28,000′

DIMENSIONS: Span 39′ 2″, Lg. 32′ 8″, Ht. 12′ 9″, Wing Area 255 sq. ft.

WEIGHT: Empty 7300 lb., Gross 9400 lb., Max. 11,200 lb. Fuel 107–421 gal.

PERFORMANCE: Speed—Top 410 mph at 25,000′, Cruising 188 mph, Landing 117 mph. Climb 25,000′/7.6 min. Range 725 miles/500 lb. bomb, 2150 miles max.

cockpit and equipment. A contract for 2930 more was canceled by the end of lend-lease. A tall tail and the V-1710-135 distinguished the only example of the P-63F.

Noncombat P-63s were reworked for tests of a Vee shaped "butterfly" tail, swept-back wings, and a second cockpit for instrument training. Nor should we forget the target versions built (RP-63A and RP-63C) to train gunners in bombers. Combat equipment was removed, and a 1488-lb. extra-thick skin applied to shatter frangible dummy bullets fired by student gunners. A red nose light blinked like a pinball machine when hits were felt. Three hundred were built during the war, followed by 32 RP-63Gs in 1946.

LATER WARTIME PROTOTYPES

Experimental fighters discussed up to this point have been those ordered by the end of the fiscal year of 1940 (June 30, 1941), the federal fiscal year in which Air Force expansion gathered impetus toward wartime goals. Although the fiscal year of 1941 added more fighter projects, production programs received higher priorities, and experimental ships lagged. The Pearl Harbor attack put further stress on service type deliveries and only unusually high priority prototypes like the XP-59A jet and XP-61 night fighter were finished in less than 18 months. Other projects drifted for two or three years, with the longest gestation being XP-58s 44 months.

An example of this delay is the twin-engined single-seat monoplane that began the career of the now well-known McDonnell Aircraft Corporation of St. Louis. Assigned the XP-67 designation on July 29, 1941,

BELL P-63F

MFR

AMC

McDONNELL XP-67
Continental XIV-1430-17, -19, 1350 hp take-off, 1600 hp at 25,000′
DIMENSIONS: Span 55′, Lg. 44′ 9″, Ht. 15′ 9″, Wing Area 414 sq. ft.
WEIGHT: Empty 17,745 lb., Gross 22,114 lb., Max. 25,400 lb. Fuel 280–735 gal.
PERFORMANCE: Speed—Top 405 mph at 25,000′ (on test), Cruising 270 mph, Landing 93 mph. Service Ceiling 37,400′, Absolute Ceiling 38,000′, Climb 2600′/1 min., 25,000′/17 min. Range 2384 miles max.

MFR

REPUBLIC XP-69 (Mockup)
Wright R-2160-3, 2350 hp
DIMENSIONS: Span 51′ 8″, Lg. 51′ 6″, Ht. 17′, Wing Area 505 sq. ft.
WEIGHT: Empty 15,595 lb., Gross 18,655 lb., Max. 26,164 lb. Fuel 240–700 gal. (1300 gal. ferry).
PERFORMANCE: (Estimated) Speed—Top 450 mph at 35,000′, Cruising 260 mph. Service Ceiling 48,900′, Climb 35,000′/20 min. Range 780 miles normal, 3000 miles max.

two prototypes were ordered October 29, 1941, and the first wasn't flown until January 6, 1944. After a generally unsatisfactory performance the XP-67 crashed on September 6, and the second example was canceled.

An airfoil-shaped fuselage and center section gave the XP-67 a unique appearance, and contained large fuel tanks, pressurized cockpit, tricycle gear, and six 37-mm. M-4 fixed cannon. Power plants were Continental XIV-1430s driving four-bladed propellers and utilizing their exhausts for extra thrust. Unfortunately, these engines delivered only 1060 of the 1350 hp expected, and left the XP-67 with an excessive take-off run. Instead of the anticipated 448 mph top speed, only 405 mph at 25,000 ft. was achieved.

MFR

REPUBLIC XP-72
Pratt & Whitney R-4360-13, 3450 hp
DIMENSIONS: Span 40′ 11″, Lg. 36′ 7″, Ht. 16′, Wing Area 300 sq. ft.
WEIGHT: Empty 11,475 lb., Gross 14,414 lb., Max. 17,492 lb. Fuel 535–755 gal.
PERFORMANCE: Speed—Top 490 mph at 25,000′, Cruising 300 mph, Landing 104 mph. Service Ceiling 42,000′, Climb 20,000′/5 min. Range 1200 miles normal, 1330 miles max.

Little is known about Vultee's XP-68, for it was canceled on November 22, 1941, shortly after it had been started. Republic's XP-69, however, was begun in July 1941 as a single-seater designed around a 2350 hp Wright R-2160-3 mounted behind the pilot and using an extension shaft to the nose. This experimental radial engine had 42 cylinders in six rows, and was cooled by air entering a scoop below and behind the mid-wing. Armament was to include two 37-mm. and four .50-caliber guns.

The XP-69s mockup passed inspection in June 1942, but the project was halted May 1943 in favor of Republic XP-72 with the more promising Pratt & Whitney R-4360-13 of 3450 hp. First flown on February 2, 1944, the XP-72 was rather similar to the P-47 Thunderbolts, but had the supercharger intake moved back under the wings. A four-bladed propeller was fitted to the first prototype, but the second tried contrarotating propellers. Six .50-caliber or four 37-mm. wing guns could be carried. One hundred P-72s were ordered to meet Nazi buzz bombs, but were canceled after Germany's defeat. Development of the P-80 jet provided the Air Force with a better interceptor.

During 1942, General Motors engineers planned a fighter to utilize the V-3420-19 of that company's Allison engine division. A proposal to the Matériel Division in September by designer Don R. Berlin resulted in a letter contract by October tenth for two prototypes to be built in Detroit. In order to assemble prototypes as fast as possible, spare parts from aircraft already in production were brought to Detroit. Tail surfaces from the Douglas Dauntless, outer wings from the Curtiss P-40, and landing gear from the Vought Corsair were joined to a fuselage in which the big engine behind the pilot, Airacobra-style, drove two co-axial, three-bladed props in the nose. This conglomeration was supposed to win the war, so historian James Fahey says they skipped P-73 and P-74 to give it "a good symbolic number. French 75 in World War I, P-75 in World War II."

Even before the XP-75-GM began flight tests, plans were made in July 1943 to produce 2500 P-75As at General Motors Fisher Body plant in Cleveland. These ships had V-3420-23s, and specifications calling for top speeds of 434 mph at 20,000 ft. and 389 at sea level. Armament included four .50-caliber synchronized nose guns with 300 rpg, up to six .50-caliber wing guns with 235 rpg, and two 1000-lb. bombs. The main order was preceded by six XP-75A-GC preproduction prototypes built at Cleveland, which differed from the XP-75-GM by modified tail and wing tips, a bubble canopy, and a V-3420-23.

Flight tests started November 17, 1943, showed the XP-75 suffering from instability, low rate of roll, poor spinning characteristics, and trouble with the engine (actually two V-1710 joined side by side). Redesigned as long-range fighters, the six XP-75As were delivered early in 1944, and followed in September by the first P-75A. Flight tests, however, showed the "Fisher Eagle" about 30 mph short of the specification's guaranteed speed, and the success of the P-47D and P-51D indicated another long-range fighter type unnecessary. On October 6, 1944, the P-75A contract was terminated, and only six ships were completed.

The last propeller-driven single-seat fighter prototype built for the Air Force, apart from P-47 and P-51

BELL XP-77
Ranger XV-770-7, 520 hp at 8500′
DIMENSIONS: Span 27′ 6″, Lg. 22′ 11″, Ht. 10′ 11″, Wing Area 100 sq. ft.
WEIGHT: Empty 2760 lb., Gross 3583 lb., Max. 3940 lb. Fuel 56–94 gal.
PERFORMANCE: Speed—Top 350 mph at 8500′, 323 mph at s l., Cruising 270 mph, Landing 92 mph. Service Ceiling 30,250′, Climb 4035′/1 min., 8500′/3 min. Range 550 miles/325-lb. bomb, 990 miles max.

AMC

GENERAL MOTORS XP-75-GM
Allison V-3420-19, 2600 hp take-off
DIMENSIONS: Span 49′ 1″, Lg. 41′ 6″, Ht. 15′ 6″, Wing Area 342 sq. ft.
WEIGHT: Empty 11,495 lb., Gross 13,807 lb., Max. 18,210 lb. Fuel 535–830 gal.
PERFORMANCE: Speed—Top 433 mph at 20,000′, Cruising 314 mph, Landing 88 mph. Service Ceiling 36,400′, Absolute Ceiling 39,500′, Climb 4200′/1 min., 20,000′/5.5 min. Range 2050 miles/535 gal., 3500 miles max.

AMC

GENERAL MOTORS XP-75-GM

GENERAL MOTORS XP-75A-GC

AF

GENERAL MOTORS P-75A-GC
Allison V-1710-23, 2600 hp take-off, 2300 hp at 20,000′
DIMENSIONS: Span 49′ 4″, Lg. 41′ 4″, Ht. 15′ 6″, Wing Area 347 sq. ft.
WEIGHT: Empty 11,255 lb., Gross 17,875 lb., Max. 19,420 lb. Fuel 210–638 gal. (858 gal. max.).
PERFORMANCE: Speed—Top 404 mph at 20,000′, Cruising 250 mph, Landing 87 mph. Service Ceiling 38,000′, Climb 20,000′/5.8 min. Range 1150 miles normal, 3150 miles/638 gal., 3850 miles max.

PMB

developments, was also the smallest and lightest type flown since the P-29. Emerging from the impression made by the maneuverability of Japan's Zero fighter, and the shortage of strategic metals, Bell's XP-77 was a lightweight single-seater of wooden construction. Designed to beat both the metal shortage and the Zero, the XP-77s procurement was authorized May 16, 1942, and after inspection of the mockup in September, two prototypes were ordered October 10, 1942.

The only all-wood American fighter, the XP-77 had a 520 hp air-cooled, inline Ranger XV-770-7 in the nose with a 20-mm. gun firing through the propeller shaft. Two .50-caliber synchronized guns and a 325-lb. bomb were included in the armament. A sharply tapered low-wing, tricycle landing gear, two-bladed propeller, and plastic canopy also distinguished the little Bell.

By the time of its first flight on April 1, 1944, a requirement for the low-altitude XP-77 no longer existed. It's too bad, in a way, for postwar sportsmen might have enjoyed aerobatics in the midgets. But from a tactical point of view, the disadvantage of such bargain-basement fighters is that they cannot force a faster opponent to do battle, and airmen on the offensive cannot afford to wait for the enemy to come to them.

Chapter 18: Shield against Annihilation 1945–59

The end of the Second World War also ended the era of propeller-driven fighters. Development of jet propulsion had obsoleted most existing fighters, and the postwar period saw production of new jet types to re-equip the world fighter units.

Invention of the atomic bomb, and strategic elements of the growing cold war between America and Russia tended to center Air Force attention on bombers, rather than fighters, and not until the unexpected appearance of Soviet atomic weapons in 1949 did jet fighter production reach really large numbers. The terrible destructive capability of bombardment now lent a new urgency to development of defensive weapons. Only the ability to clear skies of enemy intruders seemed to offer any shield against annihilation.

Although the United States had no jets ready in time for combat during the big war, wartime development had begun projects from the XP-79 to the XP-86, and had gotten the P-80 Shooting Star into successful production. At the opening of the Korean War, Air Force fighters in actual service consisted almost entirely of types begun before the end of World War II.

First of these wartime projects started in December 1942 as a tailless flying wing interceptor designed by Northrop to be operated by a pilot lying prone in the cockpit. It was hoped that this prone position would reduce strain on the pilot during violent maneuvers and sudden pull-outs, and present a minimum silhouette to enemy gunners. Three XP-79 prototypes designed for 2000-lb. thrust Aerojet rockets were ordered in January 1943, to be built under Northrop subcontract by Avion, Inc. Availability of jet engines led to a decision in March to utilize two Westinghouse 19-B axial-flow jets in the third ship, designated XP-79B.

The radical layout required tryouts in the form of towed gliders with fixed tricycle gear. One, the MX-324 was towed into the air by a P-38 on July 5, 1944, and became the first rocket-powered U.S. aircraft to fly. Aerojet was unable, however, to perfect a rocket motor suitable for the XP-79, so both prototypes were cancelled.

This left only the XP-79B, which arrived at Muroc for testing in June 1945. Sitting low on the ground it had four retractable wheels and twin vertical fins atop the jet exhaust. The welded magnesium flying wing had air bellows-operated split-flap wingtip rudders outboard of elevons, as on the XP-56, and was armed with four .50 caliber guns. The wing itself was constructed so heavily it could be used to ram enemy bombers and slice off their tails. On its first test flight, delayed to September 12, 1945, the XP-79B crashed, test pilot Harry Crosby was killed, and the project ended.

SHOOTING STARS

The most successful jet fighter to come out of the war began on June 23, 1943, when Lockheed was asked to build a single-seater around a de Havilland Goblin engine imported from England. In 143 days, 23 engineers and 105 mechanics finished a neat prototype that made its first flight on January 9, 1944. Although the engine developed only 2460-lb. thrust, instead of the 3000-lb. expected, the Lockheed XP-80 did 502 mph, and became the first American plane in that speed class.

General Electric had prepared a larger jet engine now known as the J-33 (originally I-40) and two more prototypes were ordered. Designated XP-80A and first flown June 11, 1944, they introduced the design followed on production models.

The first of 13 YP-80As flew on September 13, 1944, and as the fastest wartime AAF fighter, the Shooting Star, won orders for 5000 P-80A copies. One thousand were to be built at North American's Dallas plant, the

MFR

NORTHROP XP-79B
Westinghouse 19B, 1345 lbs.
DIMENSIONS: Span 38′, Lg. 14′, Ht. 7′, Wing Area 278 sq. ft.
WEIGHT: Empty 5840 lb., Gross 8670 lb. Fuel 300 gal.
PERFORMANCE: Speed—Top 526 mph at s. l. Climb 25,000′/4.3 min. Range 990 miles.

remainder by Lockheed, who began P-80A deliveries in February 1945. At last the United States had a fighter equal to the Messerschmitt Me 262, but the Shooting Star never got into action. With victory, Lockheed's contracts were reduced to 917 and the Dallas order dropped, leaving the P-80A the only Air Force single-seater in production after V-J Day.

Powered by a 4000-lb. thrust Allison J33-A-11[1] behind the pilot, with intakes ahead of the wing roots and jet exhaust in the tail, the P-80A sat low on tricycle gear. There was a clear plastic canopy of common practice, six .50-caliber guns with 1800 rounds in the nose, a 165-gallon drop tank below each wing tip, and a fuselage dive brake.

The last 240As delivered after March 1947 were completed as P-80Bs with an ejector seat for the pilot, underwing rocket launchers, new M-3 .50-caliber guns (firing 1200 rounds per minute, instead of the 800 rpm of the wartime M-2) and a water-alcohol injection system giving the engine bursts of emergency power. Most of the P-80As on hand were retroactively brought up to B standards, using several models of the J-33 engine (A-9B, -11B, -17A, or -21).

On March 1, 1948, the first P-80C was flown, and 798 were delivered between October 1948 and June 1950. Since F for fighter replaced the old P for pursuit in June 1948, they became known as F-80Cs, and had an Allison J33-A-23 rated at 4600-lb. thrust. Besides the two 165-gallon drop tanks (often increased to 260 in Korea), wing racks could handle ten rockets or two 1000 lb. bombs. In the first four months of the Korean War (July–October), the F-80Cs flew 15,500 sorties, and suffered 42 losses. F-51s left over from the big war flew 12,000 sorties, and lost 69 aircraft. On November 8, 1951, an F-80C engaged a MIG-15 in history's first jet air battle.

Numerous variants gave valuable supporting services. Cameras were substituted for guns in the RF-80A and RF-80C photoreconnaissance versions. A two-place trainer development, the T-33, had performance almost equal to the combat types. A special high-speed version with a J33-A-23, modified wing and fuselage, was the XP-80R which achieved 624 mph in June 1947. Another ship was fitted with an automatic rocket launcher that protruded from the nose like a swordfish's lance.

[1] Allison has produced the GE-designed J33 engine since 1945.

MFR

LOCKHEED XP-80
DeHavilland Goblin H-1b, 2460 lbs. actual thrust
DIMENSIONS: Span 37′, Lg. 32′ 10″, Ht. 10′ 3″, Wing Area 240 sq. ft.
WEIGHT: Empty 6287 lb., Gross 8916 lb. Fuel 200–285 gal.
PERFORMANCE: Speed—Top 502 mph at 20,480′. Service Ceiling 41,000′, Absolute Ceiling 41,800′, Climb 3000′/1 min., 10,000′/3.7 min.

LOCKHEED XP-80A
General Electric J33, 4000 lbs.
DIMENSIONS: Span 39′, Lg. 34′ 6″, Ht. 11′ 4″, Wing Area 238 sq. ft.
WEIGHT: Empty 7225 lb., Gross 9600 lb., Max. 13,750 lb. Fuel 485–815 gal.
PERFORMANCE: Speed—Top 553 mph at 5700′, Cruising 410 mph, Landing 95 mph. Service Ceiling 48,500′, Climb 20,000′/4.6 min. Range 560 miles normal, 1200 miles max.

MFR

MFR

LOCKHEED P-80A
Allison J33-A-11, 4000 lbs.
DIMENSIONS: Span 39′ 11″, Lg. 34′ 6″, Ht. 11′ 4″, Wing Area 238 sq. ft.
WEIGHT: Empty 7920 lb., Gross 11,700 lb., Max. 14,500 lb. Fuel 470–800 gal.
PERFORMANCE: Speed—Top 558 mph at s. l., 508 mph at 30,000′, Cruising 410 mph. Service Ceiling 45,000′, Climb 4580′/1 min. Range 540 miles normal, 1440 miles max.

PMB

LOCKHEED P-80A (with nose rocket launcher)

LOCKHEED P-80B
Allison J33-A-21, 4500 lbs. WE
DIMENSIONS: As P-80A
WEIGHT: Empty 8176 lb., Gross 11,975 lb., Max. 16,000 lb. Fuel 425–755 gal.
PERFORMANCE: Speed—Top 577 mph at 6000′, 497 mph at 35,000′, Cruising 386 mph, Landing 122 mph. Service Ceiling 36,800′, Climb 6475′/1 min. Range 1210 miles.

MFR

TWIN-ENGINED TYPES

Short range was the most obvious limitation of early jet types, and three twin-engined fighters with longer endurance were begun early in 1944 to meet this problem. First was the XP-81 single-seater proposed in January by Consolidated's Vultee division, as a combination of jet propulsion for high speeds with propeller-driven power for cruising. Two prototypes ordered February 11 were powered by a J33-GE-5 installed behind the pilot, while in the nose the first turboprop engine used in America, a General Electric XT-31 (formerly TG-100), turned a four-bladed propeller.

When first flown on February 11, 1945, a Packard V-1650 Merlin was installed in the XP-81s nose, but on December 21, 1945, flight tests with the XT-31 began. Six .50-caliber guns with 1800 rounds were mounted in the low squared-off wing, while 3200 lbs. of bombs, or drop tanks could be carried. Since the XP-81 was a pioneer effort in the turboprop field, mechanical difficulties troubled its power plant, and plans to build 13 YP-81 service test examples were dropped.

The last propeller-driven fighter purchased by the Air Force was the North American XP-82, begun in January 1944 to provide a twin-engined long-range fighter with accommodations for a relief pilot to aid navigation. Essentially two P-51H fuselages joined together on a single wing and stabilizer, the XP-82 Twin Mustang had the pilot on the left side and the co-pilot on the other, with a retractable main wheel underneath each fuselage and twin tail wheels—the last on Air Force aircraft since later ships all have nose

LOCKHEED P-80C
Allison J33-A-23, 4600 lbs., 5400 lbs. WE
DIMENSIONS: As P-80A
WEIGHT: Empty 8240 lb., Gross 15,336 lb., Max. 16,856 lb. Fuel 425–755 gal.
PERFORMANCE: (12,330 lbs., combat weight) Speed—Top 580 mph at 7000′, Cruising 439 mph, Landing 122 mph. Service Ceiling 42,750′, Climb 6870′/1 min. Range 1380 miles.

PMB

MFR

CONSOLIDATED-VULTEE XP-81

General Electric XT-31-GE-1, 2300 hp; J33-GE-5, 3750 lbs.

DIMENSIONS: Span 50′ 6″, Lg. 44′ 10″, Ht. 14′, Wing Area 425 sq. ft.

WEIGHT: Empty 12,755 lb., Gross 19,500 lb., Max. 24,650 lb. Fuel 811–1511 gal.

PERFORMANCE: Speed—Top 507 mph at 20,000′. Service Ceiling 35,500′, Climb 30,000′/7 min. Range 2500 miles.

NORTH AMERICAN P-82E

Allison V-1710-143, -145, 1600 hp

DIMENSIONS: Span 51′ 3″, Lg. 39′ 1″, Ht. 13′ 10″, Wing Area 408 sq. ft.

WEIGHT: Empty 14,914 lb., Gross 24,813 lb., Max. 24,864 lb. Fuel 576–1176 gal.

PERFORMANCE: (20,741 lbs., combat weight) Speed—Top 465 mph at 21,000′, Cruising 304 mph, Landing 124 mph. Service Ceiling 40,000′, Climb 4020′/1 min. Range 2504 miles normal, 2708 miles ferry.

MFR

NORTH AMERICAN XP-82

Packard V-1650-23, -25, 1380 hp take-off, 1860 hp at 18,400′

DIMENSIONS: Span 51′ 3″, Lg. 38′ 1″, Ht. 13′, Wing Area 408 sq. ft.

WEIGHT: Empty 13,405 lb., Gross 19,100 lb., Max. 22,000 lb. Fuel 600–1045 gal.

PERFORMANCE: Speed—Top 482 mph at 25,100′, Cruising 227 mph, Landing 102 mph. Service Ceiling 41,600′, Climb 20,000′/7 min. Range 1390 miles normal, 1280 miles/4000 lbs. bombs.

MFR

MFR

NORTH AMERICAN P-82F
Allison V-1710-143, -145, 1600 hp
DIMENSIONS: Span 51′ 3″, Lg. 42′ 2″, Ht. 13′ 10″, Wing Area 408 sq. ft.
WEIGHT: Empty 16,309 lb., Gross 26,208 lb. Fuel 576–1196 gal.
PERFORMANCE: (22,116 lbs., combat weight) Speed—Top 460 mph at 21,000′, Cruising 288 mph, Landing 128 mph. Service Ceiling 38,500′, Climb 3690′/1 min. Range 2200 miles, 2400 miles ferry.

NORTH AMERICAN F-82G [*Photo unavailable*]
Allison V-1710-143, -145, 1600 hp
DIMENSIONS: Span 51′ 3″, Lg. 42′ 5″, Ht. 13′ 10″, Wing Area 408 sq. ft.
WEIGHT: Empty 15,997 lb., Gross 25,891 lb. Fuel 576–1196 gal.
PERFORMANCE: (21,810 lbs., combat weight) Speed—Top 461 mph at 21,000′, Cruising 286 mph, Landing 127 mph. Service Ceiling 38,900′, Climb 3770′/1 min. Range 2240 miles, 2495 miles ferry.

BELL XP-83
General Electric J33-GE-5, 4000 lbs.
DIMENSIONS: Span 53′, Lg. 45′, Ht. 14′, Wing Area 431 sq. ft.
WEIGHT: Empty 14,105 lb., Gross 24,090 lb., Max. 27,500 lb. Fuel 1150–1750 gal.
PERFORMANCE: Speed—Top 522 mph at 15,660′. Service Ceiling 45,000′, Climb 30,000′/11.5 min. Range 1730 miles normal, 2050 miles max.

MFR

wheels. Armament included six .50-caliber fixed guns with 300 rpg in the wing center section. Wing racks could handle four 1000-lb. bombs, up to 25 rockets, or a center pod containing eight more guns. Internal fuel capacity could be doubled by four drop tanks, increasing range from 1390 to over 2500 miles. (For safety's sake, fuel was actually limited to 1045 gallons on the prototype.)

Powered by Packard Merlins with opposite-rotating propellers, the XP-82 was first flown April 15, 1945. A third prototype, the XP-82A, had two 1500 hp Allison V-1710-119s with propellers rotating in the same direction. Five hundred P-82Bs under order were cut back on V-J Day to 20. They were similar to the XP-82, except for two examples equipped as night fighters. Designated P-82C and P-82D, the night fighters had black finish and an SCR-720 and APS-4 radar respectively in a pod under the center section.

In March 1947, 250 more Twin Mustangs were ordered with Allison V-1710-143/-145 engines, and delivery began in May 1948. The first 100 were F-82E day fighters for escort and ground attack missions, followed in September by the F-82F night fighter. Ninety-one F-82Fs were followed by 59 F-82Gs, similar but for a longer radome. When production ended in March 1949, Twin Mustangs had replaced F-61s in USAF night fighter units, and on June 27, 1950, an F-82G became the first U.S. plane to destroy North Korean aircraft.

The Bell XP-83 was an enlargement of the Airacomet with two J33-GE-5s, bubble canopy, and six .50-caliber guns with 1800 rounds in the nose. Large fuselage fuel tanks could be supplemented by drop tanks, or two 1000-lb. bombs could be carried. Begun in March 1944, the XP-83 was ordered July 31, 1944, and made its first flight on February 27, 1945. Since performance did not justify further development, only the two prototypes were built.

THUNDERJET

The first new fighter of the postwar period was Republic's XP-84, begun in November 1944 to obtain the best speed and range obtainable from jet propulsion. General Electric's J-35 axial-flow engine permitted a long narrow fuselage whose streamlining contributed to the expected 600 mph speed and 1300-mile range. Four .50-caliber M-2 guns were mounted above the nose air intake and two more were in the wing roots. First flown on February 28, 1946, the mid-wing single-seater had the tricycle landing gear customary on jet aircraft. Fuel was carried within the fuselage, wings, and disposable wingtip tanks.

The second of three XP-84 prototypes achieved 611 mph in September 1946, but this could not be matched under standard service conditions. By April 1947, 15 YP-84As had been delivered for service tests at the Muroc and Wright development centers. The YP-84A was similar to the prototypes, but its J35-A-15 engine was now made by Allison.

Production Thunderjets began appearing in June 1947 and standardized the faster-firing M-3 guns, with 300 rpg, underwing rocket racks, and ejector seat used on service types. The first 226 were F-84Bs with J35-A-15s, followed after April 1948 by 191 F-84Cs, and in November by 154 F-84Ds. (By this time, P-84 became F-84.) The C and D were similar to the Bs in appearance, but used J35-A-13s found more serviceable than the A-15 engine. Only internal mechanical changes distinguished the D from the C.

On May 18, 1949, the F-84E was flown with the J35-A-17 of 4900-lb. thrust, and a new Sperry radar gunsight. Internal fuel capacity was increased, and four 230 gallon drop tanks could be added at the wingtips and below the wings. Alternately, two 1000-lb. bombs, two 11.75 rockets, or up to 32 5-in. rockets could be handled on attack missions. Republic built 843 F-84Es, and these Thunderjets began combat missions in Korea on December 7, 1950.

The F-84Es increased power brought the Thunderjet close to the airframe's speed limit, and Republic began an XF-84F swept-wing version. Known for a while as YF-96A, it made its first flight on June 3, 1950, with a 5200-lb. thrust J35-A-25, and 40° sweep on wings and tail. Alarm over the Korean War led in July to a large order for production models powered by 7200-lb. thrust Wright J65s, an American-built version of the British Sapphire engine. On September 8 the prototype regained the YF-84F designation, and was flown with an imported Sapphire on February 14, 1951.

Production of the F-84F was delayed by complexities of the new wing structure and the engine, and an interim type, F-84G, appeared June 1951 with the straight wing, a 5600-lb. thrust J35-A-29, and reinforced canopy. Essentially an F-84E fitted for long-range flying, the F-84G had an automatic pilot and a receptacle on the left wing for air refueling by a "flying boom" of a Boeing KC-97 or KB-29 tanker, instead of the "probe and drogue" technique tested earlier on modified F-84Es. The value of air refueling was demonstrated in 1952 by nonstop flights from California to Hawaii, Hawaii to Midway, and then a 2575-mile hop from Midway to Japan. Jet squadrons could now fly to any point in the world, refueling from flying tankers at prearranged rendezvous. The F-84G was also the first USAF jet fighter to handle a tactical atomic weapon. Many of the 3025 aircraft built went overseas to Allied nations participating in the Mutual Security Program.

Meanwhile, a preproduction F-84F appeared in March 1952 with F-84G canopy, solid nose, and wing root intakes for the Sapphire engines. A similar preproduction YRF-84F reconnaissance version was made with wing root intakes, which became standard on RF-84 Thunderflash production types delivered after March 1954, and equipped with four .50-caliber M-3s and an elongated nose for cameras.

Nose intakes were retained on production F-84F Thunderstreaks, which had six M-3s, perforated fuselage speed brakes, the J65-W-3, and, from F-84F-25, an all-flying tail. Four bombs or drop tanks could be added. The first Republic F-84F-1-RE flew November 22, 1952, and 2711 Thunderstreaks were built, including 599 F-84F-GK from General Motors Kansas City plant (formerly North American's).

The first Thunderstreaks went to the Strategic Air Command's six fighter groups, until SAC in 1957 decided escort fighters unnecessary. They were the Tactical Air Command's main fighter-bomber, until the

REPUBLIC XP-84
General Electric J35-GE-7, 3750 lbs.
DIMENSIONS: Span 36′ 5″, Lg. 37′ 2″, Wing Area 260 sq. ft.
WEIGHT: Empty 9080 lb., Gross 13,400 lb., Max. 16,200 lb.
PERFORMANCE: Speed—Top 592 mph at s. l., Cruising 425 mph. Climb 35,000′/13 min. Range 1300 miles normal.

AF

REPUBLIC YP-84A

MFR

REPUBLIC F-84B
Allison J35-A-15, 3750 lbs.
DIMENSIONS: Span 36′ 5″, Lg. 37′ 5″, Ht. 12′ 10″, Wing Area 260 sq. ft.
WEIGHT: Empty 9538 lb., Gross 16,475 lb., Max. 19,689 lb. Fuel 416–786 gal.
PERFORMANCE: (13,465 lbs., combat weight) Speed—Top 587 mph at 4000′, Cruising 436 mph, Landing 132 mph. Service Ceiling 40,750′, Climb 4210′/1 min. Range 1282 miles.

PMB
RANKIN

REPUBLIC F-84C
Allison J35-A-13, 3750 lbs.
DIMENSIONS: As F-84B
WEIGHT: Empty 9662 lb., Gross 16,584 lb., Max. 19,798 lb. Fuel 416–786 gal.
PERFORMANCE: (13,574 lbs., combat weight) Speed—Top 587 mph at 4000′, Cruising 436 mph, Landing 132 mph. Service Ceiling 40,600′, Climb 4180′/1 min. Range 1274 miles.

PMB

REPUBLIC F-84D
Allison J35-A-13, 3750 lbs.
DIMENSIONS: As F-84B
WEIGHT: Empty 9860 lb., Gross 16,862 lb., Max. 20,076 lb. Fuel 416–786 gal.
PERFORMANCE: (13,894 lbs., combat weight) Speed—Top 587 mph at 4000′, Cruising 441 mph, Landing 133 mph. Service Ceiling 39,300′, Climb 4060′/1 min. Range 1198 miles.

REPUBLIC F-84E
Allison J35-A-17, 4900 lbs.
DIMENSIONS: Span 36′ 5″, Lg. 38′ 6″, Ht. 12′ 10″, Wing Area 260 sq. ft.
WEIGHT: Empty 10,205 lb., Max. 22,463 lb. Fuel 452–1372 gal.
PERFORMANCE: (14,724 lbs., combat weight) Speed—Top 613 mph at s. l., Cruising 481 mph, Landing 142 mph. Service Ceiling 43,220′, Climb 6061′/1 min. Range 1485 miles/two 230 gal. drop tanks, 1950 miles max.

MFR

MFR

REPUBLIC YF-84F (YF-96A)
Allison XJ35-A-25, 5200 lbs.
DIMENSIONS: Span 33′ 7″, Lg. 43′ 1″, Ht. 15′ 2″, Wing Area 325 sq. ft.
WEIGHT: Empty 12,150 lb., Max. 23,230 lb. Fuel 1505 gal. max.
PERFORMANCE: Speed—Top 693 mph at s. l., Cruising 514 mph, Landing 140 mph. Service Ceiling 38,300′, Climb 35,000′/14.8 min. Range 1716 miles.

F-100C appeared, and served the Belgian, French, Italian, and German air forces. The new Luftwaffe's first fighter, over 500 F-84F went into German service beginning November 1956.

For long-range flights, 450-gallon drop tanks could be attached below the wings. In May 1953, the YF-84F tested the FICON system, utilizing a retractable hook ahead of the cockpit to engage a trapeze in a GRB-36's bomb bay; one RF-84F reconnaissance squadron was later teamed with a GRB-36 wing and equipped for FICON operations. This system enabled the jets to be carried long distances, launched for a flight over a target area, and recovered. In-flight refueling could also be used on these jets, as fighter F-84Fs demon-

PMB

REPUBLIC F-84G
Allison J35-A-29, 5600 lbs.
DIMENSIONS: Span 36′ 5″, Lg. 38′ 1″, Ht. 12′ 7″, Wing Area 260 sq. ft.
WEIGHT: Empty 11,095 lb., Gross 18,645 lb., Max. 23,525 lb. Fuel 1362 gal. max.
PERFORMANCE: Speed—Top 622 mph at s. l., Cruising 483 mph, Landing 142 mph. Service Ceiling 40,500′, Absolute Ceiling 42,100′, Climb 35,000′/9.4 min. with tanks (7.9 min. without tanks). Range 2000 miles at 21,700 lbs.

MFR

REPUBLIC F-84F
Wright J65-W-3, 7200 lbs.
DIMENSIONS: Span 33′ 7″, Lg. 43′ 5″, Ht. 15′, Wing Area 325 sq. ft.
WEIGHT: Max. 26,000 lb.
PERFORMANCE: Classified

strated in August 1955 with a 5118-mile flight from England to Texas.

Designed to explore possibilities of a turboprop fighter, the XF-84H has a 5850 hp Allison XT-40-A-1, and is reported to be the fastest propeller-driven aircraft ever built. First flown July 22, 1955, it has a large three-bladed propeller, antitorque fin behind the cockpit, and a Tee tail. Originally, the Navy had been interested in the project, but development of steam catapults, angled deck and air refueling made propeller-driven substitutes for jets unnecessary. As the Navy lost interest and mechanical difficulties persisted the project was abandoned, and a second prototype was never flown.

Two more Republic Thunderjets were modified to try the General Electric J73-GE-7. First flown May 7, 1954, the YF-84Js were similar in appearance to the F-84F except for deeper fuselage and enlarged nose scoop, but did not reach production.

MFR

REPUBLIC XF-84H
Allison XT-40-A-1, 5850 hp
DIMENSIONS: Span 33′ 7″, Lg. 51′ 6″, Ht. 15′ 5″.
WEIGHT & PERFORMANCE: Classified

MFR

REPUBLIC YF-84J

NORTH AMERICAN XP-86
(With 2nd XB-45 in background)
General Electric J35-C-3, 3750 lbs.
DIMENSIONS: Span 37′ 1″, Lg. 38′ 6″, Ht. 13′ 8″, Wing Area 274 sq. ft.
WEIGHT: Empty 9243 lb., Gross 13,311 lb., Max. 16,438 lb. Fuel 848 gal.
PERFORMANCE: Speed—Top 635 mph at 16,000′, Cruising 434 mph. Service Ceiling 44,200′, Climb 35,000′/12 min.

MFR

SABRE JETS

Shortly after Hitler's defeat, captured German scientific data indicating the advantages of swept-back wings arrived in the United States. At that time, aircraft speeds were becoming limited less by power than by compressibility effects; as sonic speeds were approached, shock waves built up over airframe projections caused buffeting and other phenomena. Sweeping wing and tail surfaces back toward their tips delays the onset of compressibility troubles, and permits higher speeds.

The first American aircraft to take advantage of this knowledge was North American's NA-140, ordered as the XP-86 on May 18, 1945. Similar to the Navy's XFJ-1, this single-seater's mockup had been approved in June with conventional straight wings, but on November 1 the Air Force accepted a proposal to sweep back wings and tail 35 degrees. First flown on October 1, 1947, at Muroc, California (now Edwards Air Force Base), the low-wing XP-86 had a 3750-lb. thrust

NORTH AMERICAN F-86A
General Electric J47-GE-13, 5200 lbs., 6000 lbs. WE
DIMENSIONS: Span 37′ 1″, Lg. 37′ 6″, Ht. 14′ 8″, Wing Area 288 sq. ft.
WEIGHT: Empty 10,495 lb., Max. 16,357 lb. Fuel 435–625 gal.
PERFORMANCE: (13,488 lbs., combat weight) Speed—Top 675 mph at 2500′, 601 mph at 35,000′, Cruising 527 mph, Landing 121 mph. Service Ceiling 48,300′, Climb 7630′/1 min. Range 1270 miles.

MFR

NORTH AMERICAN F-86E

MFR

NORTH AMERICAN F-86F
General Electric J47-GE-27, 5970 lbs.
DIMENSIONS: As F-86A
WEIGHT: Empty 10,950 lb., Gross 15,000 lb., Max. 17,000 lb. Fuel 476–876 gal.
PERFORMANCE: (Approx. at 13,500 lbs., combat weight) Speed—Top 690 mph at s. l., 610 mph at 35,000′, Landing 120 mph. Service Ceiling 50,000′, Climb 10,000′/1 min. Range 785 miles normal, 1270 miles/drop tanks.

MFR

Chevrolet-built J35-C-3, nose air scoop, fuselage dive-brakes, and leading edge slots to reduce the swept wing's stalling point.

Thirty-three production aircraft had been ordered December 1946 designated P-86A (F-86A-1 Sabre after June 1948), and 188 P-86B (F-86A-5) were later added. After the first F-86A-1 flew on May 20, 1948, 333 more Sabres were purchased in June. Power plants were a General Electric J47-GE-1 on F-86A-1, J47-GE-3 on F-86A-5, and J-47-GE-7 or -13 on F-86A-10, -15, and -20 Sabres. This jet engine offered 5200-lb. thrust and enabled the third F-86A-1 to set a world's speed record of 670.98 mph on September 15, 1948.

Six .50-caliber M-3s at the sides of the nose intake were aimed with the aid of Sperry range-finding radar in the intake's upper lip. External racks could handle two drop tanks, 1000-lb. bombs, or up to 16 5-in. rockets. On December 17, 1950, an F-86A-5 shot down a MIG-15 over Sinuiju, North Korea, and the struggle between Sabres and MIGs for air superiority and national prestige began. These first jet-vs-jet battles found the Russian-built interceptors lighter, and better in climb and ceiling, although other Sabre qualities and the skill of Air Force pilots won rather consistent victories for the Americans. There was some criticism of F-86 weight and complexity, and the situation resembled somewhat the problem presented by Japan's Zero at World War II's beginning. Once again, there was surprise that a nation thought backward industrially had developed an effective air weapon.

Work on improved versions proceeded. The F-86C became the YF-93 penetration fighter described later, while the F-86D designation was given the night fighter project known until July 24, 1950, as F-95. This aircraft, with its radar, air-to-air rockets, and afterburner, is so different in operation from day-fighting Sabres that one regrets that the more distinctive F-95 designation was abandoned. For convenience's sake, this night-fighter Sabre is considered in the next section on all-weather fighters.

After 554 F-86As were completed by December 1950, the next production version was the F-86E, identical to late production F-86As with J47-GE-13s, apart from power operated controls with elevators and tail planes linked for co-ordinated movement. Between March 1951 and April 1952, 396 F-86Es were accepted and their so-called "all-flying tail" was used on all following Sabre models.

The next day-fighter Sabre was the F-86F, flown March 19, 1952, with a 5970-lb. thrust J47-GE-27. They were similar in appearance to the F-86E, but later aircraft (F-86F-20) dispensed with wing slots for a new leading edge. Although contract totals haven't been revealed, some 2000 F-86F-NAs were built at Inglewood before production was suspended in March 1954. In addition, the government's facility at Columbus, Ohio, was used to make 700 F-86F-25-NHs. Dur-1955 the F-86F-40-NA was reinstated into production for Mutual Security Program exports, and the last one, delivered January 1957, was also the last Sabre built for the Air Force.

In the meantime, an extensive series was built for the Navy (FJ-2, -3, and -4), and a heavier fighter-bomber version was developed around the 9200-lb. thrust General Electric J73-GE-3. The first of two YF-86H-NAs built in Inglewood flew in May 1953, and had a deeper fuselage and airscoop for the J73, a clamshell type canopy, larger wings and tail, and six .50-caliber guns. On September 4, 1953, the first F-86H-1-NH production aircraft was flown at Columbus. Four 20-mm. M-39 guns, tested in Korea on modified F-86Fs, armed the F-86H-5-NH. Production of the F-86H concluded in August 1955.

Canadair Ltd. at Montreal also produced under license 1815 Sabres (Canadair CL-13) from August 1950 to October 1958. About 400 supplied to Britain were the R.A.F.'s first swept-wing types in service, and

MFR

NORTH AMERICAN F-86H
General Electric J73-GE-3, 9200 lbs.
DIMENSIONS: Span 37′ 1″, Lg. 38′ 8″, Ht. 15′, Wing Area 288 sq. ft.
WEIGHT & PERFORMANCE: Classified

300 were in the new West German air force, while most of the remainder went to the R.C.A.F. Australia also built 111 Sabres as the Commonwealth CA-27. Twenty foreign air forces have had Sabres, from Japan to Spain, making the F-86 perhaps the most widely used jet fighter.

ALL-WEATHER FIGHTERS

The development of jet propelled day fighters had made quick progress, but night fighters needed room for radar, and an electronics operator, and were a more difficult design problem. Shortly after war's end in 1945, the Air Force issued a specification for a jet plane capable of operating in darkness, or fog; a true "all-weather fighter."

The first type built for this purpose was the Curtiss XF-87 Blackhawk, developed from the XA-43 design. With a pair of Westinghouse J-34s under each wing and double wheels for the tricycle gear, the F-87 looked as big as some bombers it was supposed to chase. Specifications called for a 600 mph speed, 41,000 ft. ceiling, and armament of four 20-mm. fixed guns and two .50-caliber guns in a remote-controlled turret.

The turret was eliminated on the prototype, flown March 5, 1948, with four J34-WE-7s. Pilot and radarman sat side by side behind the bullet radar nose, and fuel tanks occupied the fuselage center section between the high wings. On June 10, 88 F-87As were ordered, to be powered, along with the second prototype (YF-87A) by two General Electric J47s; but on October 18 the contract was canceled to free funds for the newer F-89 and F-94 types. Loss of the $82,000,000 contract discouraged the firm that had built so many of America's warplanes, and the famous brand name of Curtiss has not since labeled a new airplane.

The postwar period's most successful long-range all-weather fighter was Northrop's Scorpion. This type began with a proposal to the Air Force in December

AF

CURTISS XP-87
Westinghouse XJ34-WE-7, 3000 lbs.
DIMENSIONS: Span 60′, Lg. 62′, Wing Area 600 sq. ft.
WEIGHT: Empty 25,930 lb., Gross 37,350 lb., Max. 49,900 lb. Fuel 1380–2600 gal.
PERFORMANCE: (Estimated) Speed—Top 600 mph at s. l., Cruising 450 mph. Service Ceiling 41,000′, Climb 35,000′/13.8 min. Range 1000 miles.

MFR

NORTHROP XF-89
Allison J35-A-15, 4000 lbs.
DIMENSIONS: Span 52′, Lg. 50′ 6″, Ht. 17′ 8″, Wing Area 606 sq. ft.
WEIGHT: Empty 25,864 lb., Gross 43,910 lb. Fuel 2360 gal. max.
PERFORMANCE: Speed—Top 603 mph at 2500′, Cruising 497 mph, Landing 127 mph. Service Ceiling 35,500′, Climb 35,000′/21 min. Range 1750 miles.

1945, received a developmental contract in May 1946, and after the mockup's inspection in September, the contract for two prototypes was finalized on December 18.

The first prototype, XF-89, flew on August 16, 1948, and the second, YF-89A, on November 15, 1949. They had two Allison J-35 jets tucked against the fuselage under the thin wing, with split-edge full span flaps lining the trailing edge out to wingtip fuel tanks. Pilot and radarman sat in tandem ejection seats. The XF-89 had a rounded nose, 4000-lb. thrust J35-A-15s, and black finish, but the YF-89A had a pointed nose, 5200-lb. thrust J35-A-21s with afterburners added, and dispensed with the solid black paint previously the night owl's uniform.

Northrop's design won Air Force approval but author-

NORTHROP YF-89A

MFR

COOMBS

NORTHROP F-89A
Allison J35-A-21, 5200 lbs. (6800 lbs. AB)
DIMENSIONS: Span 56′, Lg. 53′ 6″, Ht. 17′ 8″, Wing Area 606 sq. ft.
WEIGHT: (Approx.) Empty 23,600 lb., Gross 36,400 lb., Max. 42,000 lb. Fuel 1000–1600 gal.
PERFORMANCE: (Approx. at 32,000 lbs., combat weight) Speed —Top 640 mph at s. l., 570 mph at 35,000′, Cruising 500 mph, Landing 113 mph. Service Ceiling 40,000′, Climb 10,800′/1 min. Range 1300 miles.

ities were also concerned with rapid delivery, because of the Berlin blockade dispute. Lockheed offered a solution in its single-engined F-94 proposal, which could be procured quickly and cheaply because 75 per cent of its parts were included in the F-80s already in production. The Curtiss F-87A was canceled, for purchase in December 1948 of 48 F-89A and 110 F-94A all-weather fighters.

The Lockheed YF-94 (converted from a TF-80C) made its first flight on April 16, 1949, and F-94A deliveries began in December, giving the Air Force its first jet night fighter in service. Wings, tail, and landing gear were those of the F-80; only the fuselage was new. There were 940 lbs. of radar in the nose above four .50-caliber guns, a radar operator sitting behind the pilot, and behind them an Allison J33-A-33 of 4600-lb. dry thrust. An afterburner could boost this to some 6000-lb. for brief moments of climb and dash, but devoured fuel so fast that it could be used only sparingly. The F-94A was the first production job with an afterburner; they have since become standard on fighters in which short bursts of power are more important than range.

This first lot was followed by 356 F-94Bs ordered late in 1949, and arriving in early 1951. These were similar to the As, but had center-mounted tip tanks of 230 gallons of fuel, instead of 165 gallons, and added a Sperry Zero Reader for blind landings. Kits to replace the A's smaller tanks were supplied.

Delivery on 48 Northrop F-89A Scorpions began in July 1950. Similar to the YF-89A, they had J35-A-21s, were armed with six 20-mm. M-3 guns behind the radar nose, and for ground attack, could carry two 1600-lb. bombs or 16 5-in. rockets. Forty F-89As with revised internal equipment were redesignated F-89B.

MFR

NORTHROP F-89C

AF

LOCKHEED YF-94

On September 18, 1951, the first of 164 F-89Cs was flown, introducing J35-A-33 jets yielding 6950-lb. thrust each with afterburner, APG-33 radar and internal elevator mass-balances instead of the external type on older models. After fatigue failure of wing fittings had caused several crashes, all Scorpions were grounded September 1952 and returned to the factory for modifications. The aircraft were returned to service after corrections were made.

Explosion of a Soviet atomic bomb in September 1949 spurred American interceptor development, and improvements in radar navigation and bombing made it more likely that future nuclear attacks would come by night, rather than by day. Atomic weapons place exceptional demands on defense systems. No longer will prospects of heavy losses discourage an attacker when his surviving bombers may inflict fatal injuries on an enemy. Fighters may fail to stop an attack, if their guns are poorly aimed, or if the enemy bombers endure damage long enough to reach their targets. Defense now requires weapons systems capable of guaranteeing destruction of bombers at first contact.

One answer to this problem was the new weapons system, largely replacing guns on Air Defense Command fighters, consisting of 2.75 in. air-to-air rockets aimed and fired in salvo by a radar-directed automatic computer. With this system, an interceptor takes off and is vectored by directions from ground radar to a lead collision course at right angles to the bomber's path, instead of approaching from the rear in the pursuit-curve attack of the past. After the target is picked up by the fighter's radar the pilot directs his plane so as to center the target on his scope. When a certain range is closed, the Hughes electronic computer takes over flight control through an autopilot and at the proper moment automatically fires a salvo of rockets. The pilot only monitors the actual attack, resuming control to return to his base.

The system has several advantages. Exposure of the fighter to bomber defense guns is brief, accuracy is greater in all kinds of weather, and only one of the rockets need strike the target to destroy it. The four-foot, eighteen-pound FFAR (Folding Fin Aircraft Rocket) is called Mighty Mouse. Firing a salvo of mice at an invisible aircraft presumes one too large and steady to evade the missiles; one pilot shot down by mistake the B-17 guide plane instead of his radio-controlled target.

The first plane designed for the new weapon was the swept wing North American YF-95A, later designated YF-86D. This plane was begun in May 1948 as a night fighter version of the Sabre and made its first flight three days before Christmas the next year. It is the first Air Force night fighter to have only one airman and one engine, a J47-GE-17 with afterburner. Twenty-four 2.75 in. rockets are carried in a retractable tray that pops out of the belly just long enough to launch them. A second crewman seemed unnecessary because

LOCKHEED F-94A
Allison J33-A-33, 4600 lbs. (6000 lbs. AB)
DIMENSIONS: Span 38′ 11″, Lg. 40′ 1″, Ht. 12′ 8″, Wing Area 238 sq. ft.
WEIGHT: Empty 9557 lb., Gross 12,919 lb., Max. 15,330 lb. Fuel 318–648 gal.
PERFORMANCE: Speed—Top 606 mph at s. l., 546 mph at 35,000′, Cruising 443 mph, Landing 122 mph. Service Ceiling 49,750′, Climb 11,274′/1 min. Range 1079 miles.
MFR

AF

LOCKHEED F-94C (original form)
Pratt & Whitney J48-P-5, 6350 lbs. (8750 lbs. AB)
DIMENSIONS: Span 42′ 5″, Lg. 44′ 6″, Ht. 14′ 11″, Wing Area 338 sq. ft.
WEIGHT: (Approx.) Empty 12,000 lb., Max. 22,000 lb.
PERFORMANCE: (Approx. at 16,000 lbs., combat weight) Speed—Top 650 mph at s. l., 585 mph at 35,000′, Cruising 495 mph, Landing 140 mph. Service Ceiling 55,000′, Climb 17,400′/1 min. Range 1200 miles normal, 1900 miles max.

of the nearly automatic operation of the avionics system (APS-6 radar and E-4 fire control), which required 495 tubes, 6400 coils, condensers, and resistors, and cost over $90,000.

Since this type was similar to standard Sabres, except for its radar nose, rockets, and afterburner, the initial order of 122 F-95As was redesignated F-86D-1 on July 24, 1950. Deliveries began December 1951 and were followed by larger batches ordered after outbreak of war in Korea increased tension. Four hundred ordered as F-86Gs became F-86D-20. General Electric J47-GE-33s giving 7650-lb. thrust with afterburner were used on late production F-86Ds, instead of J47-GE-17s of early blocks.

On July 16, 1953, an F-86D-30 raised the world's speed record to 715.7 mph, surpassing the 698.5 mph mark set the previous November by an F-86D-5. Enough "Sabre-Dogs" were built at Inglewood to equip most Air Defense Command wings by 1955, and the type was selected for export to NATO nations under the Mutual Security Program. First flown on July 15, 1954, the YF-86K, the MSP version had a less sophisticated weapons system consisting of four 20-mm. M-39 guns and MG-4 fire control, and was slightly longer than the F-86D. Inglewood-built F-86Ks had J47-GE-33s, and were similar to the 231 built under license by Fiat in Italy.

Although F-86D production was completed in September 1955, some 800 were eventually modernized to the F-86L standard. This version first appeared in October 1956 with wingtips extended two feet, slotted wing leading edge, and "Data Link" equipment that receives data from the "SAGE" air defense ground computer and directs the pilot's instruments accordingly.

The Lockheed Starfire was the second "nearly automatic" night fighter using Mighty Mouse rockets to be purchased by the Air Defense Command. Essentially, it was similar to the earlier F-94 two-seaters, but replaced the J-33 with a Pratt & Whitney J48-P-5 with afterburner, had increased dihedral, and used a thinner wing and swept horizontal tail to increase the critical Mach number.

The most important innovation was the armament of twenty-four 2.75 in. rockets ringed around the nose radar in launching tubes concealed by snap doors. Each wing carried drop tanks at the tips, and a pod for 12 more rockets on the leading edge. Most of the Starfire's 1200 lbs. of electronics was carried in the nose, rounded on early aircraft, but replaced in 1952 by a bullet-shaped plastic bow.

The first two Starfires were modified F-94Bs, first flown January 18, 1950, which were designated YF-97A

LOCKHEED F-94C (with new nose and rocket pods)

MFR

MFR

NORTH AMERICAN F-86D-1 (F-95A)
General Electric J47-GE-17, 5700 lbs. (7630 lbs. AB)
DIMENSIONS: Span 37′ 1″, Lg. 40′ 4″, Ht. 15′, Wing Area 288 sq. ft.
WEIGHT: Empty 12,470 lb., Gross 17,100 lb., Max. 18,483 lb. Fuel 608–848 gal.
PERFORMANCE: (15,290 lbs., combat weight) Speed—Top 707 mph at s. l., 625 mph at 35,000′, Cruising 525 mph, Landing 124 mph. Service Ceiling 54,600′, Climb 17,800′/1 min. Range 836 miles.

MFR

NORTH AMERICAN F-86K
General Electric J47-GE-33, 7650 lbs.
DIMENSIONS: Span 37′ 1″, Lg. 42′ 4″, Ht. 15′, Wing Area 288 sq. ft.
WEIGHT: Gross 18,500 lb., Max. 20,347 lb.
PERFORMANCE: Classified

until September 12, when they were labeled YF-94C. A total of 387 F-94C production aircraft were delivered by February 1954. On May 1, 1951, 112 single-place F-94Ds had been ordered, but the contract was canceled after one YF-94D conversion was tested.

Third USAF fighter type with Mighty Mouse rockets was the Northrop F-89D ordered April 1951, and preceded by a YF-89D first flown October 23, 1951. In January 1953, delivery began on F-89D Scorpions, providing the ADC with a fighter carrying 104 2.75 in. rockets, the heaviest punch of any interceptor in the world. A pod on each wingtip carried fuel and 52 rockets, aimed by APG-40 radar, E-5 fire control, and E-11 auto-pilot located in the nose. Although no guns are carried, the F-89Ds nose is larger than that of earlier models, in order to accommodate an additional fuel tank and increased avionics installations. Powered by J35-A-35 engines, the F-89D had pylons under the wings for extra fuel tanks. A YF-89E was also built, actually the 12th F-89C with Allison YJ71-A-3s of 9500-lb. thrust.

The GAR-1 Falcon guided missile was first used operationally on F-89H Scorpions entering service in January 1956. This model's pods carried a total of six Falcons and 42 FFAR rockets, and additional Falcons could be carried under the wings. While Scorpion production ended with the last F-89H in December 1957, another model appeared. Converted from older models, the F-89J was the first to fire an atomic air-to-air rocket. Two Douglas MB-1 nuclear Genie rockets and four Hughes GAR-2 Falcons were carried beneath the wings.

Although the heavy Scorpions did not have the speed offered by the F-86D and F-94C types, they provided more range and fire power, and served on the outer ring of U.S. defense bases, especially in Alaska and Greenland. During the Second World War only one night fighter, the P-61, was kept in large-scale production, but the large contracts placed for three different types (F-86D, F-89, and F-94) during the Korean War showed clearly the greater concern with defensive air weapons.

PENETRATION FIGHTERS

While some engineers wrestled with the problem of stopping the bombers, others tried to build fighters to protect bombers from enemy interception. Heavy losses of bombers on daytime sorties had made escort missions penetrating deep into enemy territory the

MFR

NORTHROP F-89D
Allison J35-A-35, 5600 lbs.
DIMENSIONS: Span 59′ 8″, Lg. 53′ 10″, Ht. 17′ 6″, Wing Area 606 sq. ft.
WEIGHT & PERFORMANCE: Classified

main concern of wartime Air Force fighters, and postwar designers did not forget the problem.

An ideal fighter, of course, would function equally well both as an interceptor and as an escort, and serve a general "air superiority" function. Indeed, many World War II planes designed originally with interception in mind, did well as escorts, like the P-38 and P-47. But some of the requirements are rather contradictory—the built-in range required for escort handicaps very rapid climb for the interception function. Weapons most effective against fighters are not always best against bombers; the latter are injured most by a few large-caliber blows, but a high rate of fire is more useful against small and elusive fighters. Nevertheless, postwar American fighters standardized on six .50-caliber M-3s as the best compromise. The North American Sabre was thought of as a short-range type, while the Republic Thunderjet had greater long-range capabilities. Development of experimental fighters specifically designed for bomber escort missions continued, beginning with one carried into battle by the bombers themselves.

The most specialized of all postwar designs was the McDonnell XF-85, ordered October 1945 as a parasite fighter to be carried inside a B-36. When big bombers on a mission were menaced, certain ones might open their bomb bay, lower parasites on a trapeze, launch them and at the end of the engagement recover any survivors. Thus, the XF-85 Goblin would have to be small enough to fit inside bomb bays, yet be equal to enemy interceptors in performance.

McDonnell's answer to the unique problem was short enough to fit a 16 ft. long bay, and its swept wings folded to only 5 ft. 5 in. in width, and 10 ft. 3 in. in height. The pilot straddled a 3000-lb. thrust Westinghouse J34-WE-7 with about 30 minutes of fuel, and preliminary estimates promised a top speed of 664 mph. Four .50-caliber guns were grouped about the nose intake. Instead of landing wheels, there was a retractable hook for the trapeze of the carrier plane. Tail span was reduced by dividing the tail into six odd-shaped surfaces. As the Goblin descended on its trapeze from the mother plane, it looked like a fat little bug.

On August 23, 1948, the Goblin flew for the first time from a special B-29, but when the XF-85 attempted to return to the mother plane, the trapeze smashed the canopy, and the pilot was forced to make an emergency landing on a belly skid. Another attempt in October succeeded, but the difficulty of recovering the parasites had been demonstrated. Other difficulties presented themselves, including entirely unsatisfactory stability and control characteristics. Thirteen service test copies were canceled after the two prototypes were built.

A more conventional approach to bomber escort design was seen in the built-in range of two penetration fighters ordered June 1946. The McDonnell XF-88 and Lockheed XF-90 were armed with six 20-mm. guns, powered by two Westinghouse J-34s buried within the fuselage with enough internal fuel capacity for ranges of 1600–1700 miles, and featured 35° swept wings.

NORTHROP F-89H

MFR

MFR

McDONNELL XF-85
Westinghouse J34-WE-22, 3000 lbs.
DIMENSIONS: Span 21′ 1″, Lg. 15′, Ht. 8′, Wing Area 90 sq. ft.
WEIGHT: Empty 3740 lb., Gross 4550 lb. Fuel 135 gal.
PERFORMANCE: Speed—Top 664 mph at s. l. Service Ceiling 48,500′.

AF

McDONNELL XF-85 (launch from B-29)

McDONNELL XF-85 (launch from B-29)

AF

AF

McDONNELL XF-88
Westinghouse J34-WE-13 (also -22)
DIMENSIONS: Span 39′ 8″, Lg. 54′ 2″, Ht. 17′ 3″, Wing Area 350 sq. ft.
WEIGHT: Empty 12,140 lb., Gross 18,500 lb., Max. 23,100 lb. Fuel 734–1434 gal.
PERFORMANCE: Speed—Top 641 mph at s. l., Cruising 527 mph, Landing 140 mph. Service Ceiling 36,000′, Climb 35,000′/14.5 min. Range 1737 miles.

MFR

LOCKHEED XF-90
Westinghouse XJ34-WE-11 (later WE-15, 4000 lbs. AB)
DIMENSIONS: Span 40′, Lg. 56′ 2″, Ht. 15′ 9″, Wing Area 345 sq. ft.
WEIGHT: Empty 18,520 lb., Gross 27,200 lb., Max. 31,060 lb. Fuel 1665 gal. max.
PERFORMANCE: Speed—Top 667 mph at 1000′, Cruising 473 mph, Landing 145 mph. Service Ceiling 39,000′, Climb 25,000′/4.5 min. Range 1050 miles normal.

First to appear was the XF-88, flown on October 29, 1948, with 3000-lb. thrust XJ34-WE-13s. A second prototype, XF-88A, had 4000-lb. thrust XJ34-WE-15s with afterburners to boost speed past the 700 mph mark. Guns and radar-ranging gear were contained in the nose, and speed brakes were installed in the fuselage sides behind the jet exhausts. An Allison XT-38 turboprop was installed in the first prototype, replacing the armament, and the modified XF-88B flew April 14, 1953.

Lockheed's XF-90, flown June 6, 1949, was distinguished by a needle-nose, jet exhausts running back to the tail, and wings flush with fuselage bottom. The guns were mounted under the air intakes, and a 220 gallon drop tank could be carried on each wingtip. Westinghouse J34-WE-11s used on early flights were replaced on both prototypes by the XJ34-WE-15.

A third penetration fighter was begun by North American as a Sabre development designated F-86C. Powered by a single Pratt & Whitney J48-P-1 offering 8000-lb. thrust with afterburner, it looked good enough on paper to win an order in June 1948 for 118 F-93As with J48-P-5 engines, but in January 1949 this contract was canceled to provide more bomber funds, and only two prototypes now labeled YF-93A were completed. First flown on January 25, 1950, the YF-93A was larger than the Sabres, and had a long solid nose, flush side intakes, wider fuselage for the centrifugal-flow J-48 with afterburner, and double main wheels. Automatic wing slots were provided with an armament of six 20-mm. guns and two 1000-lb. bombs, if desired. After Air Force tests, both prototypes went to the NACA for study of various intake arrangements.

Shortages of funds, and improvement of the F-84 series delayed procurement of any of these penetration types. In June 1950, a competition between the XF-88A, XF-90, and YF-93A was expected to result in a production order, but outbreak of the Korean War again diverted attention to other types more available for quick production, and none of these planes won a contract. McDonnell's ship, however, was considered the best and became the basis of the F-101 ordered two years later.

McDONNELL XF-88A MFR

INTERCEPTORS

In the brief minutes that pass between radar warning of enemy attack and the time hostile bombers reach the bomb release point, interceptors must do their work; a rapid take-off and climb to the enemy's altitude, a swift pass across his flight path, and the interceptor's weapons are fired. Only a few minute decide the success of the defense system, and perhaps even a nation's survival.

World War II's most promising interceptor was the

MFR

NORTH AMERICAN YF-93
Pratt & Whitney J48-P-1, 6000 lbs. (8000 lbs. AB)
DIMENSIONS: Span 38′ 11″, Lg. 44′ 1″, Ht. 15′ 8″, Wing Area 306 sq. ft.
WEIGHT: Empty 14,035 lb., Gross 21,610 lb., Max. 26,516 lb. Fuel 1581 gal.
PERFORMANCE: Speed—Top 708 mph at s. l., 622 mph at 35,000′, Cruising 534 mph, Landing 150 mph. Service Ceiling 46,800′, Climb 11,960′/1 min. Range 1967 miles.

Messerschmitt Me 163B Komet, a rocket-propelled single-seater that could climb to 30,000 ft. in 2½ minutes, and reach a speed of 596 mph. First used against U.S. bombers in August 1944, it had an endurance of only about ten minutes, long enough to have done plenty of damage if there had been enough Komets. Its designer, Dr. Alexander Lippisch, planned even more advanced designs based on new ideas in wing shapes like the delta (triangle) wing.

United States designers gave great attention to German data received after the war, but short-range interceptors did not figure largely in postwar procurement, which tended to favor all-around air-superiority-type fighters capable of a more reasonable endurance. Rocket power alone consumed too much fuel, even for interceptors, so it was decided to use a jet engine plus assisting rockets in a pair of daytime interceptors.

Republic's XF-91 and Convair's XF-92 were both single-seat interceptors, but the XF-91 had unique inverse tapered wings that were wider at the tips than at the roots. Swept back 35°, they had variable incidence to provide a low angle of attack for flight and a higher angle for extra lift on take-off and landings. A pair of tandem main wheels was kept small enough to fit in the thin wings, which also had fittings for two 230-gallon drop tanks. A General Electric J47-GE-3 of 5200-lb. thrust was used for the first flight on May 9, 1949. In October, an afterburner was installed, and finally, four Reaction Motors rockets of 1500-lb. thrust each were added in pairs above and below the tail cone. In December 1952 it was announced that the XF-91 had made the "first supersonic rocket-power flight by a U.S. combat type." Two prototypes were tested by the USAF.

Since the Air Force had obtained not only delta-wing data, but Dr. Lippisch himself, it is not surprising that a delta-wing fighter was ordered from Convair to try his new theories. Designated XF-92, the supersonic four-gun delta was to have a 1500-lb. thrust Westinghouse J-30 turbojet plus six nitromethane rockets for a total thrust of 13,000 lbs., and enough fuel for five minutes of combat and ten of cruising, plus climb and descent.

Calculations suggested a top speed of 825 mph at 50,000 ft., but such a radical configuration demanded a careful approach. A flying model known first as Convair 7002 was assembled, including parts from older aircraft, like an F-80 landing gear. After a cautious hop on June 8, 1948, tests proved the tailless delta capable of stable flight. Further research was needed, and on June 3, 1949, the Air Force canceled the XF-92 project. The unarmed test aircraft, however, was accepted with the designation XF-92A.

Apparently the world's first delta-wing to actually fly, the XF-92A had a 60° sweep on its leading edge,

MFR

REPUBLIC XF-91

General Electric J47-GE-3, 5200 lbs. and Reaction Motors XLR11-RM-9, 6000 lbs. (Data for J47-GE-21, on XF-91A)

DIMENSIONS: Span 31′ 3″, Lg. 43′ 3″, Ht. 18′ 8″, Wing Area 320 sq. ft.

WEIGHT: Empty 15,853 lb., Gross (Point Intercept) 23,807 lb., (Area Intercept) 27,329 lb. Fuel 1440 gal. max.

PERFORMANCE: (With GE-21 and AB) Speed—Top 1126 mph at 50,000′, Cruising 539 mph, Landing 144 mph. Service Ceiling 55,000′, Climb 50,000′/5.33 min. Range 1171 miles max.

PMB

REPUBLIC XF-91

and elevons for control. The original Allison J33-A-23 of 5200-lb. thrust was replaced in 1950 by a J33-A-29 with afterburner. Experience with this aircraft was essential to development of the Convair F-102 interceptor.

MFR

CONVAIR XF-92A

Allison J33-A-29, 5200 lbs. (7500 lbs. AB)

DIMENSIONS: Span 31′ 4″, Lg. 41′ 4″, Ht. 11′ 8″, Wing Area 230 sq. ft.

WEIGHT: Empty 8500 lb., Gross 13,000 lb. Fuel 295 gal.

PERFORMANCE: Classified

THE CENTURY FIGHTERS

During the Korean War, the USAF had five fighters in production, including short-range F-86s and long-range F-84s for day fighting. All-weather defense was left to the F-86D, F-89, and F-94, although only early models of the latter saw any actual combat. Together these types made an impressive team, but a new trio ordered into production late in 1952 called the "century" fighters by their designations, gave USAF wings their first supersonic aircraft.

Complete details of these supersonic single-seaters are withheld by security classification, and their newness makes them a subject for journalism, rather than history. Nevertheless, a short summary of released information may serve to bring readers abreast of more recent advances in fighter design. First supersonic aircraft used by the USAF is the North American Super Sabre, whose design won USAF support in January 1951. Two YF-100 prototypes were ordered on November 1, 1951, with 110 F-100A production ships, and the mockup approved August 26, 1952. The prototype, designated YF-100A, flew May 25, 1953, and achieved a speed of 755 mph the following October 29.

Production F-100As, costing $663,354 each, began to appear the same month and were introduced into service a year later, but had to be grounded in November 1954 as a result of a series of accidents due to the newness problems of supersonic flight. Extensive tests were carried out, including a dive on February 26, 1955, in which the test pilot was forced to make an agonizing bail-out at a speed of 777 mph, the first successful escape from an aircraft traveling at supersonic speeds. After appropriate modifications to the tail,

MFR

NORTH AMERICAN YF-100A
Pratt & Whitney J57-P-7, 9700 lbs.
DIMENSIONS: Span 36′ 7″, Lg. 44′ 9″, Ht. 14′ 9″, Wing Area 376 sq. ft.
WEIGHT: Max. 28,000 lb.
PERFORMANCE: Speed—Top 755 mph.

PMB

NORTH AMERICAN F-100A-10

MFR

NORTH AMERICAN F-100C
Pratt & Whitney J57-P-21, 11,700 lbs. (17,000 lbs. AB)
DIMENSIONS: Span 38′ 9″, Lg. 47′, Ht. 15′, Wing area 385 sq. ft.
WEIGHT: (Approx.) Empty 21,000 lb., Gross 30,000 lb., Max. 34,000 lb. Fuel 1185–1735 gal.
PERFORMANCE: Classified.

MFR

NORTH AMERICAN F-100D

MFR

NORTH AMERICAN F-100A-1
Pratt & Whitney J57-P-7, 9700 lbs.
DIMENSIONS: Span 36′ 7″, Lg. 46′ 2″, Ht. 13′ 4″, Wing Area 376 sq. ft.
WEIGHT: Max. 28,000 lb.
PERFORMANCE: Classified.

wingtips, and controls, the type returned to service, with the first 70 ships being fitted with the larger wings and tail of the F-100A-5 blocks.

The F-100A is powered by a Pratt & Whitney J57-P-7 (J57-P-39 in later blocks) delivering about 10,000-lb. thrust and utilizing an afterburner for bursts of high speed. The low thin wing is swept back 45° and the horizontal surface is a movable one-piece surface combining the functions of stabilizer and elevator. An air brake is located in the squat fuselage's bottom and a drag chute at the tail reduces the fighter's landing run. Four new high-speed 20-mm. M-39 guns fire under the nose intake and up to four drop tanks may be attached to supplement the fuel within the fuselage.

Early Super Sabres (203 F-101As) were described as air superiority fighters, but the F-100C added fighter-bomber and flight-refueling capabilities. Ordered December 30, 1953, the F-100C first flew January 17, 1955, and had a more powerful J57-P-21, six underwing fixtures for up to 7000 lbs. of bombs or added fuel, and the larger wings and tail indicated by F-100A experiences. In August 1955 an F-100C established a world speed record of 822 mph.

A second source of production was begun at Columbus, Ohio, for F-100C and F-100D Super Sabres. First flown at Inglewood on January 24, 1956, the F-100D was similar to the F-100C, but introduced an automatic pilot to improve the Super Sabre's long-range usefulness.

McDonnell's F-101A Voodoo penetration fighter was based on that firm's earlier XF-88. An initial order for 31 F-101As was placed in September 1952, the first plane flown on September 29, 1954, and the contract

MFR

McDONNELL F-101A
Pratt & Whitney J57-P-13, 10,000 lbs. (15,000 lbs. AB)
DIMENSIONS: Span 39′ 8″, Lg. 67′ 5″, Ht. 18′, Wing Area 368 sq. ft.
WEIGHT: Empty 26,277 lb., Max. 42,000 lb. Fuel 2249 gal.
PERFORMANCE: Classified.

completed in April 1956. Powered by two J57-P-13 turbojets with afterburners, the Voodoo had 35° sweep, a one-piece horizontal stabilizer set high on its fin, mid-span ailerons on the thin (five per cent thickness-cord ratio) wing. Armament included four 20-mm. M-39 guns in the fuselage with optional external attachments for three Hughes Falcon air-to-air missiles, and two FFAR rocket clusters. Three external drop tanks or bombs could be carried with provision, like the F-100C, for tactical atomic weapons. Long-nosed RF-101A reconnaissance versions have also appeared. A world's speed record of 1207 mph was set with an F-101A in December 1957.

McDONNELL F-101B

MFR

MFR

MFR

CONVAIR YF-102A

CONVAIR YF-102
Pratt & Whitney J57-P-11, 10,900 lbs. (14,500 lbs. AB)
DIMENSIONS: Span 37′, Lg. 52′ 6″, Ht. 18′.
WEIGHT & PERFORMANCE: Classified

Although the F-101A had been designed as a bomber escort and fighter bomber, its long range suggested the type as an F-89 replacement and a number of two-place F-101B interceptors have been scheduled. Falcon missiles comprised the internal armament, while two MB-1 Genie unguided nuclear air-to-air missiles were carried externally.

Next century series single-seater was the delta-wing all-weather interceptor Convair developed from XF-92A experience. Using guided air-to-air missiles to attack its targets, the Convair YF-102 was designed to reach supersonic speeds. The fat fuselage contained pilot, radar, missiles, and over a thousand gallons of fuel for a J57-P-11 with afterburner.

Even before the YF-102's first flight on October 24, 1953, wind-tunnel tests warned that the drag hump at sonic speed was above the airplane's capability, and another layout using the new "area rule" of drag reduction was designed. After completion of eight YF-102s, four longer YF-102As were built with the J57-P-23, cambered leading edges for the thin wings, modified canopy, and an area-ruled fuselage incorporating lengthened nose, indented center section, and tail fairings. Supersonic speeds were achieved on the very first flight on December 21, 1954. In July 1955, delivery began on F-102A production articles, whose gray finish replaced the unpainted exteriors of YF ships. Deliveries on F-102A fighters and TF-102A two-place trainers were completed in April 1958, with about 1000 Delta Daggers accepted.

Armament consisted of six Hughes GAR-1 Falcon rockets, once designated XF-98s, released from a fuselage bay that also accommodates twenty-four 2.75 in. FFARs, or extra fuel for delivery flights. Using radar homing to seek targets, the six-foot, 100-lb. Falcons are fired by a Hughes radar fire-control system, after being extended out into the airstream from the bay, whose doors contain tubes for the FFARs.

Republic also designed a delta-wing interceptor, the XF-103, with a dual-cycle powerplant combining a 15,000-lb. thrust Wright YJ-67 and a ramjet. A 75 ft.

MFR

CONVAIR F-102A
Pratt & Whitney J57-P-23, 11,700 lbs. (16,000 lbs. AB)
DIMENSIONS: Span 38′ 1″, Lg. 68′ 3″, Ht. 21′ 2″, Wing Area 661.5 sq. ft.
WEIGHT & PERFORMANCE: Classified

PMB

CONVAIR F-102A

fuselage built of steel and titanium to meet the heat effects of very high speeds had lines broken only by the 34 ft. wing, triangular tail fins, belly scoop, and periscope for a completely faired pilot's cockpit. Mach 3 speeds were anticipated, but the Air Force preferred the proposed North American F-108, and cancelled the contract for two XF-103s on August 21, 1958.

The smallest and thinnest wings used on an American jet fighter distinguished the Lockheed XF-104 ordered March 1953 and first flown February 2, 1954. There were two prototypes powered by a Wright J65-W-6 with afterburner, and 15 similar YF-104s. Fuel was carried in the long fuselage and in drop tanks at the tips of the short, straight wings. A movable horizontal stabilizer was set high on the tail, and boundary layer separators are used on the engine air inlets. The pilot has a downward ejection seat, and fires a single T-171 20-mm. gun set low on the left side of the needle nose.

Production F-104A air superiority fighters, first flown February 17, 1956, had General Electric J79-GE-3s, new air intakes, and dorsal spine, and demonstrated phenomenal performance including a 1404 mph record speed run in May 1958, with a zoom to 91,249 feet. Although the Starfighter is said to have but half the weight of other century series types, it has been said that it is completely fitted with essential equipment, including radar. Its single gun, a six-barrel Vulcan reportedly firing 6000 rpm, can be supplemented by Sidewinder missiles on each wingtip.

Air Defense Comand units received in 1958 about 150 F-104As and some two-place F-104B tactical trainers, but lack of all-weather capability limited Starfighter usefulness to the ADC. A fighter-bomber version, the F-104C, was developed and went to the Tactical Air Command in October 1958.

Powered by a J79-GE-7, the F-104C had 900 gallons of fuel in fuselage cells supplemented by two 195 gallon tanks under the wings, and two 170 gallon tanks at the wing tips. The inside tanks can be replaced by 1000 lb. bombs or Sidewinder missiles. Clean, the F-104C retained its advanced performance, and demonstrated a zoom to 103,395 ft. in December 1958. Export versions of the F-104C have been sold to Germany, Canada, and Japan.

First type designed from the start as a Tactical Air Command fighter-bomber, the F-105 Thunderchief began in 1952 as Republic's AP-63 design. A Pratt & Whitney J57-P-25 powered the first YF-105A to fly, on October 22, 1955, but a more powerful J75-P-3 and area rule theory were incorporated on the F-105B-1 that appeared in May 1956. This was the third ship of the original fiscal 1954 fifteen-plane order, and the remaining planes (to F-105B-6) were completed for systems testing by 1957.

Production deliveries made on a 1957 contract began in 1958 with the F-105B-10, using a J75-P-5 of 17,200-lb. thrust dry and 23,500-lb with afterburner. After 75 Bs are built, TAC expects to get the F-105D which introduced the J75-P-19W (24,500–26,500-lb. thrust) and almost automatic all-weather radar navigation and bombing capabilities. A lengthened nose for its more sophisticated electronics distinguished the F-105D, whose first test example flew on June 9, 1959.

Outstanding Thunderchief feature is the internal bomb bay (first on a fighter) in the lengthy fuselage. Nuclear and conventional weapons may be delivered with the aid of a G.E. MA-18 fire control/bombing system, and pylons below the wings and fuselage can accommodate three 450 gallon external tanks, or 3000 lbs. of bombs and the internal load. A six-barrel 20-mm. M-61 (formerly T-171) is mounted in the lower left side of the nose.

Performance capabilities of the F-105 include 1216 mph demonstrated on a 100 kilometer course, a range of nearly 2000 miles, and a climb to 8200 ft. in 55 seconds from standstill. Small, thin wings swept back from root intakes with raked-forward outer lips, and petal-type dive brakes were installed behind the tailpipe.

Another swept-wing fighter-bomber tried unsuccessfully to compete with the F-105B. Republic's fighter was judged slightly superior to the J-75 powered North American YF-107A, developed from an F-100B design study and first flown September 10, 1956. Three examples were completed, distinguished by a large dorsal air intake above and behind the pilot, and armed with four 20-mm. M-39E guns and external bomb loads. Instead of separate rudder and elevators, the entire vertical and horizontal tail surfaces move.

What might be the last USAF fighter type to enter large-scale production established a 1526 mph world's speed record in December 1958. Convair's delta-wing F-106A was developed from the F-102A, but has a 17,000-lb. thrust (23,500-lbs. with afterburner) Pratt & Whitney J75-P-17, squared-off fin, dual nose wheels, and air intakes moved behind the cockpit. Built at San Diego and first flown December 26, 1956, the Delta Dart had a Hughes MA-1 aircraft and weapons control system.

This electronic system is linked with SAGE ground control and enables the all-weather interceptor to be "flown automatically from wheels-up following take-off to flare-out before touchdown." The pilot monitors the mission on a map display projected on a cockpit screen, and can take over the controls any time he desires. When radar has selected the correct target range, the F-106A fires an MB-1 Genie missile with nuclear warhead (which will destroy any aircraft within 1000 ft. of its detonation), or four Falcon GAR-3 radar-homing or GAR-4 infrared heat-seeking missiles.

AF

LOCKHEED XF-104
Wright XJ65-W-3, 7200 lbs.
DIMENSIONS: Span 21′ 11″, Lg. 54′ 9″, Ht. 13′ 6″.
WEIGHT & PERFORMANCE: Classified

AF

LOCKHEED F-104A

REPUBLIC YF-105A

AF

REPUBLIC YF-105B THUNDERCHIEF
Pratt & Whitney J75-P-3, 17,200 lbs. (22,500 lbs. AB)
DIMENSIONS: Span 34′ 11″, Lg. 63′ 1″, Ht. 19′ 8″, Wing Area 385 sq. ft.
WEIGHT: (Approx.) Empty 28,000 lb., Gross 34,000 lb., Max. 46,000 lb.
PERFORMANCE: Classified.

MFR

CONVAIR F-106A
Pratt & Whitney J75-P-17, over 17,000 lbs.
DIMENSIONS: Span 38′ 2″, Lg. 70′ 9″, Ht. 20′ 3″, Wing Area 661 sq. ft.
WEIGHT: (Approx.) Empty 26,000 lb., Gross 35,000 lb.
PERFORMANCE: Classified.

MFR

MFR

NORTH AMERICAN F-107A
Pratt & Whitney J75-P-9, 17,200 lbs. (24,500 lbs. AB)
DIMENSIONS: Span 36′ 7″, Lg. 60′ 10″, Ht. 19′ 8″.
WEIGHT & PERFORMANCE: Classified

Other performance characteristics reported include a combat radius of over 500 miles, ferry range with added fuel of 2700 miles, and a ceiling of well over 50,000 ft., with zoom possibilities beyond that.

Further development in manned fighters seemed stymied when the Air Force cancelled the North American F-108 project on September 23, 1959. Powered by two General Electric J-93 jets, the two-place F-108 was expected to be a long-range interceptor with Mach 3 capabilities.

Chapter 19: Summary

Essentially, today's fighter plane has the same mission as those of World War I: the destruction of enemy aircraft to gain control of the air. This job has steadily increased in difficulty, but has become vital to the nation's survival.

In order to destroy enemy aircraft, superior speed, climb, maneuverability, and fire power are needed, the actual requirements depending on target characteristics. Since bombers built up to 1930 were cumbersome biplanes whose speeds and ceilings seldom exceeded 120 mph and 15,000 ft., it was not difficult to surpass this performance with compact single-seat biplanes. With the advent of all-metal monoplanes, bomber capabilities advanced sharply and fighters had to keep pace. Bomber performance increased further with supercharging, and reached supersonic levels with jet propulsion. Each step required faster fighters, and increased the possibility of foreign aerial attacks.

World War II brought a tremendous increase in fighter fire power, for larger caliber guns were needed to destroy sturdy, armored bombers. Wartime increases in the quantity of guns have not been continued, however, largely because of the faster rates of fire offered by contemporary ordnance.

Electronics have played a role of growing importance since airborne radar was introduced in 1940. Not only are air attacks to be expected in all sorts of weather, but today's high speeds make purely visual gunnery almost impossible. Radar search and gunnery equipment is now a necessity, while defense requirements for the nearest thing possible to a "sure kill" have also led to radar-aimed salvos of rockets and air-to-air guided missiles fired across the path of enemy bombers.

A good interceptor may also be useful against enemy fighters, but additional qualities will be needed for gaining and maintaining control of the air. For one thing, although dogfighting seems to have gone out of style, maneuverability is still of crucial importance. Instead of the big smash of heavy-caliber guns, a higher rate of fire may be desirable. Since air battles between fighters usually require daylight, radar search equipment may not be needed, although radar gunsights proved their value in Korea. The most important attribute of the air superiority fighter as compared to the interceptor is range, because enemy fighters may have to be met deep in their own territory, in order to support friendly bombers.

Some of the range may come from disposable external tanks, which can be exchanged for bombs on fighter-bomber missions. This brings us to another function fighters have acquired, that of ground attack. Here, interceptor radar and high-altitude performance loses its importance. Like the attack planes of past Army and Navy tradition, ability to punish ground targets is the prime consideration.

Technical factors indicate that the interceptor function will be expressed in separate types from aircraft built for fighter-bomber or penetration missions. Since it will be difficult to decide in advance how fighter strength should be divided between interceptor and fighter-bomber types, it is wise to continue development of compromise air superiority types that could fill either role when strategy requires reinforcement of the more specialized squadrons.

As piloted bombers are replaced by guided missiles, defense organizations will turn to missile interception systems. Antiaircraft guided missiles are already in service for use against piloted bombers, although actual warfare has not demonstrated the extent that they may replace fighters. The Army Nike and Navy Terrier are reported to be limited to ranges under 25 miles, and are basically a replacement for high-altitude antiaircraft guns. Boeing's Bomarc, which once carried the XF-99 designation, is the leading American surface-to-air guided missile, and reputedly has a 200-mile range.

Limitations of missile range, target discrimination, and reliability, make it unlikely that piloted fighters face immediate extinction. Supersonic descendants of the wartime Spad will continue to be the primary factor in denying use of air spaces to an enemy until the bomber offensive has decided the outcome of any future war.

Part 5 Navy Patrol Planes

Chapter 20: Wings over the Basket Masts 1917–34

USN

CURTISS H-12
Rolls-Royce Eagle I, 275 hp, (Liberty 330 hp)
DIMENSIONS: Span 92′ 8″, Lg. 46′, Ht. 16′ 9″, Wing Area 1121 sq. ft.
WEIGHT: Empty 5945 lb., Gross 7989 lb.
PERFORMANCE: Speed—Top 85 mph at 2000′, Landing 55 mph.

Naval combat aviation has developed entirely as an element of sea power, and hasn't left the fleet to become an independent organization. The Navy began with shore-based flying boats for patrol, followed by shore-based torpedo planes, and finally took fighters, bombers, and torpedo planes to sea on aircraft carriers.

Patrol planes were the first used in naval service, and so they make an appropriate beginning for the story of Navy combat types. Certainly their heavy armament and long battle record qualify patrol planes as combat types, despite the monotonous nature of the average wartime patrol.

FLYING BOATS VERSUS U-BOATS

Throughout its history, the naval patrol plane has been linked to the submarine. Originally envisioned as passive observers of fleet movements, patrol planes were called into combat action when German U-boats were inflicting heavy losses on Allied shipping in World War I. With land warfare stalemated, the only possible German answer to the British blockade had been a counterblockade by submarine. Unrestricted submarine warfare by the Germans shocked American public opinion (which never dreamed the U.S. would later use the same methods against Japan) into accepting war, but was calculated to starve England out before a single U.S. division arrived. In April 1917, the sinkings rose so high it seemed the Germans calculated rightly.

In this emergency, British flying boats patrolled the most dangerous areas, and on May 20, 1917, a Curtiss H-12 hit the first U-boat sunk by aircraft. Others were not usually so successful, but flying boats handicapped the subs by reporting their location and driving them below the surface, where their speed was reduced. Other devices played a larger part in beating the subs and saving England: the convoy system, mine barrage, and hydrophones; so aircraft were responsible for only seven of nearly 200 U-boats sunk, but the flying boat had demonstrated its future possibilities.

The flying boats used then were developments of the Curtiss America, a 5000-lb., 72 ft. span biplane with a single-step boatlike hull, two 100 hp Curtiss engines and 300 gallons of fuel, designed in 1914 for a private pilot's proposed attempt to fly the Atlantic. The war prevented the America's completion, and the flight, but a British official saw its possibilities, and two experimental Curtiss H-4 flying boats were ordered in August and received in November 1914. Like five more delivered in 1915, they had two 90 hp Curtiss OX-5 water-cooled engines, but when this power plant proved inadequate, 100 hp Anzanis were used on 50 H-4s ordered March 1915 and used for training and limited patrols by the Royal Naval Air Service.

USN

CURTISS HS-1L
Liberty 12, 360 hp
DIMENSIONS: Span 62′ 1″, Lg. 38′ 6″, Ht. 14′ 7″, Wing Area 653 sq. ft.
WEIGHT: Empty 4070 lb., Gross 5910 lb. Fuel 141 gal.
PERFORMANCE: Speed—Top 87 mph, Landing 57 mph. Service Ceiling 2500′, Climb 1725′/10 min. Endurance 3.7 hrs. at top speed, 5.7 hrs. cruising.

ARC

CURTISS HS-2
Liberty 12, 350 hp
DIMENSIONS: Span 74′, Lg. 38′ 6″, Ht. 14′ 7″, Wing Area 803 sq. ft.
WEIGHT: Empty 4300 lb., Gross 6432 lb. Fuel 141 gal.
PERFORMANCE: Speed—Top 82.5 mph, Cruising 78 mph, Landing 50 mph. Service Ceiling 5200′, Climb 2300′/10 min. Endurance 4.6 hrs. at top speed, 7.6 hrs. cruising.

These flying boats were called Small Americas by the British and were followed by larger Curtiss H-8 Large Americas. Two 160 hp Curtiss engines powered the first one delivered July 1916, but again the biplane was underpowered, and 275 hp Rolls-Royce Eagles were substituted. These aircraft became the Curtiss H-12, first American plane used in combat.

Open cockpits were provided for a pilot, co-pilot, engineer, and "wireless operator," two 236-lb. bombs were carried under the wings, a pair of .30-caliber Lewis guns were in the bow cockpit, and another Lewis gun was in the rear cockpit. These guns destroyed the first enemy aircraft downed by an American airplane. On May 14, 1917, a Curtiss H-12 swept down below and alongside a German Zeppelin. A short burst from the bow guns, and the big dirigible caught fire and fell into the North Sea. Three days later, another H-12 became the first plane to sink a submarine.

Seventy-one Curtiss H-12s were built to British orders, but 20 were turned over to the United States Navy. One Navy H-12 had the original Curtiss engines, while the rest received Liberty 12s. Many North Sea patrols were made by H-12s, but the hull was subject to serious damage by rough water.

When the United States entered the war, the Navy looked for flying boats of its own. First was the Curtiss HS-1 (sometimes called HS-1L for its Liberty engine), flown on October 21, 1917, as a combination of the America-type single-step hull, a single 360 hp Liberty engine with a four-bladed pusher propeller, and wings from the R-type seaplane. Larger wings were used on HS-2 production models, first flown on May 23, 1918.

Armed with a Lewis bow gun and two 230-lb. bombs, these three-place, single-engined biplanes did most of their work off American coasts. Over a thousand HS-2s were built, including 673 by Curtiss, 250 by L.W.F., 80 by Standard, 60 by Gallaudet, 25 by Boeing, 2 by Loughead, and several erected at naval air stations from spare parts. Many were sold to private operators after the war. Modified versions were four HS-3s built by Curtiss and two HS-3s finished at the Naval Aircraft Factory.

Curtiss also designed the twin-engined H-16, a larger development of the H-12, with balanced rudder, two-step hull, and better rear armament. Britain ordered 125, and fitted the 75 that were actually delivered with 345 hp Rolls-Royce Eagles, but 74 Curtiss H-16s for the U. S. Navy had 400 hp Liberty engines. On November 20, 1917, an order for H-16s was given to the new Naval Aircraft Factory in Philadelphia, and 150 were completed between March and October 1918. Armament of the H-16 included four 230-lb. bombs, and five or six Lewis guns: one or two in the bow, two in the rear cockpit, and one at an opening on each side of the hull. This type cost $37,850, compared to $16,900 for each HS-2.

The British had designed a flying boat with an improved hull called the F-5, and an American version, the F-5-L, was built at the Naval Aircraft Factory with two 420 hp Liberty engines. Thirty-three of 138 built there were completed before the Armistice, and 480 were canceled. Sixty more were built by Curtiss, and 30 were produced in Canada. The $34,800 F-5-L carried four 230-lb. bombs under the wings and six Lewis guns at the bow and rear cockpits and waist openings. An example exhibited in the Smithsonian Institution has eight Lewis guns and a 1½ lb. cannon in the bow. The twin-engined biplane pattern of the H-12, H-16, and F-5-L established a tradition in Navy flying boats.

USN

CURTISS-NAVY F-5-L
Liberty 12A, 420 hp
DIMENSIONS: Span 103′ 9″, Lg. 49′ 4″, Ht. 18′ 9″, Wing Area 1397 sq. ft.
WEIGHT: Empty 8720 lb., Gross 13,256 lb., Max. 13,600 lb. Fuel 495 gal.
PERFORMANCE: Speed—Top 90 mph at s. l., Landing 52 mph. Service Ceiling 5500′, Climb 2625′/10 min. Range 608 miles at top speed, 830 miles cruising.

USN

CURTISS H-16
Liberty 12, 400 hp
DIMENSIONS: Span 95′ 1″, Lg. 46′ 2″, Ht. 17′ 9″, Wing Area 1164 sq. ft.
WEIGHT: Empty 7400 lb., Gross 10,900 lb. Fuel 307–410 gal.
PERFORMANCE: Speed—Top 95 mph at 2000′, Landing 56 mph. Service Ceiling 9950′, Climb 5000′/10 min. Range 378 miles.

CURTISS-NAVY NC-4
Liberty 12, 420 hp
DIMENSIONS: Span 126′, Lg. 68′ 3″, Ht. 24′ 6″, Wing Area 2380 sq. ft.
WEIGHT: Empty 15,874 lb., Gross 21,500 lb., Max. 28,000 lb. Fuel 1800 gal.
PERFORMANCE: Speed—Top 90 mph light, 81 mph fully loaded, Landing 62 mph. Service Ceiling 4500′, Climb 1050′/5 min. Range 1470 miles.

USN

ARC

NAVY PN-7

Wright T-2, 525 hp

DIMENSIONS: Span 72′ 10″, Lg. 49′ 1″, Ht. 15′ 4″, Wing Area 1217 sq. ft.

WEIGHT: Empty 9637 lb., Gross 14,203 lb. Fuel 489 gal.

PERFORMANCE: Speed—Top 104.5 mph at s. l., Landing 54.5 mph. Service Ceiling 9200′, Climb 5000′/10.2 min. Range 655 miles.

USN

NAVY PN-10

Packard 2A-1500, 525 hp

DIMENSIONS: Span 72′ 10″, Lg. 49′ 2″, Ht. 16′ 9″, Wing Area 1217 sq. ft.

WEIGHT: Empty 10,060 lb., Gross 18,994 lb., Max. 19,029 lb. Fuel 858 gal.

PERFORMANCE: Speed—Top 114 mph at s. l., Landing 66 mph. Service Ceiling 4500′, Climb 5000′/29 min. Range 1508 miles.

NAVY PN-9

Packard 1A-1500, 480 hp

DIMENSIONS: Span 72′ 10″, Lg. 49′ 2″, Ht. 16′ 6″, Wing Area 1217 sq. ft.

WEIGHT: Empty 9125 lb., Gross 19,610 lb. Fuel 1300 gal.

PERFORMANCE: Speed—Top 114.5 mph at s. l., Landing 68 mph. Service Ceiling 3080′, Climb 1750′/10 min. Range 2550 miles.

USN

Curtiss also built for Britain a single triplane flying boat in 1916, which had four 250 hp Curtiss engines. Known as the Curtiss-Wanamaker, it didn't work out, and no further information is available. Curtiss, however, planned an even larger boat which became famous for its pioneer transatlantic flight.

Four NC (Navy Curtiss) boats ordered in December 1917 were the largest American planes of 1918, designed to fly across the Atlantic to join in antisubmarine patrols. When first flown on October 4, 1918, the NC-1 had three 400 hp Libertys, but a fourth was added behind the center engine to turn a pusher propeller. Biplane tail surfaces were mounted high on spruce outriggers from the hull and huge wings, an arrangement calculated to clear waves and "permit a machine gun to be fired straight aft . . . without interference," although the field of fire in almost every other direction was cluttered. A 45 ft. hull contained a bow cockpit, side-by-side pilots' pits, rear compartment, radio, and fuel tanks. Top speed was 90 mph light, and 81 mph loaded, not much of a margin over the landing speed.

In May 1919, the NC-4 became the first plane to fly across the Atlantic. Two sister ships which also attempted the Newfoundland-Azores-Lisbon-Plymouth flight landed at sea to get their bearings and were unable to take off again.

When the Navy entered World War I it had only six flying boats; by Armistice Day 1172 were on hand, most of them single-engine HS types. After the German U-boats were gone, so was the reason, it seemed, to build any more patrol planes, although millions were invested in new battleships, with their tall basket masts and armored turrets. It was a decade before new flying boats were built in quantity. On June 30, 1925, the Navy's aging patrol force consisted of 44 F-5-L and 33 H-16 twin-engined boats, 40 single-engined HS-2s, and 80 assorted unserviceable airframes of these types. Fortunately, the Naval Aircraft Factory was developing experimentally a new class of flying boats to relieve the spruce framework of these antiques.

The first flying boat project designed at Philadelphia was to be a "Giant Boat" for use over the vast distances of the Pacific. It was to be a 63,000 lb., 164 ft. span triplane with *nine* Liberty engines; something had to be done to use up that war surplus stockpile! Fortunately, they did not complete this monstrosity; at that stage of engineering it would probably have been even less successful than the Army's Barling bomber.

TWO ENGINES AND TWO WINGS

The traditional wartime approach to twin-engined flying boats was reflected in two PN-7 biplanes built at the Naval Aircraft Factory. First tested in January 1924, they had a modified F-5 hull with new 72-ft. 10-in. span wings, only one pair of outer-wing struts on each side, and two 525 hp Wright T-2 inline engines mounted in streamlined nacelles, with the water radiators hanging from the upper wing. A crew of five, four 230-lb. bombs, and Lewis guns fore and aft were carried.

Naval Aircraft Factory records then list a PN-8 with Wright T-3s, a PN-9 with Packard 1A-1500s and a pair of PN-10s ordered May 1925 with Packard 2A-1500s. Introducing an all-metal hull with greater fuel capacity, the PN-9 made the first attempt to fly from San Francisco to Hawaii. The fuel lasted 28½ hours; long enough to cover 1841 nautical miles against headwinds and make a world's distance record, but after it ran out the PN-9 came down at sea

BOEING PB-1
Packard 2A-2540, 800 hp
DIMENSIONS: Span 87′ 6″, Lg. 59′ 5″, Ht. 22′ 2″, Wing Area 1823 sq. ft.
WEIGHT: Empty 12,742 lb., Gross 24,000 lb., Max. 26,822 lb. Fuel 1881 gal.
PERFORMANCE: Speed—Top 125 mph at s. l., Cruising 80 mph, Landing 69 mph. Service Ceiling 3300′, Climb 5000′/46 min. Range 2230 miles.

MFR

BOEING XPB-2 (XF4B-1 in front)
Pratt & Whitney GR-1690, 475 hp
DIMENSIONS: As PB-1, except height 20′ 10″.
WEIGHT: Gross 24,374 lb. Fuel 1881 gal.
PERFORMANCE: Speed—Top 112 mph at s. l., Landing 64.4 mph. Service Ceiling 4470′, Climb 2500′/10 min.

USN

PMB

NAVY XPN-11
Pratt & Whitney R-1690, 525 hp
DIMENSIONS: Span 72′ 10″, Lg. 53′ 6″, Ht. 17′ 6″, Wing Area 1154 sq. ft.
WEIGHT: Empty 7923 lb., Gross 16,870 lb.
PERFORMANCE: Speed—Top 120 mph, Landing 63 mph. Service Ceiling 7700′, Climb 5000′/16.1 min. Range 1948 miles.

some 250 miles short of Pearl Harbor. Then the hull demonstrated good flotation qualities, keeping the five-man crew safe until their rescue. Except for a wing structure of metal instead of wood, the PN-10s of 1926 were like the PN-9.

The only flying boat bought from a private firm in this period was the Boeing PB-1, acquired in 1925 for another trans-Pacific flight. Powered by two big 800 hp Packard 2A-2540s back-to-back between the hull and upper wing, turning one tractor and one pusher propeller, the PB-1 had five cockpits and composite hull with metal bottom and plywood deck.

Up to this point water-cooled engines had been used on Navy patrol planes, but in 1928 the Navy tried air-cooled radials on flying boats. Boeing's ship was rebuilt as the XPB-2 with two Pratt & Whitney R-1690 Hornets instead of the Packards which had proven unsatisfactory. Two more pairs of PN boats were built at the Naval Aircraft Factory using air-cooled radials: PN-11s powered by Pratt & Whitney R-1690s and XPN-12s using Wright R-1750Ds.

To replace the senile war leftovers still in squadron service, production of the PN series was assigned to private manufacturers. Douglas received a contract for 25 PD-1 boats in January 1928. This type was identical to the PN-12 in appearance and was powered by 525 hp Wright R-1750s. Twenty-five Martin PM-1s were ordered on May 31, 1929, together with three

DOUGLAS PD-1
Wright R-1750, 525 hp
DIMENSIONS: Span 72′ 10″, Lg. 49′ 2″, Ht. 16′, Wing Area 1162 sq. ft.
WEIGHT: Empty 8319 lb., Gross 14,988 lb. Fuel 759 gal.
PERFORMANCE: Speed—Top 121 mph at s. l., Cruising 100 mph, Landing 59 mph. Service Ceiling 11,600′, Climb 605′/1 min., 5000′/9.8 min. Range 1465 miles.

USN

PMB

NAVY XPN-12
Wright R-1750D, 525 hp
DIMENSIONS: Span 72′ 10″, Lg. 49′ 2″, Ht. 16′ 9″, Wing Area 1217 sq. ft.
WEIGHT: Empty 7669 lb., Gross 14,122 lb. Fuel 858 gal.
PERFORMANCE: Speed—Top 114 mph, Landing 58 mph. Service Ceiling 10,900′, Climb 5500′/16 min. Range 1309 miles.

MARTIN PM-1
Wright R-1820-64, 575 hp
DIMENSIONS: Span 72′ 10″, Lg. 49′ 2″, Ht. 16′ 4″, Wing Area 1236 sq. ft.
WEIGHT: Empty 8970 lb., Gross 16,117 lb. Fuel 750 gal.
PERFORMANCE: Speed—Top 118.7 mph at s. l., Landing 60.5 mph. Service Ceiling 8500′, Climb 5000′/13.3 min. Range 1305 miles.

USN

X4PN boats from the Naval Aircraft Factory. Five more aircraft were later added to the Martin contract, and the first PM-1 was delivered June 1930 with Wright R-1820-64 Cyclones and a balanced single rudder. Cyclones also powered the N.A.F. XP4N-1 of November 1930 and two heavier XP4N-2s of 1931, but these ships had larger fuel tanks and twin rudders, first tested on PN-11.

Twin rudders were also used on 18 Keystone PK-1s ordered November 30, 1929, and 25 Martin PM-2s bought June 10, 1930. The ring cowls on their R-1820-64 engines gave them a little more speed than PM-1. Keystone deliveries began in April 1931, while the Martin boats began following PM-1s in June 1931.

Meanwhile, a new balanced single tail, improved hull, and cowled GR-1750s distinguished the Hall Aluminum Company's XPH-1, which appeared in December 1929 with the usual open cockpits, and twin Lewis guns at bow and rear rings. Production PH-1s had enclosed pilots' cockpits and R-1820-86 Cyclones. Nine were ordered on June 10, 1930, and tests began in October 1931.

Fortunately, Navy patrol squadrons didn't have to depend on these biplanes for as long a time as they had had to fly 1918s survivors. Larger aircraft soon eclipsed the PN progeny and made the California to Hawaii hop a matter of routine. But the biplane was not quite through; since the Coast Guard had need of a patrol and rescue boat smaller than the PBYs,

NAVY XP4N-1
Wright R-1820-64, 575 hp
DIMENSIONS: Span 72′ 10″, Lg. 54′, Ht. 17′ 7″, Wing Area 1154 sq. ft.
WEIGHT: Empty 9770 lb., Gross 17,900 lb., Max. 20,340 lb. Fuel 1270 gal.
PERFORMANCE: Speed—Top 115 mph, Landing 65 mph. Service Ceiling 9000′, Climb 5000′/11.3 min. Range 1510 miles normal, 1930 miles max.

ARC

NAVY XP4N-2
Wright R-1820-64, 575 hp
DIMENSIONS: As XP4N-1
WEIGHT: Empty 9843 lb., Gross 17,595 lb., Max. 21,585 lb. Fuel 1420 gal.
PERFORMANCE: Speed—Top 114 mph, Landing 64 mph. Service Ceiling 9300′, Climb 5000′/11.7 min. Range 1350 miles normal, 2050 miles max.

USN

KEYSTONE PK-1
Wright R-1820-64, 575 hp
DIMENSIONS: Span 72′, Lg. 48′ 11″, Ht. 16′ 9″, Wing Area 1226 sq. ft.
WEIGHT: Empty 9387 lb., Gross 16,534 lb., Max. 17,074 lb. Fuel 750–840 gal.
PERFORMANCE: Speed—Top 120 mph at s. l., Landing 62 mph. Service Ceiling 9700′, Climb 5000′/11 min. Range 1250 miles normal, 1355 miles max.

USN

MARTIN PM-2
Wright R-1820-64, 575 hp
DIMENSIONS: Span 72′, Lg. 49′, Ht. 16′ 9″, Wing Area 1236 sq. ft.
WEIGHT: Empty 9919 lb., Gross 17,284 lb., Max. 19,062 lb. Fuel 750–878 gal.
PERFORMANCE: Speed—Top 118.5 mph at s. l., Landing 62.5 mph. Service Ceiling 9500′, Climb 5000′/13.8 min. Range 1347 miles max., 937 miles as bomber.

MFR

Hall got an order for a new version of the old design in June 1936. Five PH-2s with 750 hp Wright R-1820-F51 Cyclones were followed in 1939 by seven Hall PH-3s with improved engine cowls and pilots' enclosure. Built in the old Keystone-Fleetwings factory alongside the Delaware River at Bristol, Pennsylvania, the Hall boats were armed during the war for anti-submarine work.

While the PN series biplanes went into service, other types were developed to give the fleet different kinds of support. One such effort was the Sikorsky XPS-2 of 1928 which was followed by four PS-3 purchased October 6, 1928, and two more on April 9, 1931. Although bearing the patrol designation, they were actually Navy versions of the twin-engine Sikorsky S-38 commercial amphibian and not really combat types. Pratt & Whitney R-1340-B (XPS-2) and R-1340-C (PS-3) Wasps powered these amphibians, which had a double tail suspended on outriggers behind the sesquiplane wings.

Sikorsky tried again in June 1932 with the XP2S-1 flying boat, a biplane with twin 450 hp R-1340-88s mounted in tandem over the hull.

ARC

HALL PH-1
Wright R-1820-86, 620 hp
DIMENSIONS: Span 72′ 10″, Lg. 51′ 10″, Ht. 17′ 6″, Wing Area 1223 sq. ft.
WEIGHT: Empty 8251 lb., Gross 15,479 lb., Max. 16,379 lb. Fuel 900 gal.
PERFORMANCE: Speed—Top 134.5 mph at s. l., Landing 60 mph. Service Ceiling 11,200′, Climb 5000′/8.4 min. Range 1580 miles normal, 1868 miles max.

HALL XPH-1
Wright GR-1750, 537 hp
DIMENSIONS: Span 72′ 10″, Lg. 51′, Ht. 17′ 5″, Wing Area 1180 sq. ft.
WEIGHT: Empty 6576 lb., Gross 13,228 lb. Fuel 750 gal.
PERFORMANCE: Speed—Top 124 mph, Landing 56 mph. Service Ceiling 12,050′, Climb 5000′/9.5 min. Range 1790 miles.

USN

WILLIAMS

HALL PH-2
Wright R-1820F-51, 750 hp
DIMENSIONS: Span 72′ 10″, Lg. 51′, Ht. 17′ 10″, Wing Area 1170 sq. ft.
WEIGHT: Empty 9150 lb., Gross 15,411 lb., Max. 16,370 lb. Fuel 750–900 gal.
PERFORMANCE: Speed—Top 151 mph at 2800′, 145 mph at s. l., Cruising 126 mph, Landing 60 mph. Service Ceiling 21,000′, Climb 1550′/1 min. Range 1830 miles normal, 2170 miles max.

THE BIG BOATS

Perfection of patrol types capable of safely flying to overseas bases in Alaska, Hawaii, the Philippines, or the Canal Zone remained the major problem facing American flying boat designers. The Bureau of Aeronautics engineers planned a 100 ft. span monoplane that was a big step toward this capability, and Consolidated Aircraft, then in Buffalo, New York, built the prototype.

Completed in January 1929, the XPY-1 had two 450 hp Pratt & Whitney R-1340-38 Wasps suspended on struts between a fabric-covered, metal frame wing and an all-metal single-step hull with four open cock-

HALL PH-3
Wright R-1820F-51, 750 hp at 3200′
DIMENSIONS: Span 72′ 10″, Lg. 51′, Ht. 19′ 10″, Wing Area 1170 sq. ft.
WEIGHT: Empty 9614 lb., Gross 16,152 lb., Max. 17,679 lb. Fuel 750–892 gal.
PERFORMANCE: Speed—Top 159 mph at 3200′, 153 mph at s. l., Cruising 136 mph, Landing 60 mph. Service Ceiling 21,350′. Range 1937 miles normal, 2300 miles max.

PMB

MFR

SIKORSKY PS-3
Pratt & Whitney R-1340C, 450 hp at s. l.
DIMENSIONS: Span 71′ 8″, Lg. 40′ 3″, Ht. 13′ 10″, Wing Area 720 sq. ft.
WEIGHT: Empty 6740 lb., Gross 10,323 lb. Fuel 330 gal.
PERFORMANCE: Speed—Top 123.5 mph at s. l., Cruising 110 mph, Landing 64 mph. Service Ceiling 15,300′, Climb 5000′/8 min. Range 594 miles.

SIKORSKY XP2S-1
Pratt & Whitney R-1340-88, 450 hp
DIMENSIONS: Span 56′, Lg. 44′ 2″, Ht. 16′ 4″, Wing Area 762 sq. ft.
WEIGHT: Empty 6040 lb., Gross 9745 lb. Fuel 180–350 gal.
PERFORMANCE: Speed—Top 124 mph at s. l., Landing 59.5 mph. Service Ceiling 10,500′, Climb 660′/1 min.

MFR

USN

MARTIN P3M-2
Pratt & Whitney R-1690-32, 525 hp
DIMENSIONS: Span 100′, Lg. 61′ 9″, Ht. 16′ 8″, Wing Area 1119 sq. ft.
WEIGHT: Empty 10,032 lb., Gross 15,688 lb., Max. 17,977 lb. Fuel 844 gal.
PERFORMANCE: Speed—Top 115 mph at s. l., Landing 61 mph. Service Ceiling 11,900′, Climb 5000′/10.9 min. Range 1010 miles normal, 1570 miles max.

pits. A third Wasp was mounted above the wing, but was later deleted. The first Navy monoplane patrol type, it used outboard pontoons to keep the wingtips out of the water, and had a twin rudder tail assembly. Glenn L. Martin, however, underbid Consolidated for production of the type, starting a patrol plane rivalry that continued for over two decades. Consolidated did build a successful commercial XPY-1 development known as the Commodore.

CONSOLIDATED XPY-1
Pratt & Whitney R-1340-38, 450 hp
DIMENSIONS: Span 100′, Lg. 61′ 9″, Ht. 17′ 4″, Wing Area 1110 sq. ft.
WEIGHT: Empty 8369 lb., Gross 13,734 lb., Max. 16,492 lb. Fuel 1021 gal.
PERFORMANCE: Speed—Top 118 mph at s. l., Cruising 110 mph, Landing 56 mph. Service Ceiling 15,300′, Climb 5000′/8.3 min. Range 1716 miles normal, 2620 miles max.

MFR

ARC

MARTIN XP2M-1
Wright R-1820-64, 575 hp
DIMENSIONS: Span 100′, Lg. 61′ 2″, Ht. 22′ 8″, Wing Area 1204 sq. ft.
WEIGHT: Empty 12,467 lb., Gross 19,937 lb., Max. 22,916 lb. Fuel 1194 gal.
PERFORMANCE: Speed—Top 143 mph at s. l., Landing 68 mph. Service Ceiling 13,400′, Climb 5000′/5.9 min. Range 1257 miles normal, 1855 miles max.

Nine examples of Martin's version ordered on June 29, 1929, were designated P3M-1. The first, tested in February 1931, was similar to the twin-engined XPY-1, but the P3M-2 appeared in September with 525 hp R-1690-32 Hornets, ring cowls, and enclosed pilots' seats.

Martin also received a contract on June 28, 1929, for a developmental prototype with the same wing lowered and two cowled 575 hp Wright R-1820-64 Cyclones installed on the leading edge. It first ap-

MARTIN P3M-1
Pratt & Whitney R-1340, 450 hp
DIMENSIONS: Span 100′, Lg. 61′ 9″, Ht. 16′ 8″, Wing Area 1115 sq. ft.
WEIGHT: Empty 9988 lb., Gross 15,797 lb. Fuel 850 gal.
PERFORMANCE: Speed—Top 113 mph at s. l., Landing 60 mph. Service Ceiling 7500′, Climb 4300′/10 min. Range 1000 miles, 450 miles with bombs.

MFR

MFR

CONSOLIDATED P2Y-3

Wright R-1820-90, 750 hp take-off, 700 hp at 4000′

DIMENSIONS: Span 100′, Lg. 61′ 9″, Ht. 19′ 1″, Wing Area 1514 sq. ft.

WEIGHT: Empty 12,769 lb., Gross 21,291 lb., Max. 25,266 lb. Fuel 1620 gal.

PERFORMANCE: Speed—Top 139 mph at 4000′, 131 mph at s. l., Cruising 117 mph, Landing 63 mph. Service Ceiling 16,100′, Climb 650′/1 min. Range 1800 miles normal, 1180 miles/2000 lbs. bombs.

CONSOLIDATED P2Y-1

USN

MFR

CONSOLIDATED XP2Y-1
Wright R-1820E, 575 hp
DIMENSIONS: Span 100′, Lg. 61′ 9″, Ht. 16′ 8″, Wing Area 1430 sq. ft.
WEIGHT: Empty 10,950 lb., Gross 20,047 lb., Max. 21,547 lb. Fuel 1200 gal.
PERFORMANCE: Speed—Top 126 mph at s. l., Landing 61 mph. Service Ceiling 11,000′, Climb 5000′/10.7 min. Range 1768 miles normal, 1940 miles max.

MFR

CONSOLIDATED XP2Y-2
Wright R-1820-88
DIMENSIONS: Span 100′, Lg. 61′ 9″, Ht. 17′ 3″, Wing Area 1430 sq. ft.
WEIGHT: Empty 11,349 lb., Gross 20,251 lb., Max. 24,043 lb. Fuel 1632 gal.
PERFORMANCE: Speed—Top 135 mph (138 mph on test), Landing 61 mph. Service Ceiling 10,800′, Climb 5000′/12.6 min. Range 1890 miles normal, 2900 miles max.

peared in June 1931 as the XP2M-1 with a third Cyclone mounted above the wing, but this engine was deleted when the aircraft was modified to the XP2M-2. This reduction in power lowered performance, except for an increase in range obtained from reduced fuel consumption.

Consolidated won the next round in patrol plane competition with contracts for an XP2Y-1 on May 26, 1931, and 23 similar P2Y-1s on July 7. Adding a small lower wing to the XPY-1 layout, making it a sesquiplane (1½ wings), the XP2Y-1 was delivered on April 18, 1932, with 575 hp Wright Cyclones within the now customary ring cowls. A gunner with a .30-caliber Browning was in the bow ahead of the enclosed pilots' seats and two hatches side by side behind the wings were provided for the rear gunners. In January 1934, six P2Y-1s redeemed the PN-9s failure by a nonstop formation flight from San Francisco to Pearl Harbor.

A P2Y-1 modified by installation of R-1820-88 Cyclones on the leading edge of the wing appeared in August 1933 as the XP2Y-2, and was followed by a contract two days after Christmas in 1933 for the Consolidated P2Y-3. Twenty-three P2Y-3s delivered from January to May 1935 were powered by R-1820-90 Cyclones giving 700 hp at 4000 ft. Six export models were sold to Argentina, and examples went to Colombia and Japan.

The last patrol biplane built for the Navy, and the only one with inline engines since 1926, was the Hall XP2H-1 ordered June 30, 1930, and delivered October 31, 1932, from Bristol, Pennsylvania. The largest American flying boat since the NC-4, it had a crew

MARTIN XP2M-2 [*Photo unavailable*]
Wright R-1820-64, 575 hp (as XP2M-1, but only two engines)
DIMENSIONS: Span 100′, Lg. 61′ 2″, Ht. 15′ 10″, Wing Area 1204 sq. ft.
WEIGHT: Empty 10,115 lb., Gross 18,435 lb. Fuel 1200 gal.
PERFORMANCE: Speed—Top 128 mph, Landing 64 mph. Service Ceiling 10,800′, Climb 4420′/10 min. Range 2050 miles.

HALL XP2H-1
Curtiss V-1570-54, 600 hp
DIMENSIONS: Span 112′, Lg. 70′ 10″, Ht. 25′ 6″, Wing Area 2742 sq. ft.
WEIGHT: Empty 20,856 lb., Gross 35,393 lb., Max. 43,193 lb. Fuel 3368 gal.
PERFORMANCE: Speed—Top 139 mph at s. l., Cruising 120 mph, Landing 59 mph. Service Ceiling 10,900′, Climb 5000′/8.7 min. Range 2150 miles normal, 3350 miles max.

USN

of six and four 600 hp Curtiss V-1570-54 Conquerors mounted in tandem pairs and chemical-cooled by radiators below the front engines.

A generous quantity of struts had been necessary to support the wings of Navy patrol planes before perfection of cantilever, internally braced wings made more streamlined design possible. Douglas received a contract on May 20, 1933, for engineering studies of a twin-engine monoplane and on February 11, 1934, the Navy exercised its option for construction of an XP3D-1 prototype, first flown on February 6, 1935. Powered by two Pratt & Whitney R-1830-58 Wasps mounted above the cantilever wings, the XP3D-1 had the first enclosed gunner's turret on an American patrol plane. This turret was set back from the bow to allow room for an open mooring hatch, and was followed by an enclosed cabin for the pilots, and two open gunners' hatches behind the wings. Metal covered the hull and forward part of the wings, while fabric covered the rear wings and movable control surfaces.

This same basic design was used for the Douglas YOA-5 observation amphibian (formerly B-11) built for the Army with two 930 hp R-1820-45 Cyclones, a crew of five, and three .30-caliber guns. Since the Army's YOA-5 could be used to land on water and rescue land-plane crews forced down at sea, it pioneered the role of OA-10 Catalina rescue amphibians of World War II.

The Navy's prototype was rebuilt as XP3D-2 and reappeared in May 1936. Raised to the fuselage's top, the wing had 850 hp R-1830-64 Wasps on the leading edge, floats retracting inwardly. This type was not ordered by the Navy, since the Consolidated PBYs offered similar performance at a lower price, but Russia bought four examples of a transport version called the Douglas DF.

MFR

DOUGLAS XP3D-1

Pratt & Whitney R-1830-58, 825 hp at s. l.

DIMENSIONS: Span 95′, Lg. 69′ 10″, Ht. 22′ 5″, Wing Area 1295 sq. ft.

WEIGHT: Empty 13,799 lb., Gross 21,346 lb., Max. 26,662 lb. Fuel 1667 gal.

PERFORMANCE: Speed—Top 161 mph at s. l. Service Ceiling 15,000′, Climb 5000′/7.1 min. Range 1900 miles normal, 3530 miles max.

USN

DOUGLAS XP3D-2

Pratt & Whitney R-1830-64, 900 hp take-off, 850 hp at 8000′

DIMENSIONS: Span 95′, Lg. 69′ 7″, Ht. 22′ 5″, Wing Area 1295 sq. ft.

WEIGHT: Empty 15,120 lb., Gross 22,909 lb., Max. 27,946 lb. Fuel 1620 gal.

PERFORMANCE: Speed—Top 183 mph at 8000′, Landing 63.5 mph. Service Ceiling 18,900′, Climb 5000′/6.1 min. Range 2050 miles normal, 3380 miles max.

Chapter 21: Patrol Bombers against the Axis 1935-45

THE CATALINA

Built in greater numbers than any flying boat of World War II, the Consolidated Catalina had been used in every part of the world and by a dozen different countries. The prototype XP3Y-1 was ordered by the Navy on October 28, 1933, and was delivered from Buffalo for flight tests on March 28, 1935. Powered by two R-1830-54 Wasps giving 825 hp, it was an all-metal monoplane whose wing was attached to the hull by a superstructure and four struts. Unique retracting floats folded upward and out against the tips of the wings.

Four .30-caliber guns were carried, with up to two tons of bombs or two torpedoes beneath the wings. In the nose was a bomb-aiming window below a hand-operated pillbox turret. Pilot and co-pilot were in an enclosure ahead of a compartment for the navigator and radio operator while a flight engineer was stationed in the superstructure below the wing. Side-by-side waist gunners' pits were covered with sliding panels, and an opening in the hull's bottom behind the second step was provided for the tunnel gun.

Sixty production models were ordered June 29, 1935, from the company's new plant in San Diego, California. The prototype was returned to the factory in October 1935 for installation of R-1830-64 Wasps delivering 850 hp at 8000 ft. Redesignated XPBY-1, the modified prototype reappeared May 1936 and won a $4,898,000 contract for 50 PBY-2s on July 25. Pratt & Whitney R-1830-64s were also used on 60 PBY-1s first accepted September 1936, and on 50 similar PBY-2s first delivered the following May. Sixty-six PBY-3s ordered November 27, 1936, and delivered a year later used R-1830-66 Wasps.

When the PBY was released for export in 1938, the U.S.S.R. purchased three together with manufacturing rights. Soviet-built PBYs can be distinguished by a new front turret and characteristically Russian enclosed engine cowls. Two examples were also built for an explorer, and one for American Export Airlines. In July 1939 another PBY (Consolidated 28-5) became the first plane delivered to the Royal Air Force by transatlantic flight.

Thirty-three PBY-4s, using R-1830-72 Wasps yielding 1050 hp at take-off, were ordered December 18, 1937. The first example, tested May 1938, had the customary rear sliding hatches but the remaining ships were delivered to the Navy in 1939 with new blister enclosures over the rear gunners' positions. Armament consisted of a .50-caliber gun in each blister and a .30-caliber gun in the nose and in the tunnel.

Although the PBY had established a reputation for excellent reliability and usefulness, its days seemed numbered. Four-engined Sikorsky and Consolidated prototypes far surpassed it in performance, and Martin's PBM demonstrated a better twin-engine layout. Consolidated itself advanced flying-boat design with the twin-engine Model 31 begun as a private venture in August 1938 and first flown May 5, 1939. Using 2000 hp Wright R-3350s, Model 31 had a deep two-deck hull lacking windows. Tests were carried out with the secrecy common with combat types, for her new wing and twin rudders were to be incorporated in Consolidated's Model 32, the B-24 Army bomber. Since the PBYs wingtip floats were inappropriate to the new low-drag wing, the outboard floats retracted inwardly. Tricycle beaching gear retracted into the hull, instead of being left behind at the base.

This type was destined never to be produced in quantity, for outbreak of war gave early delivery greater importance than advanced performance. Great Britain had tested the PBY and found its performance adequate for action against German submarines. More PBYs could be built much sooner than any Model 31s, which must await tooling up and availability of untried power plants. Contracts were received for 50

MFR

CONSOLIDATED XP3Y-1 (XPBY-1)

Pratt & Whitney R-1830-58, 825 hp at s. l., (R-1830-64, 850 hp at 8000′)

DIMENSIONS: Span 104′, Lg. 63′ 6″, Ht. 18′ 6″, Wing Area 1400 sq. ft.

WEIGHT: Empty 12,512 lb. (13,000 lb.), Gross 19,793 lb. (20,226 lb.), Max. 24,803 lb. (25,236 lb.). Fuel 1750 gal.

PERFORMANCE: Speed—Top 169 mph at s. l. (184 mph at 8000′), Landing 58 mph. Service Ceiling 18,600′ (24,000′), Climb 5000′/4.1 min. (4.6 min.). Range 2070 miles normal (2110 miles), 4270 miles max. (4010 miles).

PBYs for Britain, 50 for Canada, and 18 for Australia. Needing planes in a hurry for the Neutrality Patrol, the United States Navy ordered 200 PBY-5s on December 20, 1939, and during 1940, 36 were purchased by the Dutch East Indies, while the R.A.F. Coastal Command increased its own contract to 100. British PBYs were named Catalina, a name adopted by the United States Navy on October 1, 1941.

Consolidated resumed deliveries with the first PBY-5 on September 18, 1940. Powered by R-1830-82s of 1200 hp for take-off, the PBY-5 had a modified rudder, and the PBY-4s waist blisters with a .50-caliber Browning in each, besides the usual .30-caliber bow and tunnel guns. British Catalina Is produced concurrently had S1C3G Wasps and two .303-caliber Vickers in each blister, and arrived overseas in time to track the German battleship *Bismarck* in May 1941 and to fight the growing sub menace.

Increased utility was given the Catalina design by adding retractable tricycle landing gear, turning the type into an amphibian with small loss of performance. The first amphibian version was an XPBY-5A converted from the first PBY-4 airframe returned to the factory in April 1939 and flown November 22. When the value of an amphibious version was realized, 33 of the PBY-5s under contract were modified as PBY-5A amphibians and 134 more PBY-5As were ordered on November 25, 1940. Delivery of PBY-5A amphibians commenced in December 1941.

CONSOLIDATED PBY-1

Pratt & Whitney R-1830-64, 900 hp take-off, 850 hp at 8000′

DIMENSIONS: Span 104′, Lg. 65′ 2″, Ht. 18′ 6″, Wing Area 1400 sq. ft.

WEIGHT: Empty 14,576 lb., Gross 22,336 lb., Max. 28,447 lb. Fuel 1750 gal.

PERFORMANCE: Speed—Top 177 mph at 8000′, 164 mph at s. l., Cruising 105 mph, Landing 67 mph. Service Ceiling 20,900′, Climb 840′/1 min. Range 2115 miles normal, 1210 miles/2000 lbs. bombs, 4042 miles max.

MFR

MFR

CONSOLIDATED PBY-2

Pratt & Whitney R-1830-64, 900 hp take-off, 850 hp at 8000′

DIMENSIONS: As PBY-1

WEIGHT: Empty 14,568 lb., Gross 22,490 lb., Max. 28,640 lb. Fuel 1750 gal.

PERFORMANCE: Speed—Top 178 mph at 8000′, 165 mph at s. l., Cruising 105 mph, Landing 68 mph. Service Ceiling 21,100′, Climb 860′/1 min. Range 2131 miles normal, 1242 miles/bombs.

CONSOLIDATED PBY-4

Pratt & Whitney R-1830-72, 1050 hp take-off, 900 hp at 12,000′

DIMENSIONS: As PBY-1

WEIGHT: Empty 16,837 lb., Gross 24,813 lb., Max. 32,011 lb. Fuel 1750 gal.

PERFORMANCE: Speed—Top 197 mph at 12,000′, 176 mph at s. l., Cruising 115 mph, Landing 71 mph. Service Ceiling 24,100′, Absolute Ceiling 25,700′, Climb 870′/1 min. Range 2070 miles normal, 1285 miles/2000 lbs. bombs, 4430 miles max.

USN

MFR

CONSOLIDATED PBY-3

Pratt & Whitney R-1830-66, 1000 hp take-off

DIMENSIONS: As PBY-1

WEIGHT: Empty 14,767 lb., Gross 22,713 lb., Max. 28,863 lb. Fuel 1750 gal.

PERFORMANCE: Speed—Top 191 mph at 12,000′, 171 mph at s. l., Cruising 114 mph, Landing 67 mph. Service Ceiling 24,400′, Climb 930′/1 min. Range 2175 miles normal, 1258 miles/bombs, 4170 miles max.

CONSOLIDATED PBY-5 CATALINA

Pratt & Whitney R-1830-82, 1200 hp take-off, 1050 hp at 5700′ (R-1830-92, 1050 hp at 7000′, on late models)

DIMENSIONS: Span 104′, Lg. 63′ 10″, Ht. 18′ 11″, Wing Area 1400 sq. ft.

WEIGHT: Empty 17,400 lb. (18,790 lb.), Gross 26,200 lb. (31,813 lb.), Max. 33,389 lb. (34,000 lb.). Fuel 1260–1750 gal. (1475 gal.).

PERFORMANCE: Speed—Top 200 mph at 5700′, 189 mph at s. l. (195 mph at 7000′), Cruising (110 mph), Landing 72 mph (75 mph). Service Ceiling 21,600′ (17,700′), Climb 990′/1 min. (660′/1 min.). Range 1945 miles patrol, 1245 miles/2000 lbs. bombs, 1895 miles max. (2860 miles patrol, 2370 miles/four 325 lb. bombs, 2645 miles/2000 lbs. bombs).

MFR

MFR

CONSOLIDATED PBY-5A

Pratt & Whitney R-1830-92, 1200 hp take-off, 1050 hp at 7000′

DIMENSIONS: Span 104′, Lg. 63′ 10″, Ht. 20′ 2″, Wing Area 1400 sq. ft.

WEIGHT: Empty 20,910 lb., Gross 33,975 lb., Max. 35,300 lb. Fuel 603–1478 gal.

PERFORMANCE: Speed—Top 179 mph at 7000′, Cruising 117 mph, Landing 78 mph. Service Ceiling 14,700′, Climb 10,000′/19.3 min. Range 2545 miles patrol, 1660 miles/four 325 lb. bombs, 1820 miles/2000 lbs. bombs.

Additional contracts made in 1941 and 1942 added 586 more PBY-5 flying boats, 627 more PBY-5A amphibians, and 225 PBY-5B (Catalina IB) amphibians for British lend-lease. Fifty-six PBY-5As went to the Army Air Force as OA-10 rescue amphibians, and 109 went to Britain as Catalina III and IVAs. All these aircraft used R-1830-92 Wasps, and had armor for the crew, and self-sealing tanks for 600 of the 1475-gallon fuel capacity.

Four 325-lb. depth charges or up to 4000 lbs. of bombs or two torpedoes could be carried below the wings. One .30-caliber bow gun was carried on the first 124 PBY-5A amphibians, but the remainder had two .30-caliber bow guns, as well as 511 lbs. of armor and the usual two .50-caliber and one .30-caliber rear

CONSOLIDATED PBY-6A

Pratt & Whitney R-1830-92, 1200 hp take-off, 1050 hp at 7000′

DIMENSIONS: Span 104′, Lg. 63′, Ht. 22′ 4″, Wing Area 1400 sq. ft.

WEIGHT: Empty 21,480 lb., Gross 34,550 lb., Max. 36,400 lb. Fuel 603–1778 gal.

PERFORMANCE: Speed—Top 178 mph at 7000′, 167 mph at s. l., Cruising 107 mph, Landing 79 mph. Service Ceiling 16,200′, Climb 630′/1 min. Range 2535 miles patrol, 1405 miles/four 325 lb. depth charges, 2195 miles/2000 lbs. bombs.

MFR

USN

N.A.F. PBN-1
Pratt & Whitney R-1830-92, 1200 hp take-off, 1050 hp at 7000′
DIMENSIONS: Span 104′ 3″, Lg. 64′ 8″, Ht. 21′ 3″, Wing Area 1400 sq. ft.
WEIGHT: Empty 19,288 lb., Gross 36,353 lb., Max. 38,000 lb. Fuel 622–2085 gal.
PERFORMANCE: Speed—Top 186 mph at 6700′, 174 mph at s. l., Cruising 111 mph, Landing 78 mph. Service Ceiling 15,100′. Range 2590 miles/four 325 lb. depth charges, 3700 miles max.

gun. One squadron based at the Strait of Gibraltar successfully used MAD (Magnetic Airborne Detector) gear and fired thirty 65-lb. rocket bombs back and downward at submerged U-boats.

Catalina production at San Diego was completed in March 1944 but continued in four satellite plants. On July 16, 1941, 156 PBN-1 Nomads had been ordered from Philadelphia's Naval Aircraft Factory. First accepted in February 1943, they introduced a higher rudder and enlarged fuel capacity. Armament included a .50-caliber gun in the nose turret and in each side blister as well as the usual small-caliber tunnel gun. Armor weight was 426 lbs. An order for 124 additional PBNs placed November 1942 was canceled the following September, and 137 of the PBNs built were

CONSOLIDATED XP4Y-1
Wright R-3350-8, 2300 hp take-off, 1800 hp at 13,600′
DIMENSIONS: Span 110′, Lg. 74′ 1″, Ht. 25′ 2″, Wing Area 1048 sq. ft.
WEIGHT: Empty 29,334 lb., Gross 46,000 lb., Max. 48,000 lb. Fuel 1545–3000 gal.
PERFORMANCE: Speed—Top 247 mph at 13,600′, 231 mph at s. l., Cruising 136 mph, Landing 89 mph. Service Ceiling 21,400′, Climb 1230′/1 min. Range 2300 miles/eight 325 lb. depth charges, 1745 miles/ two torpedos, 2695 miles/ 1845 gal., 3280 miles max.

MFR

lend-leased to Russia before production ended in March 1945. Two Canadian facilities were utilized: one by Boeing at Vancouver for PB2B flying boats and the other by Vickers at Montreal for PBV amphibians. All 230 Vickers Catalinas actually went to the AAF as OA-10A rescue amphibians, while 240 PB2B-1 (as PBY-5) and 50 PB2B-2 (with PBN tail) were built for the R.A.F. Coastal Command and the Royal New Zealand Air Force.

Another Consolidated factory was established in New Orleans to produce the long-dormant Model 31, which in April 1942 had been fitted with dummy turrets, designated XP4Y-1, and ordered into production. Powered by 2300 hp R-3350-8 duplex Cyclones, the P4Y-1 Corregidor was to be armed with one 37-mm. and four .50-caliber guns and up to 4000 lbs. of bombs, but this project was canceled because B-29 production devoured its engine supply, and on July 9, 1943, the plant was given instead a contract for 900 Catalinas. Between April 1944 and April 1945, 235 of these were completed at New Orleans. They were PBY-6A amphibians with new PBN tails, two .50-caliber guns in the nose turret, 455 lbs. of armor, and radar above the pilots' seats. Seventy-five went to the AAF as OA-10Bs, 21 were sent to Russia and the rest remained with the Navy.

A total of 2182 Catalinas were built by Convair, in addition to 216 prewar PBYs and 676 by other firms. Comprising almost all of 1941s patrol plane deliveries and over three-quarters of 1942 deliveries, Catalinas carried the burden of most early wartime patrol work. They were adequate for negative search and for bombing submarines, but the Catalina was slow and sometimes allowed surfaced submarines to vanish beneath the sea before they could be reached. Sending PBYs into combat zones to seek positive information, however, proved very hazardous as demonstrated by the near annihilation of Patrol Wing 10 by Japanese fighters. Catalina feats included night torpedo attacks, dive-bombing, and often the first location of Japanese forces in decisive battles like Midway, but all these actions would have been less costly in American lives had a more agile and better-protected plane been available.

FOUR-ENGINED FLYING BOATS

During the Catalina's long service life, efforts were made to develop flying boats of greater speed and fire power. One approach was the use of four engines, as in the new Army bombers, and as early as June 29, 1935, Sikorsky contracted to build a big four-engined monoplane.

First flown on August 13, 1937, the Sikorsky XPBS-1 had R-1830-68 Wasps, fixed outboard floats, and a high single tail fin. Armament included a .50-caliber gun in a manual front turret, two .30-caliber guns at side-by-side waist hatches, and a hand-operated .50-caliber tail gun; the first on an American plane, although Sikorsky had put them on Czarist bombers over 20 years earlier.

Consolidated's XPB2Y-1, ordered July 27, 1936, was rather similar in layout, but had R-1830-72s and the retractable wingtip floats used on the PBY. As on the Sikorsky, there were complete accommodations

SIKORSKY XPBS-1

Pratt & Whitney XR-1830-68, 1050 hp take-off, 900 hp at 12,000′

DIMENSIONS: Span 124′, Lg. 76′ 2″, Ht. 27′ 7″, Wing Area 1670 sq. ft.

WEIGHT: Empty 26,407 lb., Gross 46,617 lb., Max. 48,541 lb. Fuel 1970–3600 gal.

PERFORMANCE: Speed—Top 227 mph at 12,000′, 203 mph at s. l., Landing 63 mph. Service Ceiling 23,100′, Climb 640′/1 min. Range 3170 miles/4000 lbs. bombs, 4545 miles max.

MFR

for the crew, and internal wing bays for up to 12,000 lbs. of bombs. Single .50-caliber guns were mounted in the bow turret and tail position, while .30-caliber guns were provided for the two waist hatches and a tunnel mount.

Although completed in December 1937, difficulties with the tail assembly and performance on the water delayed XPB2Y-1 delivery to the Navy until August 1938. The original vertical fin had proven too small, so after trying small auxiliary fins, the XPB2Y-1 was provided with a pair of oval vertical surfaces. The hull shape, however, never was quite as satisfactory as that of the PBY.

Despite their advanced performance, these giants did not win generous orders, for admirals looked askance at their high cost and complexity, and reflected that "A large plane over a given area of sea is not, necessarily, any more effective as an observation post than is a small plane . . . the small plane . . . may be at an advantage in that the facilities which made it and maintain it can make and maintain more units." With so much money already invested in the PBYs, the Navy bought no patrol bombers at all in 1938, and during the following year concentrated funds on twin-engined types that could be obtained in quantity.

Six Consolidated PB2Y-2s were ordered March 31, 1939, at a unit cost ($300,000) triple that of a PBY. Delivered from December 1940 to July 1941, they had a new hull, R-1830-78 Wasps with two-stage superchargers, and a crew of nine. Six .50-caliber guns were distributed among the nose turret, top blister, circular side windows, tunnel orifice, and tail post. A heavier

CONSOLIDATED XPB2Y-1

MFR

CONSOLIDATED XPB2Y-1 (with twin tails)
Pratt & Whitney XR-1830-72, 1050 hp take-off, 900 hp at 12,000′
DIMENSIONS: Span 115′, Lg. 79′ 3″, Ht. 27′ 4″, Wing Area 1780 sq. ft.
WEIGHT: Empty 26,847 lb., Gross 49,754 lb., Max. 52,994 lb. Fuel 2300–3500 gal.
PERFORMANCE: Speed—Top 230 mph at 12,000′, 206 mph at s. l., Landing 65 mph. Service Ceiling 22,000′, Climb 830′/1 min. Range 4390 miles normal, 3420 miles/4000 lbs. bombs, 4950 miles max.

MFR

CONSOLIDATED PB2Y-2
Pratt & Whitney R-1830-78, 1200 hp take-off, 1000 hp at 19,000′
DIMENSIONS: Span 115′, Lg. 79′, Ht. 27′ 6″, Wing Area 1780 sq. ft.
WEIGHT: Empty 34,315 lb., Gross 60,441 lb., Max. 63,700 lb. Fuel 4400 gal.
PERFORMANCE: Speed—Top 255 mph at 19,000′, 224 mph at s. l., Cruising 141 mph, Landing 71 mph. Service Ceiling 24,100′, Climb 830′/1 min. Range 3705 miles normal, 1330 miles/12,000 lbs. bombs, 4275 miles max.

USN

CONSOLIDATED PB2Y-3
Pratt & Whitney R-1830-88, 1200 hp take-off, 1000 hp at 19,500′
DIMENSIONS: Span 115′, Lg. 79′ 3″, Ht. 27′ 6″, Wing Area 1780 sq. ft.
WEIGHT: Empty 41,031 lb., Gross 68,000 lb. Fuel 1575–3500 gal.
PERFORMANCE: Speed—Top 224 mph at 19,500′, 199 mph at s. l., Cruising 140 mph, Landing 76 mph. Service Ceiling 20,900′, Climb 550′/1 min. Range 2310 miles/four 325 lb. depth charges, 1380 miles/8000 lbs. bombs, 3120 miles ferry.

MFR

CONSOLIDATED PB2Y-5
Pratt & Whitney R-1830-92, 1200 hp at s. l., 1050 hp at 7000′
DIMENSIONS: Span 115′, Lg. 79′ 5″, Ht. 27′ 6″, Wing Area 1780 sq. ft.
WEIGHT: Empty 41,180 lb., Gross 68,000 lb. Fuel 3017–3796 gal.
PERFORMANCE: Speed—Top 211 mph at 7000′, 198 mph at s. l., Cruising 154 mph, Landing 76 mph. Service Ceiling 13,100′, Climb 490′/1 min. Range 2570 miles/four 325 lb. depth charges, 1640 miles/8000 lbs. bombs.

MFR

production version was ordered November 19, 1940; the PB2Y-3 Coronado with R-1830-88s, self-sealing fuel tanks, 2000 lbs. of armor, eight .50-caliber guns, and 4840 rounds of ammunition. Power-operated bow, top and tail turrets had two guns each, and a single hand-held gun was at each side opening. Although 210 Coronados were completed between June 1942 and June 1944, they were superseded by Liberators, and 31 were converted to PB2Y-3R transports. One fitted with Wright R-2600 Cyclones became XPB2Y-4, and some using R-1830-92s with single stage superchargers became PB2Y-5s. Ten Coronados were used by Great Britain.

MARTIN MARINERS

During 1937, Martin engineers designed a new twin-engine patrol bomber and tested its air and sea behavior on a quarter-scale man-carrying flying model. An XPBM-1 prototype was ordered June 30, 1937, together with 20 PBM-1s on December 28. The XPBM-1 was completed in February 1939 with Wright R-2600-6 Cyclones mounted high on wings gulled to keep the three-bladed propellers clear of the water. Outboard floats retracted into the wings and twin rudders were perched behind the all-metal hull.

Twenty PBM-1s accepted between September 1940 and March 1941 could be distinguished from the prototype by the diehedral on the stabilizers. The crew of seven operated five .50-caliber and one .30-caliber gun mounted in a power-operated nose turret, a power top turret, circular waist fixtures and prone tail position. Two tons of bombs or depth charges could be carried within the engine nacelles. An XPBM-2 ordered the same day was to have fuel capacity increased from 2700 to 4815 gallons, but this project was canceled.

Contracts made November 1, 1940, and August 20, 1941, were to provide 379 PBM-3 and 180 PBM-4 Mariners, as the Martin boat was named, but wartime changes caused abandonment of these types' original form. First accepted in April 1942, the new Mariners had 1700 hp R-2600-12 Cyclones, and larger nonretractable floats. The first fifty were completed without armament as PBM-3R transports, and 272 PBM-3Cs began appearing in September with in-

MARTIN XPBM-1
Wright R-2600-6, 1600 hp take-off, 1275 hp at 12,000′
DIMENSIONS: Span 118′, Lg. 77′ 2″, Ht. 24′ 6″, Wing Area 1405 sq. ft.
WEIGHT: Empty 24,006 lb., Gross 40,814 lb. Fuel 2700 gal.
PERFORMANCE: Speed—Top 213 mph at 12,000′, Landing 64 mph. Service Ceiling 20,600′, Climb 840′/1 min. Range 3450 miles/1000 lbs. bombs.

USN

ternal protection, power-operated two-gun bow and top turrets, and hand-operated .50-caliber guns at waist openings and a tail position. They were followed by 201 PBM-3Ds, which had 1900 hp R-2600-22 Cyclones with four-bladed propellers, 1058 lbs. of armor, self-sealing tanks, and eight .50-caliber guns. Radar was installed in a large housing behind the pilots' cabin. First installed experimentally on a PBM in December 1941, surface search radar had become the means to catch surfaced submarines at night or in bad weather.

As antisubmarine warfare grew in importance, an ASW Mariner was developed which had longer range and omitted power turrets. Known as the PBM-3S, they had R-2600-22 Cyclones, two hand-held .50-

MARTIN PBM-1 [*Photo unavailable*]
Wright R-2600-6, 1600 hp take-off, 1275 hp at 12,000′
DIMENSIONS: As XPBM-1
WEIGHT: Empty 24,143 lb., Gross 41,139 lb. Fuel 2700 gal.
PERFORMANCE: Speed—Top 214 mph at 12,000′, 197 mph at s. l., Cruising 128 mph, Landing 65 mph. Service Ceiling 22,400′, Climb 640′/1 min. Range 3434 miles/1000 lbs. bombs, 2590 miles/4000 lbs. bombs.

MARTIN PBM-3C
Wright R-2600-12, 1700 hp take-off
DIMENSIONS: Span 118′, Lg. 80′, Ht. 27′ 6″, Wing Area 1408 sq. ft.
WEIGHT: Empty 32,378 lb., Gross 52,665 lb., Max. 58,000 lb. Fuel 1750–2536 gal.
PERFORMANCE: Speed—Top 198 mph at 13,000′. Service Ceiling 16,900′, Climb 410′/1 min. Range 2137 miles/eight 325 lb. depth charges, 3074 miles patrol.

USN

MARTIN PBM-3D
Wright R-2600-22, 1900 hp take-off, 1350 hp at 15,400′
DIMENSIONS: Span 118′, Lg. 79′ 10″, Ht. 27′ 6″, Wing Area 1408 sq. ft.
WEIGHT: Empty 32,848 lb., Gross 51,608 lb., Max. 58,000 lb. Fuel 1950–2744 gal.
PERFORMANCE: Speed—Top 202 mph at 15,900′, 192 mph at s. l., Cruising 135 mph, Landing 76 mph. Service Ceiling 20,800′, Climb 740′/1 min. Range 2260 miles normal, 2580 miles/four 325 lb. depth charges, 3000 miles max.

WL

MARTIN PBM-3S
Wright R-2600-12, 1700 hp take-off, 1350 hp at 13,000′
DIMENSIONS: Span 118′, Lg. 79′ 10″, Ht. 27′ 6″, Wing Area 1408 sq. ft.
WEIGHT: Empty 29,915 lb., Gross 51,860 lb., Max. 54,525 lb. Fuel 2350–3138 gal.
PERFORMANCE: Speed—Top 209 mph at 13,000′, 194 mph at s. l., Cruising 134 mph, Landing 76 mph. Service Ceiling 17,600′, Climb 550′/1 min. Range 2725 miles/four 650 lb. bombs, 3530 miles max., 3130 miles/four 325 lb. depth charges.

MCNULTY

MARTIN PBM-5
Pratt & Whitney R-2800-34, 2100 hp take-off, 1700 hp at 9400′
DIMENSIONS: Span 118′, Lg. 79′ 10″, Ht. 27′ 6″, Wing Area 1408 sq. ft.
WEIGHT: Empty 32,803 lb., Gross 56,000 lb., Max. 60,000 lb. Fuel 2671 gal.
PERFORMANCE: Speed—Top 215 mph at 19,200′, 198 mph at s. l., Cruising 115 mph, Landing 82 mph. Service Ceiling 20,200′, Climb 588′/1 min. Range 2700 miles/four 325 lb. depth charges, 2480 miles/4000 lbs. bombs.

caliber nose guns, another in the waist, a fourth in the tail, and only 261 lbs. of armor. Beginning March 1944, 156 PBM-3S Mariners were delivered. Several PBM-3D and PBM-3S Mariners were lend-leased to Britain.

Two XPBM-5s introduced, in May 1943, 2100 hp Pratt & Whitney R-2800-34 Wasps. This engine was used on 589 PBM-5s first ordered January 3, 1944, and delivered from August 1944 to war's end with eight .50-caliber guns, 1067 lbs. of armor, and APS-15 radar.

Mariner production was halted with cancellation of 460 PBM-5s, but an amphibious version for rescue work was built with retractable tricycle landing gear and new radar. Thirty-six PBM-5As were finished by April 1949.

Better protected than the Catalinas, the 1290 Mariners built during the war gave excellent service and many remained in use by the postwar Navy until the end of the Korean War. A more advanced development, the P5M Marlin, is discussed in a later chapter.

OUTSIZED PB'S

Two wartime flying boats of unusual size remain to be mentioned. Largest of all patrol planes was the Martin XPB2M-1 Mars, ordered August 23, 1938, and powered by four 2200 hp Wright R-3350-18s. The size of the aircraft inspired publicity men to arrange formal ceremonies at the launching on November 5, 1941, but an accidental fire delayed the first flight to July 3, 1942.

The spacious hull contained two decks and all the room the eleven-man crew needed; we are told that there was a shower and two mess rooms—one for officers, and one for men! The Mars had been designed too early to include internal protection and other combat features, but power turrets were placed in the bow and behind the twin rudders. Later, they were removed and the Mars was used for transport work.

MARTIN XPB2M-1 (photo shows transport remodel)
Wright R-3350-18, 2200 hp take-off, 2000 hp at 4000′
DIMENSIONS: Span 200′ Lg. 117′ 3″, Ht. 38′ 5″, Wing Area 3683 sq. ft.
WEIGHT: Empty 75,573 lb., Gross 144,000 lb. Fuel 10,410 gal.
PERFORMANCE: Speed—Top 221 mph at 4500′, Landing 83.5 mph. Service Ceiling 14,600′, Climb 440′/1 min. Range 4945 miles max.

USN

MFR

BOEING XPBB-1
Wright R-3350-8, 2300 hp take-off, 1800 hp at 13,600′
DIMENSIONS: Span 139′ 8″, Lg. 94′ 9″, Ht. 34′ 2″, Wing Area 1826 sq. ft.
WEIGHT: Empty 41,531 lb., Gross 62,000 lb., Max. 101,130 lb. Fuel 2490–6890 gal.
PERFORMANCE: Speed—Top 228 mph at 14,200′, 214 mph at s. l., Cruising 127 mph. Service Ceiling 22,400′, Climb 980′/ 1 min. Range 2320 miles/1000 lbs. bombs, 6300 miles max.

Production of this big patrol type was not begun apparently because of the modifications required to bring it to combat standards, and because the productive effort required could supply a much larger number of Mariners. Twenty cargo versions (JRM) with a new hull and single tail were ordered in January 1945, but only five were completed.

Consolidated designed a flying boat almost as large, the XPB3Y-1 ordered April 2, 1942. This design was to have four Pratt & Whitney R-2800-18s, 169 ft. wing span, 121,500 lb. gross weight, two 20-mm. and ten .50-caliber guns, and carry ten tons of bombs at a top speed of 241 mph at 22,500 ft.; but on November 4 the project was canceled to expedite production of standard types.

The largest twin-engined flying boat was the Boeing XPBB-1 Sea Ranger, ordered June 29, 1940, and first flown July 5, 1942. Powered by two R-3350-8 Cyclones, it had the wing later used on B-29s, large fixed floats, a high single rudder and a crew of ten. Eight .50-caliber guns were provided in two-gun power-operated bow, top, and tail turrets, and a tear-shaped blister on each side with one .50-caliber gun. Up to 20,000 lbs. of bombs or 6890 gallons of fuel could be carried. Five hundred were to be built in the new Boeing plant at Renton, Washington, but this program was dropped so the plant and engines could be used for the B-29, leaving the prototype the Lone Ranger.

BORROWED BOMBERS

The Navy's exclusive reliance on flying boats for patrol missions was rooted in national policy giving naval aircraft responsibility for fleet support and overseas scouting, and Army aircraft responsibility for coastal defense, and co-operation with land forces. Land-based aircraft were employed by the Army, and the Navy was limited to water-based and ship-based aircraft. This had the unfortunate result that the superior performance of land planes for long-distance reconnaissance was not utilized by the Navy.

Acquisition of bases in Iceland and Newfoundland for the Neutrality Patrol, however, created a requirement for patrol craft capable of land take-offs, for water-based operations in these areas were subject to interference from winter ice conditions. This requirement was met eventually by procurement of amphibian Catalinas, but in the meantime the Lockheed Hudson being built for the R.A.F.'s Coastal Command was an available and proven antisubmarine patrol type. The long-standing flying boat tradition was broken by 20 Hudsons requisitioned in October 1941 by the Navy and labeled PBO-1. Powered by two R-1820-40 Cyclones, they were similar to the A-29s described in a previous chapter, and were armed with four 325-lb. depth charges, two fixed and three flexible .30-caliber guns.

Unlike Catalinas, they were fast enough to catch surface submarines before they crash-dived, so against competition of four flying boat squadrons and many surface ships, PBO-1s of squadron VP-82 at Argentia, Newfoundland, sank on March 1 and March 15, 1942, the first two U-boats killed by American forces.

Early in the war, as flying boats suffered grievous losses at the hands of the Zero, disadvantages of the big boats as patrol bombers became painfully apparent. Since the hull's performance handicap was all too often proving fatal, a feeling arose that ability to land on water might not be an essential requirement for patrol planes. The theory that the flying boats' blind spot due to the hull could be covered by flying close to the water seldom worked out; a forced dive to low altitude was often too late, or was more damaging than gunfire, while enemy fighters firing at long range could correct their aim by using the water splashes of their bullets.

Seldom did the flying boats' much vaunted ability to operate without prepared landing fields have great importance in the war. Instead, it was apparent that land planes could be better armed and have higher speed, enabling them to attack and escape more quickly. The Navy was now eager to acquire land-based patrol planes and requested in February 1942 a reallocation of bomber production, especially of the long-range B-24 Liberators already being used by the British for patrol work. The Army wanted every bomber it could get, so it took much negotiation before Chief of Staff George C. Marshall agreed to a Navy share on July 7, 1942.

Consolidated B-24Ds were scheduled for Navy use on July 11, 1942, redesignated PB4Y-1, and began to arrive in August. Based on Iceland, these Liberators sank their first German sub on November 5. Liberator deliveries began slowly, but gathered volume and were joined in 1943 by the entire Lockheed Ventura production, so that the majority of Navy patrol planes during the latter part of the war were land planes. Most of 1174 PB4Y-1 Liberators assigned the Navy had front turrets like later B-24s, but Erco power turrets were used, and radar replaced the belly ball-turret. Eight .50-caliber guns, with 3770 rounds, 1318 lbs. of armor, 2110 lbs. of fuel tank protection, and up to 8000 lbs. of bombs were carried.

It is notable that the patrol bomber appellation was replaced by a simple patrol label on Lockheed PV-1 Venturas, denoting overwater patrol rather than medium bombing. A good short-range supplement to long-range Liberators, the Ventura was allocated to the Navy July 24, 1942, and 1600 PV-1s were de-

USN

LOCKHEED PBO-1 HUDSON

Wright R-1820-40, 1200 hp take-off, 900 hp at 14,000′

DIMENSIONS: Span 65′ 6″, Lg. 44′ 4″, Ht. 16′ 10″, Wing Area 551 sq. ft.

WEIGHT: Empty 12,680 lb., Gross 18,837 lb., Max. 20,203 lb. Fuel 644 gal.

PERFORMANCE: Speed—Top 262 mph at 15,300′, 237 mph at s. l., Cruising 129 mph. Service Ceiling 26,200′, Climb 1450′/1 min. Range 1750 miles/four 325 lb. depth charges, 1890 miles max.

LOCKHEED-VEGA PV-1

Pratt & Whitney R-2800-31, 2000 hp take-off, 1600 hp at 11,900′

DIMENSIONS: Span 65′ 6″, Lg. 51′ 9″, Ht. 13′ 2″, Wing Area 551 sq. ft.

WEIGHT: Empty 20,197 lb., Gross 26,500 lb., Max. 31,077 lb. Fuel 981–1771 gal.

PERFORMANCE: Speed—Top 312 mph at 13,800′, 296 mph at s. l., Cruising 164 mph, Landing 91 mph. Service Ceiling 26,300′, Climb 2230′/1 min. Range 1660 miles/six 325 lb. depth charges, 1360 miles/torpedo.

MFR

livered from December 1942 to May 1944, including 388 lend-leased to the R.A.F. as Ventura G.R.V. The first Venturas actually accepted by the Navy were 27 PV-3s (AAF B-34) requisitioned from the British Ventura II contract in September 1942, but the Navy's PV-1s were specially equipped for patrol missions. Powered by two Pratt & Whitney R-2800-31s, they carried two .50-caliber fixed guns in the nose, two in a top power turret, and two .30-caliber guns in a ventral mount near the twin tails. Six 325-lb. depth charges or 500-lb. bombs, or a single torpedo could be carried in the fuselage, and a pair of drop tanks might be added below the wings. In March 1943, a three-place night-fighter version used by Marines on Bougainville in the Solomon Islands had Mark IV radar and six .50-caliber guns fixed in the nose.

On June 30, 1943, five hundred Lockheed PV-2 Harpoons were ordered. A larger and longer range development of the PV-1, the Harpoon had greater span, larger fins, 714 lbs. of armor, five .50-caliber fixed nose guns, and two in the power turret. Deliveries began in March 1944. On October 16, 1944, 100 PV-2Ds were ordered with eight .50-caliber nose guns, but only 35 were completed, because of postwar cancellations.

Five hundred North American Mitchells allotted to the Navy on January 14, 1943, were designated PBJ-1, although they actually were used by the Marine Corps for medium bombing rather than patrol missions. They retained their Army modification letters; PBJ-1H for

MFR

CONSOLIDATED PB4Y-1

Pratt & Whitney R-1830-65, 1200 hp at 25,000′

DIMENSIONS: Span 110′, Lg. 67′ 3″, Ht. 17′ 11″, Wing Area 1048 sq. ft.

WEIGHT: Empty 37,160 lb., Gross 60,000 lb., Max. 63,000 lb. Fuel 2814–3614 gal.

PERFORMANCE: Speed—Top 287 mph at 26,700′, 231 mph at s. l., Cruising 149 mph, Landing 95 mph. Service Ceiling 32,600′, Climb 990′/1 min. Range 2065 miles/8000 lbs. bombs, 3090 miles patrol.

LOCKHEED-VEGA PV-2

Pratt & Whitney R-2800-31, 2000 hp take-off, 1600 hp at 11,900′

DIMENSIONS: Span 75′, Lg. 52′ 1″, Ht. 13′ 3″, Wing Area 686 sq. ft.

WEIGHT: Empty 21,028 lb., Gross 33,668 lb., Max. 36,000 lb. Fuel 1149–1863 gal.

PERFORMANCE: Speed—Top 282 mph at 13,700′, 271 mph at s. l., Cruising 171 mph, Landing 83 mph. Service Ceiling 23,900′, Climb 1630′/1 min. Range 1790 miles/six 325 lb. depth charges, 2930 miles ferry.

MFR

248 B-25H and PBJ-1J for 252 B-25J. Since they were identical to Army Mitchells, the reader is referred to the B-25 description in Chapter 3. Later assignments added 206 more PBJ-1Js to Navy allocations.

Meanwhile, experience with Liberators indicated that a superior patrol plane could be obtained by redesigning the Consolidated ships especially for naval tasks, and in May 1943 three XPB4Y-2 prototypes were ordered converted from PB4Y-1s. The wings and tricycle landing gear were those of the B-24, but more fuel, guns, and radar were added, the fuselage lengthened, and a high single tail replaced the earlier twin rudders. Since patrol planes work at low altitudes, the turbo-superchargers were omitted, giving the Privateer a higher sea-level speed, at a cost in high-altitude performance.

The first XPB4Y-2 Privateer was flown September 20, 1943, and on October 15 a contract for 660 PB4Y-2s was made. Delivery began in March 1944, and 710 more Privateers were ordered on October 19. Cancellations, however, ended PB4Y-2 production in October 1945 after 740 were completed.

Using four R-1830-94 Wasps, the Privateer was operated by a crew of eleven, including two electronics operators for the war's most elaborate airborne radar. Twelve .50-caliber guns were disposed in six power turrets: Convair nose and tail, two Martin top domes, and tear-shaped Erco side blisters. Up to 8000 lbs. of bombs and 1171 lbs. of armor were carried in the fuselage. One squadron had special PB4Y-2Bs with a Bat antishipping missile below each wing; they were glide bombs with a 12 ft. wing, 1000-lb. warhead, and radar homing.

Landplanes like these reduced flying boats to a minority of the patrol force. On December 31, 1941, the Navy had 466 patrol bombers, including 423 Catalina and 20 Mariner twin-engined flying boats, five four-engined boats, and only 18 twin-engined landplanes. Of 4054 Navy patrol planes on hand as of June 30, 1945, there were 1629 twin-engined and 55 four-engined flying boats, and 1374 twin-engined and 996 four-engined landplanes.

PMB

NORTH AMERICAN PBJ-1J
Wright R-2600-13, -29, 1700 hp take-off, 1450 hp at 12,000′
DIMENSIONS: Span 67′ 7″, Lg. 53′ 7½″, Ht. 16′ 4″, Wing Area 610 sq. ft.
WEIGHT: Empty 20,273 lb., Gross 32,516 lb., Max. 34,846 lb. Fuel 974–1524 gal.
PERFORMANCE: Speed—Top 278 mph at 12,700′, 264 mph at s. l., Cruising 159 mph, Landing 112 mph. Service Ceiling 24,300′, Climb 1180′/1 min. Range 2010 miles patrol/1189 gal., 1940 miles/1200 lbs. bombs, 1520 miles/4000 lbs. bombs.

CONSOLIDATED PB4Y-2
Pratt & Whitney R-1830-94, 1350 hp
DIMENSIONS: Span 110′, Lg. 74′ 7″, Ht. 29′ 2″, Wing Area 1048 sq. ft.
WEIGHT: Empty 37,405 lb., Gross 64,000 lb. Fuel 2364–3964 gal.
PERFORMANCE: Speed—Top 247 mph at 14,000′, 238 mph at s. l., Cruising 158 mph, Landing 96 mph. Service Ceiling 19,500′, Climb 990′/1 min. Range 2630 miles/4000 lbs. bombs, 2900 miles patrol.

MFR

Chapter 22: Postwar Patrol Planes 1945-59

THE NEPTUNE

By war's end, patrol plane performance had greatly advanced beyond prewar standards, mainly by the substitution of landplanes for flying boats. These landplanes, however, were basically adaptations of Army bombers, and not until 1945 did a landplane designed from its inception as a patrol type become available.

Developed for the primary mission of antisubmarine and antisurface vessel patrol work, the Lockheed Model 26 Neptune was a twin-engined high-wing monoplane with tricycle landing gear and a high single fin. Secondary missions were rocket and night torpedo attack, mine laying, bombing, and reconnaissance, although these capabilities were limited to those available after providing the best possible facilities for the primary mission. Long range, ability to operate from small fields, and high speed were listed as the desired characteristics.

Two XP2V-1 and 15 P2V-1s were ordered on April 4, 1944, and 151 more Neptunes added on December 16. The prototype was flown on May 17, 1945, with 2300 hp Wright R-3350-8 Cyclones, and the P2V-1s with R-3350-8As began to appear in December 1945. Their crew of seven operated radar and six .50-caliber guns with 466 rounds each: two in a hand-operated bow emplacement, two in the rear deck power turret, and two for the tail gunner.

The Neptune's bomb bay could accommodate twelve 325-lb. depth charges, or two 2000-lb. torpedoes for night attacks, or as much as four tons for short-distance horizontal bombing, or 1000 gallons of additional fuel. For rocket attack, sixteen 5 in. or four 11.75 in. rockets could be carried on underwing studs. The third P2V-1 was specially modified by stripping off all armament, building a new streamlined nose, and adding fuel tanks in the fuselage and on the wingtips. On September 29, 1946, it took off from Australia with 8396 gallons of gasoline and 85,500 lbs. of gross weight. When the *Truculent Turtle* landed in Ohio, 55 hours later, it had established a world's nonstop, nonrefueling flight record of 11,236 miles (great circle distance).

The *Truculent Turtle*'s longer nose was incorporated into P2V-2 production models appearing in 1947. Nose armament consisted of six 20-mm. fixed guns, and additional speed was endowed by R-3350-24W engines of 2800 hp with water injection. Other additions were de-icers, and Sonobuoy launchers for underwater submarine detection. These were buoys dropped in a pattern to send out a sonar signal that rebounds from a submarine hull and is automatically transmitted by the buoy to the search plane. Several must be dropped if the submarine's area is to be enclosed and the vessel's position determined.

The original P2V-2 order had been for 151 planes, but V-J Day cancellation of 100 and the later addition of 30 brought the final total to 81. Later P2V-2s had a new tail turret with a pair of 20-mm. guns. These were standard on the P2V-3, which appeared in April 1948 with 3200 hp R-3350-26 Cyclones and four-bladed propellers. Two of 53 ordered were converted to armored special transports (P2V-3Z), and two others became P2V-3Cs modified for carrier take-off. On March 7, 1949, a P2V-3C took off from the aircraft carrier *Coral Sea*, weighing 74,000 lbs. including a 10,000-lb. dummy simulating an atomic weapon, flew 2000 miles to a target, and 2000 more to its landing. An early warning Neptune was the P2V-3W, thirty of which were built with a bulging APS-20 radar in the forward bomb bay operated by two radar men who sat with the bomber-navigator and radio operator in the cabin between the pilots and the deck turret.

In 1950, the P2V-4 model had increased fuel capacity, some of it in wingtip tanks, new radar, and after some delay, Wright R-3350-30W Compound Cyclones of 3250 hp. Fifty-two were built.

USN

LOCKHEED XP2V-1
Wright R-3350-8, 2300 hp take-off, 1900 hp at 14,000′
DIMENSIONS: Span 100′, Lg. 75′ 4″, Ht. 28′ 6″, Wing Area 1000 sq. ft.
WEIGHT: Empty 32,651 lb., Gross 54,527 lb., Max. 58,000 lb. Fuel 2350–3350 gal.
PERFORMANCE: Speed—Top 289 mph at 15,600′, 231 mph at s. l., Cruising 163 mph, Landing 93 mph. Service Ceiling 23,200′, Climb 1120′/1 min. Range 2879 miles/eight 325 lb. depth charges, 4210 miles max.

The next model was P2V-5, appearing in April 1951 with fixed guns removed and an Emerson ball turret with two 20-mm. guns in the nose, providing a lookout and bombing station. A searchlight in the nose of the starboard tip tank was controlled by movement of the bow turret, which had been first tested in 1948. The crew of nine included pilots under a raised canopy, radarmen, gunners, navigator, and radioman. Originally, 45 had been ordered by the Navy, and 12 for Australia, but orders were greatly increased during the Korean War, and Britain, France, and the Netherlands also received some of these Neptunes. Many had tail turrets replaced by an elongated housing for "MAD"—magnetic airborne detector. A longer nose,

LOCKHEED P2V-3 (P2V-3W in photo)
Wright R-3350-26W, 3200 hp WE
DIMENSIONS: As P2V-2
WEIGHT: Empty 34,875 lb., Gross 50,062 lb., Max. 64,100 lb. Fuel 2350–3350 gal.
PERFORMANCE: Speed—Top 338 mph at 13,000′, Cruising 180 mph, Landing 77 mph. Service Ceiling 28,000′, Climb 1060′/1 min. Range 3935 miles.

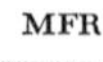

MFR

PMB

LOCKHEED P2V-1
Wright R-3350-8A, 2300 hp
DIMENSIONS: As XP2V-1
WEIGHT: Empty 33,720 lb., Gross 60,731 lb., Max. 61,153 lb. Fuel 2350–3350 gal.
PERFORMANCE: (At 47,115 lbs., combat weight) Speed—Top 303 mph at 15,300′, Cruising 176 mph. Service Ceiling 27,000′. Range 4130 miles max.

PMB

LOCKHEED P2V-2
Wright R-3350-24W, 2100 hp normal, 2800 hp WE
DIMENSIONS: Span 100′, Lg. 77′ 10″, Ht. 28′ 1″, Wing Area 1000 sq. ft.
WEIGHT: Empty 33,962 lb., Max. 63,078 lb. Fuel 2350–3350 gal.
PERFORMANCE: (At 49,040 lbs., combat weight) Speed—Top 320 mph at 13,500′, Cruising 178 mph, Landing 77 mph. Service Ceiling 26,000′, Climb 810′/1 min. Range 3985 miles.

LOCKHEED P2V-4
Wright R-3350-30W, 2650 hp normal, 3250 hp WE
DIMENSIONS: As P2V-2
WEIGHT: Empty 42,021 lb., Gross 67,500 lb., Max. 74,129 lb. Fuel 4210 gal.
PERFORMANCE: Speed—Top 352 mph at 9500′, 312 mph at s l., Landing 109 mph. Service Ceiling 31,000′. Range 4200 miles.

MFR

MFR

LOCKHEED P2V-5
Wright R-3350-30W, 3250 hp WE
DIMENSIONS: Span 102′, Lg. 81′ 7″, Ht. 28′ 1″, Wing Area 1000 sq. ft.
WEIGHT: Empty 41,754 lb., Max. 76,152 lb. Fuel 4700 gal.
PERFORMANCE: Speed—Top 341 mph. Service Ceiling 29,000′. Range 4750 miles.

new radar, mine-laying gear, and wing launchers for guided missiles was provided on the P2V-6, which also had R-3350-30W Cyclones and was first flown on October 16, 1952.

Lockheed's Neptune was successful in nearly monopolizing patrol plane procurement in the years immediately following the war. Only Martin was successful in winning any other contracts at all. In September

PMB

LOCKHEED P2V-6
Wright R-3350-30W, 3250 hp WE
DIMENSIONS: Span 102′, Lg. 82′ 7″, Ht. 28′ 1″, Wing Area 1000 sq. ft.
WEIGHT: Empty 42,818 lb., Max. 78,020 lb. Fuel 4700 gal.
PERFORMANCE: Classified

LOCKHEED P2V-7
Wright R-3350-32W, 3500 hp WE, and Westinghouse J34-WE-34, 3400 lbs.
DIMENSIONS: Span 103′ 10″, Lg. 91′ 4″, Ht. 29′ 4″, Wing Area 1000 sq. ft.
WEIGHT: Empty 47,456 lb., Gross 75,500 lb.
PERFORMANCE: Speed—Top 356 mph (all engines), 305 mph (piston only). Service Ceiling 22,000′. Range 3700 miles.

MFR

WL

MARTIN XP4M-1

Pratt & Whitney R-4360-4, 2975 hp take-off, 2400 hp at 16,200′, and Allison J33-A-17, 3825 lbs.

DIMENSIONS: Span 114′, Lg. 82′ 7″, Ht. 26′ 1″, Wing Area 1300 sq. ft.

WEIGHT: Empty 45,739 lb., Gross 77,729 lb., Max. 79,657 lb. Fuel 2800–4200 gal.

PERFORMANCE: Speed—Top (4 engines) 395 mph at 19,100′, 363 mph at s. l., (prop.) 289 mph at 17,800′, 273 mph at s. l., Cruising 170 mph, Landing 99 mph. Service Ceiling 32,800′, Climb 2380′/1 min. Range 4230 miles max., 3167 miles/two torpedos.

USN

MARTIN P4M-1

Pratt & Whitney R-4360-20, 2250 hp take-off, 2500 hp at 16,800′, and Allison J33-A-23, 4600 lbs.

DIMENSIONS: Span 114′, Lg. 84′, Ht. 26′ 1″, Wing Area 1300 sq. ft.

WEIGHT: Empty 48,536 lb., Gross 81,463 lb., Max. 83,378 lb. Fuel 2800–4200 gal.

PERFORMANCE: Speed—Top (4 engines) 415 mph at 20,100′, 379 mph at s. l., (prop.) 296 mph at 18,700′, 282 mph at s. l., Cruising 168 mph, Landing 88 mph. Service Ceiling 34,600′, Climb 2730′/1 min. Range 3800 miles max., 2840 miles/two torpedos.

1946, the Baltimore builder offered the XP4M-1 Mercator, which looked like an enlarged Neptune at first glance, but concealed behind each of the two Pratt & Whitney R-4360-4 Wasp Major was a J33-4 jet of 4000-lb. thrust. The Wasps were used for cruising, but for short dashes to catch a surfaced sub or escape an attacker, the jets were added. Top speed rose from 289 mph with propellers, to 395 with both propellers and jets.

Armament of the ten-place Mercator included six tons of bombs, depth charges, or mines, pairs of .50-caliber guns in nose and rear deck power turrets, a single .50-caliber gun on each side, and a pair of 20-mm. guns in the tail turret. Two prototypes were followed after July 1949, by 19 P4M-1 production models with R-4360-20 and J33-A-23 engines, and 20-mm. guns in the bow turret.

No more Mercators were bought, but the idea of jet boosting returned; in 1953 a Lockheed P2V-5 was fitted with a 3400-lb. thrust Westinghouse J-34 jet under each wing, and this modification was adopted for the P2V-7 and reportedly raised the top speed from 344 to 421 mph. Other features of this 1954 Neptune were a new nose enclosure omitting guns now considered unnecessary for ASW, and MAD stinger tail.

An unarmed variation on the patrol plane theme was the radar picket, intended as an airborne electronics sentry extending the reach of radar far beyond the limitations of surface stations. Twenty-three Boeing B-17Gs obtained from the AAF after the war were stripped down and fitted with extra fuel tanks and a large radar in the bomb bay, and designated PB-1W. Four similar conversions of B-29s were labeled P2B-

MARTIN XP5M-1

Wright R-3350-26, 2700 hp

DIMENSIONS: Span 118′, Lg. 88′, Ht. 37′ 11″, Wing Area 1406 sq. ft.

WEIGHT: Empty 39,000 lb., Gross 60,000 lb. Fuel 1330–2763 gal.

PERFORMANCE: Speed—Top 249 mph at 15,700′, 234 mph at s. l., Cruising 140 mph, Landing 76 mph. Service Ceiling 24,000′. Range 1036 miles/four 325 lb. depth charges, 1360 miles/1330 gal.

USN

MARTIN P5M-1
Wright R-3350-30W, 3250 hp WE
DIMENSIONS: Span 118′, Lg. 90′ 8″, Ht. 37′ 3″, Wing Area 1406 sq. ft.
WEIGHT: Empty 36,800 lb., Gross 72,837 lb. Fuel 2815 gal.
PERFORMANCE: Speed—Top 262 mph. Service Ceiling 22,400′. Range 3600 miles.

MFR

1S. The same idea was applied to a converted Lockheed Constellation transport which appeared in June 1949 with large radomes protruding from the nose, top, and belly; wingtip tanks, and a PO-1W designation. A crew of 31 included radarmen facing the consoles of six tons of electronics, at an altitude eliminating the line-of-sight limitation of surface radar. Although unattractive in appearance, this type has gone into service as the Air Force RC-121C and Navy WV-2, and will be used for radar picket, radar ferret, and combat communications center. These are not combat types, but are essentially all-weather long-range descendants of the traditional observation type.

FLYING BOATS AGAIN?

The flying boat had been eclipsed by the landplane for several years; water-based aircraft seemed to offer little to a nation that controlled land bases all over the world. During the five years after the war, the only armed hull types accepted for service were the 36 PBM-5A amphibians built for rescue work. Before the Korean War in 1950, the Navy's patrol force consisted of eight squadrons of Neptune and six of Privateer landplanes, and six with PBM-5 flying boats. Of the Reserve Air Wings, eleven used Harpoons and nine amphibian Catalinas.

The flying boat, however, got a new lease on life by development of new hulls featuring a high ratio of

MARTIN P5M-2
Wright R-3350-32W, 3400 hp
DIMENSIONS: Span 118′ 2″, Lg. 101′ 1″, Ht. 32′ 8″, Wing Area 1406 sq. ft.
WEIGHT: Empty 49,480 lb., Gross 74,442 lb., Max. 85,000 lb. Fuel 2850–3635 gal.
PERFORMANCE: Speed—Top 250 mph, Landing 90 mph. Service Ceiling 24,000′, Climb 1200′/1 min.

MFR

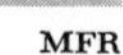

MFR

CONVAIR XP5Y-1
Allison XT-40-A-4, 5100 hp and 830 lbs.
DIMENSIONS: Span 146′ 10″, Lg. 127′ 11″, Ht. 46′ 2″, Wing Area 2102 sq. ft.
WEIGHT: Empty 71,824 lb., Gross 123,500 lb., Max. 140,374 lb. Fuel 6768–8762 gal.
PERFORMANCE: Speed—Top 388 mph at 30,000′, 372 mph at s. l., Cruising 225 mph, Landing 99 mph. Service Ceiling 39,700′, Climb 3310′/1 min. Range 2785 miles/eight 325 lb. depth charges, 3450 miles max.

length to beam and greater streamlining. These reduced the performance differential between water- and land-based craft, and renewed interest in the virtues of water landing—added safety and a less destructible base. First to demonstrate the new look in hulls was Martin's XP5M-1, begun July 1946 with a preliminary design study. Basic engineering was completed by September 1947, and on May 13, 1948, the XP5M-1 made its first flight, powered by two 2700 hp Wright R-3350-26 Cyclones. Although utilizing wings intended for the last aircraft on wartime PBM-5 contracts, the XP5M-1 introduced the new longer, narrower hull with a single step and planing bottom all the way back to a high single tail. Hydroflaps were provided for quick turns on the water, radar was placed above the flight deck, and gun turrets were mounted at the nose, rear deck, and tail.

The new hull proved successful and a small contract made December 1949 was increased to 25 P5M-1 Marlins in July 1950. First flown June 22, 1951, the P5M-1 had two 3200 hp R-3350-30W Cyclones and new fixed wing floats. Its antisubmarine warfare mission required 2500 lbs. of radar whose scanner formed a bulbous nose, and depth charges or bombs carried in the engine nacelles. Defense armament was limited to two 20-mm. guns in a power-operated tail turret.

A new T-tail, with the horizontal control surface atop the vertical fin, was introduced on P5M-2s, first flown in production form April 29, 1954. Other differ-

MARTIN XP6M-1
Allison J71-A-4, 9700 lbs. (13,000 lbs. AB)
DIMENSIONS: Span 100′, Lg. 134′, Ht. 31′, Wing Area 1900 sq. ft.
WEIGHT & PERFORMANCE: Classified

MFR

ences included a modified bow, 3400 hp R-3350-32Ws, a searchlight under the starboard wingtip, and magnetic detection gear high on the tail.

Further advance in flying boat design faced the problem of utilizing gas turbine propulsion, whose tremendous fuel consumption made difficult any adaptation to patrol type requirements. Convair's XP5Y-1 had four Allison T-40-A-4 turbines yielding 5100 hp to six-bladed contrarotating propellers, and 830-lb. residual exhaust thrust. The hull was long, narrow, and streamlined, but wingtip floats were fixed; retractable floats like the PBYs were inappropriate to the thin low-drag wing.

The first of two XP5Y-1 prototypes flew April 18, 1950. A radar scanner was in the nose, armor protected flight deck, nacelles, and turrets, 8000 lbs. of bombs could be carried, and five pairs of 20-mm. guns were mounted in remotely controlled turrets. Four turrets were on the hull's sides: two ahead of the cockpit, and two behind the wings, while a tail turret was located behind the single rudder. Although the original XP5Y-1 was destroyed July 1953 by a crash, eleven R3Y transport versions were built.

In October 1952, Convair entered a Navy design competition for a jet-propelled mine-laying seaplane, but their design was bested by the Martin Seamaster designed for the same purpose. Flown on July 14, 1955, the XP6M-1 has a long narrow hull, high T-tail, and swept wing with plastic floats at the tips for balance in the water. Four 10,000-lb. thrust Allison J71 turbojets are paired in nacelles atop the wings, a radar scanner is installed in the nose, and 20-mm. guns are mounted in a remote-controlled tail turret. A watertight rotary door in the hull carries mines, a camera pod, or other weapons, and can be loaded at sea through a hatch in the hull's roof. Pressurized compartments are provided for the crew of five, including pilot, co-pilot, navigator-mine layer, radio operator, and gunner.

Both XP6M-1 prototypes were destroyed in tests, but the similar YP6M-1 flown January 20, 1958 was followed by five sisterships. Next was the P6M-2, flown March 3, 1959 with 15,000-lb. thrust Pratt & Whitney J75-P-2s, but four were scarcely finished on a contract originally calling for 24 when the Navy suddenly terminated the Seamaster program in August. With the last of Martin's Model 275, the Navy halted American flying boat development, and Martin left the airplane business to concentrate on missiles.

Lockheed, however, has developed the four-engined P3V-1 landplane, an antisubmarine patrol version of the Electra transport. An operational prototype, flown November 25, 1959 had 4500 hp Allison T56-A-10W turboprops, radar nose, and magnetic detection gear in the tail. Until delivery of this type begins, the Navy has twenty squadrons of P2V Neptune landplanes, ten of P5M Marlin flying boats, and nine of WV Warning Star (ex-Constellation) radar-warning aircraft to perform the functions inherited from the old PBYs of World War II.

Chapter 23: Summary

Throughout the patrol plane's history, its primary function has been the destruction of enemy submarines. Hunting these elusive targets has advanced through stages set by development of the submarine itself. From the first U-boat sunk in 1917 by an H-12, to U-boats hit by the Navy Hudsons in 1942, airplanes sank submarines unlucky enough to be caught cruising on the surface. Gradually, submarines limited surface cruising to nighttime and remained underwater during the day, so airborne radar and searchlights had to be included in patrol plane equipment.

Development of the snorkel enabled subs to stay below the surface continuously, so radar had to be improved to be capable of detecting the snorkel exhaust peering out from the waves. The huge radome required by scanners of such discrimination gave aircraft the appearance of pregnant fish. But the final problem has been to attack submarines at their own depths through underwater detection devices and weapons.

Supplemented by carrier-based aircraft covering areas beyond their range, shore-based patrol planes search for the underwater enemy that seems to be today's only real threat to American control of the seas. This specialty has tended to displace surface search and attack, as foreign fleets have diminished in importance. Attacking enemy warships was always a costly business for wartime patrol types, and that mission is no longer required. Enemy fighter planes were a constant threat to patrol types, and led to heavy armor and multiple turrets. But if enemy aircraft are unlikely to be encountered on antisubmarine patrols, all that extra weight becomes unnecessary.

Even if patrol aircraft achieve greater ranges than now obtainable, it is unlikely that they can supersede carrier-based attack planes, for the endurance required for their primary mission will limit their speed and ability to fight enemy aircraft. The patrol plane's future will continue to depend on developments on and under the water, for its role today remains part of the Navy's historic mission of controlling the seas.

Part 6 Navy Attack Planes

Chapter 24: New Weapons for the Navy 1918–34

Aircraft bearing the Navy's "Attack" designation have replaced the battleship's heavy guns as the hammer of the fleet's fighting power. Whether attacking enemy vessels with torpedoes or dive-bombing, strafing with cannon and rockets, or striking hundreds of miles inland at surface targets, the carrier-based attack plane has a radius of action and striking speed never equalled by a naval weapon. The use of radar, and of atomic weapons adds further to its destructive capabilities. Attack planes have made more of a change in naval tactics and strategy than did the armored steamship when it replaced wooden sailing ships.

The weapon was not easily developed, however. It began with frail, short-range seaplanes designed to make torpedo attacks from shore bases. Then the torpedo plane was adapted to the aircraft carrier, making it a part of the fleet. Specialized scouting and dive-bombing types were also developed for the carriers, and shore-based types abandoned. After World War II substituted the carrier for the battleship as the principal arm of the fleet, scouting, bombing, and torpedo functions were successfully combined into a single attack type.

SHORE-BASED TORPEDO PLANES

At the outbreak of World War I, the Navy had no aircraft suitable for attacking either shipping or land targets. Rear Admiral Bradley A. Fiske had received a patent in July 1912 for a method of carrying and delivering a torpedo by air, but the first nation to actually use torpedo planes in warfare was Great Britain. In 1915, the British made attacks on Turkish vessels with two-place Short seaplanes handling a small torpedo between the floats. Germany began torpedo attacks on British shipping in April 1917.

In searching for a torpedo plane of its own, the United States Navy turned first to the Curtiss R-6, a two-seat, twin-float biplane. Thirty-six had been procured as trainers with 200 hp Curtiss engines, but in 1918 some (R-6-L) were fitted with a 360 hp Liberty and tested for torpedo attack. A 1036-lb. torpedo was carried between the floats, but there were no guns, and the seaplane was "not nearly rugged enough" for service conditions.

Another seaplane designed for the Navy during 1918 was the unusual Gallaudet D-4 biplane, which had a single large pontoon below the fuselage and small outboard floats near the tips of swept-back wings. The observer sat in the nose with a Lewis gun, followed by the pilot, and a 360 hp Liberty within the fuselage which turned four propeller blades on a ring around the fuselage. Wing racks could handle 390 lbs. of bombs, but there was no room for a torpedo. Excellent visibility for the observer was obtained from the novel design, even though the propeller's efficiency was badly compromised, and only two D-4s were made.

Neither of these planes saw action, but after the war the Navy continued its search for a shore-based aircraft capable of handling a torpedo, and ordered ten copies of a naval version of the Martin MB-1 Army bomber. First flown on January 31, 1920, the Martin TM-1 (MTB) was a biplane with two 400 hp Liberty engines, a front gunner, pilot, and rear gunner, and four Lewis guns. The wheeled landing gear was modified to make room for a 1618-lb. torpedo. This twin-engined landplane had a much better load and range than the single-engined seaplane, but even its folding wings did not make the Navy's first torpedo squadron suitable for shipboard use.

In 1922, Philadelphia's Naval Aircraft Factory built the PT-1 torpedo seaplane, a combination of an R-6 fuselage with HS wings and a 400 hp Liberty. Fifteen PT-1s were followed in 1923 by 18 modified PT-2s.

USN

CURTISS R-6-L (R-6 in photo)
Liberty 12, 360 hp (Curtiss, 200 hp)
DIMENSIONS: Span 57′ 1″, Lg. 33′ 5″, Ht. 14′ 2″, Wing Area 613 sq. ft.
WEIGHT: Empty 3513 lb., Gross 5662 lb. Fuel 112 gal.
PERFORMANCE: Speed—Top 104 mph at s. l., Landing 52.5 mph. Service Ceiling 9900′, Climb 5000′/12.3 min. Range 368 miles/1036 lb. torpedo.

MFR

MARTIN MTB (TM-1)
Liberty 12, 400 hp
DIMENSIONS: Span 71′ 5″, Lg. 46′ 6″, Ht. 15′, Wing Area 1080 sq. ft.
WEIGHT: Empty 7130 lb., Gross 12,078 lb. Fuel 282 gal.
PERFORMANCE: Speed—Top 105 mph, Landing 54 mph. Service Ceiling 8500′, Climb 4100′/10 min. Range 490 miles/1650 lb. torpedo.

During the summer of 1922 the Navy tested five prototypes competing for a torpedo-plane contract. Two were twin-engined three-place types venturing a low-wing monoplane layout new for that period. First flown in March 1921, the Curtiss CT-1 had two 350 hp Curtiss D-12 engines above twin floats. A short fuselage of wooden construction had pilot and navigator in tandem ahead of a rear gunner, while a biplane tail was suspended behind on tail booms. A 1446-lb. torpedo could be carried, but only one of nine CT-1s ordered was completed.

Somewhat better performance was offered by the Stout ST torpedo plane, which seems to be the first all-metal, low-wing monoplane offered the Navy. It had two 300 hp Packard V-1237 engines, twin rudders, rather clean design, and wheeled landing gear. Five had been purchased by the Navy, but the $162,000 prototype crashed after fourteen flights, and the contract was canceled.

Two foreign-built single-engine designs were also studied. Three twin-float, low, cantilever-wing Fokker FT-1 two-seaters were imported from Holland, and flown here with 400 hp Liberty engines. They were joined by a pair of Blackburn Swifts, biplanes with a 450 hp Napier Lion, wheels "releasable" in emergencies, flotation gear, and folding wings. An interesting point about this British torpedo plane is that it was a single-seater, the pilot sitting in a humped cockpit. The Navy continued, however, to feel for twenty more years that two or three men were needed to accomplish torpedo missions.

Winner of the 1922 competition was the solid, squared-off two-seater developed from the Cloudster, Donald Douglas' first airplane as an independent pro-

GALLAUDET D-4
Liberty 12, 360 hp
DIMENSIONS: Span 46′ 5″, Lg. 33′ 6″, Ht. 11′ 8″, Wing Area 620 sq. ft.
WEIGHT: Empty 4228 lb., Gross 5440 lb. Fuel 89 gal.
PERFORMANCE: Speed—Top 119 mph at s. l., Landing 58 mph. Service Ceiling 14,000′. Endurance 2.5 hrs. at top speed, 3.5 hrs. cruising.

USN

NAVY PT-1 SEAPLANE
Liberty 12, 400 hp
DIMENSIONS: Span 74′, Lg. 34′ 5″, Ht. 16′ 7″, Wing Area 808.5 sq. ft.
WEIGHT: Empty 4478 lb., Gross 6798 lb. Fuel 110 gal.
PERFORMANCE: Speed—Top 96 mph at s. l., Landing 49 mph. Service Ceiling 8800′, Climb 5000′/15.7 min. Endurance 2 hrs. at top speed, 3.5 hrs. cruising.

USN

USN

CURTISS CT-1
Curtiss D-12, 350 hp
DIMENSIONS: Span 65′, Lg. 52′, Ht. 15′ 5″, Wing Area 830 sq. ft.
WEIGHT: Empty 7684 lb., Gross 11,208 lb. Fuel 111 gal.
PERFORMANCE: Speed—Top 107 mph at s. l., Landing 58 mph. Service Ceiling 5200′, Climb 2600′/10 min. Range 350 miles.

NAVY PT-2 [*Photo unavailable*]
Liberty 12, 400 hp
DIMENSIONS: Span 73′ 11″, Lg. 36′ 4″, Ht. 16′ 6″, Wing Area 808.5 sq. ft.
WEIGHT: Empty 4231 lb., Gross 7075 lb. Fuel 112 gal.
PERFORMANCE: Speed—Top 96 mph at s. l. Service Ceiling 6100′, Climb 5000′/20.2 min. Range 286 miles at top speed, 334 miles cruising.

STOUT TORPEDO PLANE ST-1 [*Photo unavailable*]
Packard V-1237, 330 hp
DIMENSIONS: Span 60′, Lg. 37′, Ht. 14′, Wing Area 790 sq. ft.
WEIGHT: Empty 6557 lb., Gross 9817 lb. Fuel 195 gal.
PERFORMANCE: Speed—Top 110 mph, Landing 58 mph. Service Ceiling 10,000′. Range 385 miles at top speed.

DOUGLAS DT-1
Liberty, 400 hp
DIMENSIONS: Span 50′, Lg. 37′ 8″, Ht. 15′ 1″, Wing Area 707 sq. ft.
WEIGHT: Empty 4367 lb., Gross 6895 lb. Fuel 115 gal.
PERFORMANCE: Speed—Top 101 mph, Landing 45 mph. Service Ceiling 8700′, Climb 5000′/15.6 min. Range 232 miles at top speed.

USN

ARC

FOKKER FT-1
Liberty, 400 hp
DIMENSIONS: Span 69′ 8″, Lg. 46′, Wing Area 850 sq. ft.
WEIGHT: Empty 5685 lb., Gross 8620 lb. Fuel 108 gal.
PERFORMANCE: Not available.

ducer. Three ordered by the Navy in 1921 had originally been called DT-1, with radiators at the sides of a single 420 hp Liberty, but they became DT-2s, with the radiator moved to the nose. An 1835-lb. torpedo was carried between twin floats, which could be replaced by wheels for land-based operations.

After April 1922 trials, the Douglas was deemed the most serviceable torpedo type available. Thirty-eight DT-2s were ordered from Douglas, 20 from L.W.F., and 11 from Dayton-Wright. The Naval Aircraft Factory also produced 24 DT-2 and five DT-4s, a version appearing in April 1923 with a 525 hp Wright T-2. Most famous DT-2 feat was the round-the-world flight in 1924 of four examples transferred to the Army.

All of the early torpedo planes had water-cooled inline engines but a DT-5 modification tested an early 450 hp Wright Cyclone radial in April 1925. A 750 hp inline Packard 2A-2500 powered the DT-6. Standard DT-2s equipped Navy torpedo units, operating from shore bases.

DOUGLAS DT-1 (as landplane—wings folded)

MFR

DOUGLAS DT-2 LANDPLANE

USN

DOUGLAS DT-2 SEAPLANE
Liberty 12A, 420 hp
DIMENSIONS: Span 50′, Lg. 37′ 8″ (34′ 2″), Ht. 15′ 1″ (13′ 7″), Wing Area 707 sq. ft.
WEIGHT: Empty 4528 (3737) lb., Gross 7293 (6502) lb. Fuel 115 gal.
PERFORMANCE: Speed—Top 99.5 (101) mph at s. l., Landing 51 (49) mph. Service Ceiling 7400′ (7800′), Climb 3850′ (4050′)/10 min. Range 274 (293) miles/1835 lb. torpedo.

USN

December 1923 brought the first of six Curtiss CS-1s. This machine had a 525 hp inline Wright T-2, two cockpits behind the wings, and twin floats interchangeable with wheels. The upper wing was smaller in span than the lower, a reverse of usual biplane practice, and a 1618-lb. torpedo was specified as armament. Two Curtiss CS-2s with a 585 hp Wright T-3 and increased fuel capacity were delivered in April 1924.

This type was chosen to replace the DT-2s in service and contracts were let in June 1924 after open bidding in which Curtiss, asking $32,000, was underbid by Martin, asking $20,000. Thirty-five identical Martin SC-1s with T-2 engines, delivered between February and August 1925, were followed by 40 SC-2s with T-3s ordered in January and delivered by December 1925.

In May 1925, three examples of the TB-1 were ordered. Delivered in April 1926, Boeing's only torpedo plane had an 770 hp Packard inline 1A-2500, twin floats, folding wings, and the pilot and torpedoman seated side by side ahead of the wings, with a gunner seated in the rear.

A twin-engined biplane was ordered from the Naval Aircraft Factory in May 1925 and three more designed to the same BuAer specification were assigned to

USN

DOUGLAS SDW-1 (DT-2 by LWF)

MFR

CURTISS CS-1 SEAPLANE
(Landplane version in photo)
Wright T-2, 525 hp
DIMENSIONS: Span 56′ 6″, Lg. 40′ 3″ (38′ 5″), Ht. 16′ (15′ 2″), Wing Area 856 sq. ft.
WEIGHT: Empty 5390 lb. (4690 lb.), Gross 8670 lb. (7908 lb.). Fuel 214–370 gal.
PERFORMANCE: Speed—Top 100 mph at s. l. (101.5 mph), Landing 53 mph (51 mph). Service Ceiling 6900′ (9100′), Climb 5000′/17.5 min. (12.2 min.). Range 430 miles (452 miles).

MARTIN SC-1 SEAPLANE (Landplane in photo)
Wright T-2, 525 hp
DIMENSIONS: Span 56′ 6″, Lg. 40′ 3½″ (38′ 5″), Ht. 16′ (15′ 3″), Wing Area 856 sq. ft.
WEIGHT: Empty 5610 lb. (4895 lb.), Gross 9025 lb. (8310 lb.). Fuel 389 gal.
PERFORMANCE: Speed—Top 101 mph at s. l. (100 mph), Landing 55 mph (52.5 mph). Service Ceiling 5850′ (7950′), Climb 5000′/20.6 min. (14.7 min.). Range 381 miles/torpedo, 562 miles max. (403–595 miles).

USN

USN

DOUGLAS DT-4 SEAPLANE (Landplane in photo)
Wright T-2, 525 hp
DIMENSIONS: Span 50′, Lg. 37′ 8″ (34′ 5″), Ht. 15′ 1″ (13′ 5″), Wing Area 707 sq. ft.
WEIGHT: Empty 4976 lb. (4224 lb.), Gross 7741 lb. (6989 lb.). Fuel 115 gal.
PERFORMANCE: Speed—Top 107 mph (108 mph), Landing 53 mph (51 mph). Service Ceiling 6050′ (11,075′), Climb 5000′/23 min. (10 min.). Range 226 miles (240 miles).

Douglas in July. The Navy XTN-1 was completed in May 1926 and in July the first Douglas XT2D-1 was ready. Both had two 525 hp Wright R-1750 Cyclones, and a narrow fuselage with a nose gunner, pilot, and rear gunner. A 1618-lb. torpedo, or a bomb load was carried between twin floats, which could be exchanged for wheels for land operations.

Distinguished by a high, balanced rudder, the Douglas ships were followed by nine T2D-1s delivered in 1928. They had folding wings to facilitate shipboard stowage, but were actually used at shore stations. Eighteen more ordered June 1930 had 575 hp R-1820 Cyclones, more fuel, and twin rudders, but were redesignated P2D-1. Since future torpedo planes were expected to operate from carriers, these shore-based aircraft carried Patrol designations.

CURTISS CS-2 SEAPLANE (Landplane in photo)
Wright T-3, 585 hp
DIMENSIONS: Span 56′ 6″, Lg. 40′ 3″, Ht. 16′, Wing Area 856 sq. ft.
WEIGHT: Empty 6235 lb., Gross 11,333 lb.
PERFORMANCE: Speed—Top 102.5 mph at s. l., Landing 61 mph. Service Ceiling 4020′, Climb 1450′/10 min.

MFR

MFR

BOEING TB-1
Packard 1A-2500, 770 hp at s. l.
DIMENSIONS: Span 55′, Lg. 42′ 7″, Ht. 15′ 1″, Wing Area 868 sq. ft.
WEIGHT: Empty 6298 lb., Gross (scout) 10,537 lb., (torpedo) 10,703 lb. Fuel 450 gal.
PERFORMANCE: Speed—Top 106 mph at s. l., Landing (scout) 58.5 mph, (torpedo) 59 mph. Service Ceiling 2600′, Climb 1900′/10 min. Range 850 miles.

USN

NAVY XTN-1 (Seaplane)
Wright R-1750, 525 hp
DIMENSIONS: Span 57′, Lg. 44′ 10″, Ht. 15′ 7″, Wing Area 886 sq. ft.
WEIGHT: Empty 6003 lb., Gross 10,413 lb., Max. 11,926 lb. Fuel 450 gal.
PERFORMANCE: Speed—Top 121 mph at s. l. with torpedo (123 mph as bomber), Landing 58 mph. Service Ceiling 11,300′ (12,600′ as bomber), Climb 5000′/8.1 min. (7.1 min.). Range 375 miles /torpedo, 764 miles max.

MFR

MARTIN SC-2 SEAPLANE (Landplane)
Wright T-3, 540 hp
DIMENSIONS: Span 56′ 6″, Lg. 41′ 9″ (37′ 9″), Ht. 16′ (14′ 8″), Wing Area 856 sq. ft.
WEIGHT: Empty 5908 lb. (5007 lb.), Gross 9323 lb. (8422 lb.). Fuel 389 gal.
PERFORMANCE: Speed—Top 101 mph at s. l. (102 mph), Landing 56 mph (53 mph). Service Ceiling 5430′ (7470′), Climb 5000′/24.2 min. Range 335 miles/torpedo, 570 miles max. (336–540 miles).

FOR CARRIERS: ONE ENGINE, TWO WINGS, AND THREE MEN

The Navy torpedo-plane force on July 1, 1925, was hardly imposing. Forty-five Douglas DT-2s, three DT-4s, six Curtiss CSs, 31 Martin SCs on hand and 46 more on order, were all chained to shore bases. For the new carriers, *Saratoga* and *Lexington*, it was necessary to have planes capable of performing scouting, bombing, and torpedo missions, taking off and landing on the flight deck, and being stored in the hangars.

Such a type was available in the Martin T3M-1, 24 of which were delivered late in 1926. A development of the SC-2 (T2M), it had the same wings, a 575 hp Wright T3B, and an all-welded fuselage framework, with the pilot and torpedoman seated ahead of the wing, and a gunner in the rear. Twin floats or wheels

DOUGLAS T2D-1 (Landplane in photo)
Wright R-1750, 525 hp
DIMENSIONS: Span 57′, Lg. 42′, Wing Area 886 sq. ft.
WEIGHT: Empty 6011 lb., Gross 9986 lb., Max. 10,840 lb. Fuel 250 gal.
PERFORMANCE: Speed—Top 124 mph at s. l. Service Ceiling 13,830′, Climb 5000′/5.9 min.

ARC

USN

DOUGLAS T2D-1 (Seaplane)
Wright R-1750, 525 hp
DIMENSIONS: Span 57′, Lg. 44′ 4″, Ht. 16′ 11″, Wing Area 886 sq. ft.
WEIGHT: Empty 6528 lb., Gross 10,503 lb., Max. 11,357 lb. Fuel 250 gal.
PERFORMANCE: Speed—Top 124 mph at s. l. with torpedo (125 mph as bomber), Landing 58 mph. Service Ceiling 11,400′ (12,520′ as bomber), Climb 5000′/6.4 min. Range 384 miles/torpedo, 454 miles max.

MFR

DOUGLAS P2D-1
Wright R-1820E, 575 hp at s. l.
DIMENSIONS: Span 57′, Lg. 43′ 11″, Ht. 17′ 6″, Wing Area 909 sq. ft.
WEIGHT: Empty 7624 lb., Gross 12,791 lb. Fuel 356–572 gal.
PERFORMANCE: Speed—Top 135 mph at seaplane, 138 mph at landplane, Cruising 108 mph, Landing 62.5 mph. Service Ceiling 11,700′, Climb 885′/1 min., 5000′/7.6 min. Range 1010 miles.

USN

MARTIN T3M-1
Wright T-3B, 575 hp
DIMENSIONS: Span 56′ 7″, Lg. 41′ 9″, Ht. 15′ 1″, Wing Area 848 sq. ft.
WEIGHT: Empty 5462 lb., Gross (bomber) 8839 lb., (torpedo) 8979 lb. Fuel 390 gal.
PERFORMANCE: Speed—Top 108.5 mph at s. l., Cruising 78 mph, Landing 54 mph. Service Ceiling 5700′. Range 525 miles/1425 lb. torpedo.

MARTIN T3M-2
Packard 3A-2500, 710 hp at s. l.
DIMENSIONS: Span 56′ 7″, Lg. 41′ 4″, Ht. 15′ 1″, Wing Area 883 sq. ft.
WEIGHT: Empty 5814 lb., Gross 9503 lb. Fuel 300 gal.
PERFORMANCE: Speed—Top 109 mph at s. l. with torpedo, Landing 55 mph. Service Ceiling 7900′, Climb 5000′/16.8 min. Range 634 miles/torpedo.

MFR

MARTIN XT3M-3
Pratt & Whitney R-1690, 525 hp
DIMENSIONS: Span 56′ 7″, Lg. 41′ 4″, Ht. 15′ 1″, Wing Area 883 sq. ft.
WEIGHT: Empty 4600 lb., Gross 8304 lb. Fuel 300 gal.
PERFORMANCE: Speed—Top 102 mph, Landing 52 mph. Service Ceiling 3750′, Climb 5000′/15.3 min. Range 423 miles at top speed.

USN

USN

GREAT LAKES TG-1 (as seaplane)

USN

MARTIN T4M-1
Pratt & Whitney R-1690-24, 525 hp
DIMENSIONS: Span 53′, Lg. 35′ 7″, Ht. 14′ 9″, Wing Area 656 sq. ft.
WEIGHT: Empty 3931 lb., Gross 7387 lb., Max. 8071 lb. Fuel 200 gal.
PERFORMANCE: Speed—Top 114 mph at s. l. with torpedo, 113 mph with bombs, Landing 57 mph. Service Ceiling 10,150′, Climb 5000′/14 min. Range 363 miles/torpedo, 694 miles max.

ARC

GREAT LAKES TG-1
Pratt & Whitney R-1690-28, 525 hp
DIMENSIONS: Span 53′, Lg. 34′ 8″, Ht. 14′ 10″, Wing Area 656 sq. ft.
WEIGHT: Empty 4179 lb., Gross 7652 lb., Max. 7922 lb. Fuel 200 gal.
PERFORMANCE: Speed—Top 108 mph at s. l., Landing 58 mph. Service Ceiling 8000′, Climb 5000′/16 min. Range 447 miles/torpedo, 547 miles max.

GREAT LAKES TG-2
Wright R-1820-86, 620 hp
DIMENSIONS: As TG-1
WEIGHT: Empty 4670 lb., Gross 8463 lb., Max. 9236 lb. Fuel 220 gal.
PERFORMANCE: Speed—Top 127 mph at s. l., Landing 61 mph. Service Ceiling 11,500′, Climb 5000′/11 min. Range 330 miles/torpedo, 701 miles max.

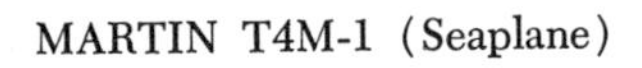
MARTIN T4M-1 (Seaplane)

USN

WL

USN

MARTIN XT6M-1
Wright R-1860, 575 hp
DIMENSIONS: Span 42′ 3″, Lg. 33′ 8″, Ht. 13′ 10″, Wing Area 502 sq. ft.
WEIGHT: Empty 3500 lb., Gross 6841 lb. Fuel 104 gal.
PERFORMANCE: Speed—Top 124 mph at s. l., Landing 61.5 mph. Service Ceiling 11,600′, Climb 5000′/8.8 min. Range 323 miles.

USN

DOUGLAS XT3D-2
Pratt & Whitney R-1830-54, 800 hp at s. l.
DIMENSIONS: Span 50′, Lg. 35′ 6″, Ht. 14′, Wing Area 649 sq. ft.
WEIGHT: Empty 4876 lb., Gross 8543 lb. Fuel 225 gal.
PERFORMANCE: Speed—Top 142 mph at s. l., Landing 62 mph. Service Ceiling 13,800′, Climb 5000′/8.8 min. Range 748 miles.

were interchangeable as landing gear. One hundred of the T3M-2 with a 710 hp inline Packard 3A-2500, equal-span wings, and three seats in tandem, were bought March 1927 and equipped the first squadron to go aboard the *Lexington* after its commissioning in December. This meant the Navy carried its aerial punch to sea, but few realized that an actual substitute for battleships was appearing.

These biplanes used water-cooled inline engines, but development of the air-cooled Pratt & Whitney Hornet radial provided a lighter power plant. This engine was tested on the XT3M-3, converted from a T3M-2, and used on the XT4M-1 (Martin 74), a new prototype introduced in April 1927. The prototype was followed by 102 T4M-1s with the R-1690-24, and tandem seats for bombardier, pilot, and gunner. Shorter wings and balanced rudder distinguished them from the T3Ms they replaced aboard the carriers in 1928–1929.

Glenn L. Martin sold his old Cleveland plant in October 1928 to the Great Lakes Aircraft Corporation, which, on June 25, 1929, received a contract for 18 of their own version of the T4M-1. With modified landing gear and an R-1690-28, the Great Lakes TG-1 appeared April 1930. Thirty-two TG-2s ordered July 2, 1930, first appeared in June 1931 with the Wright R-1820-86 Cyclone.

The Martin and Great Lakes ships remained for many years standard torpedo squadron equipment, for Navy procurement was manly devoted to dive-bomber development. There were two efforts to design a replacement; the first being Martin's XT6M-1 ordered June 28, 1929, and completed in December 1930 as an all-metal, long-nosed biplane with a Wright Cyclone. It had no more success than the Douglas XT3D-1, ordered on June 30, 1930, and tested in October 1931 with a 575 hp Hornet B single-row radial. In May 1932 this aircraft was returned for installation of an 800 hp twin-row R-1830-54. Redesignated XT3D-2, it reappeared February 1933 and had an NACA cowl, wheel pants, and low enclosures for the three crewmen. Badly streamlined, was the official verdict, and no production orders were placed.

DOUGLAS XT3D-1
Pratt & Whitney R-1860B, 575 hp at 8000′
DIMENSIONS: Span 50′, Lg. 35′ 4″, Ht. 14′ 8″, Wing Area 636 sq. ft.
WEIGHT: Empty 4319 lb., Gross 7744 lb., Max. 7941 lb. Fuel 180 gal.
PERFORMANCE: Speed—Top 134 mph at 8000′, 120 mph at s. l., Landing 59 mph. Service Ceiling 17,300′, Climb 5000′/7.7 min. Endurance 6.1 hrs. at 75 per cent power.

USN

DOUGLAS XT3D-1

USN

THE FIRST DIVE BOMBERS

During expeditions to Haiti (1919) and Nicaragua (1927) the Marines had developed dive-bombing as a technique for hitting guerrilla groups with 50-lb. bombs dropped by DH-4Bs. The Curtiss F8C Helldiver, 1928s two-seat fighter, was the first type built especially for dive-bombing, which, as war would amply show, was far more accurate against small or moving targets than horizontal bombing. If dive-bombing by fighters was effective against enemy personnel, it was apparent that large warships would be threatened by a dive bomber sturdy enough to attack with a 1000-lb. bomb. Such designs were begun first under the old "T" for torpedo designation, and later received a "B" label for bombing.

Two very similar two-seat biplanes designed for this requirement and built in 1930 were the Naval Aircraft Factory's XT2N-1 with a Wright R-1750-D, and Martin XT5M-1, tested March 1930 with a Pratt & Whitney R-1690-22. First planes capable of pulling out of a dive while carrying a 1000-lb. bomb, they had a metal fuselage, and fabric-covered metal wing structure. A single .30-caliber fixed wing gun could be mounted on the cowl, and another flexible gun was provided for the gunner.

USN

MARTIN XT5M-1
Pratt & Whitney R-1690-22, 525 hp
DIMENSIONS: Span 41′, Lg. 28′ 4″, Ht. 12′ 4″, Wing Area 417 sq. ft.
WEIGHT: Empty 3084 lb., Gross 5693 lb. Fuel 100 gal.
PERFORMANCE: Speed—Top 134 mph at s. l. Service Ceiling 13,250′, Climb 5000′/7.8 min. Range 442 miles.

NAVY XT2N-1
Wright R-1750, 525 hp
DIMENSIONS: Span 41′, Lg. 27′ 9″, Ht. 12′ 2″, Wing Area 416 sq. ft.
WEIGHT: Empty 2735 lb., Gross 5333 lb. Fuel 100 gal.
PERFORMANCE: Speed—Top 134.5 mph at s. l., Landing 60 mph. Service Ceiling 14,100′, Climb 5000′/7 min. Range 408 miles.

ARC

MARTIN BM-1
Pratt & Whitney R-1690-44, 625 hp
DIMENSIONS: Span 41′, Lg. 28′ 9″, Ht. 12′ 4″, Wing Area 417 sq. ft.
WEIGHT: Empty 3700 lb., Gross 5749 lb., Max. 6259 lb. Fuel 100–160 gal.
PERFORMANCE: Speed—Top 145 mph at 6000′, Landing 59 mph. Service Ceiling 16,400′, Climb 5000′/5.9 min. Range 409 miles/1000 lb. bomb, 689 miles max.

USN

PMB

MARTIN BM-2
Pratt & Whitney R-1690-44, 625 hp at 6000′
DIMENSIONS: Span 41′, Lg. 28′ 9″, Ht. 12′ 4″, Wing Area 436 sq. ft.
WEIGHT: Empty 3662 lb., Gross 5657 lb., Max. 6218 lb. Fuel 104–164 gal.
PERFORMANCE: Speed—Top 146 mph at 6000′, Landing 59 mph. Service Ceiling 16,800′, Climb 5000′/5.7 min. Range 413 miles/1000 lb. bomb, 695 miles max.

Martin received contracts for 12 BM-1s on April 9, 1931, and 16 BM-2s on October 17. These were to be similar to the XT5M-1, but had R-1690-22s, ring cowls, and wheel pants, although the latter streamlining details were omitted after the type went into service. The first example was received on September 28, 1931, but the pilot was killed when it failed to recover from a dive made on its first flight. Better luck was had with the second example in January 1932. The first BM-2 arrived in August 1932, after five more Martins had been added to the initial contract.

The first monoplane in this class was the Consolidated XBY-1, based on the Fleetster commercial plane with a high cantilever wing, and wheel pants. Instead of a passenger cabin, the Navy's first internal bomb bay was installed under the wing with "orange-peel" doors and a gunner firing his .30-caliber Browning behind a sliding panel in the fuselage roof. The enclosed pilot sat ahead of the wing, which contained fuel and flotation gear. Ordered on April 9, 1931, the XBY-1 appeared September 26, 1932, with a Wright R-1820-70, but resumed testes the following January with an R-1820-78. Too large for carrier stowage and limited to horizontal bombing, the type did not fit Navy tactical requirements.

Returning to a conventional biplane layout, the Navy ordered prototypes from two companies on June 22, 1932. Based on Bureau of Aeronautics design 110 for a two-place dive bomber carrying a 1000-lb. bomb beneath its belly, the Consolidated XB2Y-1 and Great Lakes XBG-1 were powered by Pratt & Whitney R-1535-64 Wasps, with neat cowls, metal fuselage and "N" struts. One .30-caliber fixed and one flexible gun were carried, with a bomb-displacement device to eject the bomb clear of the propeller when diving.

The Great Lakes XBG-1 began tests on June 12, 1933, and surpassed in performance the XB2Y-1 that arrived September 18. The latter had open cockpits, but the XBG-1 had a sliding canopy over the crewmen, open to the rear for the flexible gun. A production contract made November 22, 1933, was increased on January 9, 1934, and February 25, 1935, until 60 BG-1s were on order. Although early BG-1s had the prototype's R-1535-64, later examples went into service with the R-1535-82. Both Navy and Marine squadrons received BG-1s in 1935.

On June 30, 1934, the Navy ordered an improvement of this type, the XB2G-1. Armed with a .50-caliber fixed gun ahead of the pilot and a .30-caliber

CONSOLIDATED XBY-1
Wright R-1820-78, 600 hp at 8000′
DIMENSIONS: Span 50′, Lg. 33′ 8″, Ht. 12′ 4″, Wing Area 361 sq. ft.
WEIGHT: Empty 3800 lb., Gross 6547 lb. Fuel 130 gal.
PERFORMANCE: Speed—Top 181 mph, Landing 67 mph. Service Ceiling 22,700′.

GREAT LAKES BG-1
Pratt & Whitney R-1535-82, 750 hp take-off, 700 hp at 8900′
DIMENSIONS: Span 36′, Lg. 28′ 9″, Ht. 11′, Wing Area 384 sq. ft.
WEIGHT: Empty 3903 lb., Gross 6123 lb., Max. 6347 lb. Fuel 165–225 gal.
PERFORMANCE: Speed—Top 188 mph at 8900′ as scout, 187 mph as bomber, Landing 66 mph. Service Ceiling 20,100′, Climb 5000′/5.5 min. Range 549 miles/1000 lb. bomb, 1245 miles as scout.

PMB

MFR

USN

CONSOLIDATED XB2Y-1
Pratt & Whitney R-1535-64, 700 hp at 8900′
DIMENSIONS: Span 36′ 6″, Lg. 27′ 10″, Ht. 10′ 10″, Wing Area 362 sq. ft.
WEIGHT: Empty 3538 lb., Gross 6010 lb. Fuel 153–214 gal.
PERFORMANCE: Speed—Top 182 mph at 8900′, Landing 66 mph. Service Ceiling 21,000′, Climb 5000′/4.5 min. Range 487 miles.

GREAT LAKES XB2G-1
Pratt & Whitney R-1535-82, 700 hp at 8900′
DIMENSIONS: Span 36′, Lg. 28′ 9″, Ht. 11′ 1″, Wing Area 384 sq. ft.
WEIGHT: Empty 4248 lb., Gross 6394 lb., Max. 6802 lb. Fuel 130–190 gal.
PERFORMANCE: Speed—Top 198 mph at 8900′, Landing 61 mph. Service Ceiling 19,500′, Climb 5000′/6.5 min. Range 582 miles/1000 lb. bomb, 1115 miles max.

MFR

CURTISS XS2C-1
Wright R-1510-28, 625 hp
DIMENSIONS: Span 44′, Lg. 31′ 3″, Ht. 12′ 2″, Wing Area 285 sq. ft.
WEIGHT: Empty 3677 lb., Gross 4822 lb., Max. 5180 lb. Fuel 104–156 gal.
PERFORMANCE: Speed—Top 186 mph at s. l., Landing 71 mph. Service Ceiling 18,900′, Climb 5000′/4.4 min. Range 640 miles/488 lbs. bombs, 912 miles max.

PMB

VOUGHT XSBU-1
Pratt & Whitney R-1535-80, 700 hp at 8900′
DIMENSIONS: Span 33′ 3″, Lg. 27′ 10″, Ht. 12′, Wing Area 327 sq. ft.
WEIGHT: Empty 3558 lb., Gross 5297 lb., Max. 5520 lb. Fuel 145 gal.
PERFORMANCE: Speed—Top 208 mph at 8900′, 201 mph/500 lb. bomb, Landing 65 mph. Service Ceiling 25,300′, Climb 5000′/3.7 min. Range 561 miles/bomber, 902 miles as scout.

flexible gun for the gunner, the XB2G-1 was similar to the BG-1 but for a deep belly containing an internal bay for the 1000-lb. bomb, and wells for retracting wheels. Tested in December 1935, the XB2G-1 eventually became a Marine Command plane, but lost production contracts to more modern dive bombers. After the Cleveland firm went out of business, rights to the BG series were acquired by Bell Aircraft Corporation, but no production resulted.

VOUGHT SBU-1
Pratt & Whitney R-1535-82, 750 hp take-off, 700 hp at 8900′
DIMENSIONS: Span 33′ 3″, Lg. 27′ 9″, Ht. 12′, Wing Area 327 sq. ft.
WEIGHT: Empty 3645 lb., Gross 5394 lb., Max. 5618 lb. Fuel 145 gal.
PERFORMANCE: Speed—Top 205 mph at 8900′, 180 mph at s. l., 198 and 174 mph/500 lb. bomb, Cruising 122 mph, Landing 66 mph. Service Ceiling 24,400′, Climb 1180′/1 min. Range 548 miles/500 lb. bomb, 862 miles as scout.

MFR

EARLY SCOUT BOMBERS

A new type known as scout bombers (SB) entered history in 1934, two-seat carrier-based aircraft which could function both as scouts and as dive-bombers. The first type in this category to enter service was the culmination of a long series of two-seat biplanes built by Chance-Vought, then in East Hartford, Connecticut.

Earlier planes in this series were not combat types, and therefore detailed consideration is outside this book's scope. They began in 1918 with the Vought VE-7, a two-seat trainer that did 117 mph with a 180 hp Hispano engine. This type was widely used both with floats and with wheels, and was the first type to serve aboard the *Langley*. It was followed by the UO

VOUGHT V142-A

MFR

series begun in 1923 and powered by a 220 hp Wright J-4 radial. On November 2, 1926, Vought flew the first O2U Corsair two-seat observation type, powered by a Pratt & Whitney R-1340 Wasp. It was followed by the slightly larger O3U series begun in 1930. Hundreds of these Voughts served the fleet as observation ships, their armament being limited to a single .30-caliber fixed gun and one flexible .30-caliber gun for the observer. All had landing gear interchangeable between wheels and a single float arrangement for catapult launching.

In 1931 the scouting designation (S) began with the Vought SU series, developed from the O3U with more fuel and a more powerful engine. These ships were as successful as their predecessors and comprised nearly all the Navy's observation and scouting equipment until 1937. There was an attempt to develop an amphibian with an enclosed gunner's turret, but neither the Great Lakes XSG-1 or Loening XS2L-1 prototypes ordered June 30, 1931, could offer adequate performance. All these aircraft were biplanes, but Bellanca built a high wing monoplane for an October 19, 1931, contract (XSE-2).

The first scouting type to have real attack capabilities was actually the Curtiss XS2C-1, a naval version of the Army's YA-10 Shrike monoplane. Purchased December 13, 1932, the XS2C-1 had a Wright R-1510-28, wire-braced wing, and wheel pants. Although it could have been as useful a combat type as its Army equivalent, which carried five .30-caliber guns and 488 lbs. of bombs, this monoplane was too big for carrier stowage.

The first planes to receive the new SB designation were the Vought XSBU-1 and the Curtiss XSBC-1, which were actually begun as two-seat fighters to replace the F8C Helldiver series used by the Marine Corps. In February 1934 the Vought XF3U-1 biplane ordered in 1932 was redesignated XSBU-1 and fitted with an R-1535-80 Wasp. Armament consisted of a .30-caliber fixed gun under the cowl, a .30-caliber flexible gun for the observer, and 500 lbs. of bombs. The neat NACA cowl and cockpit enclosure were standard features of this period's Naval aircraft. Fabric covered the wings and rear fuselage, but the rest of the aircraft was of metal.

On January 1935, 84 SBU-1s were ordered and delivery began in September with the R-1535-82. Forty SBU-2s, similar to the SBU-1 but for an R-1585-98 of equal power, were ordered November 23, 1936 and went to Naval Reserve stations after May 1937. In addition, an export version, Vought V-142 was built for Argentina.

Chapter 25: Japan's Nemesis 1935–45

THE TORPEDO COMES BACK ON ONE WING

Although the Great Lakes TGs were beginning to age, the Navy had not forgotten torpedo planes. Three different prototypes ordered June 30, 1934, got the new torpedo bomber (TB) designation and the 800 hp Pratt & Whitney XR-1830-60 Twin Wasp. In order of appearance, they were the Douglas XTBD-1, Great Lakes XTBG-1, and Hall XPTBH-2.

Delivered for tests on April 24, 1935, the XTBD-1 was an all-metal, low-wing monoplane with the crew of three under a long enclosure, and wheels retracting backward into the wing, left partially protruding for emergency landings. So that the big plane could be stored aboard carriers, the 50 ft. wings folded upward, reducing span to 25 ft.-8 in. The torpedo officer sat between the pilot and gunner when acting as navigator, but in battle lay prone to sight through a window behind the engine. A Norden sight permitted horizontal aiming of a 1000-lb. bomb, or a 15 ft. torpedo could be carried with about four feet of its warhead exposed. A .30-caliber gun was provided for the pilot and another for the gunner.

This type became the first monoplane ordered for service aboard carriers when a February 3, 1936, contract called for 114 TBD-1s. Fifteen more were added August 16, 1938, after the type proved successful in service. When the first TBD-1 was received June 25, 1937, it displayed several changes: an 850 hp R-1830-64, higher pilot's canopy, and a revised cowl with the oil cooler moved under the starboard wing root.

The world's best torpedo plane when introduced, the TBD-1 had the misfortune to be the only torpedo type on hand at 1942s beginning, when 100 remaining

USN

DOUGLAS XTBD-1
Pratt & Whitney XR-1830-60, 800 hp at 7000′
DIMENSIONS: Span 50′, Lg. 35′, Ht. 14′ 2″, Wing Area 420 sq. ft.
WEIGHT: Empty 5046 lb., Gross 8385 lb., Max. 8773 lb. Fuel 180 gal.
PERFORMANCE: Speed—Top 205 mph at 8000′, 188 mph at s. l., 201 mph at 8000′/torpedo, Landing 63 mph. Service Ceiling 20,800′, Climb 5000′/4.8 min. Range 449 miles/torpedo, 907 miles/1000 lb. bomb.

DOUGLAS TBD-1
Pratt & Whitney R-1830-64, 900 hp take-off, 850 hp at 8000′
DIMENSIONS: Span 50′, Lg. 35′, Ht. 15′ 1″, Wing Area 422 sq. ft.
WEIGHT: Empty 6182 lb., Gross 9862 lb., Max. 10,194 lb. Fuel 180 gal.
PERFORMANCE: Speed—Top 206 mph at 8000′, 192 mph at s. l., Cruising 128 mph, Landing 68.5 mph. Service Ceiling 19,700′, Climb 720′/1 min. Range 435 miles/torpedo, 716 miles/1000 lb. bomb.

PMB

ARC

were named Devastators. The oldest Navy type used in the Coral Sea and Midway Island battles, they scored few hits, but proved very vulnerable to enemy fighters. Of 41 Devastators launched in the Midway battle, only six returned.

The Great Lakes XTBG-1 was the last torpedo biplane, and was received from the builder on August 20, 1935. Wheels retracted into the all-metal fuselage ahead of fabric-covered, tapered wings. A torpedoman sat behind the Twin Wasp under a low canopy with a bomb-aiming window between the wheel wells. Pilot and gunner's seats behind the wings were covered by a sliding enclosure. A torpedo or 1000-lb. bomb, and two .30-caliber guns were carried, but the flight characteristics were unstable, and the performance inferior to the XTBD-1.

Unique among this period's aircraft was the Hall XPTBH-2, a twin-engined seaplane designed for torpedo, bombing, or patrol missions. Begun in 1934 as the XPTBH-1 with Wright R-1820 Cyclones, the high-wing monoplane was built in Bristol, Pennsylvania, with XR-1830-60 Wasps, redesignated XPTBH-2, and received by the Navy on January 30, 1937. A pair of large floats were installed under the engines, while the long fuselage contained the crew of four and the bay for a torpedo or bomb. In the nose was a rotating turret with a .30-caliber gun, behind the wings a hatch slid forward and up to reveal a rear gunner and .50-caliber Browning, while a floor panel opened for a .30-caliber tunnel gun. Since water-based torpedo planes were not included in Navy procurement plans, no further contracts were let for this type.

GREAT LAKES XTBG-1
Pratt & Whitney XR-1830-60, 800 hp at 7000′
DIMENSIONS: Span 42′, Lg. 35′ 1″, Ht. 15′ 1″, Wing Area 547 sq. ft.
WEIGHT: Empty 5323 lb., Gross 8924 lb., 9275 lb./torpedo. Fuel 220 gal.
PERFORMANCE: Speed—Top 185 mph at 7000′/bomber, 171 mph at s. l./torpedo, Landing 60 mph. Service Ceiling 16,400′, Climb 5000′/6.2 min. Range 586 miles/torpedo, 998 miles/1000 lb. bomb.

HALL XPTBH-2
Pratt & Whitney XR-1830-60, 800 hp at 8000′
DIMENSIONS: Span 79′ 4″, Lg. 55′ 11″, Ht. 24′ 1″, Wing Area 828 sq. ft.
WEIGHT: Empty 11,992 lb., Gross 17,983 lb., Max. 21,414 lb. Fuel 830–1180 gal.
PERFORMANCE: Speed—Top 182 mph at 8000′, 169 mph at s. l., Landing 69.5 mph. Service Ceiling 19,200′, Climb 5000′/5.3 min. Range 850 miles/torpedo, 2620 miles max.

ARC

THE END OF THE BIPLANE

Launching of the aircraft carriers *Enterprise* and *Yorktown* in 1936 increased Navy aircraft requirements, and procurement officials selected scout-bomber types to fill the new squadrons and replace the Voughts on the older carriers. Six companies offered two-seat prototypes that year: the Great Lakes XB2G-1, Grumman XSBF-1, and Curtiss XSBC-3 biplanes, and the Northrop XBT-1, Vought XSB2U-1, and Brewster XSBA-1 monoplanes.

In order of their appearance, the Great Lakes XB2G-1 described in a previous chapter comes first, followed among the biplanes by the Grumman XSBF-1. Ordered March 26, 1935, and delivered for tests in February 1936, the XSBF-1 was a stubby development of the SF-2 two-seat biplane, with an R-1535-72, wheels retracting into the fuselage, enclosed cockpits and provision for a 500-lb. bomb. This type, however, did not win the success of single-seat fighters produced by the same company.

The Curtiss XSBC-3, which began tests April 1, 1936, was actually a culmination of a 1932 contract made for the XF12C-1 two seat, high-wing monoplane. In December 1933 this type was redesignated XS4C-1 with a Wright R-1820-80 in a revised cowl. The following month, the aircraft was labeled XSBC-1 and tested as a scout bomber, but the high wing proved unsafe for diving and a crash in September totally destroyed the prototype. In April 1935 the aircraft was reordered as a biplane with a new cockpit canopy and tail, an XR-1510-12, and redesignated XSBC-2. Bearing the original prototype's serial number, the new aircraft flew December 9, 1935. In March 1936 it was fitted with an R-1535-82 and became XSBC-3.

This long development was rewarded August 29, 1936, with a $2,045,783 contract for 83 SBC-3s powered by R-1535-94 Wasps. First delivered June 1937, the SBC-3 was similar to its prototype, with wheels retracting into an all-metal fuselage and sliding canopy for pilot and observer. Fabric-covered wings were connected by "I" struts, the swept-back upper wing

PMB

GRUMMAN XSBF-1

Pratt & Whitney R-1535-72, 700 hp take-off, 650 hp at 7000′

DIMENSIONS: Span 31′ 6″, Lg. 25′ 9″, Ht. 11′ 3″, Wing Area 310 sq. ft.

WEIGHT: Empty 3395 lb., Gross 5002 lb., Max. 5442 lb. Fuel 130 gal.

PERFORMANCE: Speed—Top 215 mph at 15,000′, 209 mph/500 lb. bomb, Landing 65 mph. Service Ceiling 26,000′, Climb 5000′/3.2 min. Range 688 miles/500 lb. bomb, 987 miles as scout.

CURTISS XSBC-2 MFR

Wright R-1510-12, 700 hp at 7000′

DIMENSIONS: Span 34′, Lg. 28′ 4″, Ht. 12′ 7″, Wing Area 317 sq. ft.

WEIGHT: Empty 3769 lb., Gross 5453 lb., Max. 5790 lb. Fuel 140 gal.

PERFORMANCE: Speed—Top 217 mph at 7000′/scout, 210 mph/bomber, Landing 63 mph. Service Ceiling 24,900′, Climb 5000′/3.5 min. Range 612 miles/500 lb. bomb, 944 miles as scout.

CURTISS XSBC-1

MFR

CURTISS XSBC-3

MFR

having ailerons and the straight lower wing utilizing flaps for landing and as dive brakes. As on most of this period's scout bombers, armament included a .30-caliber gun under the cowl and another in the rear cockpit, while a 500-lb. bomb or a drop tank could be carried beneath the fuselage.

The last aircraft on this contract was delivered with a single-row R-1820-22 Cyclone instead of the twin-row Wasp, and designated XSBC-4. A January 5, 1938, purchase of 58 SBC-4s was increased on July 27 to 89 and deliveries began in March 1939. Using an R-1820-34 and capable of handling a 1000-lb. bomb, SBC-4s can be distinguished from SBC-3 by their wider-diameter engine. Thirty-five more SBC-4s ordered August 13, 1939, were completed the following April, but on June 8, 1940, fifty were returned to the Curtiss company for transfer to France.

Most of these were held at Martinique, but five reached Britain as the Curtiss 77 Cleveland. In neither case did they do any flying, for the French aircraft were interned for the rest of the war, while the Clevelands were used for mechanics' practice. Fifty more SBC-4s built in February–May 1941 to replace those sent abroad went to Naval Reserve units. Except for a 126-gallon self-sealing tank replacing the unprotected 135-gallon fuselage tank, they were similar to their predecessors. Never used in battle, the SBC-4 has the historical distinction of being the last combat biplane built in the United States.

The dispute between biplanes and monoplanes for carrier service is illustrated by two Wasp-powered scout bombers offered by Vought to the Navy. The XSB2U-1 ordered October 11, 1934, was a low-wing monoplane with an R-1535-72, while the XSB3U-1 ordered February 7, 1935, was a biplane similar to the SBU-1, but for wheels retracting backward into the wing roots. Both prototypes were delivered in April 1936 to Anacosta Naval Air Station for evaluation. There, the monoplane's superior performance was observed, and the shipboard stowage problem was solved by folding the wings upward, as on the TBD.

All-metal construction was used on the XSB2U-1, except for fabric-covering on the rear fuselage, control surfaces, and part of the wings. A long enclosure covered both crewmen, who had a .30-caliber fixed gun with 500 rounds and a .30-caliber flexible gun with 600 rounds. Gear beneath the fuselage could handle a 500- or 1000-lb. bomb, or droppable fuel tank. Wheels retracted back, rotating to fit flat within the wing. First flight was on January 5, 1936.

A $2,240,995 contract for 54 SB2U-1s was placed October 26, 1936. The first example was ready in July 1937, but delivery on the remainder began in December. Using R-1535-96 Wasps with reversible Hamilton propellers to limit diving speeds, they were similar to the prototype, and to 58 SB2U-2s ordered January 27, 1938, whose delivery began in July. Twenty export models (Vought V-156) were built for France in 1939, and one SB2U-1 fitted with twin pontoons and ventral fin became the XSB2U-3 tested in May 1939. These trials demonstrated a top speed reduction from 251 mph with retractable wheels to 210 mph with the pontoons.

Standard retractable wheels were retained on 57 heavier SB2U-3s ordered September 25, 1939, and

PMB

CURTISS SBC-4
Wright R-1820-34, 950 hp take-off, 750 hp at 15,000′
DIMENSIONS: Span 34′, Lg. 27′ 6″, Ht. 13′ 2″, Wing Area 317 sq. ft.
WEIGHT: Empty 4552 lb., Gross 6260 lb., Max. 7141 lb. Fuel 135–180 gal.
PERFORMANCE: Speed—Top 237 mph at 15,200′, 218 mph at s. l., Cruising 127 mph, Landing 68 mph. Service Ceiling 27,300′, Climb 1860′/1 min. Range 555 miles/1000 lb. bomb, 590 miles/500 lb. bomb, 1090 miles max., 876 miles/scout.

PMB

CURTISS SBC-3
Pratt & Whitney R-1535-94, 825 hp take-off, 750 hp at 9500′
DIMENSIONS: Span 34′, Lg. 28′ 1″, Ht. 13′ 2″, Wing Area 317 sq. ft.
WEIGHT: Empty 4324 lb., Gross 6023 lb., Max. 6904 lb. Fuel 135–180 gal.
PERFORMANCE: Speed—Top 220 mph at 9500′, 203 mph at s. l., Landing 67 mph. Service Ceiling 23,800′, Climb 1340′/1 min. Range 635 miles/500 lb. bomb, 940 miles/scout, 1190 miles max.

MFR

VOUGHT XSB2U-1

Pratt & Whitney R-1535-78, 700 hp at 8900′

DIMENSIONS: Span 42′, Lg. 33′ 2″, Ht. 15′ 10″, Wing Area 305 sq. ft.

WEIGHT: Empty 4315 lb., Gross 5916 lb., Max. 6191 lb. Fuel 130 gal.

PERFORMANCE: Speed—Top 230 mph at 8900′, 222 mph/bomb, Landing 66 mph. Service Ceiling 26,600′, Climb 5000′/3.7 min. Range 532 miles/1000 lb. bomb, 564 miles/500 lb. bomb, 892 miles max.

first appearing December 1940 with R-1535-02s. Named Vindicators, they had additional fuel capacity, internal protection, and two .50-caliber fixed guns. Fifty similar Chesapeakes for Britain's Fleet Air Arm followed until production was completed in July 1941. Some Vindicators were flown by Marine Corps pilots in the fierce battle for Midway.

MFR

VOUGHT XSB3U-1

Pratt & Whitney R-1535-82, 750 hp take-off, 700 hp at 8900′

DIMENSIONS: Span 33′ 3″, Lg. 28′ 2″, Ht. 11′, Wing Area 327 sq. ft.

WEIGHT: Empty 3876 lb., Gross 5627 lb., Max. 5837 lb. Fuel 145 gal.

PERFORMANCE: Speed—Top 214.5 mph at 8900′, 209 mph/500 lb. bomb, Landing 66.5 mph. Service Ceiling 26,500′, Climb 5000′/4.2 min. Range 590 miles/500 lb. bomb, 926 miles as scout.

MFR

VOUGHT SB2U-3
Pratt & Whitney R-1535-02, 750 hp at 9500′
DIMENSIONS: As SB2U-1
WEIGHT: Empty 5634 lb., Gross 7474 lb., Max. 9421 lb. Fuel 118–420 gal.
PERFORMANCE: Speed—Top 243 mph at 9500′, Cruising 152 mph, Landing 71 mph. Service Ceiling 23,600′, Climb 1070′/1 min. Range 1120 miles/1000 lb. bomb, 2450 miles ferry.

SHERTZER

VOUGHT SB2U-1
Pratt & Whitney R-1535-96, 825 hp take-off, 750 hp at 9000′
DIMENSIONS: Span 42′, Lg. 34′, Ht. 10′ 3″, Wing Area 305 sq. ft.
WEIGHT: Empty 4676 lb., Gross 6323 lb., Max. 7278 lb. Fuel 115–180 gal.
PERFORMANCE: Speed—Top 250 mph at 9500′, 241 mph/500 lb. bomb, 231 mph at s. l., Cruising 143 mph, Landing 66 mph. Service Ceiling 27,400′, Climb 1500′/1 min. Range 635 miles/1000 lb. bomb, 699 miles/500 lb. bomb, 1004 miles as scout.

VOUGHT SB2U-2
Pratt & Whitney R-1535-96, 825 hp take-off
DIMENSIONS: As SB2U-1
WEIGHT: Empty 4713 lb., Gross 6379 lb., Max. 7332 lb. Fuel 115–180 gal.
PERFORMANCE: Speed—Top 251 mph at 9500′, 232 mph at s. l., Landing 66 mph. Service Ceiling 27,500′, Climb 1340′/1 min. Range 630 miles/1000 lb. bomb, 1002 miles as scout.

SHERTZER

DOUGLAS DAUNTLESS

The dive bomber that fought World War II's decisive battles began with a Navy contract on November 18, 1934, for the Northrop XBT-1. Delivered for tests December 16, 1935, the XBT-1 was an all-metal low-wing monoplane resembling the A-17 attack types but with shorter wings to facilitate stowage aboard carriers. Another feature was retraction of the wheels back into fairings under the wings, which had perforated split flaps at the trailing edge. These flaps were opened in dives to prevent excessive high speeds from spoiling the aim or making pull-outs dangerous.

Armament included a .50-caliber fixed gun for the pilot and an observer's .30-caliber flexible gun, as well as a 1000-lb. bomb carried below the fuselage. Original power plant was a 700 hp R-1535-66, replaced in April 1936 by the R-1535-94 used on 54 BT-1s ordered September 16, 1936. The first aircraft on the $2,084,815 contract was completed in November 1937, but a labor dispute delayed acceptance of the remaining aircraft until 1938. In August 1938 the final aircraft was completed as the XBT-2 with a 1000 hp Wright R-1820-32 Cyclone and wheels retracting inwardly into the wing roots.

By this time the original Northrop firm had become the Douglas El Segundo division. On April 8, 1939, they received a contract for 57 SBD-1s and 87 SBD-2s, the type which became known as the Douglas Dauntless. Similar to the XBT-1 except for a high tapered tail fin, the first SBD-1 appeared May 1940, and was armed with two .30-caliber fixed guns in the nose and a third .30-caliber gun for the observer. The SBD-2s which began appearing in October 1940 were similar but for increased fuel capacity.

On September 27, 1940, 174 SBD-3s were ordered and began deliveries March 1941, along with 78 similar SBD-3A (A-24) for the Army. This version introduced the R-1820-52, self-sealing fuel tanks, armor plate, and an armament of two .50-caliber fixed and two .30-caliber flexible guns.

Dauntless production might have ended when the last aircraft on this contract was completed in January 1942, had not the Pearl Harbor attack created a sudden demand for all the planes that could be built. New contracts were let and in March 1942 Douglas resumed deliveries on 500 more SBD-3s. In October acceptances began on 780 SBD-4s and 170 Army SBD-4As (A-24A), similar to the SBD-3 except for a new electrical system.

USN

NORTHROP XBT-1
Pratt & Whitney R-1535-66, 700 hp at 8900′
DIMENSIONS: Span 41′ 6″, Lg. 31′ 10″, Ht. 12′ 6″, Wing Area 315 sq. ft.
WEIGHT: Empty 4183 lb., Gross 6156 lb., Max. 6718 lb. Fuel 183 gal.
PERFORMANCE: Speed—Top 222.5 mph at 8900′, 212 mph/1000 lb. bomb, Landing 62 mph. Service Ceiling 25,800′, Climb 5000′/4.1 min. Range 564 miles/1000 lb. bomb, 1063 miles max.

MFR

NORTHROP BT-1
Pratt & Whitney R-1535-94, 825 hp take-off, 750 hp at 9500′
DIMENSIONS: Span 41′ 6″, Lg. 31′ 8″, Ht. 9′ 11″, Wing Area 319 sq. ft.
WEIGHT: Empty 4606 lb., Gross 6650 lb., Max. 7197 lb. Fuel 180 gal.
PERFORMANCE: Speed—Top 222 mph at 9500′, 212 mph/1000 lb. bomb, Cruising 192 mph, Landing 66 mph. Service Ceiling 25,300′, Climb 1270′/1 min. Range 550 miles/1000 lb. bomb, 1150 miles as scout.

MFR

NORTHROP XBT-2
(Shown before change to SBD configuration)
Wright XR-1820-32, 1000 hp take-off, 800 hp at 16,000′
DIMENSIONS: Span 41′ 6″, Lg. 31′ 9″, Ht. 12′ 10″, Wing Area 320 sq. ft.
WEIGHT: Empty 5093 lb., Gross 7231 lb., Max. 7593 lb. Fuel 210 gal.
PERFORMANCE: Speed—Top 265 mph at 16,000′, 252 mph/1000 lb. bomb, 243 mph at s. l., Cruising 155 mph, Landing 67 mph. Service Ceiling 30,600′, Climb 1450′/1 min. Range 604 miles/1000 lb. bomb, 1458 miles as scout.

USN

DOUGLAS SBD-1
Wright R-1820-32, 1000 hp take-off, 800 hp at 16,000′
DIMENSIONS: Span 41′ 6″, Lg. 32′ 2″, Ht. 13′ 7″, Wing Area 325 sq. ft.
WEIGHT: Empty 5903 lb., Gross 8138 lb., Max. 9790 lb. Fuel 180–210 gal.
PERFORMANCE: Speed—Top 253 mph at 16,000′, 231 mph at s. l., Cruising 142 mph, Landing 70.5 mph. Service Ceiling 29,600′, Climb 1730′/1 min. Range 860 miles/1000 lb. bomb, 985 miles as scout, 1165 miles ferry.

In May 1943 delivery began on 3025 SBD-5s, first ordered December 10, 1942, and powered by a 1200 hp R-1820-60 engine. Nine went to Britain for evaluation. Final version of the Dauntless was 450 SBD-6s with more fuel and a 1350 hp R-1820-66.

When the last Dauntless was completed in July 1944, 5936 had been built, including those for the Army and some given to Mexico. Their first battle experience came during the Pearl Harbor attack on December 7, 1941. A few days later an SBD sank the first Japanese submarine, and those that fought over the Coral Sea, the battle for Midway and in the Solomon Islands campaign were the principal weapons that shattered the Japanese fleet and turned the tide of the Pacific war.

MFR

DOUGLAS SBD-3
Wright R-1820-52, 1000 hp take-off, 800 hp at 16,000′
DIMENSIONS: Span 41′ 6″, Lg. 32′ 8″, Ht. 13′ 7″, Wing Area 325 sq. ft.
WEIGHT: Empty 6345 lb., Gross 9407 lb., Max. 10,400 lb. Fuel 260–310 gal.
PERFORMANCE: Speed—Top 250 mph at 16,000′, Cruising 152 mph, Landing 78 mph. Service Ceiling 27,100′, Climb 1190′/1 min. Range 1345 miles/1000 lb. bomb, 1580 miles as scout.

ARC

DOUGLAS SBD-2
Wright R-1820-32, 1000 hp take-off
DIMENSIONS: As SBD-1
WEIGHT: Empty 6293 lb., Gross 9061 lb., Max. 10,360 lb. Fuel 260–310 gal.
PERFORMANCE: Speed—Top 252 mph at 16,000′, Cruising 148 mph, Landing 75.5 mph. Service Ceiling 26,000′, Climb 1080′/1 min. Range 1225 miles/1000 lb. bomb, 1370 miles as scout.

PMB

DOUGLAS SBD-5
Wright R-1820-60, 1200 hp take-off, 1000 hp at 13,800′
DIMENSIONS: Span 41′ 6″, Lg. 33′, Ht. 12′ 11″, Wing Area 325 sq. ft.
WEIGHT: Empty 6533 lb., Gross 9352 lb., Max. 10,700 lb. Fuel 254–370 gal.
PERFORMANCE: Speed—Top 252 mph at 13,800′, 238 mph at s. l., Cruising 139 mph, Landing 80 mph. Service Ceiling 24,300′, Climb 1700′/1 min. Range 1115 miles/1000 lb. bomb, 1565 miles as scout.

PMB

DOUGLAS SBD-6
Wright R-1820-66, 1350 hp take-off, 1000 hp at 14,800′
DIMENSIONS: As SBD-5
WEIGHT: Empty 6554 lb., Gross 9608 lb., Max. 10,882 lb. Fuel 284–400 gal.
PERFORMANCE: Speed—Top 262 mph at 15,600′, 247 mph at s. l., Cruising 143 mph, Landing 75.4 mph. Service Ceiling 28,600′, Climb 1710′/1 min. Range 1230 miles/1000 lb. bomb, 1700 miles as scout.

BREWSTER'S BOMBERS

The difficulties an apparently good design may encounter in the hands of management inexperienced in aircraft production are illustrated in the story of the Brewster dive bombers. This firm's first airplane was the XSBA-1 ordered by the Navy October 15, 1934. On April 15, 1936, it appeared for tests as a mid-wing two-seat monoplane with an internal bomb bay, Wright R-1820-4, and two-bladed propeller.

In its original form, the XSBA-1 did 242 mph with a gross weight of 3695 lbs., but was returned to the company for installation of an XR-1820-22. The revised aircraft reappeared in 1937 with a new cowl and three-bladed propeller. Fastest dive bomber in the air (263 mph) it was very clean with wheels retracting into the fuselage ahead of the doors covering the 500-lb. bomb. Perforated wing flaps acted as dive brakes. The pilot was separated from the observer by a long fairing between their canopies.

Although Brewster itself did not receive a production contract for this type, 30 were ordered on September 29, 1938, from the Naval Aircraft Factory and designated SBN-1. They took uncommonly long to build; the first was not delivered until November 1940, the next 22 were not ready until June and July 1941, and the contract was not completed until March 1942. Powered by an R-1820-38 Cyclone, the SBN-1 carried a .50-caliber fixed gun, .30-caliber flexible gun, and a 500-lb. bomb.

BREWSTER XSBA-1

USN

BREWSTER XSBA-1
Wright XR-1820-22, 950 hp take-off, 750 hp at 15,200′
DIMENSIONS: Span 39′, Lg. 28′ 3″, Ht. 11′ 1″, Wing Area 259 sq. ft.
WEIGHT: Empty 4080 lb., Gross 5736 lb., Max. 5972 lb. Fuel 136 gal.
PERFORMANCE: Speed—Top 263 mph at 15,200′, Landing 69 mph. Service Ceiling 28,500′, Climb 1970′/1 min. Range 573 miles/500 lb. bomb, 890 miles as scout.

USN

USN

N.A.F. SBN-1
Wright R-1820-38, 950 hp take-off, 750 hp at 15,200′
DIMENSIONS: Span 39′, Lg. 27′ 8″, Ht. 12′ 5″, Wing Area 259 sq. ft.
WEIGHT: Empty 4503 lb., Gross 6245 lb., Max. 6759 lb. Fuel 136 gal.
PERFORMANCE: Speed—Top 254 mph at 15,200′, 231 mph at s. l., Cruising 117 mph, Landing 68 mph. Service Ceiling 28,300′, Climb 1970′/1 min. Range 1015 miles/500 lb. bomb, 1110 miles as scout.

USN

BREWSTER SB2A-2
Wright R-2600-8, 1700 hp take-off, 1450 hp at 12,000′
DIMENSIONS: Span 47′, Lg. 39′ 2″, Ht. 15′ 5″, Wing Area 379 sq. ft.
WEIGHT: Empty 9924 lb., Gross 13,068 lb., Max. 14,289 lb. Fuel 174–421 gal.
PERFORMANCE: Speed—Top 274 mph at 12,000′, 259 mph at s. l., Cruising 161 mph, Landing 87 mph. Service Ceiling 24,900′, Climb 2080′/1 min. Range 720 miles/500 lb. bomb, 1675 miles as scout.

In the meantime, Brewster had designed the larger XSB2A-1 ordered April 4, 1939. Except for wheels retracting into the wing and a dummy power-operated turret for the gunner, the XSB2A-1 was rather similar to its smaller predecessor. Known as the Brewster 340 on company records, it was powered by a 1700 hp Wright R-2600 Cyclone and a three-bladed propeller in a large spinner, and carried a 1000 lb. bomb internally.

Even before the prototype's appearance in August 1941, production contracts had been placed by Britain, the Dutch East Indies, and the United States Navy (the day before Christmas 1940). Production models had armor and self-sealing fuel tanks and a long transparent enclosure, but did not provide the turret planned for the prototype. Those built for Britain were named Bermudas while Navy versions were called Buccaneers. The first Bermudas began appearing in July 1942 and were similar to 160 planes built for the East Indies which the Navy took over on March 8, 1943, under the designation SB2A-4. With instrument panels still inscribed in Dutch, they were used by Marines for training. Armament included eight .30-caliber guns: two in the nose, four in the wings, and two in the rear cockpit, as well as a 1000-lb. bomb.

BREWSTER XSB2A-1
Wright R-2600-8, 1700 hp take-off, 1350 hp at 13,000′
DIMENSIONS: Span 47′, Lg. 38′, Ht. 16′ 1″, Wing Area 379 sq. ft.
WEIGHT: Empty 6935 lb., Gross 10,168 lb., Max. 10,982 lb. Fuel 304–395 gal.
PERFORMANCE: Speed—Top 311 mph at 15,000′, Cruising 157 mph, Landing 70 mph. Service Ceiling 27,000′, Climb 2310′/1 min. Range 980 miles/1000 lb. bomb, 1570 miles as scout.

MFR

BREWSTER SB2A-4
Wright R-2600-8A, 1700 hp take-off, 1450 hp at 12,000′
DIMENSIONS: As SB2A-2
WEIGHT: Empty 9785 lb., Gross 12,663 lb., Max. 13,811 lb. Fuel 174–421 gal.
PERFORMANCE: Speed—Top 275 mph at 12,000′, Cruising 155 mph, Landing 86 mph. Service Ceiling 25,400′, Climb 2190′/1 min. Range 750 miles/500 lb. bomb, 1750 miles as scout.

PMB

MFR

CURTISS XSB2C-1
Wright R-2600-8, 1700 hp take-off, 1450 hp at 12,000′
DIMENSIONS: Span 49′ 9″, Lg. 35′ 4″, Ht. 15′ 5″, Wing Area 422 sq. ft.
WEIGHT: Empty 7122 lb., Gross 10,261 lb., Max. 10,859 lb. Fuel 270–400 gal.
PERFORMANCE: Speed—Top 322 mph at 14,600′, 290 mph at s. l., Cruising 155 mph, Landing 69 mph. Service Ceiling 29,975′, Climb 2380′/1 min. Range 996 miles/1000 lb. bomb, 1620 miles as scout, 2260 miles ferry.

CURTISS SB2C-1 AMC

CURTISS SB2C-1
Wright R-2600-8, 1700 hp take-off, 1450 hp at 12,000′
DIMENSIONS: Span 49′ 9′, Lg. 36′ 8″, Ht. 13′ 2″, Wing Area 422 sq. ft.
WEIGHT: Empty 10,114 lb., Gross 14,730 lb., Max. 16,607 lb. Fuel 320–566 gal.
PERFORMANCE: Speed—Top 281 mph at 12,400′, 265 mph at s. l., Cruising 158 mph, Landing 79 mph. Service Ceiling 24,700′, Climb 1750′/1 min. Range 1110 miles/1000 lb. bomb, 1895 miles max.

AMC

Similar in appearance were 80 SB2A-2 Buccaneers built on the Navy contract and armed with two .50-caliber nose guns, two .30-caliber wing guns, and two .30-caliber flexible guns. The last model built was 60 SB2A-3s which had folding wings and arresting gear for carrier operation.

There were numerous production delays before the last of 750 dive bombers was completed in May 1944 at a Johnsville facility in Bucks County, Pennsylvania. Neither 450 Bermudas for Britain nor the Navy Buccaneers ever fired a shot in action as far as can be determined. Some Bermudas were used for target towing until the entire lot was "reduced to produce" in April 1945.

HELLDIVERS AT WAR

The most widely used American dive bomber was first ordered May 15, 1939, and flown as a prototype in November 1940. A chunky all-metal mid-wing monoplane, the Curtiss XSB2C-1 two-seater inherited the name Helldiver from earlier Curtiss dive bombers.

MFR

CURTISS XSB2C-2

Production models ordered November 29, 1940, incorporated over 800 changes, including a larger tail, self-sealing fuel tanks of increased capacity, and addition of 195 lbs. of armor. Instead of two .50-caliber fixed guns on the cowl, four were placed in the wings of the first 200 SB2C-1s. Later Helldivers had two 20-mm. wing guns instead. The observer operated two .30-caliber flexible guns concealed beneath the folding fairing at the rear of the cockpit enclosure. A 1700 hp Wright R-2600-8 Cyclone turned a three-bladed propeller, and wings folded upward for carrier stowage. A 1000-lb. bomb in an internal bay could be dropped from a dive braked by perforated wing flaps.

Although the first of 978 SB2C-1s was flying in June 1942, production at a new Columbus, Ohio, plant was slow gathering volume, and Helldivers did not go into action until November 11, 1943. One SB2C-1 fitted with twin floats became the XSB2C-2.

A 1900 hp R-2600-20 Cyclone with a four-bladed propeller powered 1112 SB2C-3s delivered in 1944, and followed by 2045 SB2C-4s, which added wing fittings for eight 5 in. rockets or 1000 lbs. of additional bombs, and an early type of radar. The 970 SB2C-5s which began appearing in February 1945 had a larger fuel capacity than the previous models. A 2100 hp R-2600-22 and larger internal fuel tanks were modifications made to the single XSB2C-6.

When Helldiver production ended October 1945, 5106 had been finished at Columbus, and 900 fixed wing A-25As had been built for the Air Force at St. Louis. In addition, two Canadian factories had produced Helldivers: 300 from Fairchild designated SBF and 894 from the Canadian Car and Foundry plant designated SBW. Twenty-six of the latter went to the Fleet Air Arm of Britain, but were not used operationally.

Helldivers were the standard Navy dive bombers during the last two years of the war, and the last squadron was not retired from service until 1949. Some went to Italy after the war, and 50 were given to Greece for use in the civil war there.

USN

CURTISS SB2C-3 (XSB2C-3 shown)
Wright R-2600-20, 1900 hp take-off, 1450 hp at 15,000′
DIMENSIONS: As SB2C-1
WEIGHT: Empty 10,400 lb., Gross 14,042 lb., Max. 16,471 lb. Fuel 320–566 gal.
PERFORMANCE: Speed—Top 294 mph at 16,700′, 269 mph at s. l., Cruising 158 mph, Landing 79.5 mph. Service Ceiling 29,300′, Climb 1830′/1 min. Range 1165 miles/1000 lb. bomb, 1925 miles max.

CURTISS SB2C-4
Wright R-2600-20, 1900 hp take-off, 1450 hp at 15,000′
DIMENSIONS: As SB2C-1
WEIGHT: Empty 10,547 lb., Gross 14,189 lb., Max. 16,616 lb. Fuel 320–566 gal.
PERFORMANCE: Speed—Top 295 mph at 16,700′, 270 mph at s. l., Cruising 158 mph, Landing 84 mph. Service Ceiling 29,100′, Climb 1800′/1 min. Range 1165 miles/1000 lb. bomb, 1235 miles normal as scout.

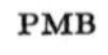
PMB

CURTISS SB2C-5
Wright R-2600-20, 1900 hp take-off, 1450 hp at 15,000′
DIMENSIONS: As SB2C-1
WEIGHT: Empty 10,589 lb., Gross 14,415 lb., Max. 16,287 lb. Fuel 355–655 gal.
PERFORMANCE: Speed—Top 290 mph at 16,500′, 267 mph at s. l., Cruising 161 mph, Landing 92 mph. Service Ceiling 27,600′, Climb 1850′/1 min. Range 1324 miles.

PMB

MFR

NORTHROP N-3PB
Wright R-1820G-205A, 1200 hp
DIMENSIONS: Span 48′ 11″, Lg. 38′, Ht. 12′, Wing Area 377 sq. ft.
WEIGHT: Empty 6560 lb., Gross 10,600 lb. Fuel 320 gal.
PERFORMANCE: Speed—Top 257 mph at 16,400′, Cruising 215 mph, Landing 65 mph. Service Ceiling 28,800′, Climb 2540′/1 min. Range 1400 miles max.

THE AVENGERS

The prewar period that produced so many dive bombers showed less interest in the more expensive torpedo planes. After 1935s XTBD-1, a new single-engined torpedo type did not appear until 1941.

One might consider the Northrop[1] N-3PM low-wing seaplane a torpedo type, because it had the capacity to carry a torpedo or a ton of bombs between its twin floats. Designed for Norway in April 1940 to patrol fiords, it was used by Norwegian pilots based in Iceland for antisubmarine operations. Twenty-four were completed from January to March 1941, powered by Wright R-1820-G205A Cyclones giving 1200 hp for take-off. They carried three men, four .50-caliber fixed wing guns, a .30-caliber flexible gun, and another .30-caliber gun aimed through a trap door in the belly.

[1] The original Northrop firm was bought out by Douglas, but this was a new firm set up by John Northrop, who left his old firm on January 1, 1938.

However, the standard torpedo type through all but the first six months of the war was the Grumman Avenger. A contract for two XTBF-1 prototypes was ordered April 8, 1940. Two days before Christmas in 1940, 286 production TBF-1s were ordered, for the need to replace the older Devastators could not await the prototype's first flight on August 1, 1941. Wartime needs led to orders for more TBFs on January 2, 1942, and March 16, and General Motors also received a contract for Avengers on March 23. Designated TBM-1, they were built at the Eastern Aircraft Division in Trenton, New Jersey.

A fat-bodied mid-wing monoplane with a 1700 hp R-2600-8, the TBF-1 had a crew of three, internal bays for a torpedo or a 2000-lb. bomb, and a power-operated turret. The landing gear retracted into the wings, which folded back for carrier stowage. The Avenger's pilot released the torpedo and fired a .30-caliber fixed gun on the cowl's right side, and the gunner's turret was provided with a .50-caliber gun. Between them sat a bombardier who could climb down to a compartment behind the bomb bay to set the torpedo, operate the bombsight or fire the .30-caliber ventral gun.

The Avenger somewhat resembled the Wildcat fighter, enough to deceive at least one Japanese ace who flew into a near-fatal blast from the turret gun. Torpedoing enemy warships, bombing enemy bases, and making the Navy's first air-to-surface rocket attack—January 11, 1944, on a U-boat—the Avenger played a brilliant war role.

GRUMMAN TBF-1
Wright R-2600-8, 1700 hp take-off, 1450 hp at 12,000′
DIMENSIONS: Span 54′ 2″, Lg. 40′, Ht. 16′ 5″, Wing Area 490 sq. ft.
WEIGHT: Empty 10,080 lb., Gross 13,667 lb., Max. 15,905 lb. Fuel 335–395 gal.
PERFORMANCE: Speed—Top 271 mph at 12,000′, 269 mph/torpedo, 251 mph at s. l., Cruising 145 mph, Landing 76 mph. Service Ceiling 22,400′, Climb 1430′/1 min. Range 1215 miles/torpedo, 1450 miles as scout.

USN

JANSSON

GENERAL MOTORS TBM-1C
Wright R-2600-8, 1700 hp take-off, 1450 hp at 12,000′
DIMENSIONS: As TBF-1
WEIGHT: Empty 10,555 lb., Gross 16,412 lb., Max. 17,364 lb. Fuel 335–726 gal.
PERFORMANCE: Speed—Top 257 mph at 12,000′, Cruising 153 mph, Landing 77 mph. Service Ceiling 21,400′, Climb 10,000′/13 min. Range 1105 miles/torpedo, 2335 miles max.

PMB

GENERAL MOTORS TBM-3
Wright R-2600-20, 1900 hp take-off, 1450 hp at 15,000′
DIMENSIONS: As TBF-1
WEIGHT: Empty 10,843 lb., Gross 16,761 lb., Max. 18,250 lb. Fuel 335–810 gal.
PERFORMANCE: Speed—Top 267 mph at 15,000′, Cruising 151 mph, Landing 78 mph. Service Ceiling 23,400′, Climb 1170′/1 min. Range 1130 miles/torpedo, 1565 miles/drop tanks, 2530 miles max.

Grumman built 2290 TBF-1s from February 1942 to December 1943, including 402 lend-leased to Britain as the Avenger I. One modified with an XR-2600-10 Cyclone became the XTBF-2. Delivery on the TBM-1 began in September 1942, and was followed in September 1943 by the TBM-1C which could carry two .50-caliber wing guns, extra drop tanks, and additional armor.

A Wright R-2600-20 powered the TBM-3, which appeared April 1944 with fittings under the wings for rockets, or extra drop tanks, and radar. Later versions included the TBM-3E and the TBM-3W, the latter with a large APS-20 radome protruding from the bomb bay. Eastern Aircraft built 2882 TBM-1s and 4664 TBM-3s, including 334 TBM-1 (Avenger II) and 222 TBM-3 (Avenger III) lend-leased to the Royal Navy.

GENERAL MOTORS TBM-3E
Wright R-2600-20, 1900 hp take-off, 1450 hp at 15,000′
DIMENSIONS: Span 54′ 2″, Lg. 40′ 11½″, Wing Area 490 sq. ft.
WEIGHT: Empty 10,545 lb., Gross 14,160 lb., Max. 17,895 lb. Fuel 335–810 gal.
PERFORMANCE: Speed—Top 276 mph at 16,500′, 251 mph at s. l., Cruising 147 mph, Landing 81 mph. Service Ceiling 30,100′, Climb 2060′/1 min. Range 1010 miles/torpedo, 1145 miles normal, 1920 miles as scout.

PMB

The first British squadron to use Avengers formed at Norfolk and actually operated from the U.S.S. *Saratoga* in the spring of 1943, before transferring to a British carrier. Although withdrawn from fleet service after the war, some 80 Avenger A.S.4s (TBM-3E) reentered service in 1953. At home, the TBM-3 was the standard U. S. Navy torpedo plane at the end of the war and remained in service until retirement in June 1954.

An attempt to develop a second source of supply for wartime torpedo types did not prove successful. On April 22, 1940, the Vought XTBU-1, powered by a Pratt & Whitney R-2800-20 Wasp, was ordered. Completed December 1941, it was rather similar to the Avenger's layout, but had a high rounded fin and rounded wingtips. Armament included a .50-caliber fixed cowl gun, another .50-caliber gun in the power-operated rear turret, and a .30-caliber ventral gun, as well as the torpedo or bomb load.

The XTBUs high speed made it an attractive alternate to the Avenger, but Vought was too occupied with fighters to undertake its production. On September 6, 1943, Consolidated contracted to build 1100 of this type, now designated TBY-2 Sea Wolf, in a new Allentown, Pennsylvania, plant. The first TBY was delivered in November 1944 but only 180 were completed before the contract was canceled due to the slowness in getting the type into production. Similar in appearance to its prototype, the TBY-2 had three .50-caliber fixed guns, one .50-caliber gun in the power turret, a .30-caliber ventral gun, 380 lbs. of armor, and radar on the starboard wing. None were ever used in combat.

At the very outset of the war, the combined attack of dive bombers and torpedo planes demonstrated a striking power and reach far beyond that of the traditional warship battle line. No Allied capital ship was ever lost to the guns of a Japanese battleship, but in the very first week of the war Japanese planes destroyed four U.S. and British battleships and disabled six others. The great naval battles of the war became, in the main, contests between opposing fleets of aircraft. As American aircraft grew in numbers and efficiency, carrier-type attack planes sank six of ten Japanese battleships sunk during the war, as well as eleven of 15 carriers and ten of 14 heavy cruisers lost. Of the 12 remaining large Japanese ships, eight were sunk by submarines, and four by surface ships. Horizontal bombing of Army types caused no losses of heavy ships.

Achieving these results required a remarkable increase in the number of Naval attack aircraft from 709 scout bombers, and 100 torpedo planes in December 1941, to a total of 5101 scout bombers and 4937 torpedo bombers on June 30, 1945. These air weapons destroyed the Japanese Navy, virtually ended the era of the battleship, and established a naval superiority over the rest of the world never before seen in history.

COMBINATION: ONE-MAN TORPEDO BOMBERS

The carrier attack planes which won the victory at sea were of two patterns established a decade before the war: two-seat dive bombers and three-seat torpedo bombers. A new pattern developed during the war combined dive-bombing and torpedo attack in one single-seat aircraft. This was now possible because the airplane's increasing power and strength permitted accommodation of either bombs or a torpedo, and because the weight handicap of a gunner and his weapons seemed to have been made unnecessary by control of the air by American fighters.

MFR

CONSOLIDATED-VULTEE TBY-2

Pratt & Whitney R-2800-20, 2000 hp take-off, 1600 hp at 13,500′

DIMENSIONS: Span 56′ 11″, Lg. 39′ 2½″, Ht. 15′ 6″, Wing Area 439.5 sq. ft.

WEIGHT: Empty 11,022 lb., Gross 17,011 lb., Max. 18,488 lb. Fuel 495 gal.

PERFORMANCE: Speed—Top 306 mph at 13,000′, 293 mph at s. l., Cruising 168 mph, Landing 80 mph. Service Ceiling 27,200′, Climb 1720′/1 min., 10,000′/7.2 min. Range 1505 miles/one torpedo.

Wartime development of this type began with the Douglas XSB2D-1 two-seater, which had an internal bomb bay, a 20-mm. fixed gun at the bend of each gulled low wing, and a .50-caliber gun in an upper and a lower remote-controlled rear turret. Two prototypes ordered June 30, 1941, but not completed until April 1943, had a Wright R-3350-14 and were the first carrier planes designed with retractable tricycle landing gear, first tested on a modified BT-1 in October 1938.

When the Navy called for a single-place type combining bombing and torpedo work, Douglas redesigned

VOUGHT XTBU-1

Pratt & Whitney R-2800-20, 2000 hp take-off, 1600 hp at 13,500′

DIMENSIONS: Span 57′ 2″, Lg. 39′, Ht. 18′ 7″, Wing Area 439 sq. ft.

WEIGHT: Empty 10,504 lb., Gross 16,247 lb. Fuel 317–587 gal.

PERFORMANCE: Speed—Top 311 mph at 14,700′, 295 mph at s. l., Cruising 165 mph, Landing 77 mph. Service Ceiling 27,900′, Climb 1820′/1 min. Range 1400 miles/torpedo.

MFR

MFR

DOUGLAS XSB2D-1
Wright R-3350-14, 2300 hp take-off, 1900 hp at 14,000′
DIMENSIONS: Span 45′, Lg. 38′ 7″, Ht. 16′ 11″, Wing Area 375 sq. ft.
WEIGHT: Empty 12,458 lb., Gross 16,273 lb., Max. 19,140 lb. Fuel 350–550 gal.
PERFORMANCE: Speed—Top 346 mph at 16,100′, Cruising 180 mph, Landing 88 mph. Service Ceiling 24,400′, Climb 1710′/1 min. Range 1480 miles/1000 lb. bomb.

MFR

CURTISS XBTC-2
Pratt & Whitney R-4360-14, 3000 hp take-off, 2400 hp at 13,500′
DIMENSIONS: Span 50′, Lg. 38′ 7″, Ht. 16′ 8″, Wing Area 406 sq. ft.
WEIGHT: Empty 13,947 lb., Gross 17,910 lb., Max. 20,944 lb. Fuel 360–690 gal.
PERFORMANCE: Speed—Top 386 mph at 16,200′, 322 mph/torpedo, Cruising 180 mph, Landing 85 mph. Service Ceiling 28,000′, Climb 2610′/1 min. Range 1245 miles/torpedo with 460 gal.

PMB

PMB

DOUGLAS BTD-1
Wright R-3350-14, 2300 hp take-off, 1900 hp at 14,000′
DIMENSIONS: Span 45′, Lg. 38′ 7″, Ht. 13′ 7″, Wing Area 373 sq. ft.
WEIGHT: Empty 12,900 lb., Gross 18,140 lb., Max. 19,000 lb. Fuel 460–640 gal.
PERFORMANCE: Speed—Top 344 mph at 16,100′, 340 mph/torpedo, 319 mph at s. l., Cruising 188 mph, Landing 91.5 mph. Service Ceiling 23,600′, Climb 1650′/1 min. Range 1480 miles/torpedo, 2140 miles max.

DOUGLAS XTB2D-1
Pratt & Whitney XR-4360-8, 3000 hp take-off, 2400 hp at 13,500′
DIMENSIONS: Span 70′, Lg. 46′, Ht. 22′ 7″, Wing Area 605 sq. ft.
WEIGHT: Empty 18,405 lb., Gross 28,545 lb., Max. 34,760 lb. Fuel 774–1374 gal.
PERFORMANCE: Speed—Top 340 mph at 15,600′, 312 mph/torpedo, 292 mph at s. l., Cruising 141 mph, Landing 75 mph. Service Ceiling 24,500′, Climb 1390′/1 min. Range 1250 miles/torpedo, 2880 miles max.

KAISER XBTK-1
Pratt & Whitney R-2800-34W, 2100 hp take-off, 1850 hp at 16,000′
DIMENSIONS: Span 48′ 8″, Lg. 38′ 11″, Ht. 15′ 8″, Wing Area 380 sq. ft.
WEIGHT: Empty 9959 lb., Gross 12,728 lb., Max. 15,782 lb. Fuel 275–375 gal.
PERFORMANCE: Speed—Top 373 mph at 18,000′, 342 mph at s. l., 297–258 mph/torpedo, Cruising 158 mph, Landing 80 mph. Service Ceiling 33,400′, Climb 3550′/1 min. Range 1250 miles/torpedo, 1370 miles/1000 lb. bomb.

PMB

the XSB2D-1 by removing the rear gunner and his turrets and enlarging the bomb bay to accommodate a torpedo, 3200 lbs. of bombs, or added fuel tankage. The pair of 20-mm. guns in the gulled wings was retained, along with the R-3350-14, the prop spinner, and tricycle gear. Dive brakes were installed on the fuselage sides. The original April 9, 1942, contract was increased on August 31, 1943, to 358 Douglas BTD-1 Destroyers and delivery began in June 1944. Only 28 were completed, however, because of cancellations.

The next Douglas torpedo bomber was the large three-place XTB2D-1 ordered October 31, 1943, and powered by a Pratt & Whitney XR-4360-8 turning eight-bladed counterrotating propellers. Intended for the big *Midway* class carriers, the two XTB2D-1 prototypes had tricycle landing gear, and a low wing with a flat center section and dihedral on the outer panels. Not completed until February 1945, the heavy Douglas carried four .50-caliber fixed guns in the wings, three .50-caliber guns in remote-controlled turrets, 527 lbs. of armor, and up to 4000 lbs. of bombs.

Using one man and one aircraft to do work previously assigned to two different types with two or three crewmen had obvious advantages for carrier operation, whatever increased strain was put on the pilot. Elimination of defensive guns seemed justified by the superiority of Navy fighters, and the limited success of rear gunners in action. During 1944, four single-seat bomber-torpedo designs were begun, all of them low-wing monoplanes with conventional tail-down landing gear and bomb load carried externally. Internal racks like those of the BTD enabled higher cruising speeds to the target, but external racks present fewer design problems and can accommodate a greater variety of weapons shapes. In the order contracts were let, the new single-seaters were the Curtiss BTC, Kaiser-Fleetwings BTK, Martin BTM, and Douglas BT2D.

Using the Pratt & Whitney 3000 hp Wasp Major, the Curtiss design began with an XBTC-1 contract on December 31, 1943, became the XBTC-2 with a change in engine model and was not accepted until July 1946. Armed with four 20-mm. wing guns and powered by an R-4360-14 with contrarotating six-bladed propellers, the XBTC-2 had the sturdy appearance typical of the low-wing attack types.

Lightest of the new bomber-torpedo single-seaters was the Kaiser-Fleetwings XBTK-1, ordered March 31, 1944, and flown early in April 1945. Four were completed, and a fifth used for static tests at the Bristol, Pennsylvania, plant. A Pratt & Whitney R-2800-34W was the first engine installation cooled by using exhaust gases to pump air through the nose cowl and exhausting it in stainless steel ducts at the fuselage sides. The wings had picket-type trailing-edge dive brakes and folded vertically to reduce stowage span to 20 feet. Two 20-mm. wing guns, 230 lbs. of armor, and a self-sealing fuel tank behind the pilot were installed, along with external racks for up to 5000 lbs. of bombs, rockets, torpedo, or radar or drop tanks for scouting.

Neither the Curtiss nor Kaiser types were adopted by the Navy, which instead placed large orders for the Douglas and Martin types that became so familiar in the postwar period.

Chapter 26: Postwar Attack Types 1945-59

THE SKYRAIDER AND ITS COMPETITORS

The most widely used attack type of the post-war period was the Douglas Skyraider, designed in June 1944. Twenty-five XBT2D-1 pre-production prototypes were ordered July 21, 1944, and the first was flown March 18, 1945. Instead of the gulled low-drag wing of the BTD, the Skyraider used a straight high-lift wing to enable quicker take-offs with larger loads. Powered by a Wright R-3350-24W with four-bladed propeller, the Skyraider carried two 20-mm. wing guns with 400 rounds, 208 lbs. of armor, two or three tons of bombs, rockets or torpedoes, or drop tanks and APS-4 radar.

These weapons, and any scouting necessary were the responsibility of a single pilot under the bubble canopy. The wheels turned through 90° as they retracted backward into the wings, which folded upward for stowage, and dive brakes were placed at the fuselage sides. On April 18, 1945, an order was placed for 548 production Skyraiders, reduced to 277 after V-J Day, and redesignated AD-1, under the new designation system. Delivery began November 1946 on 242 AD-1 and 35 AD-1Q, the latter a radar countermeasures version with a technician in the fuselage behind the pilot operating devices to identify and jam hostile radar. An XAD-1W early warning prototype, converted from a BT2D-1, had a huge belly radome, two radarmen in the fuselage, and no dive brakes or guns. Two AD-1N, also converted from BT2Ds, had radar and a searchlight under the wings and two radar operators for night attacks.

Competing with the Douglas Skyraider for attack contracts was Martin's Mauler powered by a 3000 hp Pratt & Whitney R-4360-4 Wasp Major and four-bladed propeller. Similar in appearance to the Skyraider, it was a heavier type with four 20-mm. guns in the wings, 297 lbs. of armor, and picket-type dive brakes. Two XBTM-1 prototypes were ordered May 31, 1944, and 750 production BTMs puchased January 15, 1945. The prototypes began tests in November 1945 and the production contract, redesignated AM-1 and cut back to 149 planes, was delivered between late 1947 and October 1949. In service they proved remarkable weight lifters, on one occasion lifting a 14,179-lb. useful load, including 10,689 lbs. of ordnance (3 torpedoes, 12 250-lb. bombs, guns and ammunition). Gross weight on that flight was 29,332 lbs.

Ten Curtiss XBT2C-1s ordered March 27, 1945, used the same engine as the AD-1. First appearing January 1946, they resembled the XBTC-2, and had two 20-mm. wing guns, up to 4000 lbs. of bombs or torpedoes, 182 lbs. of armor, and APS-4 radar. The pilot sat under a bubble canopy and a second crewman could be accommodated behind him within the fuselage. Only nine of the Navy's last Curtiss type were actually completed.

Grumman had not neglected the possibility of building themselves the weapon to replace the Avenger. They had designed an XTB2F-1 with two R-2800-22 Wasps, an enlargement of the twin-engined F7F fighter. This was canceled in January 1945 in favor of the Grumman G-70, designed October 1944 and winning a February 19, 1945, contract for two XTB3F prototypes.

On December 1, 1945, the XTB3F-1 made its first flight, with a 2300 hp Pratt & Whitney R-2800-46 and pilot and observer sitting side by side over an internal weapons bay that accommodated two torpedoes or 4000 lbs. of bombs. The wings had provision for two 20-mm. guns, wells for the outward-retracting main wheels, and folded backward in typical Grumman fashion. The prototype had a Westinghouse 19XB jet ejecting 1600-lb. thrust from a tail nozzle, providing an estimated top speed of 356 mph for short bursts. This idea was abandoned before the jet was ever

MFR

DOUGLAS XBT2D-1
Wright R-3350-24W, 2500 hp take-off, 2200 hp at 11,000′
DIMENSIONS: Span 50′, Lg. 39′ 5″, Ht. 9′, Wing Area 400 sq. ft.
WEIGHT: Empty 10,093 lb., Gross 13,500 lb., Max. 17,500 lb. Fuel 365–665 gal.
PERFORMANCE: Speed—Top 375 mph at 13,600′, 357 mph at s. l. clean, 303–271 mph/torpedo, Cruising 164 mph, Landing 83 mph. Service Ceiling 33,200′, Climb 3680′/1 min. Range 1427 miles/torpedo with 515 gal.

MARTIN XBTM-1
Pratt & Whitney XR-4360-4, 3000 hp take-off, 2400 hp at 13,500′
DIMENSIONS: Span 50′, Lg. 41′ 2″, Ht. 16′ 10″, Wing Area 496 sq. ft.
WEIGHT: Empty 14,296 lb., Gross 19,000 lb., Max. 23,000 lb. Fuel 500–800 gal.
PERFORMANCE: Speed—Top 367 mph at 16,000′, 341 mph at s. l., Cruising 178 mph, Landing 88 mph. Service Ceiling 26,800′, Climb 2480′/1 min. Range 1200 miles/torpedo, 2350 miles max.

MARTIN AM-1
Pratt & Whitney R-3350-4, 2975 hp take-off, 2400 hp at 16,200′
DIMENSIONS: As XBTM-1
WEIGHT: Empty 14,500 lb., Gross 19,200 lb., Max. 23,386 lb. Fuel 510–810 gal.
PERFORMANCE: Speed—Top 367 mph at 11,600′, 350 mph at s. l., Cruising 189 mph, Landing 97 mph. Service Ceiling 30,500′, Climb 2780′/1 min. Range 1800 miles/2000 lbs. bombs and 810 gal.

WL

PMB

DOUGLAS AD-1
Wright R-3350-24W, 2500 hp take-off, 2200 hp at 11,500′
DIMENSIONS: Span 50′, Lg. 39′ 5″, Ht. 9′, Wing Area 400 sq. ft.
WEIGHT: Empty 10,508 lb., Gross 13,924 lb., Max. 18,030 lb. Fuel 365–665 gal.
PERFORMANCE: Speed—Top 366 mph at 13,500′, 348 mph at s. l., Cruising 185 mph, Landing 84 mph. Service Ceiling 33,000′, Climb 3590′/1 min. Range 1935 miles/2000 lbs. bombs.

WL

GRUMMAN XTB3F-1S
Pratt & Whitney R-2800-46W, 2300 hp take-off
DIMENSIONS: Span 60′, Lg. 42′ 11″, Ht. 14′ 3″, Wing Area 549 sq. ft.
WEIGHT: Empty 15,035 lb., Gross 19,125 lb., Max. 21,352 lb. Fuel 420–720 gal.
PERFORMANCE: Speed—Top 278 mph at 2100′, 272 mph at s. l., Cruising 155 mph, Landing 85 mph. Service Ceiling 21,900′. Range 1578 miles.

H. G. MARTIN

MFR

CURTISS XBT2C-1
Wright R-3350-24, 2500 hp take-off, 1900 hp at 14,800′
DIMENSIONS: Span 47′ 7″, Lg. 38′ 8″, Ht. 16′ 5″, Wing Area 416 sq. ft.
WEIGHT: Empty 12,268 lb., Gross 15,975 lb., Max. 19,022 lb. Fuel 410–710 gal.
PERFORMANCE: Speed—Top 349 mph at 17,000′, 313 mph/torpedo, Cruising 175 mph, Landing 90 mph. Service Ceiling 28,100′, Climb 2590′/1 min. Range 1435 miles/torpedo.

GRUMMAN AF-2S (AF-2W in foreground)
Pratt & Whitney R-2800-48W, 2400 hp take-off, 1800 hp at 6500′
DIMENSIONS: Span 60′ 8″, Lg. 43′ 4″, Ht. 16′ 2″, Wing Area 560 sq. ft.
WEIGHT: Empty 14,580 lb., Gross 22,500 lb., Max. 25,500 lb.
PERFORMANCE: Speed—Top 317 mph at 16,000′, 302 mph at s. l., Landing 82.5 mph. Service Ceiling 32,500′, Climb 1850′/1 min. Range 1500 miles, or 8 hrs. endurance.

MFR

tested. Instead, the prototype was retailored for antisubmarine search, the jet engine removed, and a large radome installed in the bomb bay. This version was labeled XTB3F-1S. Antisubmarine warfare increasingly concerned the postwar Navy and a production contract first placed May 3, 1948, and eventually increased to cover 62 AF-2S and 63 AF-2W Grumman Guardians, provided the Navy with its first specialized carrier-based ASW aircraft.

First flown November 17, 1949, production Guardians used the 2400 hp R-2800-48W and came in two versions, AF-2W and AF-2S. They worked in pairs; an AF-2W with the big belly radome and four men flew at low altitudes searching the surface for a submarine periscope. When the AF-2W located a target, an accompanying AF-2S pinpointed it with APS-30 radar under the starboard wing, illuminated the target, if necessary, with a searchlight under the port wing, and dropped depth charges or homing torpedo from the weapons bay. A pair of vertical fins were added to the Guardian's stabilizer to compensate for the radome's effect.

While Grumman Guardians were issued to special antisubmarine "Killer" carrier groups, Douglas Skyraiders made up the bulk of attack equipment. The AD-1 was followed in 1948 by the AD-2, which had a 2700 hp R-3350-26W, new cockpit arrangement, and more fuel. A total of 156 AD-2s and 22 AD-2Qs were purchased, followed by the AD-3, differing only in a strengthened internal structure. A total of 125 AD-3, 23 AD-3Q, 31 AD-3W, and 15 AD-3N aircraft were purchased.

Fiscal 1949 funds were used to order 236 AD-4, 69 AD-4W, 65 AD-4N, and 39 AD-4Qs, which introduced automatic pilot and new electronics equipment. Out-

PMB

DOUGLAS AD-2Q
Wright R-3350-26W, 2700 hp take-off, 3020 hp mil.
DIMENSIONS: As AD-2
WEIGHT: Empty 11,159 lb., Gross 17,140 lb., Max. 19,143 lb. Fuel 380 gal.
PERFORMANCE: Speed—Top 317 mph at 18,300′, Cruising 205 mph, Landing 85 mph. Service Ceiling 31,500′, Climb 2590′/1 min. Range 850 miles.

break of the Korean War brought combat action and new orders for the Skyraider, which served as the standard dive bomber throughout three years of warfare, striking from both carrier and land bases. It was well armed for this purpose, for besides the twin 20-mm. guns, there were three large pylons which could each hold a 2150-lb. torpedo, 2000-lb. bomb, or 11.75 in. rocket, and twelve small studs handled either 5 in. rockets or 250-lb. bombs. Three 150-gallon drop tanks could be attached to the larger pylons to supplement internal fuel tankage. An AD-4D special weapons version of 1953 had four 20-mm. wing guns, provisions for an atomic weapon, and once lifted a useful load of 14,941 lbs. in addition to its basic weight of 11,798 lbs.

DOUGLAS AD-2
Wright R-3350-26W, 2700 hp take-off, 3020 hp mil.
DIMENSIONS: Span 50′, Lg. 38′ 2″, Ht. 15′ 5″, Wing Area 400 sq. ft.
WEIGHT: Empty 10,546 lb., Gross 16,268 lb., Max. 18,263 lb. Fuel 380 gal.
PERFORMANCE: Speed—Top 321 mph at 18,300′, Cruising 198 mph, Landing 83 mph. Service Ceiling 32,700′, Climb 2800′/1 min. Range 915 miles.

DON WALSH

WL

DOUGLAS AD-3 (also AD-3N data)
Wright R-3350-26W, 2700 hp take-off, 3020 hp mil.
DIMENSIONS: As AD-2
WEIGHT: Empty 10,812 (11,483) lb., Gross 16,520 (18,044) lb., Max. 18,515 (19,664) lb. Fuel 380 gal.
PERFORMANCE: Speed—Top 321 (296) mph at 18,300′, Cruising 200 (197) mph, Landing 84 (87) mph. Service Ceiling 32,300′ (28,800′), Climb 2760′/1 min. (2260′/1 min.). Range 900 miles (1175 miles).

All this was a lot of ordnance for one busy airman; one is somehow not surprised to read of the AD pilot who climbed into his cockpit, began his take-off, and was airborne without noticing that the wings were still folded over his head. The AD, of course, stalled and crashed.

The next version was the AD-5, whose prototype first flew August 17, 1951, with a larger tail, four wing guns and an expanded fuselage serving as a universal chassis on which several different conversions could be made from prepared kits. The two-man flight crew sat side by side under the canopy, and up to eight passengers or four litter patients could be squeezed into the fuselage. Day or night attack, early warning, antisubmarine warfare, ambulance, cargo, or

DOUGLAS AD-4 (AD-4N in photo)
Wright R-3350-26W, 2700 hp take-off, 3020 hp mil.
DIMENSIONS: As AD-2
WEIGHT: Empty 11,138 lb., Gross 16,888 lb., Max. 18,861 lb. Fuel 380 gal.
PERFORMANCE: Speed—Top 321 mph at 18,300′, Cruising 202 mph, Landing 85 mph. Service Ceiling 32,200′, Climb 2660′/1 min. Range 900 miles.

DON WALSH

PMB

DOUGLAS AD-5
Wright R-3350-26W, 2700 hp take-off, 3020 hp mil.
DIMENSIONS: Span 50′, Lg. 40′ 1″, Ht. 15′ 10″, Wing Area 400 sq. ft.
WEIGHT: Empty 12,313 lb., Gross 18,799 lb.
PERFORMANCE: Classified

personnel transport conversions were possible. By August 1953, 670 AD-5s began superseding the AD-4s in production, but the AD-6 reverted to the standard attack configuration.

Final version of the Skyraider was the AD-7, which appeared in August 1956. When production was completed in March 1957, 3180 Skyraiders had been built in 12 years at El Segundo.

An attempt at a radical improvement in performance was made with the Douglas XA2D-1 Skyshark, powered by an Allison XT40-A-6 turboprop engine delivering 5100 hp to contrarotating six-bladed propellers and 830-lb. exhaust thrust. The wing plan was that of the AD but a thinner airfoil was used. The pilot

PMB

DOUGLAS XA2D-1
Allison XT-40-A-2, 5100 hp and 830 lbs. take-off
DIMENSIONS: Span 50′, Lg. 54′, Ht. 17′, Wing Area 400 sq. ft.
WEIGHT: Empty 12,944 lb., Gross 16,224 lb., Max. 21,764 lb. Fuel 500–800 gal.
PERFORMANCE: Speed—Top 492 mph at 27,000′, 450 mph at s. l., 442 mph/2000 lbs. bombs, Cruising 276 mph, Landing 94 mph. Service Ceiling 48,100′, Climb 7280′/1 min. Range 2200 miles max.

sat high above the engine and ahead of the fuel tank, which required a larger capacity than that of the AD because of higher fuel consumption. Four 20-mm. guns were mounted in the wings and 2000 lbs. of bombs or 300 gallons of fuel could be carried externally.

DOUGLAS AD-6 (with AD-5W in background)
Wright R-3350-26W, 2700 hp take-off, 3020 hp mil.
DIMENSIONS: Span 50′, Lg. 38′ 10″, Ht. 15′ 8″, Wing Area 400 sq. ft.
WEIGHT: Empty 11,968 lb., Gross 18,106 lb., Max. 25,000 lb.
PERFORMANCE: Classified

MFR

MFR

NORTH AMERICAN XAJ-1

Pratt & Whitney R-2800-44, 2300 hp take-off, 2215 hp at 30,000′, and Allison J33-A-19, 4000 lbs.

DIMENSIONS: Span 71′ 5″, Lg. 62′, Ht. 20′ 5″, Wing Area 835.5 sq. ft.

WEIGHT: Empty 28,307 lb., Gross 47,630 lb., Max. 51,580 lb. Fuel 1217–3317 gal.

PERFORMANCE: (Estimated) Speed—Top (all engines) 466 mph at 35,000′, 379 mph at s. l., (prop.) 393 mph at 30,000′, 304 mph at s. l., Cruising 379 mph. Service Ceiling (all engines) 41,100′, Climb 2690′/1 min. Range 2200 miles/ 10,500 lbs. bombs and 1817 gal.

The Skyshark made its first flight on May 26, 1950, but an order for ten service test examples was terminated in 1953 when mechanical troubles with the power transmission persisted.

THE BIG PUNCH

Versatile as the Navy's single-engined bombers were, they compared poorly with the strategic striking power of the Air Force's bigger weapons. This was inherent in the limitations imposed by flight-deck operations; a carrier plane can only be so big and so heavy, must have arresting gear, folding wing and specialized shipboard equipment, and thus can't have the tremendous power and armament of their heavier competitors. Comparing the AD with Army light bombers, we find it much slower, minus defensive guns, and of more limited bomb capacity; an important point when early atomic bombs were so bulky.

MFR

NORTH AMERICAN AJ-2

NORTH AMERICAN AJ-1

MFR

MFR

NORTH AMERICAN XA2J-1
Allison T40-A-6, 5100 hp
DIMENSIONS: Span 71′ 5″, Lg. 62′, Ht. 20′, Wing Area 835.5 sq. ft.
WEIGHT & PERFORMANCE: Classified

As the postwar Air Force won the predominant influence and share of the budget, the Navy hoped for an atomic punch of its own that could contribute to a strategic bombing offensive.

To acquire this capability required fitting strategic bombers to carriers, and building carriers large enough to handle strategic bombers. If the former task was a severe one for engineers, the latter involved a struggle with the national budget. Completion of the *Midway* class carriers at war's end did offer larger flight decks, and two days before V-J Day the Navy ordered from North American a prototype far advanced beyond existing equipment. A high-wing monoplane with two 2300 hp Pratt & Whitney R-2800-44 Wasps under the wings and a 4000-lb. thrust Allison J-33 jet in the fuselage, the XAJ-1 Savage carried a crew of three in a pressurized cockpit, nose radar, and an internal bomb bay with room for an atomic weapon, or over 5 tons of conventional bombs. No guns were carried, the type depending on its speed for protection. Preliminary estimates promised a range of 2200 miles with a 10,500-lb. bomb, and a top speed of 393 mph at 30,000 ft. using propellers only. The jet could be cut in to increase speed to 466 mph for short distances. Despite its size and weight, the Savage could land

MFR

DOUGLAS A3D-2
Pratt & Whitney J57-P-10, 10,500 lbs.
DIMENSIONS: Span 72′ 6″, Lg. 76′ 4″, Ht. 22′ 9″, Wing Area 780 sq. ft.
WEIGHT: Empty 38,298 lb., Gross 70,000 lb. Fuel 4385 gal.
PERFORMANCE: Classified

on the carrier with its tricycle gear, folding its wings up and the fin down to ease stowage.

After the XAJ-1s first flight on July 12, 1948, an initial production order for 28 was increased to 43 and the first production AJ-1 flew May 1949 with a reinforced canopy and the addition of wingtip tanks. Five crashes in the first 20 months of operation were more painful because of the cost; one AJ-1 cost as much as eight ADs or 18 wartime Avengers.

The first series had been built at North American's home plant in California, but the second series was produced in Columbus, Ohio, at the leased ex-Helldiver plant. The first of these appeared March 1952 as the AJ-2P with R-2800-48, a higher fin, bulbous nose, seven cameras, and more fuel for reconnaissance missions. Standard AJ-2s began appearing February 1953, but most were used as flying tankers to refuel fighters in flight, by a probe-and-drogue system fitted into the bomb bay with fuel tanks.

Another Savage development was North American's XA2J-1, flown January 4, 1952, which was similar but was powered by two Allison T40-A-6 turboprop engines turning six-bladed contrapropellers. Other changes included swept tail fin, narrower fuselage, dual nose wheel, more fuel, and two radar-aimed remote-controlled 20-mm. tail guns. Production of this type was discouraged by the same mechanical problems that frustrated the XA2D-1.

Real progress toward a naval strategic bomber required full jet power with all the fuel and weight that implied. The obvious answer was an aircraft carrier large enough to handle bigger bombers, but funds for this were hard to get. Hadn't the Navy over a hundred carriers already, including three *Midways* and 25 of the *Essex* class, several times more than all the rest of the world put together? Besides, the Air Force felt itself perfectly capable of doing all the strategic bombing necessary, and wanted any available funds invested in its own big bombers.

A huge 65,000 ton carrier was ordered August 10, 1948, by pro-Navy Defense Secretary James V. Forrestal, but was canceled April 23, 1949, by his successor in the Cabinet post, Louis Johnson. Another chance came with the Korean War, and a 59,900-ton carrier ordered on July 12, 1951, was named *Forrestal* after the late Secretary and made a flight deck for large-size bombers available.

Prospects of larger carriers led to the design of the Douglas XA3D-1 Skywarrior, which overcame the usual limitations of carrier-based aircraft so well that the Air Force ordered the same type as the B-66 light bomber. First flown October 28, 1952, the three-place XA3D-1 was the first all-jet attack type, and had an internal bay for atomic weapons, bombs, or mines. The high wing was swept back 36° and fitted with slots, folding for stowage. The fuselage contained wells for the retractable tricycle landing gear, a radar bombing system in the nose, pressure cabin, fuel tanks, and a remote-controlled radar-aimed Westinghouse tail turret with two 20-mm. guns.

Two prototypes used 7500-lb. thrust Westinghouse J40-WE-12 jets in pods below the wings, but production A3D-1s had the 10,000-lb. thrust Pratt & Whitney J57-P-6, when first flown September 16, 1953. Although type characteristics are classified, a top speed of over 600 mph, high ceiling, and long range give the Skywarrior strategic capabilities. More recent variants include the A3D-2 of 1957 with J57-P-10s, the A3D-2P (photographic) of July 1958, the A3D-2Q, a seven-place electronics countermeasures type, and the A3D-2T trainer.

Chapter 27: Summary

SEARCH AND ATTACK

Since the Korean War, details of attack-plane development and procurement have been secret, but a survey of contemporary types shows a situation far different than before World War II, when this category existed mainly to torpedo enemy battleships or bomb enemy carriers. Today there are few potentially hostile capital ships left to sink, and targets of the future will most often be submarines and land installations.

Douglas designs have always strongly influenced naval attack development and their Skyraiders were for many years the primary carrier-based weapon and served in Korea as ground support aircraft. Today they are being replaced by aircraft designed for three separate attack specialties. The Grumman S2F Tracker was designed from the very beginning to find and attack enemy submarines, the Douglas A3D Skywarrior has long-range nuclear bombing capability, and the little Douglas A4D Skyhawk does the work in between, against sea or short targets.

Special carrier air groups have been formed with the mission of attacking submarines in high priority areas, especially in mid-ocean areas outside the range of shore-based patrol planes. Rather than speed or defensive firepower, this mission requires the endurance and elaborate detection equipment formerly common only to large patrol bombers. The first effort of carrier types to acquire this capability was the uneconomical two-plane search and attack partnership of the Grumman AF-2 Guardians or special conversions of the Douglas AD Skyraiders.

Combining search and attack functions into one aircraft, the Grumman XS2F-1 first flew December 4 ,1952. Although powered by two 1425 hp Wright R-1820-76 Cyclones, this high-wing monoplane is small enough to operate from escort carriers, using long span flaps and other devices to allow low stalling speed for landing and for hovering when tracking submarines. Pilot and co-pilot enjoy excellent visibility from the nose, and two electronics operators behind them have complete equipment for detecting radar signals transmitted by enemy craft, as well as a retractable radome that can be lowered behind the bomb bay for surface search. Undersea detection devices included sonobuoys dropped from the rear of the engine nacelles, a magnetic airborne detector in the tail, and a long-range searchlight is provided for use at night. Homing torpedo or depth charges are accommodated in the weapons bay, and six rockets can be carried below the wings. Tricycle landing gear is retractable. Production models of the S2F-1, using 1525 hp R-1820-82s went into service in 1954.

In October 1952 Douglas presented the mockup of a single-seat attack type so promising that it was ordered into production before the prototype's first flight on June 22, 1954. In contrast with the big Skywarrior, the XA4D-1 Skyhawk is the smallest and lightest jet yet built for the Navy. Powered by a 7200-lb. thrust Wright J65-W-2 it has a triangular low wing, tricycle gear, and features simple design, light weight and low cost. Armed with two 20-mm. guns in the wing roots, the Skyhawk has external attachments for bombs, drop tanks, or tactical atomic weapons, and has displayed a 695 mph speed over a 621 mile course.

This trio of carrier-based weapons, the Skyhawk, Skywarrior, and Tracker, has replaced the battleship as the main element in controlling the sea, and may maintain the American Navy as the world's strongest for many years.

The Navy's first supersonic bomber appeared in May 1958, introducing an advanced all-weather, carrier-based weapon system that eventually may replace the Skywarrior as the fleet's big punch. Powered by two General Electric J79-GE-2s of 15,000-lb. thrust, the North American A3J-1 Vigilante has high, swept wings, droopable leading edges, all-movable slab tail surfaces, and tandem cockpits. Radar-guided attacks at Mach Two speeds could launch atomic stores from a rearward-facing tube. Wings and tail fold for storage aboard the larger carriers.

PMB

GRUMMAN S2F-1 TRACKER

MFR

GRUMMAN S2F-1 TRACKER
Wright R-1820-82, 1525 hp
DIMENSIONS: Span 69′ 8″, Lg. 42′ 3″, Ht. 16′ 3″, Wing Area 260 sq. ft.
WEIGHT: Gross 24,000 lb.
PERFORMANCE: Classified

MFR

NORTH AMERICAN A3J-1
General Electric J79-GE-2, 15,000 lb.
DIMENSIONS: Span 53′, Lg. 73′, Ht. 20′
WEIGHT & PERFORMANCE: Classified

Compare this Navy two-seater with those used twenty years before Vigilante's first flight on August 31, 1958; the speed has multiplied some five times, and destructive power has multiplied infinitely. In 1938, the Navy and Marines had 16 squadrons of BG, BT, SBC, SBU, SB2U, and TBD aircraft. By 1958, some 83 attack or antisub squadrons used ADs (30) squadrons), A4D (12), S2F (10), FJ-4B (10), F9F-8B (10), A3D (8), AJ (4), and F11F-1 (1). (The FJ-4B, F9F-8B, and F11F-1 are modified forms of fighters discussed in chapters 31 and 32.) Since then, the Navy has been disbanding prop-driven AD units, has added more antisubmarine S2F squadrons, and has scheduled the supersonic A3J to replace the A3Ds in Heavy Attack outfits. Whether the targets be submarines, surface ships, ground forces, or strategic centers, there is an appropriate weapons system.

PMB

DOUGLAS A4D-1 SKYHAWK
Wright J65-W-4, 7200 lbs.
DIMENSIONS: Span 27′ 6″, Lg. 39′ 1″, Ht. 15′ 2″, Wing Area 260 sq. ft.
WEIGHT: Gross 15,000 lb.
PERFORMANCE: Classified

MFR

DOUGLAS A4D-2
Wright J65-W-4, 7200 lbs.
DIMENSIONS: Span 27′ 6″, Lg. 39′ 6″, Ht. 15′ 2″, Wing Area 260 sq. ft.
WEIGHT: Empty 8300 lb., Gross 15,000 lb. Fuel 770–1270 gal.
PERFORMANCE: Classified

Part 7 Navy Fighters

Chapter 28: Adapting the Fighter to the Flight Deck 1922-32

A HUMBLE BEGINNING

The Navy's fighters have had the same basic mission as those of the Air Force: destruction of enemy aircraft. However, since they are based on aircraft carriers, they present a more difficult designing problem. The carrier fighter must have a short take-off and landing run for operations from a limited flight deck. To conserve space, carrier types should have either small wings, or some way of folding large ones. An arresting hook is necessary for deck landing, and safety gear should be available for overwater flying.

When the first U.S. carrier, the *Langley,* was commissioned in 1922 the Navy had two "fighter" squadrons but they were equipped only with two-place Vought VE-7s built for training. During World War I, the only fighters the Navy had were a few transferred from the Army for training purposes. They included 12 Nieuport 28s, two Sopwith Camels, two Curtiss-built S.E.5s, and ten Hanriots, a light rotary-powered French-designed single-seater built at the Naval Aircraft Factory. In 1919 some American-built fighters were acquired for test purposes: eleven Thomas-Morse MB-3 single-seaters, one Loening M-8 two-seat monoplane (used as prototype for ten M-8-O observation), and two Curtiss 18-T two-place triplanes tested on floats in May 1920. Details of these aircraft are included in the chapter on Army fighters.

The first type specially designed for the Navy was the Curtiss TS-1 which appeared in June 1922. A 200 hp Wright J-1 air-cooled radial provide the power at a time when nearly all other service types used water-cooled inline engines. Built small enough to fit aboard ships, the TS-1 single-seater could operate with wheels from shore bases, or with twin floats from ships. It was a single-bay biplane, like most early Navy fighters, but the lower wing hung below the fuselage, carrying fuel in a center-section tank droppable in an emergency. A single .30-caliber synchronized Browning was the armament.

Thirty-four Curtiss TS-1s were built by Curtiss, and the Naval Aircraft Factory built five TS-1s, two TS-2s with a 240 hp Aeromarine, and one TS-3 with a 220 hp

RILEY

HANRIOT HD-1 (Naval Aircraft Factory)
LeRhone 110 hp
DIMENSIONS: Span 28′ 6″, Lg. 19′ 2″, Wing Area 188 sq. ft.
WEIGHT: Empty 904 lb., Gross 1521 lb.
PERFORMANCE: Speed—Top 100 mph.

CURTISS TS-1 (Landplane)
Wright J-4, 200 hp
DIMENSIONS: Span 25′, Lg. 22′ 1″, Ht. 9′, Wing Area 228 sq. ft.
WEIGHT: Empty 1240 lb., Gross 1920 lb. Fuel 50 gal.
PERFORMANCE: Speed—Top 125 mph, Landing 48 mph. Service Ceiling 16,250′, Climb 5000′/5.5 min. Range 482 miles.

MFR

MFR

CURTISS TS-1 (Seaplane)
Wright J-4, 200 hp
DIMENSIONS: As TS-1 landplane, except height 9′ 7″.
WEIGHT: Gross 2123 lb. Fuel 50 gal.
PERFORMANCE: Speed—Top 123 mph. Service Ceiling 14,450′. Range 339 miles.

Wright E-2. The latter were experimental modifications using water-cooled engines and a different airfoil. The TS series aircraft were later redesignated FC-1, F2C-1, and F3C-1. Two examples of another version, F4C-1, were built in 1924 with fabric-covered metal internal structure, raised lower wing, and Wright J-3 radial engine.

These designs were clearly inferior in performance to land-based types, and the only fast Navy single-seaters were experimental noncombat racers such as the twin-float Curtiss Navy racers, Wright NW-2, and the Wright F2W-1. To replace the TS types on hand the Navy turned to single-seaters then being offered by Boeing and Curtiss to the U. S. Army.

CURTISS F4C-1
Lawrence-Wright J-4, 200 hp
DIMENSIONS: Span 25′, Lg. 18′ 4″, Ht. 8′ 9″, Wing Area 185 sq. ft.
WEIGHT: Empty 1027 lb., Gross 1707 lb. Fuel 50 gal.
PERFORMANCE: Speed—Top 126 mph, Landing 49 mph. Service Ceiling 17,400′, Climb 5000′/3. 9 min. Range 340 miles at top speed, 525 miles cruising.

ARC

BOEING'S BIPLANES

In December 1924, 14 Boeing FB-1s were ordered for delivery the following August with 400 hp Curtiss D-12 inline engines. Based on the Army's PW-9, they had tapered single-bay biplane wings and a water radiator below the engine. Armament included two .30-caliber synchronized guns on the cowl, one of which could be replaced by a .50-caliber weapon if desired. This arrangement remained standard on Navy fighters up to World War II.

Some FB-1s became FB-2s when arresting gear for landings on the *Langley* was installed. Two FB-3s were built with 510 hp Packard 1A-1500 engines and balanced controls, and could exchange their wheels for twin floats. They were followed in 1927 by an FB-4 which was an earlier ship modified by a 450 hp air-cooled Wright P-1 radial. Twenty-seven FB-5s delivered in 1927 were powered by 525 hp Packard 2A-1500s. An FB-6 modification tested a 400 hp Pratt & Whitney R-1340 Wasp.

USN

BOEING FB-1
Curtiss D-12, 400 hp
DIMENSIONS: Span 32′, Lg. 23′ 6″, Ht. 8′ 9″, Wing Area 241 sq. ft.
WEIGHT: Empty 2132 lb., Gross 2944 lb. Fuel 112 gal.
PERFORMANCE: Speed—Top 167 mph at s. l., Landing 57.5 mph. Service Ceiling 21,200′, Climb 5000′/2.8 min. Range 509 miles.

BOEING FB-4
Wright P-2, 440 hp
DIMENSIONS: Span 32′, Lg. 22′ 10″, Ht. 8′ 9″, Wing Area 241.5 sq. ft.
WEIGHT: Empty 2000 lb., Gross 2817 lb. Fuel 112 gal.
PERFORMANCE: Speed—Top 160 mph, Landing 58 mph. Service Ceiling 22,500′, Climb 5000′/3.18 min. Range 428 miles.

MFR

USN

BOEING FB-3
Packard 1A-1500, 510 hp
DIMENSIONS: Span 32′, Lg. 22′ 11″, Ht. 8′ 9″, Wing Area 241.5 sq. ft.
WEIGHT: Empty 2387 lb., Gross 3204 lb. Fuel 112 gal.
PERFORMANCE: Speed—Top 170 mph, Landing 59 mph. Service Ceiling 23,100′, Climb 5000′/3 min. Range 460 miles.

Designed especially for carrier use, the Boeing XF2B-1 appeared November 1926 with a Pratt & Whitney R-1340B, and a balanced straight rudder. Thirty-two production F2B-1s ordered March 1927, and first delivered the following October, were completely equiped for carrier operation and had a 50-gallon fuel tank within the fuselage and 50 gallons more in an auxiliary tank that could be attached below the fuselage.

A further development was the Boeing XF3B-1 of March 1927, whose larger wings permitted lower landing speeds. Further distinguished from their predecessors by a rounded dural balanced rudder on a very

BOEING FB-5
Packard 2A-1500, 525 hp
DIMENSIONS: Span 32′, Lg. 23′ 8″, Ht. 9′ 1″, Wing Area 241 sq. ft.
WEIGHT: Empty 2416 lb., Gross 3196 lb. Fuel 50–100 gal.
PERFORMANCE: Speed—Top 169 mph at s. l., 163 mph at 5000′, Cruising 110 mph, Landing 60 mph. Service Ceiling 20,200′, Climb 5000′/3.2 min. Range 323 miles.

USN

MFR

BOEING F2B-1
Pratt & Whitney R-1340B, 450 hp
DIMENSIONS: Span 30′ 1″, Lg. 22′ 11″, Ht. 10′ 1″, Wing Area 243 sq. ft.
WEIGHT: Empty 2058 lb., Gross 2874 lb., Max. 3204 lb. Fuel 50–100 gal.
PERFORMANCE: Speed—Top 158 mph at s. l., Landing 58 mph. Service Ceiling 21,500′, Climb 5000′/3 min. Range 372 miles normal, 704 miles max.

BOEING F3B-1
Pratt & Whitney R-1340-80, 450 hp
DIMENSIONS: Span 33′, Lg. 24′ 10″, Ht. 10′ 1″, Wing Area 275 sq. ft.
WEIGHT: Empty 2183 lb., Gross 2950 lb., Max. 3340 lb. Fuel 60–110 gal.
PERFORMANCE: Speed—Top 156 mph at s. l., Landing 55 mph. Service Ceiling 20,900′, Climb 5000′/3.1 min.

WL

small fin, 74 F3B-1s began going into service in February 1928. The Pratt & Whitney Wasp of 450 hp was, on one article, temporarily fitted with a ring cowl.

EARLY CURTISS HAWKS

There was now a fighter squadron each for the new *Lexington*, *Saratoga*, and old *Langley*, as well as two Marine fighter units. But not all used Boeings, for Curtiss offered strong competition with the Navy Hawks, which, like the Boeing types, evolved from a water-cooled standard Army pursuit to an air-cooled type specially designed for carriers. In March 1925 the Navy ordered nine seagoing versions of the successful Army

USN

CURTISS F6C-1
Curtiss D-12, 400 hp
DIMENSIONS: Span 31′ 6″, Lg. 22′ 8″, Ht. 10′, Wing Area 252 sq. ft.
WEIGHT: Empty 2055 lb., Gross 2803 lb. Fuel 50–100 gal.
PERFORMANCE: Speed—Top 163.5 mph at s. l., Cruising 110 mph, Landing 59 mph. Service Ceiling 21,700′, Climb 5000′/2.9 min. Range 350 miles.

CURTISS F6C-2
Curtiss D-12, 400 hp
DIMENSIONS: As F6C-1
WEIGHT: Empty 2090 lb., Gross 2838 lb. Fuel 50–100 gal.
PERFORMANCE: Speed—Top 159 mph at s. l., Landing 59 mph. Service Ceiling 22,700′, Climb 5000′. Range 330 miles.

USN

P-1 Hawk. Delivery began in September on five F6C-1s and four similar F6C-2s, which used 400 hp Curtiss D-12s and were like the Army pursuit except for interchangeable landing gear with either twin floats or wheels. (The F5C designation was skipped in order to avoid confusion with F-5 flying boats still in service.)

Thirty-five F6C-3s with wheels and carrier arresting gear were built in 1927. Like their predecessors and the Boeing FBs they had tapered wings, "N" struts, and water-cooling radiators below the D-12 engines.

By 1927, the Navy had decided to substitute air-cooled radials for the inline engines, which were more difficult to maintain at sea. After tests of an XF6C-4 in September 1926, 31 F6C-4s powered by 410 hp

USN

CURTISS F6C-3
Curtiss D-12, 400 hp
DIMENSIONS: Span 31′ 6″, Lg. 22′ 10″, Ht. 10′ 8″, Wing Area 252 sq. ft.
WEIGHT: Empty 2161 lb., Gross 2963 lb., Max. 3349 lb. Fuel 50–100 gal.
PERFORMANCE: Speed—Top 154 mph at s. l., Landing 59 mph. Service Ceiling 20,300′, Climb 5000′/3.5 min. Range 351 miles normal, 655 miles max.

Pratt & Whitney R-1340s went into service. They proved lighter and more maneuverable than the F6C-3.

Experimental variations on this airframe were the XF6C-5, introducing a 525 hp Pratt & Whitney R-1690 Hornet, and the unarmed XF6F-6, specially built for the 1930 air races with lower wing removed, wheel pants, and a Curtiss Conqueror inline engine. The latter machine's fatal crash killed the pilot and ended Navy competition in the air races. Wind tunnel experiments and careful engineering were proving a more efficient method of advancing performance than trial-and-error racers unsuitable for actual service work. The last modification of this series was an XF6C-7 with a 450 hp air-cooled inverted inline Ranger.

Designed from the very beginning as a carrier type, the Curtiss XF7C-1 made its first flight on February 28, 1927. A 450 hp R-1340B Wasp was neatly mounted behind a large prop spinner, the upper wing was swept back over a straight lower wing, and a life raft was carried in a tube behind the pilot's open cockpit. Eighteen F7C-1s began appearing November 1928.

USN

CURTISS F6C-4
Pratt & Whitney R-1340, 410 hp
DIMENSIONS: Span 31′ 6″, Lg. 22′ 6″, Ht. 10′ 11″, Wing Area 252 sq. ft.
WEIGHT: Empty 1980 lb., Gross 2785 lb., Max. 3171 lb. Fuel 50–100 gal.
PERFORMANCE: Speed—Top 155 mph at s. l., Landing 57 mph. Service Ceiling 22,900′, Climb 5000′/2.5 min. Range 361 miles normal, 676 miles max.

PMB

CURTISS XF6C-5
Pratt & Whitney R-1690, 525 hp
DIMENSIONS: Span 31′ 6″, Lg. 22′ 6″, Ht. 9′ 8″, Wing Area 252 sq. ft.
WEIGHT: Empty 2109 lb., Gross 2960 lb. Fuel 50–100 gal.
PERFORMANCE: Speed—Top 159 mph, Landing 60 mph. Service Ceiling 21,900′, Climb 5000′/2.5 min. Range 329 miles.

USN

CURTISS F7C-1
Pratt & Whitney R-1340B, 450 hp
DIMENSIONS: Span 32′ 8″, Lg. 22′ 2″, Ht. 10′ 4″, Wing Area 276 sq. ft.
WEIGHT: Empty 2038 lb., Gross 2782 lb., Max. 3219 lb. Fuel 80–110 gal.
PERFORMANCE: Speed—Top 151 mph at s. l. Service Ceiling 23,350′, Climb 5000′/2.6 min. Range 330 miles normal, 671 miles max.

VOUGHT FU-1 (Seaplane)

MFR

THREE INDEPENDENT CONTENDERS

Boeing and Curtiss were not alone in their interest in Navy contracts, for other firms offered single-seat biplane fighters of varying quality. None, however, reached quantity production.

The Vought FU-1 appeared in January 1927 as a "training fighter" with straight equal-span double-bay wings. Twenty were built with 200 hp Wright J-5s (R-1790s) with a Root integral supercharger. Some landed on wheels but others had a single float for catapult launchings from warships. They were the last fighters so equipped, for since then Navy fighters have worked from carriers, with regular warships' limited space reserved for observation planes.

Contrasting with the Vought's rather antique appearance was the Wright XF3W-1 with an R-1340B and single-bay wings. Another design was the Eberhart

VOUGHT FU-1
Wright R-790, 220 hp
DIMENSIONS: Span 34′ 4″, Lg. 24′ 5″, Ht. 8′ 10″, Wing Area 290 sq. ft.
WEIGHT: Empty 1715 lb., Gross 2409 lb. (Seaplane 2774 lb.). Fuel 46 gal.
PERFORMANCE: Speed—Top 147 mph at 13,000′, 125 mph at s. l., Landing 53 mph. Service Ceiling 27,300′, Absolute Ceiling 29,600′, Climb 5000′/5.1 min. Range 430 miles.

USN

WRIGHT XF3W-1 (Seaplane version shown)
Pratt & Whitney R-1340B, 450 hp
DIMENSIONS: Span 27′ 4″, Lg. 22′ 1″, Ht. 8′ 6″, Wing Area 215 sq. ft.
WEIGHT: Empty 1414 lb., Gross 2128 lb. Fuel 47 gal.
PERFORMANCE: Speed—Top 162 mph at s. l., Landing 54 mph.

USN

PMB

EBERHART XFG-1
Pratt & Whitney R-1340C, 425 hp
DIMENSIONS: Span 32′, Lg. 27′ 3″, Ht. 9′ 10″, Wing Area 241 sq. ft.
WEIGHT: Empty 2145 lb., Gross 2938 lb., Max. 3208 lb.
PERFORMANCE: Speed—Top 154 mph. Service Ceiling 18,700′, Climb 5000′/3.7 min.

XFG-1, which was completed as the F2G-1 Comanche and appeared June 1927 with a swept-back upper wing and 425 hp R-1340C, but was destroyed during tests.

TWO-SEAT FIGHTERS

Two-seat fighters emerged from a Marine Corps requirement for aircraft capable of observation, light bombing, and fighting on expeditions made by the Corps to Caribbean trouble spots. Since World War I, the Marines had been equipped with DH-4Bs with which they had developed a dive-bombing technique with small fragmentation bombs against guerrilla opponents in Haiti and Nicaragua.

The first type to meet this requirement was the Curtiss F8C-1 introduced in January 1928, as a development of the Falcon O-1 and A-3 observation and attack types being built for the Army. The Navy version was powered by an air-cooled R-1340 Wasp instead of the water-cooled engines of the Falcon, but had the same fabric-covered fuselage and biplane wing structure, with the upper wing swept back from the center section, and a balanced rudder. Two .30-caliber Brownings mounted in the lower wings fired outside of the propeller arc, and a Lewis gun was mounted on a ring around the observer's cockpit. Six F8C-1 and 21 F8F-3s delivered to the Marines were redesignated OC-1 and OC-2, and became known as Helldivers, a trademark for all future Curtiss dive bombers.

USN

CURTISS F8C-1 (OC-1)
Pratt & Whitney R-1340, 432 hp
DIMENSIONS: Span 32′, Lg. 25′ 11″, Ht. 10′ 6″, Wing Area 308 sq. ft.
WEIGHT: Empty 2440 lb., Gross 3918 lb., Max. 4367 lb. Fuel 120 gal.
PERFORMANCE: Speed—Top 137.5 mph at s. l., 129 mph at 10,000′, Landing 58 mph. Service Ceiling 17,300′. Range 378 miles.

MFR

CURTISS XF8C-2
Pratt & Whitney R-1340-80, 450 hp
DIMENSIONS: As F8C-1
WEIGHT: Empty 2229 lb., Gross 3347 lb., Max. 3548 lb. Fuel 86 gal.
PERFORMANCE: Speed—Top 145 mph at s. l., Landing 55 mph. Service Ceiling 20,800′, Climb 5000′/4 min. Range 333 miles.

PMB

CURTISS F8C-4
Pratt & Whitney R-1340-88, 400 hp at s. l.
DIMENSIONS: As F8C-1
WEIGHT: Empty 2513 lb., Gross 3783 lb., Max. 4238 lb. Fuel 86–136 gal.
PERFORMANCE: Speed—Top 137 mph at s. l., Landing 59 mph. Service Ceiling 15,000′, Climb 5000′/6 min. Range 455 miles normal, 722 miles max.

CURTISS F8C-3 (OC-2) [*Photo unavailable*]
Pratt & Whitney R-1340, 432 hp
DIMENSIONS: As F8C-1
WEIGHT: Empty 2515 lb., Gross 4191 lb. Fuel 120 gal.
PERFORMANCE: Speed—Top 136 mph at s. l., 130 mph at 10,000′, Landing 60 mph. Service Ceiling 16,425′, Absolute Ceiling 18,230′, Climb 1010′/1 min.

CURTISS F8C-5 (O2C-1)
Pratt & Whitney R-1340C
DIMENSIONS: Span 32′, Lg. 26′, Ht. 10′ 3″, Wing Area 308 sq. ft.
WEIGHT: Empty 2520 lb., Gross 4020 lb. Fuel 120 gal.
PERFORMANCE: Speed—Top 140 mph, Cruising 110 mph, Landing 63 mph. Service Ceiling 16,050′. Range 560 miles.

USN

CURTISS XF8C-6 [*Photo unavailable*]
Pratt & Whitney R-1340C, 450 hp at 6000′
DIMENSIONS: As F8C-1
WEIGHT: Empty 2618 lb., Gross 3886 lb.
PERFORMANCE: Speed—Top 153 mph at 5000′. Service Ceiling 20,500′.

CURTISS XF8C-7
Wright R-1820-64, 575 hp
DIMENSIONS: Span 32′, Lg. 26′, Ht. 11′, Wing Area 308 sq. ft.
WEIGHT: Empty 2958 lb., Gross 4274 lb. Fuel 120 gal.
PERFORMANCE: Speed—Top 179 mph at s. l., Landing 63 mph. Service Ceiling 20,800′, Climb 5000′/3.2 min.

MFR

MFR

VOUGHT XF2U-1
Pratt & Whitney R-1340C, 450 hp
DIMENSIONS: Span 36′, Lg. 27′, Ht. 10′, Wing Area 318 sq. ft.
WEIGHT: Empty 2539 lb., Gross 3907 lb., Max. 4208 lb. Fuel 110 gal.
PERFORMANCE: Speed—Top 146 mph, Cruising 110 mph, Landing 57.5 mph. Service Ceiling 18,700′, Climb 9100′/10 min. Range 495 miles.

An XF8C-2 prototype was built and fitted with bomb racks that could carry two 116-lb. bombs under each wing, or a 500-lb. bomb below the fuselage. Although the first prototype crashed, a second was flown in August 1929 with a cowl around the engine cylinders. The pilot had a telescopic sight for dive-bombing alongside the ring sight for the two .30-caliber guns in the upper wing. In June 1929 orders were placed for an XF8C-4, 27 F8C-4s, and nine F8C-5s. The F8C-4 appeared on May 1, 1930, with an R-1340-88, while the F8C-5s began appearing in September. Together with 43 more ordered June 1930 and delivered in 1931, the F8C-5s were redesignated O2C-1s. Two were modified to XF8C-6s, with a supercharged engine and wing slots. One deluxe example of the Helldiver (XF8C-7) with a Wright R-1820-64, wheel pants, and the first enclosed cockpits seen on a Navy fighter, was purchased November 6, 1930, as a command transport.

On June 25, 1929, the Vought XF2U-1 was delivered to the Navy. Another two-seat biplane with a cowled R-1340C, it had wider straight wings than its Curtiss competitor, and could exchange its wheel landing gear for floats. While the design was unsuccessful as a fighter, it was similar to the O3U Corsairs produced for observation squadrons.

THE F4B'S

Boeing's Model 83 was a single-seat fighter powered by a 500 hp Pratt & Whitney R-1340B, first flown June 25, 1928, and sent to the Navy on August 2 for tests. Like the similar Model 89, it became the XF4B-1, and was ordered by both the Navy (F4B-1) and Army (P-12). Equipment included two .30-caliber guns with 1200 rounds and a rack for a 500-lb. bomb or 49-gallon belly tank. Twenty-nine F4B-1 (Model 99) with R-1340-8 Wasps were built, and the first was flown on May 6, 1929.

Another Boeing private venture was the Model 205, which after demonstration tests at Anacosta was purchased May 10, 1930, as the XF5B-1. Resembling the F4B-1, it was a high-wing monoplane and, like the XP-15 offered to the Army at the same time, used a 450 hp R-1340D. Trials were made with a ring cowl, which added 15 mph to the top speed with bare cylinders. The Navy, however, was not yet ready for monoplanes aboard carriers, and instead contracted for 46 F4B-2s in June 1930. First delivered in January 1931, they were similar to the F4B-1 except for ring cowl, Frieze ailerons, and a split-axle landing gear replacing the longer cross-axle type used earlier.

In December 1930 Boeing offered Model 218 with a new all-metal fuselage to both the Army and Navy,

MFR

BOEING XF4B-1 (Model 83)
Pratt & Whitney R-1340B, 500 hp at s. l.
DIMENSIONS: Span 30′, Lg. 20′ 7″, Ht. 9′ 3″, Wing Area 227.5 sq. ft.
WEIGHT: Empty 1811 lb., Gross 2557 lb., Max. 3087 lb.
PERFORMANCE: Speed—Top 169 mph at s. l., Landing 56 mph. Service Ceiling 26,900′, Climb 2920′/1 min.

WL

BOEING F4B-1
Pratt & Whitney R-1340-8, 500 hp at 6000′
DIMENSIONS: Span 30′, Lg. 20′ 1″, Ht. 9′ 4″, Wing Area 227.5 sq. ft.
WEIGHT: Empty 1950 lb., Gross 2750 lb., Max. 3169 lb. Fuel 57–107 gal.
PERFORMANCE: Speed—Top 176 mph at 6000′, Landing 59 mph. Service Ceiling 27,700′, Climb 5000′/2.9 min. Range 371 miles normal, 771 miles max.

USN

BOEING XF5B-1
Pratt & Whitney R-1340D, 500 hp at 6000′
DIMENSIONS: Span 30′ 6″, Lg. 21′, Ht. 9′ 4″, Wing Area 157 sq. ft.
WEIGHT: Empty 2091 lb., Gross 2848 lb. Fuel 50–132 gal.
PERFORMANCE: Speed—Top 183 mph at 6000′, Landing 71 mph. Service Ceiling 27,100′, Climb 5000′/2.7 min.

MFR

BOEING XF4B-1 (Model 89)

WL

BOEING F4B-1

BOEING F4B-2
Pratt & Whitney R-1340-8, 500 hp at 6000′
DIMENSIONS: Span 30′, Lg. 20′ 1″, Ht. 9′ 1″, Wing Area 227.5 sq. ft.
WEIGHT: Empty 2067 lb., Gross 2799 lb., Max. 3260 lb. Fuel 55–110 gal.
PERFORMANCE: Speed—Top 186 mph at 6000′, 170 mph at s l., Landing 59 mph. Service Ceiling 26,900′, Climb 5000′/2.5 min. Range 403 miles normal, 812 miles max.

USN

leading to orders for the P-12E and F4B-3. Contracts let on April 23, 1931, and August 15 called for 75 F4B-3s, but 54 of these aircraft were delivered as F4B-4s. The F4B-3s began to appear in January 1932 powered by R-1340-10s, and the F4B-4, with an R-1340-16, wider fin, and enlarged headrest appeared in July. Thirty-eight more F4B-4s were ordered August 15, 1932, and completed by February 1933, after 14 Boeing fighters were sold to Brazil with nine more in 1933. Another F4B-4 is carried on Navy lists as being assembled from spare parts. Armed with two .30-caliber guns under the cowl, the F4B-4 had wing bomb racks for two 116-lb. bombs, and a 55-gallon drop tank under the fuselage could double the internal fuel load. A telescopic sight for dive-bombing alongside the gunsight helps distinguish the F4B from its Army P-12 sister ships. Boeing built 586 of these fighters, including 188 for the Navy, 32 for export, and 366 for the Army.

Although the F4B series were used by both the Army and the Navy, it was two decades before another fighter type could be successful in both roles (North American F-86 and FJ series). The Army's shift to high-speed monoplanes could not be followed for many years, and when it was, monoplanes designed for carrier work were basically different from their land-based counterparts.

Several other companies made unsuccessful attempts to capture Navy contracts from the successful Boeing ships. Hall Aluminum, then at Buffalo, New York, introduced their XFH-1 in June 1929. Another biplane with an R-1340, it had a fat, all-metal watertight fuselage, and could drop its landing gear for emergency water landings.

In order to compare American technique with developments abroad, the Navy imported the British Bristol Bulldog fighter for tests. The first example crashed in November 1929 but a second was purchased in March 1930. Powered by a 515 hp Bristol Jupiter VII, the Bulldog was considered not as rugged as American types, but of good performance.

Among this period's most interesting types was the Berliner-Joyce XFJ-1, which was distinguished by a gap between the metal fuselage and the lower wing, while the upper wing was gulled into the fuselage behind a 450 hp R-1340C Wasp. Ordered May 16, 1929, the XFJ-1 was tested in May 1930, but was damaged in a crash and was returned to the Dundalk, Maryland,

BOEING F4B-4
Pratt & Whitney R-1340-16, 550 hp at 6000′
DIMENSIONS: As F4B-3
WEIGHT: Empty 2354 lb., Gross 3128 lb., Max. 3611 lb. Fuel 55–110 gal.
PERFORMANCE: Speed—Top 188 mph at 6000′, Landing 62.5 mph. Service Ceiling 26,900′. Range 370 miles normal, 734 miles max.

PMB

USN

BOEING F4B-3
Pratt & Whitney R-1340-10, 500 hp
DIMENSIONS: Span 30′, Lg. 20′ 5″, Ht. 9′ 9″, Wing Area 227.5 sq. ft.
WEIGHT: Empty 2242 lb., Gross 2958 lb., Max. 3419 lb. Fuel 55–110 gal.
PERFORMANCE: Speed—Top 187 mph at 6000′, 167 mph at s l., Cruising 160 mph, Landing 61 mph. Service Ceiling 27,500′, Climb 5000′/2.9 min. Range 401 miles normal, 829 miles max.

USN

HALL XFH-1
Pratt & Whitney R-1340B, 450 hp
DIMENSIONS: Span 32′, Lg. 22′ 6″, Ht. 11′, Wing Area 255 sq. ft.
WEIGHT: Empty 1773 lb., Gross 2514 lb. Fuel 80 gal.
PERFORMANCE: Speed—Top 153 mph at s. l., Landing 55 mph. Service Ceiling 25,300′, Climb 5000′/2.8 min. Range 275 miles.

factory for modification in November. On May 22, 1931, the prototype, now designated XFJ-2, resumed tests at Anacosta using an R-1340D of 500 hp, wheel pants, ring cowl, prop spinner, and a larger vertical tail. Top speed increased from 177 to 193 mph, but the aircraft was now unstable, and no longer satisfactory.

Another biplane with the upper wings gulled into an all-metal fuselage was the XFA-1 built by General Aviation, formerly Atlantic-Fokker. A 450 hp R-1340C

USN

BRISTOL BULLDOG (Navy test)
Bristol Jupiter VII, 515 hp at 9000′
DIMENSIONS: Span 33′ 10″, Lg. 27′ 6″, Ht. 9′ 4″, Wing Area 306 sq. ft.
WEIGHT: Empty 2174 lb., Gross 3264 lb. Fuel 70 gal.
PERFORMANCE: Speed—Top 173 mph at 9000′, 141 mph at s. l., Landing 59 mph. Service Ceiling 27,300′, Climb 5000′/2.7 min.

MFR

BERLINER-JOYCE XFJ-1
Pratt & Whitney R-1340C, 450 hp at s. l.
DIMENSIONS: Span 28′, Lg. 20′ 7″, Ht. 9′ 10″, Wing Area 179 sq. ft.
WEIGHT: Empty 2046 lb., Gross 2797 lb. Fuel 91 gal.
PERFORMANCE: Speed—Top 172 mph at s. l., Landing 65 mph. Service Ceiling 23,800′, Climb 5000′/3.9 min. Range 404 miles normal, 716 miles max.

USN

BERLINER-JOYCE XFJ-2
Pratt & Whitney R-1340-92, 500 hp
DIMENSIONS: Span 28′, Lg. 20′ 10″, Ht. 9′ 10″, Wing Area 179 sq. ft.
WEIGHT: Empty 2102 lb., Gross 2847 lb., Max. 3116 lb. Fuel 91 gal.
PERFORMANCE: Speed—Top 193 mph at 6000′, Landing 64 mph. Service Ceiling 24,700′, Climb 14,300′/10 min. Range 520 miles.

USN

FOKKER XFA-1
Pratt & Whitney R-1340C, 450 hp
DIMENSIONS: Span 25′ 6″, Lg. 22′ 2″, Ht. 9′ 3″, Wing Area 175 sq. ft.
WEIGHT: Empty 1837 lb., Gross 2508 lb. Fuel 60 gal.
PERFORMANCE: Speed—Top 170 mph, Landing 64 mph. Service Ceiling 20,200′, Climb 5000′/3.4 min. Range 375 miles normal, 518 miles max.

Wasp was fitted with a two-bladed propeller and a ring cowl. Ordered June 24, 1930, the XFA-1 could be distinguished by a fairing over the landing-gear strut, and was also seen with a three-bladed propeller. It was tested by the Navy in March 1932, but neither it nor the Berliner-Joyce ship succeeded in surpassing the Boeing single-seaters so popular during this period.

Unique among Navy single-seaters, the Curtiss XF9C-1 Sparrowhawk was ordered June 30, 1930, appeared March 27, 1931, and was intended for oper-

CURTISS F9C-2
Wright R-975-22, 420 hp at s. l.
DIMENSIONS: Span 25′ 6″, Lg. 20′ 1″, Ht. 7′ 1″, Wing Area 173 sq. ft.
WEIGHT: Empty 2114 lb., Gross 2776 lb., Max. 2888 lb. Fuel 60–90 gal.
PERFORMANCE: Speed—Top 176.5 mph at s. l., Landing 65 mph. Service Ceiling 19,200′, Climb 5000′/3.5 min. Range 366 miles normal, 507 miles max.

USN

MFR

CURTISS XF9C-1
Wright R-975C, 421 hp
DIMENSIONS: Span 25′ 6″, Lg. 19′ 5″, Ht. 7′ 1″, Wing Area 173 sq. ft.
WEIGHT: Empty 1836 lb., Gross 2502 lb. Fuel 59 gal.
PERFORMANCE: Speed—Top 176.5 mph at s. l., 160 mph at 10,000′, Landing 63 mph. Service Ceiling 22,600′, Climb 5000′/2.6 min. Range 396 miles normal, 536 miles max.

ations from the dirigibles *Akron* and *Macon*.[1] A little biplane with upper wings gulled into the metal fuselage behind a 400 hp Wright R-975C Whirlwind with ring cowl, the XF9C-1 was followed in December 1931 by an XF9C-2 with modified tail surfaces and landing gear with wheel pants.

Six F9C-2s ordered on Columbus Day 1931, and first delivered May 3, 1932, had a 420 hp R-975-22, two .30-caliber guns, and a hook ahead of the cockpit to engage a trapeze lowered from the airship's belly. During maneuvers, these airships proved unable to defend themselves from attacking aircraft, despite efforts of the Sparrowhawks they carried. After both dirigibles were destroyed in accidents, no other large rigid lighter-than-air craft were built for the Navy.

[1] Not all authorities agree that the XF9C-1, and perhaps the gull-winged XFA-1, were designed with airship operations in mind. Cf. *AAHS Journal*, Vol. 3, No. 2, p. 100, (Concord, Calif., 1958).

Chapter 29: Biplanes or Monoplanes? 1931–38

MORE TWO-SEATERS

Up to 1931 naval aircraft used the open cockpits and fixed landing gear traditional on combat planes since the First World War. Gradually, however, metal was replacing the fabric for airframe covering, and efforts to decrease drag led to retractable landing gear and enclosed cockpits.

Retractable landing gear was used for the first time by a Navy fighter on the Grumman company's first product, the XFF-1, ordered April 2, 1931. The wheels folded into a bulge in the deep metal fuselage behind a Wright Cyclone, ahead of fully enclosed cockpits. Although a two-seater, the XFF-1 was faster than any single-seater carrier-based type then available. When first delivered on December 29, 1931, it reached a speed of 195 mph with an R-1820E developing 616 hp. In October 1932, the Grumman reappeared with a 750 hp R-1820F, which raised speed to 201 mph. A second prototype equipped for scouting missions was the Grumman XSF-1.

Seven FF-1 and 20 similar FF-2 ordered December 19, 1932, and powered by the R-1820-78 were delivered from May to November 1933. Thirty-four SF-1 scouts with the R-1820-84, ordered December 4, 1933, were delivered the following year, and followed in December 1934 by an XSF-2 powered by a Pratt & Whitney Wasp. An export lot was built for China, and 52 were built in Canada in 1938–39 by Canadian Car & Foundry Co., Ltd. Of these, 40 went to the Spanish Republicans, one to Nicaragua, one to Japan, and the last ten to the Canadian Air Force as the Goblin I.

The next two-seat fighter biplane was the Berliner-Joyce XF2J-1, which had the upper wing gulled into the fuselage behind a 625 hp Wright R-1510-92. Or-

GRUMMAN XFF-1
Wright R-1820E, 616 hp (modified with R-1820F, 675 hp)
DIMENSIONS: Span 34′ 6″, Lg. 24′ 6″, Ht. 9′ 8″, Wing Area 310 sq. ft.
WEIGHT: Empty 2667 lb., Gross 3933 lb. (4565 lb.). Fuel 120 gal.
PERFORMANCE: Speed—Top 195 mph at s. l. (201 mph with R-1820F), Landing 60 mph (63 mph). Service Ceiling 23,600′ (20,700′), Climb 5000′/4.3 min. Range 818 miles.

PMB

GRUMMAN FF-2
Wright R-1820-78, 700 hp at 4000′
DIMENSIONS: Span 34′ 6″, Lg. 24′ 6″, Ht. 11′ 1″, Wing Area 310 sq. ft.
WEIGHT: Empty 3250 lb., Gross 4828 lb. Fuel 140 gal.
PERFORMANCE: Speed—Top 207 mph at 4000′, Landing 65 mph. Service Ceiling 21,100′, Climb 5000′/2.9 min. Range 921 miles.

PMB

MFR

GRUMMAN SF-1
Wright R-1820-78, 700 hp at 4000′
DIMENSIONS: As FF-2
WEIGHT: Empty 3250 lb., Gross 5079 lb. Fuel 165 gal.
PERFORMANCE: Speed—Top 206 mph at 4000′, Landing 65 mph. Service Ceiling 23,400′.

dered June 30, 1931, the XF2J-1 was not delivered until two years later, when its fixed landing gear held performance below standards set by the fast Grumman ships. Visibility from the enclosed cockpits was also considered poor.

Three more two-seat fighters were ordered June 30, 1932. The Douglas XFD-1 and Vought XF3U-1 were both developed from Bureau of Aeronautics design 113, with a conventional biplane layout, fixed gear, enclosed cockpits, and the 700 hp Pratt & Whitney R-1535-64

BERLINER-JOYCE XF2J-1
Wright R-1510-92, 625 hp at 6000′
DIMENSIONS: Span 36′, Lg. 28′ 10″, Wing Area 303.5 sq. ft.
WEIGHT: Empty 3211 lb., Gross 4539 lb., Max. 4851 lb. Fuel 80–160 gal.
PERFORMANCE: Speed—Top 193 mph at 6000′, Landing 66 mph. Service Ceiling 21,500′, Climb 5000′/3.1 min. Range 522 miles normal, 1015 miles max.

DOUGLAS XFD-1
Pratt & Whitney R-1535-64, 700 hp at 8900′
DIMENSIONS: Span 31′ 6″, Lg. 25′ 4″, Ht. 11′ 1″, Wing Area 295 sq. ft.
WEIGHT: Empty 3227 lb., Gross 4745 lb., Max. 5000 lb. Fuel 110 gal.
PERFORMANCE: Speed—Top 204 mph at 8900′, Landing 64 mph. Service Ceiling 23,700′, Climb 5000′/3.3 min. Range 576 miles.

MFR

VOUGHT XF3U-1
Pratt & Whitney R-1535-64, 700 hp at 8900′
DIMENSIONS: Span 31′ 6″, Lg. 26′ 6″, Ht. 10′ 11″, Wing Area 295 sq. ft.
WEIGHT: Empty 3078 lb., Gross 4616 lb. Fuel 110 gal.
PERFORMANCE: Speed—Top 214 mph, Landing 64 mph. Service Ceiling 24,600′. Range 570 miles.

Wasp. The Douglas ship was delivered on June 18, 1933, and differed from the Vought that arrived four days later, by a spreader bar between the wheels. Armament consisted of the usual two synchronized guns under the cowling and the observer's .30-caliber flexible Browning.

Although ordered the same day, the Curtiss XF12C-1 offered a bolder approach. This all-metal high-wing monoplane had slots and flaps on a swept-back wing braced by Vee main struts, and folded backward for shipboard stowage. Like the Grumman, the XF12C-1

CURTISS XF12C-1
Wright R-1510-92, 625 hp at 6000′
DIMENSIONS: Span 41′ 6″, Lg. 29′ 1″, Ht. 12′ 11″, Wing Area 272 sq. ft.
WEIGHT: Empty 3884 lb., Gross 5461 lb., Max. 5840 lb. Fuel 110–170 gal.
PERFORMANCE: Speed—Top 217 mph at 6000′, Landing 64 mph. Service Ceiling 22,500′. Range 738 miles normal, 1074 miles max.

MFR

BOEING XF6B-1 (XBFB-1)
Pratt & Whitney R-1535-44, 625 hp at 6000′
DIMENSIONS: Span 28′ 6″, Lg. 22′ 2″, Ht. 10′ 6″, Wing Area 252 sq. ft.
WEIGHT: Empty 2823 lb., Gross 3705 lb., Max. 4007 lb. Fuel 64–109 gal.
PERFORMANCE: Speed—Top 195 mph at 6000′, Landing 64 mph. Service Ceiling 20,700′, Climb 5000′/4.2 min. Range 437 miles normal, 737 miles max.

PMB

MFR

CURTISS XF11C-1
Wright R-1510-98, 600 hp at 6000
DIMENSIONS: Span 31′ 6″, Lg. 23′ 1′, Ht. 10′, Wing Area 262 sq. ft.
WEIGHT: Empty 3290 lb., Gross 4368 lb. Fuel 94 gal.
PERFORMANCE: Speed—Top 203 mph, Landing 67 mph. Service Ceiling 23,800′, Climb 5000′/8.2 min. Range 530 miles.

had wheels retracting into the fuselage behind the engine, a 625 hp Wright R-1510-92 Twin Whirlwind. It was the last two-seat fighter of the period, for that aircraft class vanished into the new scout-bomber category. Tested as a fighter in October 1933, the XF12C-1 became the S4C-1 with a Cyclone engine in December, and was redesignated SBC-1 in January 1934. The Vought XF3U-1 also became a scout bomber when it was given new wings and redesignated XSBU-1 in February 1934.

THE BOMBER-FIGHTER IDEA

The success of the Helldivers had led the Navy to include light dive-bombing as a single-seat fighter capability, and so Boeing and Curtiss types tested in

NACA

CURTISS XBFC-1 (converted from XF11C-1)

1933 were fitted with bomb racks and relabeled bomber-fighters.

The first was Boeing's XF6B-1 ordered June 30, 1931, and delivered some two years later. Using a 625 hp R-1535-44, equal span biplane wings with ailerons only on the lower wing, and faired wheel struts, it was later redesignated XBFB-1.

More successful was the later Curtiss Goshawk, another open cockpit biplane, whose basic airframe was similar to that of the older F6Cs and the current Army P-6Es. Two prototypes were purchased April 16, 1932. The first to appear was an XF11C-2 with a single-row Wright SR-1820-78 Cyclone and two-bladed propeller, and an XF11C-1 with a twin-row Wright R-1510-98 Whirlwind and a three-bladed propeller was tested in May 1933. Wheels were covered by pants at the end of a single-strut gear.

On October 18, 1932, 28 F11C-2s were ordered with the R-1820-78 Cyclone, and a modified cockpit. The last aircraft on this contract was delivered May 27, 1933, with an R-1820-80, landing gear retracting into the fuselage, and redesignated XF11C-3.

CURTISS BFC-2 (F11C-2)
Wright R-1820-78, 700 hp
DIMENSIONS: Span 31′ 6″, Lg. 25′, Ht. 10′ 7″, Wing Area 262 sq. ft.
WEIGHT: Empty 3037 lb., Gross 4120 lb., Max. 4638 lb. Fuel 94–146 gal.
PERFORMANCE: Speed—Top 205 mph as fighter, 198 mph as bomber, Landing 65 mph. Service Ceiling 24,300′, Climb 5000′/2.6 min. Range 560 miles normal, 628 miles max.

PMB

CURTISS XF11C-2
Wright R-1820-78 ,700 hp at 8000′
DIMENSIONS: Span 31′ 6″, Lg. 25′, Ht. 10′ 7″, Wing Area 262 sq. ft.
WEIGHT: Empty 3000 lb., Gross 4132 lb., Max. 4601 lb. Fuel 94 gal.
PERFORMANCE: Speed—Top 202 mph at 8000′, Landing 65 mph. Service Ceiling 25,100′, Climb 10,400′/10 min. Range 303 miles at top speed.

USN

USN

CURTISS XF11C-3 (XBF2C-1)
Wright R-1820-80, 700 hp at 8000′
DIMENSIONS: Span 31′ 6″, Lg. 23′, Ht. 10′ 7″, Wing Area 262 sq. ft.
WEIGHT: Empty 3230 lb., Gross 4495 lb., Max. 5020 lb. Fuel 98–150 gal.
PERFORMANCE: Speed—Top 229 mph at 8000′, Landing 69 mph. Service Ceiling 26,000′, Climb 11,600′/10 min.

Twenty-seven production models ordered February 26, 1934, had 700 hp R-1820-04s and enclosed cockpits. Like their predecessors they carried two .30-caliber synchronized Brownings, four 116-lb. bombs under wing racks, or one 474-lb. bomb or streamlined 50-gallon drop tank beneath the fuselage. In recognition of the type's dive-bombing capabilities, F11C-2s then serving aboard the *Saratoga* were redesignated BFC-2 and the F11C-3s on order became BF2C-1s on March 21, 1934. First delivered on October 7, 1934, the BF2C-1 was the first single-seater assigned to the new light carrier *Ranger*, and the last Curtiss fighter in actual Navy service.

The Curtiss Hawk also gained great success in the export trade, 251 being sold in addition to those built for the Army and Navy. The Hawk I and II had the BFC-2s fixed gear and open cockpit, and were powered by 710 hp R-1820F-3 Cyclones. The I had 50 gallons of internal fuel while the II had 94 gallons within the fuselage. The Hawk III had the B2F-1s retractable landing gear and enclosed cockpit, with special Navy equipment omitted and a three-bladed propeller and 750 hp R-1820F-53 installed, Type IV Hawks built for Argentina had an R-1820F-56 and modified canopy.

China was the Hawk's best customer, buying over 100 types II and III from 1932 to 1936. The latter model was built there under license, and formed the bulk of Chinese fighter equipment at the opening of the war with Japan in 1937. Twenty-four type IIs went to Turkey, while others went to Bolivia, Colombia, and Cuba. Two type IIs became the first modern fighter purchased by Nazi Germany and some type IIIs went to Siam.

While discussing exports, it is appropriate to mention here the Vought V-80 sold to Argentina in 1933. Built to naval specifications, it was a conventional biplane with a 675 hp Pratt & Whitney Hornet, enclosed cockpit, and panted wheels interchangeable with floats. Armament included two cowl guns, two more fixed guns on the upper wing and wing racks for four 116-lb. bombs.

PMB

BACHMANN

CURTISS BF2C-1 (F11C-3)
Wright R-1820-04, 700 hp at 8000′
DIMENSIONS: Span 31′ 6″, Lg. 23′, Ht. 10′ 10″, Wing Area 262 sq. ft.
WEIGHT: Empty 3329 lb., Gross 4555 lb., Max. 5086 lb. Fuel 110–160 gal.
PERFORMANCE: Speed—Top 225 mph at 8000′ (210 mph/474 lb. bomb), Landing 69 mph. Service Ceiling 27,000′, Climb 5000′/2.6 min. Range 797 miles normal, 1054 miles max.

CURTISS HAWK II (CUBA)
Wright R-1820F-3, 710 hp at 7000′
DIMENSIONS: Span 31′ 6″, Lg. 22′ 4″, Ht. 9′ 9″, Wing Area 252 sq. ft.
WEIGHT: Empty 2903 lb., Gross 3876 lb. Fuel 94–144 gal.
PERFORMANCE: Speed—Top 208 mph at 6900′, 187 mph at s. l., Cruising 179 mph, Landing 63 mph. Service Ceiling 26,400′, Absolute Ceiling 27,400′. Range 414 miles normal, 635 miles max.

MFR

MFR

CURTISS HAWK III (CHINA)
Wright R-1820F-53, 750 hp at 7600′
DIMENSIONS: Span 31′ 6″, Lg. 23′ 6″, Ht. 9′ 11″, Wing Area 262 sq. ft.
WEIGHT: Empty 3213 lb., Gross 4317 lb. Fuel 110–160 gal.
PERFORMANCE: Speed—Top 240 mph, Cruising 203 mph, Landing 68 mph. Service Ceiling 25,800′, Climb 2280′/1 min. Range 575 miles.

CURTISS HAWK IV
Wright R-1820F-56, 745 hp at 12,000′
DIMENSIONS: Span 31′ 6″, Lg. 23′ 6″, Ht. 10′ 10″, Wing Area 262 sq. ft.
WEIGHT: Empty 3404 lb., Gross 4598 lb. Fuel 110 gal.
PERFORMANCE: Speed—Top 248 mph at 12,500′, Cruising 211 mph, Landing 69 mph. Service Ceiling 29,700′, Absolute Ceiling 30,300′. Range 577 miles.

MFR

VOUGHT V-80
Pratt & Whitney R-1690, 675 mph at 6000′
DIMENSIONS: Span 36′, Lg. 27′ 7″, Ht. 10′ 5″, Wing Area 337 sq. ft.
WEIGHT: Empty 3287 lb., Gross 4597 lb. Fuel 110–150 gal.
PERFORMANCE: Speed—Top 197 mph at 6000′, Landing 61 mph. Service Ceiling 27,800′, Climb 1850′/1 min. Range 760 miles.

PMB

BERLINER-JOYCE XF3J-1
Wright R-1510-26, 625 hp at 6000′
DIMENSIONS: Span 29′, Lg. 22′ 11″, Ht. 10′ 9″, Wing Area 240 sq. ft.
WEIGHT: Empty 2717 lb., Gross 4016 lb., Max. 4264 lb. Fuel 120 gal.
PERFORMANCE: Speed—Top 209 mph at 6000′, Landing 66 mph. Service Ceiling 24,500′, Climb 5000′/2.7 min. Range 719 miles/232 lbs. bombs.

MFR

GRUMMAN XF2F-1
Pratt & Whitney XR-1535-44, 625 hp at 8400′
DIMENSIONS: Span 28′ 6″, Lg. 21′ 1″, Ht. 8′ 6″, Wing Area 230 sq. ft.
WEIGHT: Empty 2525 lb., Gross 3490 lb., Max. 3690 lb. Fuel 80–110 gal.
PERFORMANCE: Speed—Top 229 mph at 8400′, Cruising 198 mph, Landing 64 mph. Service Ceiling 29,800′, Climb 3080′/1 min. Range 543 miles normal, 750 miles max.

GRUMMAN F2F-1
Pratt & Whitney R-1535-72, 700 hp take-off, 650 hp at 7500′
DIMENSIONS: Span 28′ 6″, Lg. 21′ 5″, Ht. 9′ 1″, Wing Area 230 sq. ft.
WEIGHT: Empty 2691 lb., Gross 3847 lb. Fuel 110 gal.
PERFORMANCE: Speed—Top 231 mph at 7500′, 203 mph at s. l., Landing 66 mph. Service Ceiling 27,100′, Climb 2050′/1 min., 5000′/2.1 min. Range 985 miles max.

USN

STREAMLINED BIPLANES

The last biplane fighter with old-fashioned fixed landing gear was the Berliner-Joyce XF3J-1, ordered June 30, 1932. Completed January 1934 and tested in April by the Navy, it was a handsome aircraft with elliptical wings tapered at the tips and roots, and a turtleback running from the enclosed cockpit to the rounded rudder. Powered by an SR-1510-26, the XF3J-1 had two .30-caliber cowl guns and could carry two 116-lb. bombs under the wings. During its long construction, it was surpassed by more advanced types and with its failure to win a production contract, the Berliner-Joyce firm retired from business.

Although the aviation business has resulted in many such failures, it has also produced such successes as Grumman, whose chunky little XF2F-1 biplane ordered November 2, 1932, and first flown on October 18, 1933, won quick recognition. Fabric covered the wings, and metal covered a tear-drop shaped fuselage with an enclosed cockpit. Wheels retracted into a bulge behind a Pratt & Whitney R-1535-44, and armament included two synchronized guns and two 116-lb. bombs in wing racks.

Fifty-four F2F-1s with R-1535-72 Wasps were ordered on St. Patrick's Day, 1934, and another was added after deliveries began in January 1935. These Grumman biplanes began a long series of single-seaters by this company, which has had fighter types under contract for the Navy without interruption ever since.

PREMATURE MONOPLANES

Although by 1933, monoplanes were in production for all classes of Army Air Corps aircraft, the Navy had hesitated to adopt the more streamlined aircraft for carrier operation. Only the high-wing XF5B-1 and XF12C-1 had attempted to utilize the speed offered by monoplane configurations, but problems of shipboard stowage, structural strength, and relatively high landing speed had barred adoption of those types.

Boeing's XF7B-1, ordered March 20, 1933, and powered by a 550 hp Pratt & Whitney R-1340-30, was the first low-wing monoplane fighter ever tested by the Navy. Of all-metal construction, the Boeing had wheels folding back partially into a cantilever wing, and had a long turtleback running from the cockpit to the tail. When first flown on Armistice Day 1933, the XF7B-1 had an enclosed cockpit, weighed 3579 lbs., and did 239 mph. Visibility from under the canopy proved poor, and an open cockpit was used on later tests. Additional weight further depressed the performance, and the plane was criticized for excessively long take-off runs, high landing speed, poor maneuverability, and general instability.

Curtiss also attempted a monoplane design, the XF13C-1 ordered November 23, 1932, with a Wright R-1510-94 and wheels retracting into a clean metal fuselage. Designed originally as a high-wing monoplane with the pilot's enclosure and external struts connecting the wings to the fuselage, it was delivered February 10, 1934, with a spare set of biplane wings for comparative study. The original 35 ft. high wing had slots and flaps to reduce the landing speed, but the alternate arrangement had narrower chord wings without the lift devices, utilizing instead the added area of a 24 ft. lower wing. As a biplane the type was known as XF13C-2, although the original type number was retained on the tail fin. Actually, it was first flown, in December 1933 by company pilots, in the biplane form.

BOEING XF7B-1 (Photo shows original form)
Pratt & Whitney R-1340-30, 550 hp at 10,000′
DIMENSIONS: Span 32′, Lg. 27′ 7″, Ht. 10′, Wing Area 213 sq. ft.
WEIGHT: Empty 2698 lb., Gross 3868 lb. Fuel 112 gal.
PERFORMANCE: Speed—Top 231 mph at 10,000′, Landing 73 mph. Service Ceiling 26,900′, Climb 5000′/3.4 min. Range 824 miles.

MFR

CURTISS XF13C-1
Wright XR-1510-94, 600 hp at 10,000′
DIMENSIONS: Span 35′, Lg. 25′ 8″, Ht. 12′ 9″, Wing Area 205 sq. ft.
WEIGHT: Empty 3238 lb., Gross 4400 lb. Fuel 110 gal.
PERFORMANCE: Speed—Top 236 mph at 10,000′, Landing 67 mph. Service Ceiling 23,800′, Climb 5000′/3.5 min. Range 864 miles.

MFR

CURTISS XF13C-2
Wright XR-1510-94, 600 hp at 10,000′
DIMENSIONS: Span 35′, Lg. 25′ 8″, Ht. 12′ 9″, Wing Area 282 sq. ft.
WEIGHT: Empty 3183 lb., Gross 4343 lb. Fuel 110 gal.
PERFORMANCE: Speed—Top 218 mph, Landing 68 mph. Service Ceiling 23,900′, Climb 5000′/3.6 min. Range 863 miles.

USN

CURTISS XF13C-3
Wright XR-1510-12, 700 hp at 7000′
DIMENSIONS: Span 35′, Lg. 26′ 3″, Ht. 12′, Wing Area 205 sq. ft.
WEIGHT: Empty 3499 lb., Gross 4721 lb. Fuel 110 gal.
PERFORMANCE: Speed—Top 232 mph at 7000′, Landing 70 mph. Service Ceiling 24,100′, Climb 5000′/2.5 min. Range 726 miles.

The added drag of the lower wing reduced the top speed and so the aircraft returned to the high-wing form for the XF12C-3 modification, which appeared with a 700 hp XR-1510-12 in May 1935.

The Northrop XFT-1 was ordered May 8, 1933, and tested at Anacosta in March 1934. Powered by a 625 hp Wright R-1510-26, it was an all-metal low-wing monoplane with a long turtleback from the enclosed cockpit to the tail, and the deep wheel pants characteristic of early Northrops. Two synchronized cowl guns, two 116-lb. bombs, and 120 gallons of fuel were carried.

In August 1935, the Navy ordered the aircraft reworked as the XFT-2 with a 650 hp Pratt & Whitney R-1535-72. Delivered in March 1936, the XFT-2 had modified landing gear, only 80 gallons of fuel, and improved performance.

NORTHROP XFT-1
Wright R-1510-26, 625 hp at 6000′
DIMENSIONS: Span 32′, Lg. 21′ 1″, Ht. 9′ 5″, Wing Area 177 sq. ft.
WEIGHT: Empty 2469 lb., Gross 3756 lb., Max. 4003 lb. Fuel 120 gal.
PERFORMANCE: Speed—Top 235 mph at 6000′, Landing 63 mph. Service Ceiling 26,500′, Climb 6000′/2.6 min. Range 976 miles normal, 902 miles/232 lbs. bombs.

USN

Failure of these monoplanes to win Navy contracts has been attributed to their high landing speed and stowage difficulties, although all had wing flaps and were relatively small. In any case, the Navy chose to stick to biplanes, even though the Army was now concentrating on faster monoplanes. Discouraged by their unsuccessful efforts, neither Boeing, Curtiss, nor Northrop was to offer a Navy fighter for many years.

GRUMMAN F3F BIPLANES

Grumman's first single-seater, the F2F-1, had been successful but Navy engineers desired more maneuverability and better directional stability. The XF3F-1, which had an R-1535-72, larger wings and longer fuse-

NORTHROP XFT-2
Pratt & Whitney R-1535-72, 650 hp at 7500′
DIMENSIONS: As XFT-1
WEIGHT: Empty 2730 lb., Gross 3770 lb., Max. 4017 lb. Fuel 80 gal.
PERFORMANCE: Speed—Top 240 mph at 7500′, Landing 67 mph. Service Ceiling 27,500′, Climb 5000′/2.2 min.

USN

MFR

GRUMMAN XF3F-1
Pratt & Whitney R-1535-72, 700 hp take-off, 650 hp at 7500′
DIMENSIONS: Span 32′, Lg. 23′, Ht. 10′ 6″, Wing Area 261 sq. ft.
WEIGHT: Empty 2868 lb., Gross 4094 lb., Max. 4327 lb. Fuel 110 gal.
PERFORMANCE: Speed—Top 226 mph at 7500′, Landing 64.5 mph. Service Ceiling 29,500′, Climb 5000′/2.5 min. Range 910 miles.

GRUMMAN F3F-1
Pratt & Whitney R-1535–84, 700 hp take-off, 650 hp at 7500′
DIMENSIONS: Span 32′, Lg. 23′ 3″, Ht. 9′ 4″, Wing Area 261 sq. ft.
WEIGHT: Empty 2952 lb., Gross 4170 lb., Max. 4403 lb. Fuel 110 gal.
PERFORMANCE: Speed—Top 231 mph at 7500′, 215 mph at s. l., Landing 66 mph. Service Ceiling 28,500′, Climb 1900′/1 min. Range 882 miles normal, 1000 miles max.

lage, was ordered October 15, 1934, to meet this requirement. The first prototype crashed four days after its delivery on May 13, 1935, but a second prototype completed in June won a new contract for 54 F3F-1s on August 24, 1935. Powered by a 650 hp Pratt & Whitney R-1535-84, this lot was delivered from January to August 1936.

Instead of the earlier models twin-row Wasps and two-bladed propeller, the Grumman XF3F-2 had a single-row Wright XR-1820-22 Cyclone of 750 hp and a three-bladed propeller. Purchased July 25, 1936, and tested at Anacosta the following January, it could be distinguished from the F3F-1 by the wider-diameter engine and modified rudder.

Eighty-one production F3F-2s were ordered March 23, 1937, and deliveries began in December, followed by 27 similar F3F-3s ordered June 21, 1938, whose acceptances began the following December. A private version of this type became famous as the Grumman Gulfhawk flown by a Major Williams and now preserved in the National Air Museum.

By 1939, Grumman biplanes equipped all Navy and Marine fighter squadrons. These machines were the last biplane fighters produced in the United States, because the drag of their strut-braced wings prevented performance advances comparable with those of the Army's monoplanes.

The Navy tried the monoplanes then on order for

USN

USN

GRUMMAN F3F-2
Wright R-1820-22, 950 hp take-off, 750 hp at 15,200′
DIMENSIONS: Span 32′, Lg. 23′ 2″, Ht. 9′ 4″, Wing Area 260 sq. ft.
WEIGHT: Empty 3254 lb., Gross 4498 lb., Max. 4750 lb. Fuel 130 gal.
PERFORMANCE: Speed—Top 260 mph at 17,250′, 234 mph at s. l., Landing 69 mph. Service Ceiling 32,300′, Climb 2800′/1 min. Range 975 miles at 123 mph, 1130 miles max.

G. S. WILLIAMS

GRUMMAN F3F-3
Wright R-1820-22, 950 hp take-off, 750 hp at 15,200′
DIMENSIONS: As F3F-2
WEIGHT: Empty 3285 lb., Gross 4543 lb., Max. 4795 lb. Fuel 130 gal.
PERFORMANCE: Speed—Top 264 mph at 15,200′, 239 mph at s. l., Landing 68 mph. Service Ceiling 33,200′, Climb 2750′/1 min. Range 980 miles normal, 1150 miles max.

USN/WL

SEVERSKY XFN-1
Wright R-1820-22, 950 hp take-off, 750 hp at 15,200′
DIMENSIONS: Span 36′, Lg. 25′ 2″, Ht. 9′ 1″, Wing Area 220 sq. ft.
WEIGHT: Empty 4020 lb., Gross 5231 lb. Fuel 90–200 gal.
PERFORMANCE: Speed—Top 267 mph at 15,000′, Landing 69 mph. Service Ceiling 30,700′, Climb 2760′/1 min.

the Army, in order to see if carrier-based adaptions would be practical. In July 1936, Curtiss Design 75, the P-36's prototype, was tested at Anacosta. Powered by an 840 hp Wright R-1820G-5, it did 277 mph at 5,265 lbs. gross, better than the Grumman biplane. A Naval version of the Seversky P-35 was the XFN-1, received September 24, 1937. Similar to the Army job but for a Wright R-1820-22, it did not prove adaptable for carrier-based purposes. Nevertheless, something had to be done to develop monoplanes for carrier use, if the 300 mph speeds of land-based fighters were to be equalled. Landing speeds thought too dangerous in the '30s were to become commonplace during the war years, and ingenious methods of wing folding would solve the stowage problem.

Chapter 30: Fighters against Japan 1938–45

USN/M. SALO

BREWSTER XF2A-1
Wright XR-1820-22, 950 hp take-off, 750 hp at 15,200′
DIMENSIONS: Span 35′, Lg. 25′ 6″, Ht. 11′ 9″, Wing 209 sq. ft.
WEIGHT: Empty 3711 lb., Gross 5017 lb. Fuel 164 gal.
PERFORMANCE: Speed—Top 277.5 mph at 15,200′, Landing 67 mph. Service Ceiling 30,900′, Climb 2750′/1 min.

BREWSTER BUFFALO

The first monoplane fighter actually used by Navy squadrons was the barrel-shaped Brewster Buffalo. A mid-wing all-metal single seater with wheels retracting into the fuselage and a Wright R-1820-22, the XF2A-1 prototype was ordered June 22, 1936, and began tests in January 1938.

Fifty-four F2A-1s ordered June 11, 1938, had an R-1820-34, enlarged fin, and cowl alterations. Delivery began June 1939, and the first machines operated from the *Saratoga*. Eleven went to the Navy, but the remaining aircraft were released to Finland for use against Russia. This contract was completed in February 1940. Too late for the "Winter War" they were operated by the Finns in the later fight from 1941 to 1944 with unusual success.

Forty more Brewsters (Model 439) were completed from April to July 1940 for Belgium, but 38 were turned over to Britain and named Buffalo I. Used by one RAF squadron, they were considered too slow for operations against Germany, and 170 additional Buffalos on order were scheduled for shipment to Singapore and Rangoon to meet the threat of war in the Far East.

In the meantime, the Navy had ordered on March 22, 1939, the original prototype modified to an XF2A-2, with a more powerful R-1820-40, and modified fin. This version was tested in July 1939, and its improvements included on 43 F2A-2s delivered to the Navy beginning September 1940, to replace the Finnish lot.

In December 1940, delivery began on the 170 Buffalos for the Far East and, beginning in March 1941, 72 Buffalos for the Dutch East Indies. The next Buffalo contract, delivered July to December 1941, was for 108 Navy F2A-3s, ordered the previous January 21. When 20 more Buffalos for the Dutch East Indies were completed by March 1942, 507 had been built.

USN/M. SALO

Armament of the Buffalo included two .50-caliber guns on the upper cowl, and two more in the wings. A 100-lb. bomb could be attached under each wing, and later models were provided with armor and leak-proof tanks. The additional weight put into production models greatly increased the loading on the smallest

BREWSTER F2A-1

Wright R-1820-34, 940 hp take-off, 750 hp at 17,000′

DIMENSIONS: Span 35′, Lg. 26′, Ht. 11′ 8″, Wing Area 209 sq. ft.

WEIGHT: Empty 3785 lb., Gross 5055 lb., Max. 5370 lb. Fuel 160 gal.

PERFORMANCE: Speed—Top 301 mph at 17,000′, 271 mph at s. l. Service Ceiling 32,500′, Climb 3060′/1 min. Range 1095 miles normal, 1545 miles max.

USN

USN

BREWSTER XF2A-2

Wright R-1820-40, 1200 hp take-off, 900 hp at 14,000′

DIMENSIONS: Span 35′, Lg. 25′ 7″, Ht. 12′ 1″, Wing Area 209 sq. ft.

WEIGHT: Empty 4131 lb., Gross 5409 lb., Max. 5643 lb. Fuel 164 gal.

PERFORMANCE: Speed—Top 325 mph at 16,100′, 290 mph at s. l., Cruising 144 mph, Landing 70 mph. Service Ceiling 35,000′, Climb 3100′/1 min. Range 1015 miles.

USN

BREWSTER F2A-3

Wright R-1820-40, 1200 hp take-off, 900 hp at 14,000′

DIMENSIONS: Span 35′, Lg. 26′ 4″, Ht. 12′, Wing Area 209 sq. ft.

WEIGHT: Empty 4732 lb., Gross 6321 lb., Max. 7159 lb. Fuel 110–240 gal.

PERFORMANCE: Speed—Top 321 mph at 16,500′, 284 mph at s. l., Cruising 161 mph, Landing 81 mph. Service Ceiling 33,200′, Climb 2290′/1 min. Range 965 miles normal, 1680 miles max.

wing of any U.S. production fighter, crippling climb and maneuverability.

The Buffalo's combat record proved pretty dismal, for it was consistently outperformed and outmaneuvered by the Japanese Zero during fighting over Burma, Singapore, and the East Indies. The only U.S. combat use was that of Marine F2A-3s based at Midway. Fortunately, another Navy fighter developed side by side with the Buffalo proved much more successful.

PMB

BREWSTER F2A-2
Wright R-1820-40, 1200 hp take-off, 900 hp at 14,000′
DIMENSIONS: Span 35′, Lg. 25′ 7″, Ht. 12′, Wing Area 209 sq. ft.
WEIGHT: Empty 4576 lb., Gross 5942 lb., Max. 6890 lb. Fuel 240 gal.
PERFORMANCE: Speed—Top 323 mph at 16,500′, 285 mph at s. l., Cruising 157 mph, Landing 78 mph. Service Ceiling 34,000′, Climb 2500′/1 min. Range 1015 miles normal, 1670 miles max.

USN

BREWSTER BUFFALO I
Wright GR-1820-G105A, 1200 hp take-off
DIMENSIONS: Span 35′, Lg. 26′, Ht. 12′ 1″, Wing Area 209 sq. ft.
WEIGHT: Empty 4479 lb., Max. 6840 lb.
PERFORMANCE: Speed—Top 324 mph at 21,000′, 313 mph at 13,000′, Cruising 256 mph. Service Ceiling 30,675′, Climb 3070′/1 min., 15,000′/6.3 min.

USN

GRUMMAN XF4F-2
Pratt & Whitney R-1830-66, 1050 hp take-off, 900 hp at 10,000′
DIMENSIONS: Span 34′, Lg. 26′ 5″, Ht. 11′, Wing Area 232 sq. ft.
WEIGHT: Empty 4036 lb., Gross 5535 lb. Fuel 130 gal.
PERFORMANCE: Speed—Top 288 mph at 10,000′. Service Ceiling 29,450′.

WILDCATS AT WAR

Grumman's first monoplane fighter had been ordered March 2, 1936, as the XF4F-1 with an R-1535-92, but when first flown December 23, 1937, it was the XF4F-2, powered by a Pratt & Whitney R-1830-66 Wasp with a single stage supercharger. The wing had rounded tips and was mounted at the center of the fuselage, into which the wheels retracted in the manner distinguishing Navy fighters of that period from Army aircraft whose wheels retracted into the wing. Two guns protruded from the top of the cowling ahead of the enclosed cockpit.

In October 1938 the aircraft was ordered modified to the XF4F-3, which had enlarged wings with square tips, raised squared-off stabilizer, and an XR-1830-76 with two-stage supercharger and intake moved forward to the front of the cowl. After tests in March 1939 a contract for 78 F4F-3s was let on August 8, 1939.

France had purchased 81 Grumman G-36As, but the contract was transferred to Britain, who named the type Martlet I. Powered by a Wright R-1820-G205A Cyclone (R-1820-40), and armed with four .50-caliber wing guns, the Martlet I was first flown July 27, 1940. Two XF4F-5s built for the Navy used the same engine.

The first F4F-3 was tested August 20, 1940, with an R-1830-76 Wasp, prop spinner and two guns ahead of the cockpit, but the remaining ships on this contract began appearing late in November 1940 with four .50-caliber wing guns and no spinner. An XF4F-6 finished the same month was similar but for an R-1830-90.

In March 1941 delivery began on the next production batch, 100 G-36B (Martlet II), with Pratt & Whitney R-1830-S3C4G and wings folding backwards for carrier stowage. The Martlet III also built for Britain at the same time, had fixed wings and an R-1830-90. Known as the F4F-3A on Navy records, the 95 plane lot included 30 originally scheduled for Greece.

Another Navy contract was let August 5, 1940, and deliveries began in May 1941. The first 107 were fixed-wing F4F-3s but the remainder were F4F-4s with folding wings, R-1830-86 Wasps, self-sealing fuel tank, 164 lbs. of armor, and six .50-caliber wing guns with 1440 rounds of ammunition. The XF4F-4 of May 1941 was followed in November by the first of 1269 Navy F4F-4s and 220 F4F-4Bs (Martlet IV) for the United Kingdom. Navy Grummans were known as Wildcats, the name eventually adopted by the British instead of Martlet.

Several Wildcat modifications appeared, including an F4F-3 fitted with twin float landing gear. Twenty-one F4F-7s built in 1942 had the guns replaced by unprotected internal wing tanks to increase fuel capacity to 685 gallons, while cameras were installed in the belly for long-range reconnaissance. The last of Grummans 1971 Wildcats was finished in May 1943, and that plant turned to production of more advanced Hellcats.

Navy requirements for fighters for the growing fleet of escort carriers led to continuation of Wildcat production by the Eastern Aircraft Division of General Motors. Similar to the F4F-4 except for armament of four .50-caliber guns with 1720 rounds, the General Motors FM-1 Wildcat first flew September 1, 1942. General Motors built 1150 FM-1s, including 312 lend-leased to Britain's Fleet Air Arm as the Wildcat V.

In September 1943, delivery began on the FM-2, production version of two XF4F-8s tested the previous December. The FM-2 had a Wright R-1820-56 Cyclone, new cowl, high fin, 142 lbs. of armor, and was armed with four .50-caliber guns, two 250-lb. bombs, or six 5 in. rockets. Production continued to August

GRUMMAN XF4F-3

Pratt & Whitney XR-1830-76, 1200 hp take-off, 1000 hp at 19,000′

DIMENSIONS: Span 38′, Lg. 28′ 10″, Ht. 12′ 5″, Wing Area 260 sq. ft.

WEIGHT: Empty 4907 lb., Gross 6103 lb., Max. 6404 lb. Fuel 160 gal.

PERFORMANCE: Speed—Top 335 mph at 21,300′, 284 mph at s. l., Cruising 145 mph, Landing 68 mph. Service Ceiling 33,500′, Climb 3100′/1 min. Range 890 miles normal, 1270 miles max.

PMB

GRUMMAN F4F-3
Pratt & Whitney R-1830-76, 1200 hp take-off, 1000 hp at 19,000′
DIMENSIONS: Span 38′, Lg. 28′ 9″, Ht. 11′ 10″, Wing Area 260 sq. ft.
WEIGHT: Empty 5342 lb., Gross 7002 lb., Max. 8152 lb. Fuel 147–231 gal.
PERFORMANCE: Speed—Top 330 mph at 21,100′, 281 mph at s. l., Cruising 147 mph, Landing 76 mph. Service Ceiling 37,500′, Climb 2265′/1 min. Range 845 miles normal, 1690 miles max.

USN

GRUMMAN F4F-4
Pratt & Whitney R-1830-86, 1200 hp take-off, 1000 hp at 19,000′
DIMENSIONS: As F4F-3
WEIGHT: Empty 5785 lb., Gross 7406 lb., Max. 7952 lb. Fuel 144 gal.
PERFORMANCE: Speed—Top 318 mph at 19,400′, 275 mph at s. l., Cruising 155 mph, Landing 78 mph. Service Ceiling 34,900′, Climb 1950′/1 min. Range 770 miles normal, 1100 miles max.

MFR

GRUMMAN G-36A (MARTLET I)
Wright R-1820-G205A, 1000 hp at 13,500′
DIMENSIONS: As F4F-3
WEIGHT: Empty 4425 lb., Gross 5876 lb. Fuel 160 gal.
PERFORMANCE: Speed—Top 325 mph at 15,500′, 290 mph at s. l., Cruising 285 mph, Landing 66.5 mph. Service Ceiling 28,000′, Climb 3300′/1 min. Range 1150 miles max.

USN

GRUMMAN XF4F-5
Wright R-1820-40, 1200 hp take-off, 900 hp at 14,000′
DIMENSIONS: As F4F-3
WEIGHT: Empty 4942 lb., Gross 6134 lb., Max. 6711 lb. Fuel 160 gal.
PERFORMANCE: Speed—Top 312 mph at 15,250′, 279 mph at s. l., Cruising 148 mph, Landing 68 mph. Service Ceiling 34,000′, Climb 2240′/1 min. Range 910 miles normal, 1250 miles max.

PMB

GRUMMAN F4F-3 (as seaplane)

1945, when 4777 FM-2 Wildcats had been built, including 370 Wildcat VIs for Britain.

First U. S. Wildcats to fight were Marine F4F-3s lost with Wake Island. By 1942, Wildcats equipped all carrier fighter squadrons, and remained our sole carrier fighter in action for the first half of the war, fighting in all the major naval battles. Of all the U.S. wartime fighters, they were the slowest, even among carrier-based types, yet the Wildcat was fairly successful, for the generous wing's low loading permitted a better climb and maneuverability than some of its faster contemporaries. Inferior to the Mitsubishi Zero in performance, but possessing internal protection and more firepower, the Wildcat's victories were really due to the superior tactics and training of U.S. fighter pilots. Turning their own strong points against the enemy's weaknesses, American pilots used a two-plane element to dive, fire, and dive away, avoiding any attempt to turn and twist with the lighter Zeros. These tactics had been developed by pilots of the American Volunteer Group in China commanded by General Claire L. Chennault.

USN

GENERAL MOTORS FM-1
Pratt & Whitney R-1830-86, 1200 hp take-off, 1040 hp at 18,400′
DIMENSIONS: As F4F-3
WEIGHT: Empty 5895 lb., Gross 7975 lb., Max. 8762 lb. Fuel 144–260 gal.
PERFORMANCE: Speed—Top 320 mph at 18,800′, 284 mph at s. l., Cruising 161 mph, Landing 81 mph. Service Ceiling 34,000′, Climb 10,000′/5.6 min. Range 830 miles normal, 1275 miles max.

USN

GENERAL MOTORS FM-2
Wright R-1820-56, 1350 hp take-off, 1000 hp at 14,700′
DIMENSIONS: Span 38′, Lg. 28′ 11″, Ht. 11′ 5″, Wing Area 260 sq. ft.
WEIGHT: Empty 5448 lb., Gross 7487 lb., Max. 8271 lb. Fuel 126–242 gal.
PERFORMANCE: Speed—Top 332 mph at 28,800′, 306 mph at s. l., Cruising 164 mph, Landing 76 mph. Service Ceiling 34,700′, Climb 3650′/1 min. Range 900 miles normal, 1310 miles max.

VOUGHT CORSAIRS

Three new fighter projects were launched in 1938 in an effort to bring carrier-based performance up to the level of land-based contemporaries. The Grumman XF5F-1 and Vought XF4U-1 were ordered June 30, 1938, and the Bell XFL-1 was ordered November 8.

The first twin-engined single-seater built for the Navy, the XF5F-1, was first flown on the first of April 1940 with Wright R-1820-40 Cyclones slung ahead and below the leading edge of stubby square-cut wings. The short fuselage began behind the wing's leading edge and extended back to twin rudders. Known as the G-34 Skyrocket on company records, it was originally armed with two Madsen cannon, but four .50-caliber guns were installed instead ahead of the pilot's cockpit. Main wheels folded back into the engine nacelles, while the tail wheel was fixed and the wings folded for carrier stowage.

Delayed by cooling troubles, the prototype did not complete tests until February 1941, and from March to July was returned to the factory for rework with an extended nose and prop spinners added. After 211 flights the project was abandoned in favor of the XF7F-1, and the XP-50 Army version had no greater success.

First flown May 13, 1940, the Bell XFL-1 was a carrier version of the P-39 Airacobra, with an Allison V-1710-6 placed behind the pilot and turning the propeller by a driveshaft extended to the nose. Instead of tricycle wheels, however, the XFL-1 had conventional tail-down landing gear, with an arrester hook added for carrier landings. Radiators below the wing cooled the only inline engine in the last 25 years of Navy fighters, and provisions were made for a 37-mm. cannon and two .50-caliber guns in the nose.

Both of these experiments were surpassed by the Vought XF4U-1 Corsair, first Navy plane built around the Pratt & Whitney 1850 hp XR-2800-4 Double Wasp, with a 13 ft.-4 in. diameter three-bladed propeller. In order to give the big propeller sufficient ground clearance without making the landing gear too stilted and heavy, the wing was gulled downward, a technique that also promised reduced drag at the juncture of wing and body. The wheels retracted backward and swiveled 90° flat into the wing, which folded upward for stowage. Two .50-caliber guns were mounted in the nose, with another pair in the wings. Finished with a smooth spot-welded skin, the XF4U-1 made its first flight on May 29, 1940.

An initial production contract for 584 F4U-1s was placed June 30, 1941, but war expanded requirements and the VGB program was set up to pool the resources of Vought, Goodyear, and Brewster to produce Corsair fighters. On June 25, 1942, the first production F4U-1 was flown with a 2000 hp R-2800-8, lengthened fuselage, and cockpit moved back to make room for additional fuel. Six .50-caliber guns in the wings with 2350 rounds of ammunition, self-sealing fuel tanks, and 155 lbs. of armor was installed.

In September 1942 the Corsair was tested on an aircraft carrier, but it landed rather fast and downward visibility was poor. In any case, the Corsair was satisfactory for land-based operations and was therefore issued to Marine units, who took it into its first battle February 15, 1943. By the following August all eight Marine fighter squadrons in the Pacific used Corsairs.

Goodyear began delivery on the FG-1 in April 1943,

MFR

GRUMMAN XF5F-1

Wright R-1820-40, 1200 hp take-off, 900 hp at 14,000′

DIMENSIONS: Span 42′, Lg. 28′ 11″, Ht. 12′, Wing Area 303 sq. ft.

WEIGHT: Empty 7990 lb., Gross 10,021 lb., Max. 10,892 lb. Fuel 178–277 gal.

PERFORMANCE: Speed—Top 358 mph at 17,300′, 312 mph at s. l., Landing 72 mph. Service Ceiling 34,500′, Climb 10,000′/4.2 min. Range 780 miles normal, 1170 miles max.

MFR

BELL XFL-1

Allison V-1710-6, 1150 hp take-off, 1000 hp at 10,000′

DIMENSIONS: Span 35′, Lg. 29′ 9″, Ht. 11′ 5″, Wing Area 232 sq. ft.

WEIGHT: Empty 5161 lb., Gross 6651 lb., Max. 7212 lb. Fuel 126–200 gal.

PERFORMANCE: Speed—Top 338 mph at 11,000′, 306 mph at s. l., Cruising 172 mph, Landing 72 mph. Service Ceiling 30,900′, Climb 2630′/1 min. Range 965 miles normal, 1475 miles max.

BELL XFL-1

MFR

USN

VOUGHT XF4U-1

Pratt & Whitney XR-2800-4, 1850 hp take-off, 1460 hp at 21,500′

DIMENSIONS: Span 41′, Lg. 31′ 11″, Ht. 15′ 7″, Wing Area 314 sq. ft.

WEIGHT: Empty 7505 lb., Gross 9357 lb., Max. 10,074 lb. Fuel 273 gal.

PERFORMANCE: Speed—Top 405 mph, Landing 73 mph. Service Ceiling 35,200′, Climb 2660′/1 min. Range 1070 miles.

similar to the F4U-1, but without folding wings. Brewster's F3A-1 Corsairs began appearing July 1943. Many minor modifications were made, including F4U-1Bs with wingtips clipped so that they could fold inside the smaller hangars on British carriers. A night fighter version had been proposed as early as November 8, 1941, and the Naval Aircraft Factory converted a dozen Corsairs to F4U-2s with a radome on the starboard wingtip, and two guns deleted. On October 31, 1943, over New Georgia, one made the Navy's first successful radar-guided interception.

USN

VOUGHT F4U-1D

VOUGHT F4U-2 [*Photo unavailable*]

Pratt & Whitney R-2800-8, 2000 hp take-off, 1650 hp at 21,000′

DIMENSIONS: As F4U-1

WEIGHT: Empty 9170 lb., Gross 11,446 lb., Max. 13,112 lb. Fuel 178–363 gal.

PERFORMANCE: Speed—Top 381 mph at 23,500′, 325 mph at s. l., Cruising 187 mph, Landing 82 mph. Service Ceiling 33,900′, Climb 2970′/1 min. Range 955 miles normal, 1790 miles max.

VOUGHT F4U-1

Pratt & Whitney R-2800-8, 2000 hp take-off, 1650 hp at 21,000′

DIMENSIONS: Span 41′, Lg. 33′ 4″, Ht. 16′ 1″, Wing Area 314 sq. ft.

WEIGHT: Empty 8982 lb., Gross 12,039 lb., Max. 14,000 lb. Fuel 237–537 gal.

PERFORMANCE: Speed—Top 417 mph at 19,900′, 359 mph at s. l., Cruising 182 mph, Landing 87 mph. Service Ceiling 36,900′, Climb 2890′/1 min. Range 1015 miles normal, 2220 miles ferry.

USN

MFR

VOUGHT XF4U-3
Pratt & Whitney XR-2800-16, 2000 hp at 30,000′
DIMENSIONS: As F4U-1
WEIGHT: Empty 9039 lb., Gross 11,623 lb., Max. 13,143 lb.
PERFORMANCE: Speed—Top 412 mph at 30,000′, 314 mph at s. l., Cruising 180 mph, Landing 83 mph. Service Ceiling 38,400′, Climb 2990′/1 min. Range 780 miles normal, 1430 miles max.

USN

VOUGHT F4U-4
Pratt & Whitney R-2800-18W, 2100 hp take-off, 1950 hp at 23,300′
DIMENSIONS: Span 41′, Lg. 33′ 8″, Ht. 14′ 9″, Wing Area 314 sq. ft.
WEIGHT: Empty 9205 lb., Gross 12,420 lb., Max 14,670 lb. Fuel 234–534 gal.
PERFORMANCE: Speed—Top 446 mph at 26,200′, 381 mph at s. l., Cruising 215 mph, Landing 89 mph. Service Ceiling 41,500′, Climb 3870′/1 min. Range 1005 miles normal, 1560 miles max.

After 1550 F4U-1s were completed by Vought, further copies had the cockpit raised seven inches, with a new canopy to improve vision, and an R-2800-8W with water injection. The F4U-1D, which substituted fittings for a 160 gallon drop tank, two 1000-lb. bombs, or eight 5 in. rockets for internal outboard wing tanks, was introduced in February 1944. Vought built 4102 F4U-1s, including 95 Corsair Is (old cockpit) and 510 Corsair IIs (new canopy) for the Fleet Air Arm, and 370 for New Zealand.

The Navy closed the badly managed Brewster Johnsonville, Pennsylvania, facility in July 1944, after 735 F3A-1s were finished, thereby causing a brief "sit-in" strike by workers demanding more war work to do. Goodyear, however, continued Corsair production to the end of the war, completing 3808 FG-1s and 200 FG-4s. Britain received 430 of the Brewster Corsair IIIs and 977 Goodyear Corsair IVs under lend-lease.

In March 1942, three high-altitude XF4U-3s with a turbo-supercharged R-2800-16 fed by a belly intake were projected, but not until 1946 was one example completed. More successful were the five XF4U-4s, which resulted in the F4U-4 production series that began appearing in October 1944. This Corsair had a new cowl over an R-2800-18W turning a four-bladed propeller with 2100 hp for take-off. The use of water injection in this engine's supercharger raised top speed from a normal 425 mph to 446 mph. The F4U-4 carried six .50-caliber wing guns, two 1000-lb. bombs or eight 5 in. rockets, and 197 lbs. of armor. Variations of this type included the F4U-4B for Britain, the F4U-4C with four 20-mm. guns, F4U-4E with APS-4 radar, F4U-4N with APS-6 radar, F4U-4P photoreconnaissance, and the Goodyear FG-4.

In January 1945 Marine F4U-1D and F4U-4 squadrons finally began combat operations from U.S. aircraft carriers and functioned with successes that made previous reluctance to operate Corsairs from flight decks seem timid. V-J Day cancellations reduced F4U-4 contracts from 3149 to 2356 copies, not including 287 F4U-4Bs, but the last F4U-4 was not finished until June 1947.

Goodyear produced a special Corsair for the interception of low-altitude kamikazes, with the big 3000 hp Pratt & Whitney R-4360-4. A March 22, 1944, contract called for 418 F2G-1s and ten F2G-2s with carrier gear, but only five of each type were finished in 1945 before victory ended production. Faster at low altitudes than the standard Corsair, they had a bubble canopy and an intake above the engine. Four .50-caliber guns with 1200 rounds were carried in the wings, together with fittings for two 1600-lb. bombs. All F2Gs were eventually sold as surplus and some were used as private racers.

The end of the war didn't end Corsair history, for postwar Navy requirements for a suitable fighter bomber and night fighter prolonged its life well into the jet age. In July 1946, Vought proposed the F4U-5 version with an R-2800-32W and four 20-mm. guns, and two earlier aircraft were modified to XF4U-5 prototypes. The Navy ordered 223 F4U-5, 75 F4U-5N, and 30 F4U-5P in fiscal 1947, and added 240 F4U-5N night fighters the following year. Work began in the old Connecticut plant, but shifted to Dallas, Texas, in April 1949.

The F4U-5N had a radar scanner on the starboard wing, rearranged cockpit, and two small side intakes on the new cowl for the 2300 hp R-2800-32W. Four 20-mm. guns with 924 rounds were carried in the wings, and either two 1000-lb. bombs, eight 5 in. rockets, or two 150-gallon drop tanks could be attached externally.

A new requirement for a close-support Corsair version was created by the Korean War, and the XF4U-6,

PMB

GOODYEAR F2G-1 (Data for F2G-2)
Pratt & Whitney R-4360-4, 3000 hp take-off, 2400 hp at 13,500′
DIMENSIONS: Span 41′, Lg. 33′ 10″, Ht. 16′ 1″, Wing Area 314 sq. ft.
WEIGHT: Empty 10,249 lb., Gross 13,346 lb., Max. 15,422 lb. Fuel 309–609 gal.
PERFORMANCE: Speed—Top 431 mph at 16,400′, 399 mph at s. l., Cruising 190 mph, Landing 92 mph. Service Ceiling 38,800′, Climb 4400′/1 min. Range 1190 miles normal, 1955 miles max.

MFR

VOUGHT F4U-5
Pratt & Whitney R-2800-32W, 2300 hp at 26,200′
DIMENSIONS: Span 41′, Lg. 33′ 6″, Ht. 14′ 9″, Wing Area 314 sq. ft.
WEIGHT: Empty 9583 lb., Gross 12,902 lb., Max. 15,079 lb. Fuel 234–534 gal.
PERFORMANCE: Speed—Top 462 mph at 31,400′, 403 mph at s. l., Cruising 190 mph, Landing 91 mph. Service Ceiling 44,100′, Climb 4230′/1 min. Range 1036 miles normal, 1532 miles max.

later designated AU-1, was designed for this purpose. Delivered after January 1952, it had a narrow cowl with the oil coolers moved in from the wing roots into the fuselage. An R-2800-83W with a single-stage supercharger provided low-altitude power, and additional armor was placed under the cockpit, fuel tank, and engine accessory compartment. Fuel and 20-mm. armament was the same as that of the F4U-5, but external racks could handle up to 4000 lbs. of bombs or ten rockets. Marine squadrons received 110 AU-1s and used them in Korea.

Final Corsair model was the F4U-7, which differed from the AU-1 by R-2800-18W two-stage supercharged engines and a scoop on the cowl's bottom. Ninety were built for French forces in Indochina.

When the last F4U-7 rolled off the line on Christmas Eve 1952, production of the last propeller-driven fighter built in the United States was complete after 12,571 planes had been built. In length of time in production, the Corsair surpassed any fighter in America. During World War II, F4U pilots flew 64,051 combat sorties; 54,470 from land bases and 9581 off aircraft carriers. For a loss of 189 Corsairs they claimed the destruction of 2140 Japanese aircraft.

MFR

VOUGHT F5U-5N
Pratt & Whitney R-2800-32W, 2300 hp at 26,200′
DIMENSIONS: Span 41′, Lg. 34′ 6″, Ht. 14′ 9″, Wing Area 314 sq. ft.
WEIGHT: Empty 9683 lb., Gross 12,901 lb., Max. 14,106 lb. Fuel 234–534 gal.
PERFORMANCE: Speed—Top 470 mph at 26,800′, 379 mph at s. l., Cruising 227 mph. Service Ceiling 41,400′, Climb 3780′/1 min. Range 1120 miles.

MFR

VOUGHT AU-1
Pratt & Whitney R-2800-83W, 2300 hp take-off, 2800 hp WE
DIMENSIONS: Span 41′, Lg. 34′ 1″, Ht. 14′ 10″, Wing Area 314 sq. ft.
WEIGHT: Empty 9835 lb., Gross 18,979 lb., Max. 19,398 lb. Fuel 234–534 gal.
PERFORMANCE: Speed—Top 238 mph at 9500′, Cruising 184 mph, Landing 83 mph. Service Ceiling 19,500′, Climb 920′/1 min. Range 484 miles.

VOUGHT F4U-7

MFR

HELLCATS

Since the Corsair was not accepted for carrier operations earlier in the war, it is fortunate that another type more suitable for flight deck work was available. The Grumman Hellcat also had a 2000 hp Pratt & Whitney Wasp and six wing guns, but sacrificed speed for better maneuverability, climb, and visibility.

The Navy ordered the XF6F-1 prototype June 30, 1941, and F6F-3 production aircraft May 23, 1942. Grumman began deliveries with unusual speed, flying the first prototype on June 26, 1942, and completing production models as early as November, with ten finished by the end of 1942.

Hellcats replaced Wildcats at Grumman, although the older type's production was continued at General

MFR

GRUMMAN XF6F-3 (begun as XF6F-1)

USN

GRUMMAN F6F-3

Pratt & Whitney R-2800-10W, 2000 hp take-off, 1975 hp at 16,900′

DIMENSIONS: Span 42′ 10″, Lg. 33′ 7″, Ht. 13′ 1″, Wing Area 334 sq. ft.

WEIGHT: Empty 9101 lb., Gross 12,441 lb., Max. 15,487 lb. Fuel 250–400 gal.

PERFORMANCE: Speed—Top 375 mph at 17,300′, 335 mph at s. l., Cruising 160 mph, Landing 84 mph. Service Ceiling 37,300′, Climb 3500′/1 min. Range 1090 miles normal, 1590 miles max.

GRUMMAN F6F-5

Pratt & Whitney R-2800-10W, 2000 hp take-off, 1975 hp at 16,900′

DIMENSIONS: As F6F-3

WEIGHT: Empty 9238 lb., Gross 12,740 lb., Max. 15,413 lb. Fuel 250–408 gal.

PERFORMANCE: Speed—Top 380 mph at 23,400′, 315 mph at s. l., Cruising 168 mph, Landing 88 mph. Service Ceiling 37,300′, Climb 2980′/1 min. Range 945 miles normal, 1355 miles max.

USN

MFR

GRUMMAN F6F-3N
Pratt & Whitney R-2800-10W, 2000 hp take-off, 1975 hp at 16,900′
DIMENSIONS: As F6F-3
WEIGHT: Empty 9331 lb., Gross 13,015 lb., Max. 14,074 lb. Fuel 250–400 gal.
PERFORMANCE: Speed—Top 360 mph at 18,000′, 305 mph at s. l., Cruising 161 mph. Service Ceiling 38,100′, Climb 3090′/1 min. Range 865 miles normal, 1235 miles max.

PMB

GRUMMAN F6F-5N
Pratt & Whitney R-2800-10W, 2000 hp take-off, 1975 hp at 16,900′
DIMENSIONS: As F6F-3
WEIGHT: Empty 9421 lb., Gross 13,190 lb., Max. 14,250 lb. Fuel 250–400 gal.
PERFORMANCE: Speed—Top 366 mph at 23,200′, Cruising 166 mph, Landing 89 mph. Service Ceiling 36,700′, Climb 2840′/1 min. Range 880 miles normal, 1260 miles max.

Motors. On the first of September 1943, the first Hellcat combat sorties were made, some 14 months after the prototype's first flight. (Corresponding time on the Corsair was over 32 months.) High mark of the Hellcats' success was the battle of the Philippine Sea in June 1944 when the Grummans smashed the Japanese attack with very small losses to themselves.

Powered by an R-2800-10W with Hamilton three-bladed propeller, the Hellcat had the largest wing area of any U.S. single-engine service fighter, to keep wing loading low. The wheels folded backward flat into the wings, which folded backward aboard ship. Seating the pilot high on top of the fuel tanks gave him fine visibility. A downward angle given the engine thrust line enhanced his view, and keeping the tail down in relation to the thrust line made climb the aircraft's natural tendency. The prototype XF6F-3 could be distinguished from production models by a Curtiss propeller in a large spinner, natural aluminum finish, and bulkier landing gear fairings. A second prototype, the XF6F-2, was to use a turbo-supercharged R-2800-21, but this project was canceled and the aircraft delivered March 1943 with an R-2800-27 and designated XF6F-4.

Installations on the F6F-3 consisted of six .50-caliber guns with 2400 rounds in the wings, 212 lbs. of armor, and the self-sealing fuel tanks standard on all wartime Navy types. The F6F-3N was similar but had APS-6 radar, while the F6F-3E had APS-4 radar. A total of 4423 F6F-3s, 205 F6F-3Ns, and 18 F6F-3Es were completed before the F6F-5 began appearing in May 1944.

Also powered by an R-2800-10W, the F6F-5 had a modified cowl and windshield, armor increased to 242 lbs., and later models could substitute 20-mm. guns for the two inner wing weapons. Contracts for 6436 F6F-5s and over a thousand F6F-5Ns were placed, and production continued until V-J Day, with a total of 12,272 Hellcats completed. The British Royal Navy received 252 F6F-3s as the Hellcat I and 930 F6F-5s as the Hellcat II, including some night-fighter versions. Two XF6F-6s with the 2100 hp R-2800-18W were tested in July 1944, but the type wasn't put into production.

While not nearly as fast as the Corsair, the Hellcat had enough margin over the Zero to completely frustrate the enemy type in combat. The Japanese introduced fighters of superior performance in 1945, but they were too late to turn the tide of battle. With its radome on the starboard wing, the night-fighter

MFR

GRUMMAN XF6F-6
Pratt & Whitney R-2800-18W, 2100 hp take-off, 1800 hp at 21,900′
DIMENSIONS: As F6F-3
WEIGHT: Empty 9526 lb., Gross 12,768 lb., Max. 13,823 lb. Fuel 250–400 gal.
PERFORMANCE: Speed—Top 417 mph at 21,900′, Cruising 171 mph, Landing 85 mph. Service Ceiling 39,000′, Climb 3070′/1 min. Range 1170 miles normal, 1730 miles max.

MFR

CURTISS XF14C-2
Wright XR-3350-16, 2300 hp take-off, 2250 hp at 32,000′
DIMENSIONS: Span 46′, Lg. 37′ 9″, Ht. 17′, Wing Area 375 sq. ft.
WEIGHT: Empty 10,582 lb., Gross 13,405 lb., Max. 14,582 lb. Fuel 230–380 gal.
PERFORMANCE: Speed—Top 424 mph at 32,000′, 317 mph at s. l., Cruising 172 mph. Service Ceiling 39,500′, Climb 2700′/1 min. Range 950 miles normal, 1355 miles max.

USN

GRUMMAN F7F-1 (XF7F-1 prototype shown)
Pratt & Whitney R-2800-22W, 2100 hp take-off, 1600 hp at 16,000′
DIMENSIONS: Span 51′ 6″, Lg. 45′ 4½″, Ht. 15′ 2″, Wing Area 455 sq. ft.
WEIGHT: Empty 15,943 lb., Gross 21,425 lb., Max. 22,560 lb. Fuel 426–576 gal.
PERFORMANCE: Speed—Top 427 mph at 19,200′, 394 mph at s. l., Cruising 177 mph, Landing 89 mph. Service Ceiling 36,200′, Climb 4360′/1 min. Range 1170 miles normal, 1485 miles max.

GRUMMAN F7F-2N
Pratt & Whitney R-2800-22W, 2100 hp take-off, 1850 hp at 14,000′
DIMENSIONS: As F7F-1
WEIGHT: Empty 16,321 lb., Gross 21,857 lb., Max. 26,194 lb. Fuel 375–975 gal.
PERFORMANCE: Speed—Top 421 mph at 20,600′, 362 mph at s. l., Cruising 183 mph, Landing 84 mph. Service Ceiling 39,800′, Climb 4540′/1 min. Range 960 miles normal, 1250 miles/525 gal.

MFR

PMB

GRUMMAN F7F-3
Pratt & Whitney R-2800-34W, 2100 hp take-off, 1850 hp at 15,500′
DIMENSIONS: Span 51′ 6″, Lg. 45′ 4″, Ht. 16′ 7″, Wing Area 455 sq. ft.
WEIGHT: Empty 16,270 lb., Gross 21,720 lb., Max. 25,720 lb. Fuel 455–755 gal.
PERFORMANCE: Speed—Top 435 mph at 22,200′, 367 mph at s. l., Cruising 222 mph, Landing 91 mph. Service Ceiling 40,700′, Climb 4530′/1 min. Range 1200 miles normal, 1572 miles max.

MFR

GRUMMAN F7F-3N
Pratt & Whitney R-2800-34W, 2100 hp take-off, 1850 hp at 15,500′
DIMENSIONS: As F7F-3
WEIGHT: Empty 16,400 lb., Gross 21,476 lb., Max. 25,846 lb. Fuel 375–675 gal.
PERFORMANCE: Speed—Top 423 mph at 21,900′, Cruising 170 mph, Landing 91 mph. Service Ceiling 40,800′, Climb 4580′/1 min. Range 960 miles/525 gal., 1595 miles max.

GRUMMAN F7F-4N
Pratt & Whitney R-2800-34W, 2100 hp take-off, 1850 hp at 14,000′
DIMENSIONS: Span 51′ 6″, Lg. 46′ 10″, Ht. 16′ 7″, Wing Area 455 sq. ft.
WEIGHT: Empty 16,954 lb., Gross 21,960 lb., Max. 26,167 lb. Fuel 375–675 gal.
PERFORMANCE: Speed—Top 430 mph at 21,900′, 360 mph at s. l., Cruising 235 mph, Landing 92 mph. Service Ceiling 40,450′, Climb 4385′/1 min. Range 810 miles normal, 1360 miles max.

WL

version had a better rate of climb than heavier land-based machines; at Leyte they pulled out an Army P-61 squadron and substituted F6F-5Ns.

TOO LATE FOR THE WAR

On the same day, June 30, 1941, the Navy ordered the Hellcat prototypes, it ordered two prototypes each of the Curtiss XF14C-1 and the Grumman XF7F-1. First Curtiss Navy fighter since 1935, the XF14C-1 was to be powered by a 2200 hp Lycoming H-2470-4, and the second prototype was redesigned to take a 2300 hp Wright R-3350-16 Cyclone. When the inline Lycoming proved unsatisfactory, the XF14C-1 was canceled in December 1943, but the second prototype was accepted as the XF14C-2 in July 1944. Co-axial contrarotating propellers were provided for the big Cyclone, along with an intake under the cowl for the turbo-supercharger. The wheels folded inwards into the roots of the low wing, which could fold upward for stowage. Four 20-mm. guns protruded from the wing leading edge.

Grumman's twin-engined XF7F-1 Tigercat introduced in December 1943 a tricycle landing gear for the first time on a naval fighter, and had the heaviest armament yet seen. Short shoulder-high square-tip wings folded upwards outboard of two R-2800-22W Wasps. The pilot sat ahead of the wings with four .50-caliber guns mounted low in the pointed nose with 1200 rounds. Four 20-mm. guns with 800 rounds were mounted in the wing roots and 377 lbs. of armor was installed. External fittings could carry two 1000-lb. bombs, drop tanks, or a standard torpedo; the first time this weapon could be handled by a service fighter.

Five hundred Tigercats had been ordered for Marine Corps squadrons and delivery began April 1944. The first 34 were F7F-1 single-seaters, but in November 1944 delivery began on the F7F-2N two-seater. This version had a radar operator seated behind the pilot, omitting some fuel and the nose guns. An XF7F-2N and 64 F7F-2Ns were followed in March 1945 by the F7F-3, a single-place version with R-2800-34Ws, 388 lbs. of armor, and the F7F-1s armament. Cancellations limited F7F-3 completions to 189, but a new contract provided for 60 F7F-3N (appeared February 1946) and 13 F7F-4N (June 1946) two-place night fighters. The last-mentioned type was the only one actually equipped for carrier operations. An enlarged fin and bulging radar nose also distinguished the 1946 models, which had four 20-mm. wing guns and 484 lbs. of armor.

The Grumman Bearcat was designed as a Hellcat replacement which would have better climb and maneuverability and be able to operate from even the smallest carriers. Two XF8F-1 prototypes ordered

GRUMMAN XF8F-1

Pratt & Whitney R-2800-22W, 2100 hp take-off, 1600 hp at 16,000′

DIMENSIONS: Span 35′ 6″, Lg. 28′ 8″, Ht. 13′ 8″, Wing Area 244 sq. ft.

WEIGHT: Empty 6733 lb., Gross 8788 lb., Max. 9537 lb. Fuel 150–250 gal.

PERFORMANCE: Speed—Top 424 mph at 17,300′, 393 mph at s. l., Cruising 170 mph. Service Ceiling 33,700′, Climb 4800′/1 min. Range 955 miles normal, 1450 miles max.

ARC

GRUMMAN F8F-1

Pratt & Whitney R-2800-34W, 2100 hp take-off, 1850 hp at 15,500′

DIMENSIONS: Span 35′ 10″, Lg. 28′ 3″, Ht. 13′ 10″, Wing Area 244 sq. ft.

WEIGHT: Empty 7070 lb., Gross 9386 lb., Max. 12,947 lb. Fuel 183–333 gal.

PERFORMANCE: Speed—Top 421 mph at 19,700′, 382 mph at s. l., Cruising 163 mph, Landing 92 mph. Service Ceiling 38,700′, Climb 4570′/1 min. Range 1105 miles normal, 1965 miles ferry.

USN

GRUMMAN F8F-2
Pratt & Whitney R-2800-34W, 2300 hp take-off, 1600 hp at 22,000′
DIMENSIONS: Span 35′ 6″, Lg. 27′ 8″, Ht. 12′ 2″, Wing Area 244 sq. ft.
WEIGHT: Empty 7690 lb., Gross 10,426 lb., Max. 13,494 lb. Fuel 185–335 gal.
PERFORMANCE: Speed—Top 447 mph at 28,000′, 387 mph at s. l., Cruising 182 mph, Landing 105 mph. Service Ceiling 40,700′, Climb 4420′/1 min. Range 865 miles normal, 1435 miles max.

PMB

November 27, 1943, had a Pratt & Whitney R-2800-22W with a four-bladed propeller, a bubble canopy, and low square-tipped wings that could be folded upwards. Appearing September 1944, the XF8F-1 lacked the fin fairing of production jobs. Small and strictly limited in weight, the Bearcat was armed with four .50-caliber guns and 1200 rounds in the wings, had 169 lbs. of armor, and external fittings for two 1000-lb. bombs, drop tanks, or four rockets. Contracts for 2023 Bearcats were approved on October 6, 1944, and deliveries began in February 1945 on the F8F-1, which had the R-2800-34W.

General Motors received a February 5, 1945, order for 1876 Bearcats, to be designated F3M-1. An XF2M-1 project with a Wright R-1820-70W was canceled, but the end of the war halted the plan to have F3M-1s

MFR

BOEING XF8B-1

Pratt & Whitney XR-4360-10, 3000 hp take-off, 2540 hp at 22,000′

DIMENSIONS: Span 54′, Lg. 43′ 3″, Ht. 15′ 11″, Wing Area 489 sq. ft.

WEIGHT: Empty 13,519 lb., Gross 20,508 lb., Max. 21,691 lb. Fuel 384–954 gal.

PERFORMANCE: Speed—Top 432 mph at 26,900′, 340 mph at s. l., Cruising 162 mph, Landing 82 mph. Service Ceiling 37,500′, Climb 2800′/1 min. Range 1305 miles normal, 2780 miles max.

MFR

VOUGHT XF5U-1

Pratt & Whitney R-2000-2, 1600 hp at 23,000′

DIMENSIONS: Span 23′ 4″, Lg. 28′ 1½″, Ht. 16′ 8″, Wing Area 475 sq. ft.

WEIGHT: Empty 13,107 lb., Gross 16,722 lb., Max. 18,772 lb. Fuel 300–450 gal.

PERFORMANCE: (Estimated) Speed—Top 476 mph at 28,000′, 366 mph at s. l., Cruising 202 mph. Service Ceiling 34,500′, Climb 3590′/1 min. Range 710 miles normal, 910 miles max.

VOUGHT XF5U-1

MFR

replace FM-2s in production. Victory reduced Grumman F8F-1 contracts to 765 planes, but postwar orders provided for 100 F8F-1Bs which began appearing May 1946 with four 20-mm. guns, and 36 F8F-1N night fighters. A modified fin and new cowl distinguished 293 F8F-2s and a dozen F8F-2Ns. Four 20-mm. guns, 800 rounds, and 173 lbs. of armor were carried. Sixty F8F-2P photo jobs had cameras and two 20-mm. guns.

Boeing interrupted its retirement from fighter design with the XF8B-1. Three prototypes were ordered May 4, 1943, but were not completed in time to win any wartime contracts. A large low-wing monoplane built around a 3000 hp Pratt & Whitney R-4360-10 with contrarotating propellers, the Boeing's wheels rotated 90° to retract backward into the wing. Armament included six wing guns and external racks for two 2000-lb. bombs. Recognition features included the large scoop below the engine and a bubble canopy.

The last propeller-driven fighter Vought offered the Navy was also the oddest. The XF5U-1 was based on a proposal by C. H. Zimmerman for a circular flying wing aircraft designed to be capable of hovering by standing on its tail and using its propeller as helicopter rotors. A full-scale wood and fabric flying model with panted fixed landing gear, the V-173, was flown November 23, 1942, and construction began on a single-place fighter development known as XF5U-1. This was powered by two 1600 hp turbo-supercharged Pratt & Whitney R-2000-2 radials buried within the thick circular wing on each side of the cockpit and driving two large four-bladed propellers located at the wingtips. Twin rudders were mounted at the wing's trailing edge, and horizontal controls extended outboard of the weird saucer-shaped airframe. Dual main wheels and a tail wheel retracted backward.

Armed with six .50-caliber guns, the aircraft had a span of 23 ft.-4 in. at the wingtips and 36 ft.-5 in. at the propeller tips. When the prototype was completed in 1946, the Navy declined to allot any funds to a test program and the XF5U-1 was discarded without ever being flown. The airframe, rolled out in August 1945, was finally scrapped in March 1948. Therefore, the flurry of flying saucer sightings cannot be blamed upon this aircraft.

None of these types saw action in World War II, because the Corsairs, Hellcats, and older Wildcats finished the job. From 514 fighters on hand at the end of 1941, the Navy expanded to 13,940 fighters on June 30, 1945. During the war, Navy and Marine fighters flew 85,862 carrier-based and 60,603 land-based action sorties, lost 2360 planes to various causes (including about 664 to enemy aircraft), and claimed destruction of over 8600 enemy aircraft.

Chapter 31: Blowtorches at Sea 1945–59

THE NAVY'S FIRST JETS

Wartime gas turbine development greatly interested the Navy, but actual adoption of jets for carrier service presented many difficulties. Jet aircraft required great quantities of fuel, and tricycle landing gear, which was not used on flight decks at that time. The long take-off run required by jet types made catapult launching desirable, and their high landing speed required improved arresting technique.

With such difficulties, it is not surprising that the first approach should be via composite aircraft using a normal engine and propeller for cruising, and a jet unit only for high speed and quick climb. Such a machine was first proposed in December 1942, and three Ryan XFR-1 prototypes and 100 FR-1s were ordered December 2, 1943. The Ryan Model 28 Fireball, as it was called by the company, first flew June 25, 1944, powered by a Wright R-1820-56, and at first glance resembled the usual single-seat low-wing monoplane. Behind the pilot, however, was a General Electric I-16 jet giving 1600-lb. thrust through a tail nozzle, and fed by wing root intakes. Landing gear was of the tricycle type, and the wings could fold upward.

Production FR-1 delivery began June 1945, with an R-1820-72W Cyclone and the I-16 jet. Four .50-caliber wing guns, 189 lbs. of armor, and external fittings for two 1000-lb. bombs, two 150-gallon drop tanks, or four 5 in. rockets were carried. Top speed was 295 mph with the propeller only, but increased to 404 mph when the jet unit was turned on.

A thousand more FR-1s were ordered January 1945,

MFR

RYAN FR-1
Wright R-1820-72W, 1425 hp take-off, 1000 hp at 14,800′, and General Electric I-16, 1600 lbs.
DIMENSIONS: Span 40′, Lg. 32′ 4″, Ht. 13′ 11″, Wing Area 275 sq. ft.
WEIGHT: Empty 7689 lb., Gross 9958 lb., Max. 11,652 lb. Fuel 180–380 gal.
PERFORMANCE: Speed—Top (both engines) 404 mph at 17,800′, (prop. only) 295 mph at 16,500′, Cruising 152 mph, Landing 91 mph. Service Ceiling 43,100′. Range 1620 miles max.

MFR

RYAN XF2R-1
General Electric XT31-GE-2, 1700 hp + 550 lbs., and J31-GE-3, 1600 lbs.
DIMENSIONS: Span 42′, Lg. 36′, Ht. 14′, Wing Area 305 sq. ft.
WEIGHT: Gross 11,000 lb.
PERFORMANCE: (Approx.) Speed—Top 500 mph at s. l. Service Ceiling 39,100′, Climb 10,000′/2 min.

MFR

CURTISS XF15C-1
Pratt & Whitney R-2800-34W, 2100 hp take-off, and de Havilland Halford, 2700 lbs.
DIMENSIONS: Span 48', Lg. 44', Ht. 15' 3", Wing Area 400 sq. ft.
WEIGHT: Empty 12,648 lb., Gross 16,630 lb., Max. 18,698 lb. Fuel 376–526 gal.
PERFORMANCE: Speed—Top (both engines) 469 mph at 25,300', 432 mph at s. l., (prop. only) 373 mph at 25,300', 322 mph at s. l., Cruising 163 mph. Service Ceiling 41,800', Climb 5020'/1 min. Range 1385 miles max.

PMB

CURTISS XF15C-1 (with T tail)

but were canceled at war's end. Sixty-six Fireballs were delivered by December 1945, and several were used for modifications in 1946. These included the XFR-2 with an R-1820-74W and I-16, XFR-3 with R-1820-74W and GE I-20, and an XFR-4 with the R-1820-74W and side fuselage intakes for a 4200-lb. thrust Westinghouse J-34. A General Electric TG-100 giving 1700 hp to a four-bladed propeller and 550-lb. residual thrust was fitted to the XF2R-1, together with a General Electric I-16. In November 1946, the XF2R-1 became the Navy's first turboprop aircraft flight tested.

Another composite fighter was the Curtiss XF15C-1, also a low-wing monoplane with tricycle landing gear. Three prototypes ordered April 7, 1944, were completed with a Pratt & Whitney R-2800-34W turning a four-bladed propeller in the nose and a de Havilland Halford jet of 2700-lb. thrust fitted under the fuselage. Originally mounted low, the stabilizer was later perched atop the fin. Armed with four 20-mm. wing guns, the prototypes were delivered to the Navy in November 1946 and the project was discontinued.

The Navy's first three all-jet prototypes were ordered August 30, 1943. As the major aircraft producers were then tied up by mass production problems, responsibility for airframe development was given the young McDonnell firm in St. Louis, while Westinghouse undertook development of axial-flow turbojets. Six small engines were originally planned for each prototype, but fortunately development of the 1600-lb. thrust Westinghouse 19XB-2B reduced requirements to two. Each 19 in. diameter engine was buried in the wing roots on each side of the smoothly streamlined fuselage. When first flown on January 26, 1945, the type was known as the McDonnell XFD-1, but the designation was later changed to XFH-1 to

ARC

McDONNELL XFD-1 (XFH-1)
Westinghouse WE-19-XB-2B, 1600 lbs. military, 1300 lbs. normal
DIMENSIONS: Span 40' 9", Lg. 37' 3", Ht. 14' 2", Wing Area 276 sq. ft.
WEIGHT: Empty 6156 lb., Gross 8626 lb., Max. 9531 lb. Fuel 260–400 gal.
PERFORMANCE: Speed—Top 487 mph at s. l., 483 mph at 20,000', Cruising 250 mph, Landing 80 mph. Service Ceiling 43,700', Climb 4960'/1 min. Range 540 miles normal, 750 miles max.

avoid confusion with Douglas types, and the engine became known as the J-30.

On March 7, 1945, the first Navy jet production contract was placed; originally for 100 planes, but cut back to 60 after the war. Production FH-1s delivered from January 1947 to May 1948 had J30-WE-20s, and were similar to the prototype but for additional fuel and modified tail fin. Four .50-caliber guns were mounted in the upper side of the nose, and a 295-gallon drop tank could be fitted flush to the belly.

MFR

McDONNELL FH-1

Westinghouse J30-WE-20, 1600 lbs.

DIMENSIONS: Span 40′ 9″, Lg. 38′ 9″, Ht. 14′ 2″, Wing Area 276 sq. ft.

WEIGHT: Empty 6683 lb., Gross 10,035 lb., Max. 12,035 lb. Fuel 375–670 gal.

PERFORMANCE: Speed—Top 479 mph at s. l., Cruising 248 mph, Landing 87 mph. Service Ceiling 41,100′, Climb 4230′/1 min. Range 695 miles normal, 980 miles max.

On July 21, 1946, a prototype became the first jet to fly from a U.S. carrier, while production Phantoms were the first actually in service with Marine groups.

Vought's first jet type was the XF6U-1 Pirate, ordered December 29, 1944, and first flown October 2, 1946. A 3000-lb. thrust Westinghouse J34-WE-22 behind the pilot was fed by intakes in the wing roots. Four 20-mm. cannon were grouped in the rounded nose, and drop tanks were attached to each wing tip. Like the Phantom and most subsequent Navy jet fighters, the three XF6U-1s utilized retractable tricycle landing gear. Construction was of Metalite—two thin sheets of alloy bonded to a balsa wood core. In April 1948, one prototype flew with a J34-WE-30A giving 3250-lb. normal thrust, and 4225-lb. thrust for

MFR

VOUGHT XF6U-1

Westinghouse J34-WE-22, 3000 lbs.

DIMENSIONS: Span 32′ 10″, Lg. 32′ 10″, Ht. 11′ 9″, Wing Area 203.5 sq. ft.

WEIGHT: Empty 5876 lb., Gross 9306 lb., Max. 11,125 lb. Fuel 370–650 gal.

PERFORMANCE: Speed—Top 535 mph at s. l., 530 mph at 20,000′, Cruising 370 mph, Landing 98 mph. Service Ceiling 40,900′, Climb 4560′/1 min. Range 783 miles normal, 1285 miles max.

H. LEVY

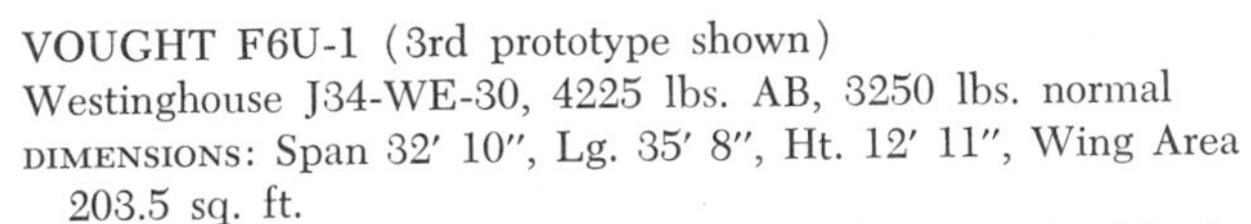

VOUGHT F6U-1 (3rd prototype shown)
Westinghouse J34-WE-30, 4225 lbs. AB, 3250 lbs. normal
DIMENSIONS: Span 32′ 10″, Lg. 35′ 8″, Ht. 12′ 11″, Wing Area 203.5 sq. ft.
WEIGHT: Empty 7000 lb., Gross 10,741 lb., Max. 12,571 lb. Fuel 420–700 gal.
PERFORMANCE: Speed—Top 600 mph at s. l., 564 mph at 20,000′/AB, Cruising 340 mph. Service Ceiling 49,000′, Climb 8480′/1 min. Range 730 miles normal, 1150 miles max.

PMB

NORTH AMERICAN XFJ-1
General Electric J35, 3820 lbs.
DIMENSIONS: Span 38′ 1″, Lg. 33′ 5″, Ht. 14′ 1″, Wing Area 221 sq. ft.
WEIGHT: Empty 8182 lb., Gross 12,135 lb., Max. 14,386 lb. Fuel 465–805 gal.
PERFORMANCE: Speed—Top 542 mph at 16,000′, 533 mph at s. l., Cruising 340 mph, Landing 98 mph. Service Ceiling 47,400′, Climb 4690′/1 min. Range 858 miles normal, 1393 miles max.

NORTH AMERICAN FJ-1
Allison J35-A-2, 4000 lbs take-off and military
DIMENSIONS: Span 38′ 2″, Lg. 34′ 5″, Ht. 14′ 10″, Wing Area 221 sq. ft.
WEIGHT: Empty 8843 lb., Gross 15,115 lb., Max. 15,600 lb. Fuel 805 gal. max.
PERFORMANCE: Speed—Top 547 mph at 9000′, Cruising 432 mph, Landing 121 mph. Service Ceiling 32,000′, Climb 3300′/1 min. Range 1500 miles.

MFR

short periods when using the first afterburner on a Navy fighter. The afterburner added about 50 mph to the top speed at sea level. Delivery began August 1949 on 30 production F6U-1s.

First flown November 27, 1946, the North American XFJ-1 Fury was also a single-seat monoplane, but the fat fuselage had a nose intake for the General Electric J35 engine. Three prototypes were to be followed by 100 FJ-1s ordered May 18, 1945, but the contract was cut to 30. Allison-built J35-A-2s of 4000-lb. thrust powered the FJ-1, which in March 1948 became the first jet type operating in squadron strength from the aircraft carrier *Boxer.*

Six .50-caliber guns were mounted at the sides of the nose scoop; the last of this caliber on Navy fighters, for the 20-mm. cannon has been standard since that time. The Air Force continued using the .50-caliber M-3 gun, however, until the faster-firing M-39 20-mm. gun became available in 1953.

McDONNELL F2H-1
Westinghouse J34-WE-22, 3000 lbs.
DIMENSIONS: Span 41′ 6″, Lg. 39′, Ht. 14′ 5″, Wing Area 294 sq. ft.
WEIGHT: Empty 9794 lb., Gross 14,234 lb., Max. 18,940 lb. Fuel 526 gal.
PERFORMANCE: Speed—Top 587 mph at s. l., 563 mph at 20,000′, Cruising 351 mph, Landing 101 mph. Service Ceiling 48,500′, Climb 7380′/1 min. Range 1278 miles.

The Phantoms, Pirates, and early Furys were a transitional phase between props and jets. They demonstrated that jet types could operate from carriers, and paved the way for complete replacement of propeller-driven fighters by more advanced jet types.

JET PLANES GO TO WAR

During 1947 and 1948, four new fighter types appeared and were ordered into production. They became known to the public as the Banshee, Panther, Skyknight, and Cutlass, and the outbreak of the Korean War found them the available Navy jet fighters.

First was the McDonnell XF2H-1 Banshee, a twin-engine enlargement of the Phantom, powered by 3000-lb. thrust Westinghouse J34-WE-22s. Two prototypes ordered March 1945 were first flown January 11, 1947. Fifty-six F2H-1s, ordered May 1947 and delivered from August 1948 to February 1949, were identical to the prototype, but for elimination of stabilizer dihedral. Four 20-mm. guns were mounted low in the nose, and the wings folded upward for stowage.

In June 1948, a contract was made for the F2H-2, which had 3150-lb. thrust J34-WE-34s, more internal fuel, and a 200-gallon drop tank on each wingtip. In

MFR

MFR

McDONNELL F2H-2
Westinghouse J34-WE-34, 3250 lbs. take-off and military
DIMENSIONS: Span 44′ 10″, Lg. 40′ 2″, Ht. 14′ 6″, Wing Area 294 sq. ft.
WEIGHT: Empty 11,146 lb., Gross 20,612 lb., Max. 22,312 lb. Fuel 1277 gal.
PERFORMANCE: Speed—Top 532 mph at 10,000′, Cruising 501 mph, Landing 99 mph. Service Ceiling 44,800′, Climb 3910′/1 min. Range 1475 miles.

addition to the usual four 20-mm. guns, two 500-lb. bombs could be carried. Beginning in August 1949, 334 F2H-2s were delivered, plus 14 F2H-2Ns with radar added in the nose for night fighting. Fifty-eight F2H-2P reconnaissance types had no guns, but mounted six cameras in an elongated nose.

The F2H-3 appeared in April 1952 with the 3600-lb. thrust J34-WE-36, longer nose with radar for all-weather operations, and increased fuel. Final Banshee version was another all-weather model, the F2H-4 with the Westinghouse J34-WE-38. The last of 175 F2H-3s and 55 F2H-4s was delivered in October 1953, bringing Banshee totals to 784, including 39 F2H-3s later transferred to Canada. The F2H-2 was used as a fighter bomber in Korea beginning in August 1951, while later models served as the fleet's standard carrier-based all-weather fighter.

The Grumman Panther is a smaller single-engine single-seater, but the design began as the XF9F-1 with four 1500-lb. thrust Westinghouse J-30s. Searching for a more efficient way of getting the power required, Grumman decided to import from Britain the 5000-lb. thrust Rolls-Royce Nene (the engine also sold to Russia for the MIG-15 prototype), and in August 1946 the XF9F-2 design (Grumman G-79) was submitted to the Navy. The Nene-powered XF9F-2 Panther was first flown November 24, 1947.

The third prototype was flown August 16, 1948, as the XF9F-3 with an Allison J33-A-8 of 4600-lb. normal thrust. This engine was similar in size to the Nene, and was planned as a second source power plant in case the program to produce Nenes by Pratt & Whitney, as the J-42, was unsuccessful. The first production contract for the Panther called for 47 F9F-2s with the Pratt & Whitney J42-P-6, and 54 F9F-3s with the Allison J33-A-8. The two engines were interchangeable, and all F9F-3s were later converted to F9F-2s, of which 437 were eventually delivered.

In November 1948, F9F-2 acceptances began. Similar to the prototype, they were armed with four 20-mm. nose guns, six 5 in. rockets or two 500-lb. bombs. Permanent wingtip tanks carried auxiliary fuel, which could be jettisoned in emergencies from outlets in the

MFR

McDONNELL F2H-3

WL

McDONNELL F2H-4
Westinghouse J34-WE-38, 3600 lbs.
DIMENSIONS: Span 44′ 11″, Lg. 47′ 6″, Ht. 14′ 5″, Wing Area 294 sq. ft.
WEIGHT: Gross 19,000 lb.
PERFORMANCE: Classified

MFR

GRUMMAN XF9F-2
Rolls-Royce Nene, 5000 lbs. normal, 5700 lbs. military
DIMENSIONS: Span 35′ 3″, Lg. 37′ 8″, Ht. 11′ 3″, Wing Area 250 sq. ft.
WEIGHT: Empty 7107 lb., Gross 10,840 lb., Max. 12,442 lb. Fuel 358–597 gal.
PERFORMANCE: Speed—Top 594 mph at s. l., 573 mph at 20,000′, Cruising 350 mph, Landing 100 mph. Climb 7700′/1 min. Range 1100 miles max.

MFR

GRUMMAN F9F-2

Pratt & Whitney J42-P-8, 5750 lbs. WE take-off, 5000 lbs. military

DIMENSIONS: Span 38′, Lg. 37′ 3″, Ht. 11′ 4″, Wing Area 250 sq. ft.

WEIGHT: Empty 9303 lb., Gross 16,450 lb., Max. 19,494 lb. Fuel 932 gal.

PERFORMANCE: Speed—Top 526 mph at 22,000′, Cruising 487 mph, Landing 105 mph. Service Ceiling 44,600′, Climb 5140′/1 min. Range 1353 miles.

WL

GRUMMAN F9F-5

Pratt & Whitney J48-P-6, 7000 lbs. WE take-off, 6250 lbs. military

DIMENSIONS: Span 38′, Lg. 38′ 10″, Ht. 12′ 3″, Wing Area 250 sq. ft.

WEIGHT: Empty 10,147 lb., Gross 17,766 lb., Max. 18,721 lb. Fuel 1003 gal.

PERFORMANCE: Speed—Top 579 mph at 5000′, Cruising 481 mph, Landing 108 mph. Service Ceiling 42,800′, Climb 5090′/1 min. Range 1300 miles.

DOUGLAS XF3D-1

Westinghouse J34-WE-22, 3000 lbs.

DIMENSIONS: Span 50′, Lg. 45′ 5″, Ht. 16′ 1″, Wing Area 400 sq. ft.

WEIGHT: Empty 12,683 lb., Gross 18,668 lb., Max. 21,500 lb. Fuel 1290 gal.

PERFORMANCE: Speed—Top 543 mph at 11,000′, 533 mph at s. l., Cruising 330 mph, Landing 98 mph. Service Ceiling 42,800′, Climb 4423′/1 min. Range 717 miles normal, 1120 miles max.

USN

PMB

DOUGLAS F3D-2
Westinghouse J34-WE-36, 3400 lbs.
DIMENSIONS: As XF3D-1
WEIGHT: Empty 18,160 lb, Gross 27,000 lb.
PERFORMANCE: Classified

rear. Fuselage brakes under the nose reduced speed in descent, and wings folded upward for stowage.

Seventy-three F9F-4s were ordered, to get Allison J33-A-16s, but were incorporated into contracts for 641 F9F-5s. First flown December 21, 1949, the XF9F-5 and F9F-5 production aircraft had a 6250-lb. thrust Pratt & Whitney J48-P-2 (based on the Rolls-Royce Tay), longer fuselage and higher tail fin.

On August 6, 1950, F9F-2s from the carrier *Philippine Sea* were launched against North Korea, becoming the first naval jets used in combat. The majority of carrier-based fighters used from 1949 to 1952 were Grumman Panthers.

The Navy's first jet-propelled night fighter was the two-place Douglas XF3D-1 Skyknight. Over 1000 lbs. of radar were carried within the plane, including a scanner under the plastic nose and a warning device in the plastic tail cone. The radar operator and pilot sat side by side in a pressurized cockpit from which they could escape, even at high speeds, by bailing out through a tunnel to the fuselage's bottom. A high-wing monoplane, the XF3D-1 had a pair of Westinghouse 3000-lb. thrust J34-WE-22 jets low on the fuselage sides, and the now usual four 20-mm. guns behind and below the nose scanner. Fittings beneath the wing could accommodate two 300-gallon drop tanks or 1000-lb. bombs.

The first of two prototypes flew March 23, 1948, and 28 F3D-1s were purchased in June. Delivered from February to September 1950, they had J34-WE-32s. Seventy F3D-2s ordered August 1949 were to have larger 4600-lb. thrust Westinghouse J-46 engines, but these were unavailable when the F3D-2 was first flown February 14, 1951, so J34-WE-36s of 3400-lb. thrust were substituted.

Although the Skyknight was equipped for carrier operations, the single-place Banshee night fighter had a higher performance and Skyknights were used only by Marine Corps squadrons, including one based in Korea.

This period's most radical design was the Vought XF7U-1 Cutlass, a tailless single-seater with two Westinghouse J34-WE-32 units and twin rudders mid-way out on the 38° swept-back wing. Pressurized cockpit, ejection seat, and ailevators (combined ailerons and elevators) were used. The short, stubby wings had an aspect ratio of 3 : 1 and leading edge slots. At rest, the Cutlass had a nose-high attitude due to the long strut for the dual nose wheels, a feature designed to maintain a high angle of attack for the wing during take-off and landing. Each turbojet gave 3000-lb. thrust normally, but afterburners were installed to temporarily boost thrust to 3700-lb., according to preliminary estimates. These same estimates calculated that top speed would increase from 595 mph to over 670 mph through use of these afterburners.

Cutlass design began in August 1945, and three prototypes ordered June 1946 began flight tests September 29, 1948. Fourteen similar pre-production F7U-1s, purchased June 1948, were first flown on the first of March 1950. An F7U-2 version was abandoned on the drawing board, but the F7U-3 was ordered, to be powered by 4600-lb. thrust Westinghouse J46-WE-8As with afterburners. This engine's production was delayed and the first F7U-3 had to be flown with

MFR

VOUGHT XF7U-1
Westinghouse J34-WE-32, 3000 lbs. (3700 lbs. AB)
DIMENSIONS: Span 38′ 8″, Lg. 39′ 7″, Ht. 9′ 10″, Wing Area 496 sq. ft.
WEIGHT: Empty 9565 lb., Gross 14,505 lb., Max. 16,840 lb. Fuel 582–971 gal.
PERFORMANCE: Speed—Top 672 mph at 20,000′, 661 mph at s. l., Cruising 300 mph, Landing 98 mph. Service Ceiling 41,400′, Climb 9400′/1 min. Range 1170 miles max.

Allison J35-A-29s without afterburners, when it was tested December 20, 1951. The more advanced J-46 became available in 1953, but the F7U-3 didn't enter carrier service until 1955. Various refinements of the nose, fins, and airframe distinguished the heavier F7U-3 from the F7U-1. Four 20-mm. guns, set low in the nose of the prototypes, were mounted on the upper lips of the F7U-3s intakes and laid by a radar-ranging gunsight. In July 1955, the Navy got photo-reconnaissance F7U-3Ps, and the F7U-3M equipped to fire four Sperry Sparrow I beam-riding missiles. The last F7U-3 was delivered in December 1955, but service accidents were high and the Cutlass dropped out of Fleet squadrons three years later.

MFR

VOUGHT F7U-3
Westinghouse J46-WE-8A, 4600 lbs. (6100 lbs. AB)
DIMENSIONS: Span 38′ 8″, Lg. 44′ 3″, Ht. 14′ 7″, Wing Area 496 sq. ft.
WEIGHT: Empty 18,210 lb., Gross 27,340 lb., Max. 31,642 lb.
PERFORMANCE: Classified

SWEPT-WINGS FOR THE CARRIERS

Since the Korean War's beginning, fighter development has been under the shroud of secrecy natural to military affairs. Although details of procurement programs and aircraft characteristics have not been released, an examination of contemporary fighters does reveal the broad tendency of modern design. Most outstanding characteristic of contemporary fighter aircraft is the use of swept or delta wings to delay the effects of compressibility encountered at sonic or near-sonic speeds.

The first new prototype to appear after the outbreak of war in Korea was the Douglas XF4D-1 Skyray, a

VOUGHT F7U-1 (with F6U-1 above)

MFR

MFR

DOUGLAS F4D-1
Pratt & Whitney J57-P-2, 9700 lbs. (13,500 lbs. AB)
DIMENSIONS: Span 33′ 6″, Lg. 45′ 8″, Ht. 13′, Wing Area 557 sq. ft.
WEIGHT: Empty 16,024 lb., Gross 27,000 lb. Fuel 640–1240 gal.
PERFORMANCE: Classified

MFR

DOUGLAS F4D-1

DOUGLAS XF5D-1
Pratt & Whitney J57-P-12
DIMENSIONS: Span 34′, Lg. 50′, Ht. 15′.
WEIGHT & PERFORMANCE: Classified

MFR

single-engine, single-place delta wing interceptor designed in 1948 and first flown January 23, 1951. An Allison J35-A-17 of 5000-lb. thrust powered the first two prototypes as a temporary expedient until the first Westinghouse J-40s were available. Another temporary installation was that of a J40-WE-6, used until the J40-WE-8 giving 11,600-lb. thrust with afterburner was installed. The second prototype, using this engine, established a speed record of 753 mph in October 1953. This was the first time the world's speed record was held by a carrier-based aircraft.

Because of production difficulties encountered with the Westinghouse turbojet, the Navy in June 1953 decided to install Pratt & Whitney J57-P-2s in production Skyrays. The first F4D-1 with the 9700-lb. thrust J-57 (13,500-lb. with afterburning) was flown June 5, 1954. Armament included four 20-mm. guns in the wings, while underwing attachments could carry drop tanks or four pods containing a total of 76 2.75 in. air-to-air rockets. The Skyray's mission was that of intercepting enemy bombers through a very fast rate of climb and involved an endurance of less than 45 minutes.

Skyray production was completed at El Segundo in January 1959, after both Marine and Navy squadrons received the type. One unit, VF(AW)-3 at San Diego, was the only Navy squadron attached to the Air Defense Command. On practice intercepts, its F4D-1s carried an electronics stone on the central pylon, a pair of 19 2.75-in. rocket packs, two 300 gallon drop tanks, and on the outer pylons two Sidewinder missiles. With such loads, they still climbed spectacularly, although not as fast as the "clean" F4D-1 whose 9842 ft. in 44 seconds, 39,370 ft. in 111 seconds, and 49,212 ft. in 156 seconds established climb records in May 1958. On this and most other F4Ds, a J57-P-8 (10,500–14,500-lbs.) replaced the P-2.

Originally known as F4D-2N, the Douglas XF5D-1 Skylancer is an all-weather fighter development of the Skyray with increased internal fuel capacity and more elaborate electronics. First flown April 21, 1956, the XF5D-1 had a J-57 turbojet, larger vertical tail, thinner wing, and longer fuselage. Production models were to have General Electric J-79 engines, but this program was curtailed in 1956.

Another interceptor type appearing in 1951 was the McDonnell XF3H-1 Demon, a single-seater with a 7200-lb. thrust Westinghouse XJ40-WE-6 and swept wings and tail. This prototype had originally been ordered in July 1949, and a program was planned as early as March 1951 for 150 Demons. Production aircraft, known as F3H-1Ns, were to have more fuel and the increased radar required for all-weather capabilities. Gross weight increased from 22,000 to 29,000 lbs., but a more powerful J40-WE-24 turbojet was expected to compensate for the increase.

The XF3H-1 prototype flew August 7, 1951, and the production program was increased to 528 aircraft, with an additional quantity to be built by Temco. In April 1952 McDonnell recommended utilization of the Allison J71-A-2 instead of the J40, which was suffering various difficulties, and in November the Navy decided that, beginning with the 61st Demon, the J-71 turbojet would be used. In September 1953 it became apparent that the J40-WE-24 would not materialize, and that the F3H-1N would have to be content with the 7200-lb. thrust J40-WE-22.

The first of 56 F3H-1Ns was delivered in January 1954, and the handicap of the additional weight soon became apparent. In November the contract was reduced to 280, and in July 1955, after the fourth pilot was killed in a series of 11 accidents that had destroyed six F3H-1Ns during tests, the type was permanently grounded. The engine's power was judged insufficient for the airframe's weight. Twenty-one aircraft, costing $28,350,000, could be used only for mechanics' ground training, and 29 were converted by installation of Allison J-71s into F3H-2 standards. The failure of the F3H-1N program cost the Navy some $200,000,000, most of which was expended on the unsuccessful J-40 engine.

McDONNELL F3H-2N
Allison J71-A-2, 9700 lbs. (14,250 lbs. AB)
DIMENSIONS: Span 35′ 4″, Lg. 58′ 11″, Ht. 14′ 7″, Wing Area 519 sq. ft.
WEIGHT: Empty 22,133 lb., Gross 33,900 lb. Fuel 1506 gal.
PERFORMANCE: Classified

MFR

USN

McDONNELL XF3H-1

McDONNELL F3H-1N [*Photo of XF3H-1*]
Westinghouse J40-WE-22, 7200 lbs.
DIMENSIONS: Span 35′ 4″, Lg. 58′ 4″, Ht. 13′ 11″
WEIGHT: Gross 29,000 lb.
PERFORMANCE: Classified

The F3H-2N, which first appeared in June 1955, had the 9700-lb. thrust Allison J71-A-2 and an afterburner to increase thrust to a reported 14,250-lb. Wing area was increased by widening the chord at the roots. A radar scanner in the nose was fitted, along with four 20-mm. guns, under the pilot's cockpit, and intakes for the turbojet were provided on each side of the fuselage.

In service the Demon proved excellent for air-to-air missiles, with four wing pylons for infrared Sidewinders (F3H-2N), beam-riding Sparrow Is (F3H-2M) or radar homing Sparrow IIIs (F3H-2). Production contracts were increased to 519 Demons, carrying deliveries up to November 1959.

The next Navy swept-wing fighter was the Grumman G-93 Cougar, whose prototype, the XF9F-6, flew first September 20, 1951. The fuselage and power plant were those of the F9F-5 Panther, but the wing and tail surfaces were swept back. Production deliveries began only five months later, and Cougars became the first swept-wing types actually in service on carriers. Armed with four 20-mm. guns, and capable of handling two 1000-lb. bombs, the Cougar replaced the Panther as the most widely used Naval fighter type. Most F9F-6s used the Pratt & Whitney J48-P-8

McDONNELL F3H-2N

PMB

USN

McDONNELL F3H-2M (with Sparrow missiles)

MFR

GRUMMAN F9F-8
Pratt & Whitney J48-P-8, 7200 lbs.
DIMENSIONS: Span 34′ 6″, Lg. 41′ 7″, Ht. 12′ 3″.
WEIGHT & PERFORMANCE: Classified

of 6250-lb. thrust. If an alternate Allison J33-A-16 was used, the Cougar was designated F9F-7.

On December 18, 1953, the F9F-8 was flown for the first time, with lengthened fuselage, cambered leading edge extensions on the wings, and an increase of 140 gallons in internal fuel capacity. A photoreconnaissance variant was the F9F-8P with camera nose.

In the hasty search for a quickly available swept-wing fighter that occurred after the appearance of the MIG-15s in Korea, the Navy determined in February

GRUMMAN F9F-6

USN

MFR

NORTH AMERICAN XFJ-2

PMB

NORTH AMERICAN FJ-2
General Electric J47-GE-27, 6100 lbs.
DIMENSIONS: Span 37′ 1″, Lg. 37′ 6″, Ht. 14′ 8″, Wing Area 288 sq. ft.
WEIGHT: Empty 10,500 lb., Gross 15,000 lb., Max. 18,000 lb.
PERFORMANCE: (Approx.) Speed—Top 690 mph at s. l., 610 mph at 35,000′, Landing 120 mph. Service Ceiling 50,000′. Range 785 miles normal, 1270 miles/drop tanks.

MFR

NORTH AMERICAN FJ-3
Wright J65-W-2, 7200 lbs.
DIMENSIONS: Span 37′ 1″, Lg. 37′ 7″, Ht. 13′ 8″, Wing Area 288 sq. ft.
WEIGHT & PERFORMANCE: Classified

RILEY

NORTH AMERICAN FJ-3

MFR

NORTH AMERICAN XFJ-4
Wright J65-W-4, 7800 lbs.
DIMENSIONS: Span 39′ 1″, Lg. 37′ 6″, Ht. 12′ 8″, Wing Area 338 sq. ft.
WEIGHT & PERFORMANCE: Classified

USN

NORTH AMERICAN FJ-4B
Wright J65-W-16A, 7700 lbs.
DIMENSIONS: Span 39′ 1″, Lg. 36′ 6″, Ht. 13′ 11″, Wing Area 338 sq. ft.
WEIGHT: (Approx.) Empty 15,000 lb., Gross 19,900 lb., Max. 26,000 lb.
PERFORMANCE: Classified

1951 to procure a navalized version of the North American F-86 Sabrejet. On February 19, 1952, an XFJ-2 prototype was flown, similar in appearance to the Air Force's F-86E but for installation of arresting gear, four 20-mm. guns, and Navy blue finish. Production FJ-2s were built in the North American leased facility at Columbus, Ohio, and were similar to the F-86F except for folding wings, carrier gear, and 20-mm. gun armament. Only modern Navy fighters with an Air Force counterpart, the North American FJ-2s were powered by a 6100-lb. thrust General Electric J47-GE-27.

On July 3, 1953, the North American flew the first XFJ-3, which introduced the Wright J65-W-2 of 7200-lb. thrust. Production FJ-3s began appearing in December, and in January 1956 were the first aircraft to operate from the giant aircraft carrier *Forrestal.*

The next Fury version was the FJ-4 which had a 7800-lb. thrust J65-W-4 and was completely redesigned

MFR

CONVAIR XF2Y-1
Westinghouse J34-WE-42, 3400 lbs.
DIMENSIONS: Span 30′ 6″, Lg. 41′ 2″, Ht. 21′ 1″.
WEIGHT & PERFORMANCE: Classified

GRUMMAN XF10F-1 JAGUAR [*Photo unavailable*]
Westinghouse J40-WE-8, 11,600 lbs. AB
DIMENSIONS: Span 50′ 7″, Lg. 55′.
WEIGHT: Max. 33,000 lb.
PERFORMANCE: Speed—Top 722 mph.

with a larger wing, new fuselage, high tail fin, and new landing gear. The first XFJ-4 prototype flew on October 28, 1954, and production models began appearing the following May.

Marine squadrons got the FJ-2 Furies, while FJ-3 and FJ-4s went to both Marine and Navy units. Sidewinder heat-seeking missiles equipped the FJ-3M, while FJ-4Bs issued to attack squadrons were fitted for atomic bombs or Bullpups, a 540-lb. air-to-surface missile with a 250-lb. warhead. First flown in December 1956, the FJ-4B could substitute 700-gallon drop

MFR

CONVAIR XF2Y-1

tanks for its bombs, and handle any load up to 26,000 lbs. gross.

By 1955, the sky above the fleet was filled with the new shapes of the fighters that replaced the straight-winged types of the past. Grumman Cougars, North American Furys, Douglas Skyray interceptors, all-weather McDonnell Demons, and Vought Cutlasses provided the carriers with a variety of weapons to insure air superiority. All could utilize probe and drogue for flight refueling. Not content with this selection, however, the Navy studied four experimental types of radical configuration.

The Grumman XF10F-1 Jaguar was powered by a Westinghouse J40-WE-8 of 11,600-lb. thrust with afterburner, and featured variable sweep wings mounted high on the fuselage. These wings were held straight out to the full 50 ft.-7 in. span for landings and take-off, but swept back 40°, reducing span to 36 ft.-8 in. for high speed flight. A delta-shaped horizontal tail was mounted atop the vertical fin, replacing a con-

MFR

CONVAIR XFY-1
Allison T40-A-14, 5850 hp
DIMENSIONS: Span 25′ 8″, Lg. 34′ 10″, Ht. 23′ 11″, Wing Area 355 sq. ft.
WEIGHT & PERFORMANCE: Classified

LOCKHEED XFV-1
Allison T40
DIMENSIONS: Span 23′ 7″, Lg. 29′ 6″.
WEIGHT & PERFORMANCE: Classified

MFR

ventional swept surface originally used. The first of two prototypes flew May 19, 1953, but an order for 30 was canceled when the XF10F-1, designed for a 722 mph speed, proved unsatisfactory.

Alternatives to carrier-launching for fighters were explored by the vertical take-off (VTO) Convair XFY-1 and Lockheed XFV-1, and the water-based Convair XF2Y-1. The first to appear was the XF2Y-1 Sea Dart, a single-place delta wing fighter powered by two 3400-lb. thrust J34-WE-42 turbojets, and taking off from water by use of retractable hydroskis. Retracting into the fuselage, these skis promised water-based aircraft the same low drag of land-based types, and offered an opportunity to operate from areas without prepared landing fields. The first Sea Dart was flown April 18, 1953, but the program was terminated in 1955 after four aircraft were completed.

Most radical experimental type of its time was the Convair XFY-1, a delta-wing single-seater powered by an Allision 5850 hp T40-A-14 turning 16 ft. diameter six-bladed contra-props. Designed to take-off vertically from an erect position and swing into horizontal flight, the XFY-1 hung on its prop to land vertically on four-point landing gear consisting of small castering wheels. The strange aircraft was ordered in March 1951, made its first flight on the first of August 1954, and its first complete transition from vertical to horizontal flight on November 2.

Built at the same time as the Convair type, the Lockheed XFV-1 was also designed for VTO, which made possible operations from restricted areas such as the decks of destroyers or freighters. Although using the same engine as its competitor, the Lockheed had short straight wings with wingtip fuel tanks, and the small landing wheels were at the tips of a four-fin tail.

Detailed information about the testing of these aircraft has not been announced by the Navy, but since none have gone into production, it is evident that a satisfactory alternative to carrier-based fighters is not yet on hand.

Chapter 32: Summary

NAVY FIGHTERS TODAY

The most striking result of progress in American carrier-based fighters is the existence of supersonic air superiority fighters. The first of these was the Grumman G-98 Tiger, which was originally designated XF9F-9, but is now the F11F-1. Begun in January 1953, it made its first flight July 30, 1954, exhibiting for the first time in American aircraft the principle of area rule design, with the indented fuselage. Six XF11F-1 prototypes were followed by 39 additional F11F-1 Tigers on a contract made October 1954, and a larger order was completed in 1959.

Powered by a 7800-lb. thrust Wright J65-W-4, with afterburner added for additional power, and fitted with small, very thin wings, the Tiger has gone through many modifications since its original appearance. In 1956 a modification (F11F-1F) powered by a 12,000-lb. thrust General Electric J-79 appeared and a speed of over 1220 mph was attained.

First 1000 mph plane actually in Navy service was the Chance Vought F8U-1 Crusader, which had shoulder-mounted thin swept wings with two-position incidence, pivoting on the rear spar so that their angle of attack may be increased for landing or take-off. Armament included four 20-mm. guns mounted, like on the F11F-1, behind and below the pilot, together with Sidewinders and 32 2.75-in. rockets. Air for the Pratt & Whitney J57 entered a scoop under the radar nose scanner.

Crusader history actually began with a Navy request in September 1952 for supersonic day fighter designs. Vought's proposal won the design contract in May 1953, and the XF8U-1, powered by a J57-P-11, surpassed Mach 1 on its first flight, March 25, 1955.

Quantity production of the Crusader was ordered in December 1955, and a speed record of 1015 mph was set by an F8U-1 in August 1956. When the F8U-1 (now using the J57-P-12) reached squadron service in March 1957, the two-position wing was proven to be satisfactory for carrier landings.

Even higher speeds were possible for the F8U-2, with a J57-P-16, airscoops for the afterburner, and two long, narrower fins under the tail section for added stability. These features were tested on a modified F8U-1 early in 1958 and incorporated on production F8U-2s that superseded the earlier model in August. By September 1959, over 500 Crusaders were in service, and orders had been placed for the F8U-2N, with improved radar and a J57-P-20.

A more radical change in configuration was attempted in the F8U-3, first flown on June 2, 1958. Powered by a Pratt & Whitney J75 of 17,500–27,000-lbs. (AB) thrust, the Crusader III was larger than previous models and was armed with three Sparrow III missiles. All-weather radar, push-button controls, and movable ventral fins were among its features. Defeated in competition with the F4H-1, the F8U-3 lost its 18 plane contract in December 1958, and only three examples were completed.

Latest Navy fighter ordered into production is the twin-engined all-weather McDonnell F4H-1. First two-seater for many years, the F4H-1 is armed with four Sparrow III missiles semi-submerged underneath the fuselage, and external stores. Powered by General Electric J79-GE-2s, its configuration includes turned-up wingtip and turned-down horizontal tail surfaces. Performances include speeds over Mach 2, a zoom to 98,560 ft., and exceptional range.

Actually, this type began with a Navy development contract for an attack type labeled AH-1, in September 1953. By July 1955 the type had become a fighter, and two XF4H-1s were ordered in August. Eighteen F4H-1s were added August 1956, and the first prototype flew on May 27, 1958. Production ships were expected to join the Navy's Crusaders, Demons, Furies, Skyrays, and Tigers in 1960.

When these supersonic types, with their radar-assisted 20-mm. guns and packs of air-to-air rockets, are compared to the Navy's earlier open cockpit biplane fighters, with their .30-caliber guns, the immense

MFR

GRUMMAN F11F-1
Wright J65-W-6, or W-18, 10,500 lbs.
DIMENSIONS: Span 31′ 8″, Lg. 40′ 10″, Ht. 12′ 9″, Wing Area 250 sq. ft.
WEIGHT: Empty 13,428 lb., Gross 21,174 lb., Max. 24,078 lb.
PERFORMANCE: Classified

MFR

GRUMMAN F11F-1F

progress made in the last thirty years is apparent. The highly complex all-metal aircraft of today has replaced the fabric-covered, propeller-driven type of the past, but the basic combat mission remains. The Navy fighter must operate from aircraft carriers dispatched to any part of the world and guarantee air superiority against whatever bombardment threat an enemy may offer. In the presence of today's atomic weapons, the very survival of the fleet, and therefore control of the world's seaways, will depend on the carrier fighter's success in performing its mission.

MFR

VOUGHT F8U-1
Pratt & Whitney J57-P-12
DIMENSIONS: Span 35′ 9″, Lg. 54′ 3″, Ht. 15′ 9″, Wing Area 350 sq. ft.
WEIGHT & PERFORMANCE: Classified

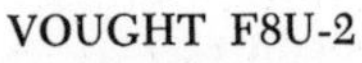

VOUGHT F8U-2

MFR

Notes on Sources

Perhaps the most controversial element in a description of military airplanes is the data describing each type's performance. Since the actual data on most military aircraft is kept secret for some time, there is opportunity for unofficial and often inaccurate estimates of each type's capability to be published. Conflicting sets of data have appeared on many of the aircraft described in this book, and therefore it is necessary to specify the sources from which the data here presented was selected. Every effort has been made to select data based on an actual flight test of a typical example of the type described, or when test flights are not available, to give the specifications guaranteed by the manufacturer in his contract with the government. Such data, of course, cannot necessarily be true of every article of that type produced, for there has been much variation from the brand new aircraft tested, by modification and service wear and tear. Pilots usually regard official figures as being decidedly optimistic.

In this book, data on aircraft built for United States air services is taken from the official characteristics charts prepared by each service for the use of the officers in charge. These charts were usually issued annually from 1920 to 1942 and included aircraft on hand or on order at time of issue. Since 1942, charts are issued individually for each aircraft. The Technical Data Branch, Matériel Division, at Wright Field prepared the "Characteristics and Performance of U. S. Army Airplanes" charts, and these were examined at the Central Air Force Museum at the Wright-Patterson Air Force Base. Data on World War II aircraft has been combined in "Army Airplane Characteristics" (TSEST-A-2) April 1, 1946, prepared by William Englehardt of the Air Matériel Command's Design Branch, Characteristics Section. Mr. Englehardt's office also has those charts on individual postwar aircraft which have been declassified to date and are the Official Standard Aircraft Characteristics. In addition, serial technical reports of Official Airplane Performance Tests made at Wright Field up to 1938 are available in the Central Air Force Museum.

Characteristics charts for Naval aircraft were made available by the Office of Technical Information of the Bureau of Aeronautics, U. S. Navy. The Bureau of Aeronautics Library at its headquarters in Washington, D.C., contains official flight test reports made at Anacosta Naval Air Station previous to World War II.

Data on recent combat aircraft used by the U.S. is still classified, including the majority of aircraft built since 1947. This writer has utilized only declassified documents, and therefore most information on contemporary types is limited to what has appeared in the aeronautical press. In some cases approximations of aircraft performance are permissible.

Data on aircraft built for export is drawn from specifications issued by the manufacturers and published in annual surveys of the aircraft industry made by *Jane's All the World's Aircraft*, the *Aircraft Yearbook*, and *Aero Digest* and *Aviation Week* magazines.

The Historical Division of the Air Matériel Command has prepared a number of case history monographs of AAF wartime types. Some of these are restricted for official use only, but others are available at the Air Force Museum, and the author's queries to the Division have been helpfully answered. The Modern Army Section of the National Archives in Washington, D.C., has been another useful source, with Record Group 18 containing the Army Air Forces Central Files 1919–45 including valuable correspondence, memoranda, and reports filed under 452.1 Aircraft. The Documentary Collection of the Air Corps Library in the same record group contains under D52.1 many of the old Technical Reports from McCook Field (1918–27) and historical material on early Air Service types.

The Department of Air Commerce published a list of *U. S. Military Aircraft Acceptances 1940–1945* (Washington: U. S. Government Printing Office, 1946). Bureau of Aeronautics lists of Naval Aircraft, Record of Acceptances, and U. S. Army publications on Aircraft Model Designations were used to establish the numbers of aircraft delivered to each service. Articles in the American and British aeronautical press provided much data on the production of aircraft for export.

The hearings before the Morrow Board in 1925, and official reports of the Truman Committee of the Senate, Admiral Ernest J. King of the Navy, and General Henry H. Arnold of the Air Force have also provided useful information. Hundreds of articles on various types of airplanes appearing in the aeronautical press since 1917 have been consulted to provide information for this book. A complete acknowledgment of these sources would take up nearly as much space as the text itself, but the work of Peter Bowers, James C. Fahey, Robert C. Hare, William Larkins, and Robert McLarren deserves particular mention. Company periodicals sometimes contain surprising contributions to aviation history, such as Thomas Walker's series in the Thermix Company's *The Project Engineer.* Numerous individuals mentioned in the Preface have also provided items of information.

The following list of books is not an exhaustive bibliography of the topic, but mentions those books which provided particular information for this work.

BOOKS

Aircraft Yearbook (Washington, D.C.: Lincoln Press, annually 1919 to date).

Arnold, Henry H., *Global Mission* (New York: Harper & Brothers, 1949).

Bruchiss, Louis, *Aircraft Armament* (New York: Aerosphere, Inc., 1945).

Chennault, Claire L., *Way of a Fighter* (New York: G. P. Putnam's Sons, 1948).

Collison, Thomas, *The Superfortress Is Born* (New York: Duell, Sloan & Pearce, 1945).

Dollfus, C. and H. Bouche, *Histoire de l'Aeronautique* (Paris: L'illustration, 1932).

Edmonds, Walter D., *They Fought with What They Had* (Boston: Little, Brown & Co., 1951).

Fahey, James C., *U.S. Army Aircraft 1908–1946* (New York: Ships and Aircraft, 1946).

——— *USAF Aircraft 1947–1956* (Falls Church, Va.: Ships and Aircraft, 1956).

——— *Ships and Aircraft of the U.S. Fleet* (Washington, D.C.: Ships and Aircraft, seven editions 1939 to 1959).

Fokker, Anthony H., and Gould, Bruce, *Flying Dutchman* (New York: Henry Holt & Co., 1931).

Green, William, and Cross, Roy, *The Jet Aircraft of the World* (New York: Hanover House, 1955).

Green, William, *Famous Fighters of the Second World War* (New York: Hanover House, 1958).

Green, William, *Famous Bombers of the Second World War* (Garden City, New York: Hanover House, 1959).

Green, William, and Pollinger, Gerald, *The World's Fighting Planes* (Garden City, N.Y.: Hanover House, 1959).

Gorrell, Edgar S., *The Measure of America's World War Aeronautical Effort* (Northfield, Vermont: Norwich University, 1940).

Grey, Charles G., *History of Combat Airplanes* (Northfield, Vermont: Norwich University, 1941).

Hinton, Harold B., *Air Victory* (New York: Harper & Brothers, 1948).

Historical Office of the Army Air Forces, *Official Pictorial History of the AAF* (New York: Duell, Sloan & Pearce, 1947).

——— *The Army Air Forces in World War II,* eds. J. L. Cate and W. F. Craven, 6 vols. (Chicago: University of Chicago Press, 1947–55).

——— *A History of the United States Air Force, 1907–1957,* ed. Alfred Goldberg (Princeton, N.J.: D. Van Nostrand Company, Inc., 1957).

Holley, Irving B., *Ideas and Weapons* (New Haven: Yale University Press, 1953).

Jane's All the World's Aircraft (New York: McGraw-Hill, 1909 to date).

Larkins, William T., *U.S. Marine Corps Aircraft 1914–1959* (Concord, California: Aviation History Publications, 1959).

Levine, Issac Don, *Mitchell, Pioneer of Air Power* (New York: Duell, Sloan & Pearce, 1944).

Loening, Grover, *Our Wings Grow Faster* (New York: Doubleday, Doran & Co., Inc., 1935).

Mansfield, Harold, *Vision* (Story of Boeing Aircraft) (New York: Duell, Sloan & Pearce, 1956).

Morison, Samuel Eliot, *History of United States Naval Operations in World War II,* 11 vols. to date (Boston: Little, Brown & Company, 1947–57).

Morris, Joseph, *German Air Raids on Britain* (London: 1928).

Morris, Lloyd, and Smith, Kendall, *Ceiling Unlimited* (New York: Macmillan, 1953).

Office of Naval Operations, *U.S. Naval Aviation in the Pacific* (Washington, D.C.: U.S. Gov't Printing Office, 1947).

Paust, Gilbert, and Lancelot, Milton, *Fighting Wings* (New York: Duell, Sloan & Pearce, 1944).

Sherrod, Robert, *History of Marine Corps Aviation in World War II* (Washington, D.C.: Combat Forces Press, 1952).

Sikorsky, Igor, *Story of the Winged S* (New York: Dodd, Mead & Co., 1943).

Stimson, Henry L., and Bundy, McGeorge, *On Active Service in Peace and War* (New York: Harper & Brothers, 1947).

Thetford, Owen, *Aircraft of the 1914–1918 War* (Bucks, England: Harleyford Publications, 1954).

——— *Aircraft of the Royal Air Force 1918–57* (London: Putnam, 1957).

——— *British Naval Aircraft 1912–58* (London: Putnam, 1958).

Turnbull, Archibald D., and Lord, C. L., *History of United States Naval Aviation* (New Haven: Yale University, 1949).

Warlick, William W., and Grant, V. F., *Naval Aviation* (Annapolis: U.S. Naval Institute, 1929).

PERIODICALS

Aero Digest (Washington, monthly 1921 to 1956).

Aviation Week (New York, weekly since 1947, formerly *Aviation monthly*).

Flying (Chicago, monthly 1927 to date, formerly *Popular Aviation*).

Journal of the American Aviation Historical Society (Concord, California, quarterly 1956 to date).

Model Airplane News (New York, monthly 1929 to date).

Index